Copy 1

STATISTICS IN PSYCHOLOGY
AND EDUCATION

"If we take in our hand any volume . . . let us ask, *Does it contain any abstract reasoning concerning quantity or number?* No. *Does it contain any experimental reasoning concerning matter of fact and existence?* No. Commit it then to the flames: for it can contain nothing but sophistry and illusion!"

Hume, David, *An Enquiry Concerning Human Understanding,* (1777).

STATISTICS IN PSYCHOLOGY AND EDUCATION

HENRY E. GARRETT, Ph.D.
PROFESSOR OF PSYCHOLOGY
COLUMBIA UNIVERSITY

with an introduction by
R. S. WOODWORTH
PROFESSOR EMERITUS OF PSYCHOLOGY
COLUMBIA UNIVERSITY

Fourth Edition

LONGMANS, GREEN AND CO.
NEW YORK • LONDON • TORONTO
1953

LONGMANS, GREEN AND CO., INC.
55 FIFTH AVENUE, NEW YORK 3

LONGMANS, GREEN AND CO. LTD.
6 & 7 CLIFFORD STREET, LONDON W 1

LONGMANS, GREEN AND CO.
215 VICTORIA STREET, TORONTO 1

GARRETT
STATISTICS IN PSYCHOLOGY AND EDUCATION

COPYRIGHT • 1926, 1937, 1947, AND 1953
BY LONGMANS, GREEN AND CO., INC.

ALL RIGHTS RESERVED, INCLUDING THE RIGHT TO REPRODUCE
THIS BOOK, OR ANY PORTION THEREOF, IN ANY FORM

FIRST EDITION, JANUARY 1926
TEN PRINTINGS
SECOND EDITION, REWRITTEN JUNE 1937
EIGHT PRINTINGS
THIRD EDITION, REWRITTEN JANUARY 1947
JULY 1947, NOVEMBER 1947
OCTOBER 1948, SEPTEMBER 1949
FOURTH EDITION, REWRITTEN JANUARY 1953
REPRINTED SEPTEMBER 1953

Printed in the United States of America

INTRODUCTION

by R. S. Woodworth

Modern problems and needs are forcing statistical methods and statistical ideas more and more to the fore. There are so many things we wish to know which cannot be discovered by a single observation, or by a single measurement. We wish to envisage the behavior of a man who, like all men, is rather a variable quantity, and must be observed repeatedly and not once for all. We wish to study the social group, composed of individuals differing one from another. We should like to be able to compare one group with another, one race with another, as well as one individual with another individual, or the individual with the norm for his age, race or class. We wish to trace the curve which pictures the growth of a child, or of a population. We wish to disentangle the interwoven factors of heredity and environment which influence the development of the individual, and to measure the similarly interwoven effects of laws, social customs and economic conditions upon public health, safety and welfare generally. Even if our statistical appetite is far from keen, we all of us should like to know enough to understand, or to withstand, the statistics that are constantly being thrown at us in print or conversation—much of it pretty bad statistics. The only cure for bad statistics is apparently more and better statistics. All in all, it certainly appears that the rudiments of sound statistical sense are coming to be an essential of a liberal education.

Now there are different orders of statisticians. There is, first in order, the mathematician who invents the method for performing a certain type of statistical job. His interest, as a mathematician, is not in the educational, social or psychological problems just alluded to, but in the problem of devising instruments for handling such matters. He is the tool-maker of the statistical industry, and one good tool-maker can supply many skilled workers. The latter are quite another order of statisticians. Supply them with the mathematician's formulas, map out the procedure for them to follow, provide working charts, tables and calculating machines, and they will compute from your data the necessary averages, probable errors and correlation coefficients. Their interest, as computers, lies in the quick and accurate handling of the tools of the trade. But there is a statistician of yet another order, in between the other two. His primary interest is psychological, perhaps, or it may be educational. It is he who has selected the scientific or practical problem, who has organized his attack upon the problem in such fashion that the data obtained can be handled in some sound statistical way. He selects the statistical tools to be employed, and, when the computers have done their work, he scrutinizes the results for their bearing upon the scientific or practical problem with which he started. Such an one, in short, must have a discriminating knowledge of the kit of tools which the mathematician has handed him, as well as some skill in their actual use.

The reader of the present book will quickly discern that it is intended primarily for statisticians of the last-mentioned type. It lays out before him the tools of the trade; it explains very fully and carefully the manner of handling each tool; it affords practice in the use of each. While it has little to say of the tool-maker's art, it takes great pains to make clear the use and limitations of each tool. As anyone can readily see who has tried to teach statistics to the class of students who most need to know the subject, this book is the product of a genuine teacher's experience, and is exceptionally well adapted to the student's use. To an unusual degree, it succeeds in meeting the student upon his own ground.

COLUMBIA UNIVERSITY
(1926)

PREFACE

to the Fourth Edition

Perhaps the author who revises an elementary textbook in statistical method is always tempted to add new material and to eliminate old. If he has tried to keep up even approximately with the field, he will have encountered new techniques which will seem to him important and worth including in a new text. Furthermore, if he has taught the beginning course in statistics for many years, elementary (but perhaps fundamental) procedures may, through sheer repetition, have become so simple and routine as no longer to be considered worthy of attention. Undoubtedly either or both of these attitudes can work to the disadvantage of the revised book, not to mention the beginning student. The addition of extensive new materials may easily make a book almost unusable to a beginner—especially if the added material is of an advanced nature and not too well integrated with the rest of the text. And the toning down or elimination of necessary preliminary methods neglects the fact that each new generation of students begins from scratch and that things simple to the instructor are not always equally simple to the student.

In preparing the present (fourth) edition of this book I have tried to avoid the pitfalls of overextension as well as of underemphasis. My purpose is the same as it was in 1926 when the first edition of this book was written, namely, to present the *fundamentals* of statistical method most useful to students in psychology and education. In accordance with this plan, I have not included highly specialized techniques (factor analysis, psychophysical methods, curve fitting), nor methods which are applicable mainly to test construction, item analysis and the like. It is my experience that specialized as well as advanced topics belong in courses designed to follow the elementary course.

viii • PREFACE TO THE FOURTH EDITION

Chapters dealing with reliability and inference have been completely rewritten and several obsolete and marginally useful techniques dropped out. One new chapter (Chapter 10) dealing with analysis of variance has been included for those who wish to introduce this topic in the first course. For the convenience of the instructor the present edition has been divided into three parts. Part I (Descriptive Statistics) includes Chapters 1–6; Part II (Prediction and Inference), Chapters 7–11; and Part III (Special Topics), Chapters 12–16. More than a hundred and fifty examples with answers will be found at the ends of the chapters.

Although the present edition is about thirty pages shorter than the earlier, I suspect that it still contains too much material for the usual beginning course. In a short course—one semester or summer session—I suggest that the instructor concentrate on Part I, as I doubt if he can cover more. If the course extends over a year or meets several times a week, I would add to Part I Chapters 7, 8, 9, 12 and 13. Also, if time permits, I would teach Chapters 10, 11, 14 and 15, or assign them as outside work to the better students. Chapter 16 is supplementary to Chapter 15 and is intended to be used mainly for reference.

Many teachers who have used this book in the past have been kind enough to offer suggestions looking to its improvement. To all of these go my sincere thanks even though I have not been able in every case to follow their advice. I am indebted to Dr. Lincoln E. Moses for a critical reading of Chapters 8, 9 and 10.

HENRY E. GARRETT

COLUMBIA UNIVERSITY

CONTENTS

Part I: DESCRIPTIVE STATISTICS

1. THE FREQUENCY DISTRIBUTION

    I. Measures in General 1
    II. Drawing Up a Frequency Distribution 4
    III. The Graphic Representation of the Frequency Distribution 9
    IV. Standards of Accuracy in Computation 20

2. MEASURES OF CENTRAL TENDENCY

    I. Calculation of Measures of Central Tendency 28
    II. Calculation of the Mean by the "Assumed Mean" or Short Method 36
    III. When To Use the Various Measures of Central Tendency 39

3. MEASURES OF VARIABILITY

    I. Calculation of Measures of Variability 44
    II. Calculation of the SD by the Short Method 52
    III. The Coefficient of Variation, V 57
    IV. When To Use the Various Measures of Variability ... 60

4. CUMULATIVE DISTRIBUTIONS, GRAPHIC METHODS, AND PERCENTILES

    I. The Cumulative Frequency Graph 63

II. Percentiles and Percentile Ranks 66
III. The Cumulative Percentage Curve or Ogive 69
IV. Other Graphical Methods 78

5. THE NORMAL PROBABILITY CURVE

I. The Meaning and Importance of the Normal Probability Distribution 85
II. Properties of the Normal Probability Distribution 94
III. Measuring Divergence from Normality 97
IV. Applications of the Normal Probability Curve 103
V. Why Frequency Distributions Deviate from the Normal Form 113

6. LINEAR CORRELATION

I. The Meaning of Correlation 122
II. The Coefficient of Correlation 126
III. The Calculation of the Coefficient of Correlation by the Product-Moment Method 134

Part II: INFERENCE AND PREDICTION

7. REGRESSION AND PREDICTION

I. The Regression Equations 152
II. The Reliability of Predictions 161
III. The Effect of Variability of Scores upon the Size of r 166
IV. The Solution of a Second Correlation Problem 168
V. The Interpretation of the Coefficient of Correlation ... 172

8. THE RELIABILITY OF THE MEAN AND OF OTHER STATISTICS

I. The Meaning of Reliability 181
II. The Reliability of the Mean and of the Median 182
III. The Reliability of Measures of Variability 194
IV. The Reliability of Percentages and Correlation Coefficients 196
V. Sampling and the Use of Reliability Formulas 201

9. THE RELIABILITY OF THE DIFFERENCE BETWEEN MEANS AND OTHER MEASURES

    I. The Significance of Differences between Means and Medians 212
    II. The Significance of the Difference between σ's 232
    III. The Significance of the Difference between Percentages and Correlation Coefficients 236
    IV. The Significance of Deviations from Normality 240

10. TESTING EXPERIMENTAL HYPOTHESES

    I. The Null Hypothesis 247
    II. The χ^2 (Chi-square) Test and the Null Hypothesis ... 254

11. ANALYSIS OF VARIANCE IN DETERMINING THE SIGNIFICANCE OF DIFFERENCES BETWEEN MEANS

    I. How Variance Is Analyzed 270
    II. The Significance of the Difference between Means Derived from Independent or Uncorrelated Measures or Scores 273
    III. The Significance of the Difference between Means Obtained from Correlated Groups 285

Part III: SPECIAL TOPICS:
Correlation and Test Construction

12. THE SCALING OF MENTAL TESTS AND OTHER PSYCHOLOGICAL DATA

    I. The Scaling of Test Items 302
    II. The Scaling of Judgments 316

13. THE RELIABILITY AND VALIDITY OF TEST SCORES

    I. The Reliability of Test Scores 332
    II. The Validity of Test Scores 344
    III. Item Analysis 349

14. FURTHER METHODS OF CORRELATION

    I. Computing Correlation from Ranks 353
    II. Measuring Correlation from Data Grouped into Categories 356
    III. Curvilinear or Non-Linear Relationship 371

15. PARTIAL AND MULTIPLE CORRELATION

    I. The Meaning of Partial and Multiple Correlation 378
    II. An Illustrative Correlation Problem Involving Three Variables 380
    III. General Formulas for Use in Partial and Multiple Correlation 387
    IV. Spurious Correlation 399

16. MULTIPLE CORRELATION IN TEST SELECTION

    I. The Wherry-Doolittle Test Selection Method 404
    II. Limitations to the Use of Partial and Multiple Correlation 419
    Appendix of Tables 423
    Table of Squares and Square Roots 442
    Index 455

STATISTICS IN PSYCHOLOGY
AND EDUCATION

1

THE FREQUENCY DISTRIBUTION

I. Measures in General

1. What is meant by measurement

The measurement of individuals and objects may be of various kinds, and may be taken to varying degrees of precision. When individuals or things have been *ranked* or arranged in a series with respect to some attribute or trait, we have perhaps the simplest sort of measurement. Children may be put in order for height, weight, or regularity of school attendance; salesmen may be ranked for years of experience, or amount of sales over a year; advertisements or pictures may be ranked for amount of color, or for cost, or for sales appeal. Rank order tells us serial position in the group but it does not give us a measurement. We cannot add or subtract ranks as we can inches or pounds since a person's rank is always relative to the ranks of other members of his group, and is never absolute, i.e., in terms of some known unit.

Measurements of individuals may also be expressed as *scores*. Scores are usually given in terms of *time* taken to complete a task, or *amount* done in a given time; less often scores are expressed in terms of difficulty of the task performed, or excellence of the final result. Scores vary with performance, although score-changes rarely parallel performance-changes exactly. When scores are expressed in equal units, they constitute a *scale*. Scaled tests in psychology and education have equal units or steps but do *not* possess an absolute zero point. On the other hand, the "c.g.s. scales" (centimeters, grams, seconds) of physics do have equal units and an absolute zero point. "Scores" from physical scales are called *measures*; they may be added or subtracted and a "score" of twenty inches, say, is twice a "score" of ten inches. Scaled scores from mental tests may also be added or subtracted just as we add and subtract inches. But we cannot say that a score of 40 achieved on a test is twice as good as a score of 20, since neither is measured from a zero point of just no ability. Traits and other characteristics, measurements of which are expressible as scores, are known generally as *variables*.

2. Continuous and discrete series

In the measurement of mental and social traits, most of the variables with which we deal fall into *continuous series*. A continuous series is one which is capable of any degree of subdivision, although in practice divisions smaller than some convenient unit are rarely employed. Measurements of general intelligence illustrate scores which fall into continuous series. I.Q.'s, for example, may be thought of as increasing by increments of 1 on an ability continuum which extends from the idiot to the genius. But there is no reason why with more refined methods of measurement we should not be able to get I.Q.'s of 100.8 or even of 100.83. Physical measures such as height, weight, and cephalic index as well as scores from mental and educational tests fall into continuous series: within the given range any measure, integral or fractional, may exist and have meaning. When gaps occur in a truly continuous series, these are to be attributed to a failure to measure enough cases, to the relative crudity of the measuring instrument, or to some other factor of a like sort, rather than to the lack of measures within the gaps.

Not all variables fall into continuous series. A salary scale in a department store may run from $10 per week to $20 per week in units of $1; no one receives, let us say, $17.53 per week. Again, the average family in a certain locality may work out mathematically to have 2.57 children, although there is obviously a real gap between two children and three children. Series which exhibit real gaps are called *discrete* or *discontinuous*. It is fortunate that nearly all of the variables with which we deal in psychology and education fall into continuous series or may be profitably treated as continuous. This makes it possible for us to be concerned primarily with methods of handling continuous data.

In the following sections we shall define more precisely what is meant by a score and shall then show how scores may be classified into what is called a *frequency distribution*.

THE FREQUENCY DISTRIBUTION • 3

3. The meaning of scores in continuous series

Scores or other numbers in continuous series are to be thought of as *distances* along a continuum, rather than as discrete points. An inch is the linear magnitude between two divisions on a foot-rule; and, in like manner, a score in a mental test is a unit distance between two limits. A score of 150 upon an intelligence examination, for example, represents the interval 149.5 up to 150.5. The exact midpoint of this score-interval is 150 as shown below.

```
            Score 150
|             150             |
149.5          ∧            150.5
```

Other scores are to be interpreted in the same way. A score of 8 on the Thorndike Handwriting Scale, for instance, includes all values from 7.5 up to 8.5; i.e., any value from a point .5 unit *below* 8, to .5 unit *above* 8. Hence, 7.7, 8.0, and 8.4 may all be scored 8. An interval extending from .5 unit below to .5 unit above the given value is the usual mathematical meaning of a single score.

There is another and somewhat different meaning which a test score may have. According to this second view, a score of 150 means that an individual has done *at least* 150 items correctly, but not 151. Hence, a score of 150 represents any value *between* 150 and 151. Any fractional value greater than 150, but less than 151, e.g., 150.3 or 150.8, since it falls within the interval 150–151 is scored simply as 150. The middle of the score is 150.5. (See below.)

```
            Score 150
|            150.5            |
150            ∧             151
```

Both of these ways of defining a score are valid and useful. Which to use will depend upon the way in which the test is scored and on the meaning of the units of measurement employed. If each of ten boys is recorded as having a height of sixty-four inches this will ordinarily mean that these heights fall between 63.5 and 64.5 inches (middle value 64 in.), and not between sixty-four and sixty-five inches (middle value 64.5 in.). On the other hand, the ages of twenty-five children, all recorded as being nine years old, will most probably lie between nine and ten years; will be greater than nine and less than ten years (middle value 9.5). But "nine years old" must be taken in many studies to mean 8.5 up to 9.5 years with a middle value of nine years. The point to remember is that results obtained from treating scores under our second definition will always be .5 unit higher than results obtained when scores are taken under the first or mathematical definition. The student will often have to decide, perhaps somewhat arbitrarily, which meaning a score should have. As a general rule it is safer to take the first meaning of a score unless clearly indicated otherwise. This will be the method followed throughout this book. That is, scores of 62 and 231, say, will usually mean 61.5 up to 62.5, and 230.5 up to 231.5, and not 62 up to 63, and 231 up to 232.

II. Drawing Up a Frequency Distribution

1. The classification of measures

Data collected from tests and experiments often have little meaning or significance until they have been rearranged or classified in a systematic way. The first task that confronts us, then, is the organization of our material and this leads naturally to a grouping of the measures or scores into classes or categories. The procedure in grouping falls under three main heads:

(1) Determination of the *range* or the interval between the largest and smallest scores. The range is found by subtracting the smallest from the largest score.

(2) Decision as to the *number* and *size* of the groups to be used in classification. The number and size of these *class-intervals* will depend upon the range of scores and the kind of measures with which we are dealing.

(3) Tabulation of the separate scores within their proper class-intervals.

These three principles of classification are illustrated in Table 1. The figures in this table represent the Army Alpha scores earned by fifty college men. Since the highest score is 197, and the lowest 142, the range (197–142) is exactly 55. In deciding upon the number of classes to be used in grouping, a good general rule is to select by trial an interval which will yield not more than twenty nor less than ten classes.*

The number of class-intervals which a given range will yield can be determined approximately (within one interval) by dividing the range by the interval tentatively chosen. In the present problem, 55

---

* This rule must often be broken when the number of scores is very large or very small.

THE FREQUENCY DISTRIBUTION • 5

(the range) divided by 5 (the interval) gives 11, which is one less than the actual number of intervals, namely, 12. An interval of three units will yield nineteen classes; an interval of ten units, six classes.

TABLE I The tabulation of Army Alpha scores made by fifty college students

1. The original scores ungrouped

185	166	176	145	166	191	177	164	171	174
147	178	176	# 142	170	158	171	167	180	178
173	148	168	187	181	172	165	169	173	184
175	156	158	187	156	172	162	193	173	183
*197	181	151	161	153	172	162	179	188	179

* Highest score   # Lowest score

2. The same fifty scores grouped into a frequency distribution

(1)	(2)	(3)
Class-Intervals	Tallies	f(frequency)
195 up to 200	/	1
190 " " 195	//	2
185 " " 190	////	4
180 " " 185	////	5
175 " " 180	//// ///	8
170 " " 175	//// ////	10
165 " " 170	//// /	6
160 " " 165	////	4
155 " " 160	////	4
150 " " 155	//	2
145 " " 150	///	3
140 " " 145	/	1
		$N = \overline{50}$

The tabulation of the separate scores within their class-intervals is shown in Table 1. In the first column of this table the class-intervals have been listed serially from the smallest score at the bottom of the column to the largest score at the top. Each class-interval comprises exactly five scores. The first interval "140 up to 145" begins with score 140 and ends with 144, thus including the five scores 140, 141, 142, 143, and 144. The second interval "145 up to 150" begins with 145 and ends with 149, i.e., at score 150. The last interval "195 up to 200" begins with score 195 and ends at score 200, thus including the scores 195, 196, 197, 198, 199. In column (2), marked "Tallies," the separate scores have been listed opposite their proper intervals. The first score, 185, is represented by a tally placed opposite interval "185 up to 190"; the second score, 147, by a tally placed opposite interval "145 up to 150"; and the third score, 173, by a tally placed opposite "170 up to 175." The remaining scores have been tabulated in the same way. When all fifty scores have been listed, the total number of tallies on each class-interval (i.e., the frequency) is written in column (3) headed f (frequency). The sum of the f column is called N. When the total frequency within each class-interval has been tabulated opposite the proper interval, as shown in column (3), our fifty Army Alpha scores are arranged in a *frequency distribution*.

The student will note that the beginning score of the first interval in the distribution (140 up to 145) has been set at 140 although the lowest score in the series is 142. When the interval selected for tabulation is five units it facilitates tabulation as well as computations which come later if the score limits of the first interval, and, accordingly, of each successive interval, are multiples of five. A class-interval "142 up to 147" is just as good theoretically as a class-interval "140 up to 145"; but the second is easier to handle from the standpoint of the arithmetic involved.

2. Methods of describing the limits of the class-intervals in a frequency distribution

Table 2 illustrates three ways of expressing the limits of the class-intervals in a frequency distribution. In (A), the interval "140 up to 145" means, as we have already seen, that all scores from 140 up to but not including 145 fall within this grouping. The intervals in

TABLE 2 Methods of grouping scores into a frequency distribution

(The data are the fifty Army Alpha scores tabulated in Table 1, p. 5)

(A)				(B)				(C)			
Class-Intervals		Mid-point	f	Class-Intervals		Mid-point	f	Class-Intervals	Mid-point	f
195 up to 200		197	1	194.5 up to 199.5		197	1	195–199	197	1
190 " "	195	192	2	189.5 " "	194.5	192	2	190–194	192	2
185 " "	190	187	4	184.5 " "	189.5	187	4	185–189	187	4
180 " "	185	182	5	179.5 " "	184.5	182	5	180–184	182	5
175 " "	180	177	8	174.5 " "	179.5	177	8	175–179	177	8
170 " "	175	172	10	169.5 " "	174.5	172	10	170–174	172	10
165 " "	170	167	6	164.5 " "	169.5	167	6	165–169	167	6
160 " "	165	162	4	159.5 " "	164.5	162	4	160–164	162	4
155 " "	160	157	4	154.5 " "	159.5	157	4	155–159	157	4
150 " "	155	152	2	149.5 " "	154.5	152	2	150–154	152	2
145 " "	150	147	3	144.5 " "	149.5	147	3	145–149	147	3
140 " "	145	142	1	139.5 " "	144.5	142	1	140–144	142	1
		$N = 50$				$N = 50$				$N = 50$

THE FREQUENCY DISTRIBUTION • 7

(B) cover the same distances as in (A), but the upper and lower limits of each interval are defined more exactly. We have seen (p. 5) that a score of 140 in a continuous series ordinarily means the interval 139.5 up to 140.5; and that a score of 144 means 143.5 up to 144.5. Accordingly, to express precisely the fact that an interval *begins* with 140 and *ends* with 144, we may write 139.5 (the beginning of score 140) as the lower limit, and 144.5 (end of score 144 or beginning of score 145) as the upper limit of this step. The class-intervals in (C) express the same facts more clearly than in (A) and less exactly than in (B). Thus, "140–144" means that this interval begins *with* score 140 and ends *with* score 144; but the precise limits of the interval are not given. The diagram below will show how (A), (B), and (C) are three ways of expressing identically the same facts:

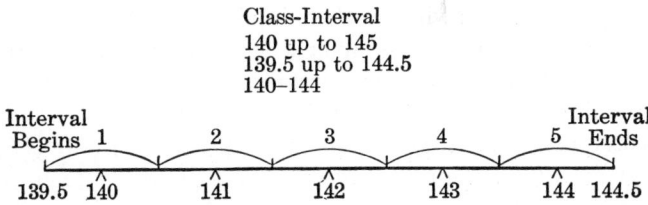

For the rapid tabulation of scores within their proper intervals, method (C) is to be preferred to (B) or (A). In (A) it is fairly easy, even when one is on guard, to let a score of 160, say, slip into the interval "155 up to 160," owing simply to the presence of 160 at the upper limit of the interval. Method (B) is clumsy and time-consuming because of the need for writing .5 at the beginning and end of every interval. Method (C), while easiest for tabulation, offers the difficulty that in later calculations one must constantly remember that the *expressed* class limits are not the *actual* class limits: that interval "140–144" begins at 139.5 (not 140) and ends at 144.5 (not 144). If this is clearly understood, method (C) is as accurate as (B) or (A). It will be generally used throughout this book.

The scores grouped within a given interval in a frequency distribution are assumed to be spread evenly over the entire interval. This assumption is made whether the interval is three, five, or ten units. If we wish to represent *all* of the scores within a given interval by some single value, the midpoint of the interval is taken to be the logical choice. For example, in the interval 175–179 [Table 2, method (C)] all eight scores upon this interval are represented by the single value 177, the midpoint of the interval.* Why 177 is the midpoint of this interval is shown graphically below:

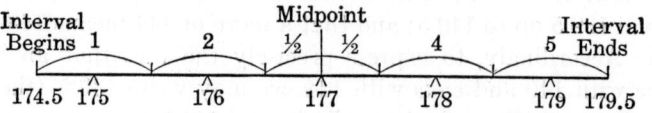

A simple rule for finding the midpoint of an interval is Midpoint = lower limit of interval + $\dfrac{(\text{upper limit} - \text{lower limit})}{2}$. In our illustration, $174.5 + \dfrac{(179.5 - 174.5)}{2} = 177$. Since the interval is five units, it follows that the midpoint must be 2.5 units from the *lower limit* of the class, i.e., $174.5 + 2.5$; or 2.5 units from the *upper limit* of the class, i.e., $179.5 - 2.5$.

It is often a question whether the midpoint is, in fact, fairly representative of *all* of the scores upon a given interval. Referring to Table 1, we find that of the ten scores in the class-interval "170 up to 175" (midpoint 172), three (170, 171, 171) are *below* the midpoint; three (172, 172, 172) are *on* the midpoint; and four (173, 173, 173, 174) are *above* the midpoint. Of the five scores upon interval "180 up to 185," three (180, 181, 181) are *below* the midpoint (182); and two (183, 184) are *above*. The single score of 197 upon interval "195 up to 200" falls exactly on the midpoint. In these examples the midpoint represents quite adequately the scores within the given intervals; but it must be admitted that the balancing of scores above and below the midpoint is not always so satisfactory as it is here. When the data are scanty, or when the distribution is badly skewed (p. 97), there may be many more scores on one side of a midpoint than on the other. When this happens, the midpoint does not fairly represent *all* of the scores within the given interval.

The assumption that the midpoint is the most representative score within an interval holds best when the number of scores in the distribution is large, and when the intervals are not too broad. But even when neither of these conditions fully obtains, the midpoint assumption is not greatly in error and is the best that we can make. In the long run, about as many scores will fall above as below the various midpoint values; and lack of balance in one interval will usually be offset by the opposite condition in another interval.

---

*The same value (namely, 177) is, of course, the midpoint of the interval when methods (*A*) and (*B*) are used.

THE FREQUENCY DISTRIBUTION • 9

Measures of central tendency (p. 28) and of variability (p. 43) calculated from data grouped into intervals of five units, say, will usually vary slightly from the same measures calculated from these data when ungrouped, or when grouped into intervals of, say, three or ten units. These variations arise from (1) differences in the size of the groups in which the data are classified, and (2) the fact that each score within an interval is assigned the value of the middle of the interval instead of its actual value. Corrections are sometimes applied to the measures of variability to correct the *grouping error* thus introduced. But usually the error which results from grouping is so small that it may be neglected in ordinary statistical work.

III. The Graphic Representation of the Frequency Distribution

Aid in analyzing numerical data may often be obtained from a graphic or pictorial treatment of the frequency distribution. The advertiser has long used graphic methods because these devices catch the eye and hold the attention when the most careful array of statistical evidence fails to attract notice. For this and other reasons the research worker also utilizes the attention-getting power of visual presentation; and, at the same time, seeks to translate numerical facts—often abstract and difficult of interpretation—into more concrete and understandable form.

Four methods of representing a frequency distribution graphically are in general use. These methods yield the *frequency polygon*, the *histogram*, the *cumulative frequency graph*, and the *cumulative percentage curve* or *ogive*. The first two graphic devices will be treated in the following sections; the second two in Chapter 4.

1. Graphical representation of data; General principles

Before considering methods of constructing a frequency polygon or histogram, we shall review briefly the simple algebraic principles which apply to all graphical representation of data. Graphing or plotting is done with reference to two lines or *coördinate axes*, the one the vertical or *Y-axis*, the other the horizontal or *X-axis*. These basic lines are perpendicular to each other, the point where they intersect being called O, or the *origin*. Figure 1 represents a system of coördinate axes.

10 • STATISTICS IN PSYCHOLOGY AND EDUCATION

The origin is the zero point or point of reference for both axes. Distances measured along the X-*axis* to the *right* of O are called positive, distances measured along the X-*axis* to the *left* of O negative. In the same way, distances measured on the Y-*axis above* O are positive; distances *below* O negative. By their intersection at O, the X- and Y-*axes* form four divisions or quadrants. In the upper right division or first quadrant (see Fig. 1), both x and y measures are positive

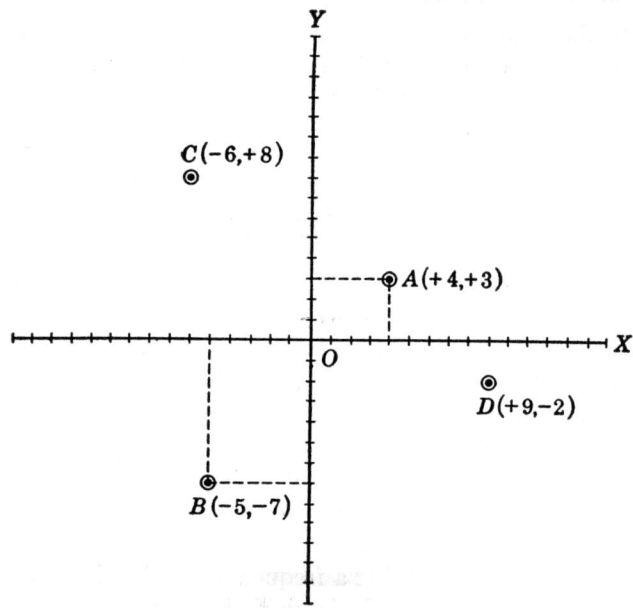

FIG. I A system of coördinate axes

(++). In the upper left division or second quadrant, x is minus and y plus (−+). In the lower left or third quadrant, both x and y are negative (−−); while in the lower right or fourth quadrant, x is plus and y minus (+−).

To locate or plot a point "A" whose coördinates are $x = 4$, and $y = 3$, we go out from O four units on the X-*axis*, and up from the origin three units on the Y-*axis*. Where the perpendiculars to these points intersect, we locate the point "A" (see Fig. 1). The point "B," whose coördinates are $x = -5$, and $y = -7$, is plotted in the third quadrant by going left from O along the X-*axis* five units, and then down seven units, as shown in the figure. In like manner, any points "C" and "D" whose x and y values are known can be located with reference to OY and OX, the coördinate axes. The distance of a point from O on the X-axis is commonly called the *abscissa*; and the distance of the point from O on the Y-axis the *ordinate*. The abscissa of point "D" is $+9$, and the ordinate, -2.

2. The frequency polygon

(1) CONSTRUCTION OF THE FREQUENCY POLYGON

Figure 2 illustrates the use of the coördinate system in the construction of a frequency polygon. This graph pictures the frequency

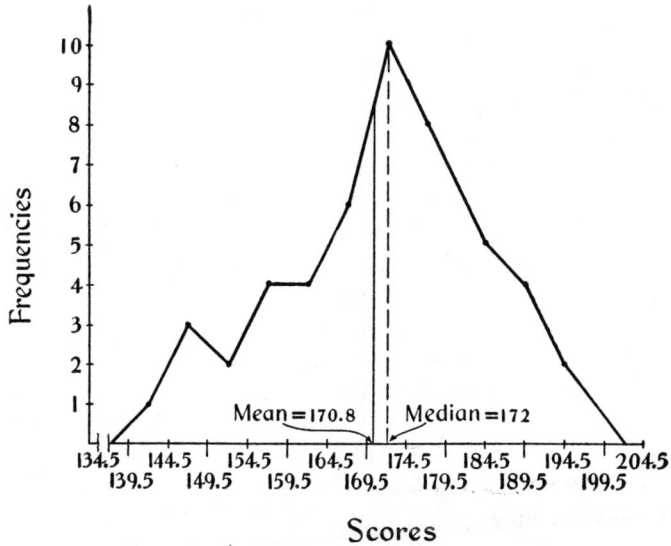

FIG. 2 Frequency polygon plotted from the distribution of fifty Army Alpha scores given in Table I, page 5

distribution of the 50 Army Alpha scores shown in Table 1, page 5. The exact limits of the intervals are laid off at regular distances along the base line (the X-axis) from the origin; and the frequencies within each interval are measured off upon the Y-axis. There is one score on the first interval, 140 up to 145 (Table 1, p. 5). To represent this score on the diagram, we go out on the X-axis to 142, midway between 139.5 and 144.5, and count up one Y-unit. The frequency on the next interval, 145 up to 150, is three, hence the second point falls midway between 144.5 and 149.5, three units above the X-axis. The two scores on interval 150 up to 155, the four scores on 155 up to 160, and the frequency on each succeeding interval, are represented in every case by a point the specified number of scores (Y-units) above the X-axis, and midway between the upper and lower limits of the interval upon which the f lies. It is important in plotting a frequency polygon to remember that the midpoint of an interval is always taken to represent the entire interval. The height of the ordinate at the midpoint represents *all* of the scores within the given interval.

When all of the points have been located, they are joined in regular order to give the frequency polygon * shown in Figure 2. In order to complete the figure, one interval (134.5 to 139.5) at the low end, and one interval (199.5 to 204.5) at the high end of the distribution have been included on the X-scale. The frequency on each of these intervals is zero at the midpoint; hence by including them we begin the frequency polygon one-half interval *below* the first, and end it one-half interval *above* the last, class-interval on the X-axis.

In order to give symmetry and balance to a polygon, one must exercise care in the selection of unit-distances to represent the intervals on the X-axis and the frequencies on the Y-axis. A too-long X-unit tends to stretch out the polygon, while a too short X-unit crowds the separate points. On the other hand, a too-long Y-unit exaggerates the changes from interval to interval, and a too-short Y-unit makes the polygon too flat. A good general rule is to select X- and Y-units which will make the *height* of the figure approximately 75% of its *width*. The ratio of height to width may vary from 60–80% and the figure still have good proportions; but it can rarely go below 50% and leave the figure well balanced. The frequency polygon in Figure 2 illustrates the "75% rule." There are thirteen class-intervals laid off on the X-axis—twelve full intervals plus one-half interval at the beginning and at the end of the range. Hence, our polygon should be 75% of thirteen, or about ten X-axis units high. These ten units (each equal to *one* interval) are laid off on the Y-axis. To determine how many scores (f's) should be assigned to *each unit* on the Y-axis, we divide 10, the largest f (on interval 169.5 up to 174.5) by 10, the number of intervals laid off on Y. The result (i.e., 1) shows that each Y-unit is exactly equal to one f or score, as shown in Figure 2.

The polygon in Figure 5, page 18, furnishes another illustration of this method of plotting a frequency polygon so as to preserve balance. This polygon represents the distribution of 200 cancellation

* Polygon means "many-sided figure."

scores shown in Table 3. There are ten intervals laid off along the base line or X-axis—nine full intervals plus one-half interval at the beginning and at the end of the range. Since 75% of 10 is 7.5, the height of our figure could be either seven or eight X-axis units. To determine the "best" value for each Y-unit, we divide 52, the largest f (on 119.5 up to 123.5) by 7, getting $7\frac{3}{7}$; and then by 8, getting 6.5. Using whole numbers for convenience, evidently we may lay off on the Y-axis seven units, each representing eight scores; or eight units each representing seven scores. The first combination was chosen because a unit of eight f's is somewhat easier to handle than one of seven. A slightly longer Y-unit representing ten f's would perhaps have been still more convenient.

TABLE 3 Scores made by 200 adults upon a cancellation test

Class-Interval = 4

Class-Intervals Scores	Midpoint X	f
135.5 up to 139.5	137.5	3
131.5 " " 135.5	133.5	5
127.5 " " 131.5	129.5	16
123.5 " " 127.5	125.5	23
119.5 " " 123.5	121.5	52
115.5 " " 119.5	117.5	49
111.5 " " 115.5	113.5	27
107.5 " " 111.5	109.5	18
103.5 " " 107.5	105.5	7
	$N =$	200

The total frequency (N) of a distribution is represented by the *area* of its polygon; that is, the area bounded by the frequency surface and the X-axis. The area lying above any given interval, however, cannot be taken as proportional to the number of cases within the interval because of the irregularities in the distribution and consequently in the frequency surface. To show the positions of the mean and the median in the graph, we may locate these measures on the X-axis as shown in Figures 2 and 5. Perpendiculars erected at these points show the approximate frequency at the mean and at the median.

Steps involved in constructing a frequency polygon may be summarized as follows:

(1) Draw two straight lines perpendicular to each other, the vertical line near the left side of the paper, the horizontal line near the bottom.

14 • STATISTICS IN PSYCHOLOGY AND EDUCATION

Label the vertical line (the Y-axis) OY, and the horizontal line (the X-axis) OX. Put the O where the two lines intersect. This point is the *origin*.

(2) Lay off the intervals of the frequency distribution at regular distances along the X-axis. Begin with the lower limit of the interval *next below* the lowest in the distribution, and end with the upper limit of the interval *next above* the highest in the distribution. Label the successive X distances with the interval limits. Select an X-unit which will allow all of the intervals to be represented easily on the graph paper.

(3) Mark off on the Y-axis successive units to represent the scores (the frequencies) on the different intervals. Choose a Y-scale which will make the largest *frequency* (the height) of the polygon approximately 75% of the width of the figure.

(4) At the midpoint of each interval on the X-axis go up in the Y direction a distance equal to the number of scores on the interval. Place points at these locations.

(5) Join the points plotted in (4) with straight lines to give the frequency surface.

(2) SMOOTHING THE FREQUENCY POLYGON

Because the sample is small ($N = 50$) and the frequency distribution somewhat irregular, the polygon in Figure 2 tends to be jagged in outline. To iron out chance irregularities, and also get a better notion of how the figure might look if the data were more numerous, the frequency polygon may be "smoothed" as shown in Figure 3, below. In smoothing, a series of "moving" or "running" averages are taken from which new or adjusted frequencies are determined. The method is illustrated in Figure 3. To find an adjusted or

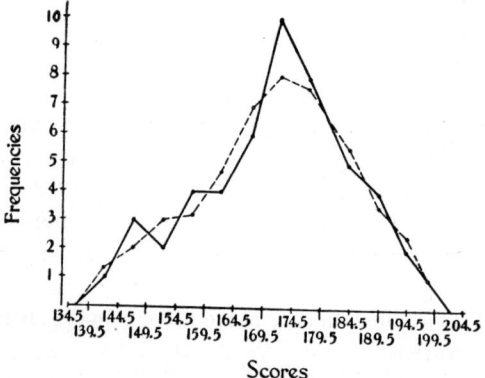

FIG. 3. Original and smoothed frequency polygon. The original and smoothed f's are given below

"smoothed" f, we add together the f on the given interval and the f's on the two adjacent intervals (the one just *below* and the one just *above*) and divide the sum by 3. For example, the smoothed f for interval 174.5 up to 179.5 is $\frac{5+8+10}{3}$ or 7.67; for interval 154.5 up to 159.5, $\frac{4+4+2}{3}$ or 3.33. The smoothed f's for the other intervals may be found in the table below Figure 3. To find the smoothed

(Data from Table 1, p. 5)

Scores	f	Smoothed f
200–204	0	.33
195–199	1	1.00
190–194	2	2.33
185–189	4	3.67
180–184	5	5.67
175–179	8	7.67
170–174	10	8.00
165–169	6	6.67
160–164	4	4.67
155–159	4	3.33
150–154	2	3.00
145–149	3	2.00
140–144	1	1.33
135–139	0	.33
	50	50.00

f's for the two intervals at the extremes of the original distribution, namely, 139.5 up to 144.5, and 194.5 up to 199.5, a slightly different procedure is necessary. Here we add 0, the f on the step *below* or *above*, the f on the given step, and the f on the adjacent step and divide by 3. This procedure makes the smoothed f for 139.5 up to 144.5, $\frac{0+1+3}{3}$ or 1.33, and the smoothed f for 194.5 up to 199.5, $\frac{2+1+0}{3}$ or 1.00. The smoothed f for the intervals 134.5 up to 139.5 and 199.5 up to 204.5, for which the frequency in the original distribution is 0, is in each case $\frac{1+0+0}{3}$ or .33. Note that if we omit these two intervals the N for the smoothed distribution will be less than 50, since the smoothed distribution has frequencies outside the range of the original distribution.

If the already smoothed f's in Figure 3 are subjected to a second smoothing, the outline of the frequency surface will become more nearly a continuous flowing curve. It is doubtful, however, whether so much adjustment of the original f's is often warranted. When an investigator presents only the smoothed frequency polygon and does not give his original data, it is impossible for a reader to tell with what he started. Moreover, smoothing gives a picture of what an investigator *might* have gotten (not what he did get) if his data had been more numerous, or less subject to error than they were. If N is large, smoothing may not greatly change the shape of a graph, and hence is often unnecessary. The frequency polygon in Figure 5, page 18, for example, which represents the distribution of 200 cancellation test scores, is quite regular without any adjustment of the ordinate (i.e., the Y) values. Probably the best course for the beginner to follow is to smooth data as little as possible. When smoothing seems to be indicated in order better to bring out the facts, one should be careful always to present original data along with "adjusted" results.

3. The histogram or column diagram

A second way of representing a frequency distribution graphically is by means of a histogram or column diagram. This type of graph is illustrated in Figure 4, page 17, for the same distribution of scores represented by the frequency polygon in Figure 3, page 14. The two figures are constructed in much the same way, with this important difference: In a frequency polygon all of the scores within a given interval are represented by the midpoint of that interval, while in a histogram the assumption is made that scores are spread uniformly over their intervals. The measures within each interval of a histogram, therefore, are represented by a rectangle, the base of which equals the interval, and the height of which equals the number of scores (the f) within the interval. Thus the one score upon interval 139.5 up to 144.5 is represented by a rectangle whose base equals the length of the interval, and whose height equals one unit measured off on the Y-axis. The three scores within the next interval, 144.5 up to 149.5, are represented by a rectangle one interval long and three Y-units high. The altitudes of the other rectangles vary with the number of f's upon the intervals, the bases all being one interval long. When the same number of scores falls within two or more adjacent intervals, as in the intervals 154.5 up to 159.5, and 159.5 up to 164.5, the top of the rectangle covers two or more intervals on the X-axis. The highest rectangle is, of course, that one (on interval 169.5 up to 174.5) which has 10, the largest frequency, as its altitude. In selecting scales for the X- and Y-axes, the same considerations, as to height and width of figure, outlined on page 12 for the frequency polygon, should be observed.

Although in a histogram each interval is represented by a separate rectangle, it is not necessary to project the sides of the rectangles to the base line as is done in Figure 4, below. The rise or fall of

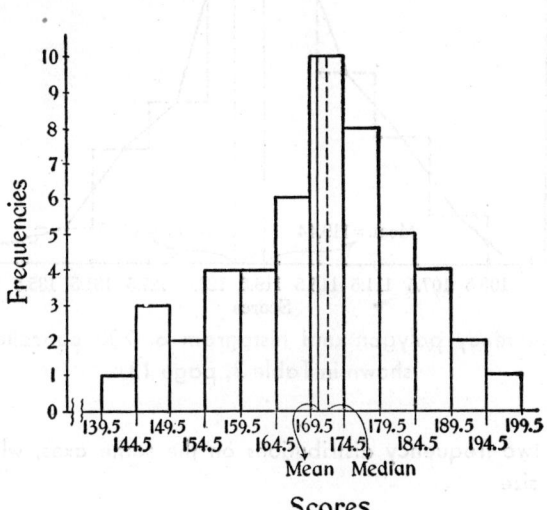

Scores

FIG. 4 Histogram of the fifty Army Alpha scores shown in Table 1, page 5

the boundary line shows the increase or decrease in the number of scores from interval to interval and is usually the important fact to be brought out (see Fig. 5). As in a frequency polygon, the total frequency (N) is represented by the *area* of the histogram. In contrast to the frequency polygon, however, the area of *each rectangle* in a histogram is directly proportional to the number of measures within the interval. For this reason, the histogram presents an accurate picture of the relative proportions of the total frequency from interval to interval.

In order to provide a more detailed comparison of the two types of frequency graph, the distribution in Table 3, page 13, is plotted upon the same coördinate axes in Figure 5, page 18, as a frequency polygon and as a histogram. The increased number of cases and the more symmetrical arrangement of scores in the distribution make these figures more regular in appearance than those in Figures 2 and 4.

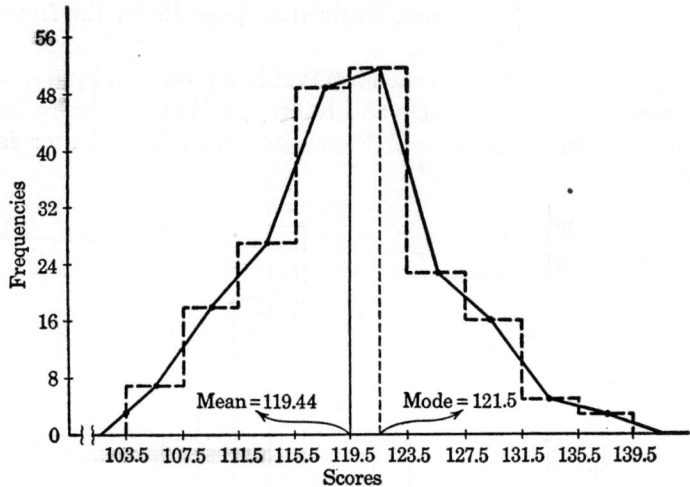

FIG. 5 Frequency polygon and histogram of 200 cancellation scores shown in Table 3, page 13

4. Plotting two frequency distributions on the same axes, when samples differ in size

Table 4 gives the distributions of scores on an achievement examination made by two groups, A and B, which differ considerably in size. Group A has 60 cases, Group B, 160 cases. If the two distributions in Table 4 are plotted as polygons or as histograms on the same coördinate axes, the fact that the f's of Group B are so much larger than those of Group A makes it hard to compare directly the range

TABLE 4

(1) Achievement Examination Scores	(2) Group A f	(3) Group B f	(4) Group A Percent-Frequencies	(5) Group B Percent-Frequencies
80–89	0	9	0.0	5.6
70–79	3	12	5.0	7.5
60–69	10	32	16.7	20.0
50–59	16	48	26.7	30.0
40–49	12	27	20.0	17.0
30–39	9	20	15.0	12.5
20–29	6	12	10.0	7.5
10–19	4	0	6.7	0.0
	60	160	100.1	100.1

and quality of achievement in the two groups. A useful device in cases where the N's differ in size is to express both distributions in percentage frequencies as shown in Table 4. Both N's are now 100, and the f's are comparable from interval to interval. For example, we know at once that 26.7% of Group A and 30% of Group B made scores of 50 through 59, and that 5% of the A's and 7.5% of the B's scored from 70 to 79. Frequency polygons representing the two distributions, in which percentage frequencies instead of original f's have been plotted on the same axes, are shown in Figure 6. These polygons provide an immediate comparison of the relative achievement of our two groups not given by polygons plotted from original frequencies.

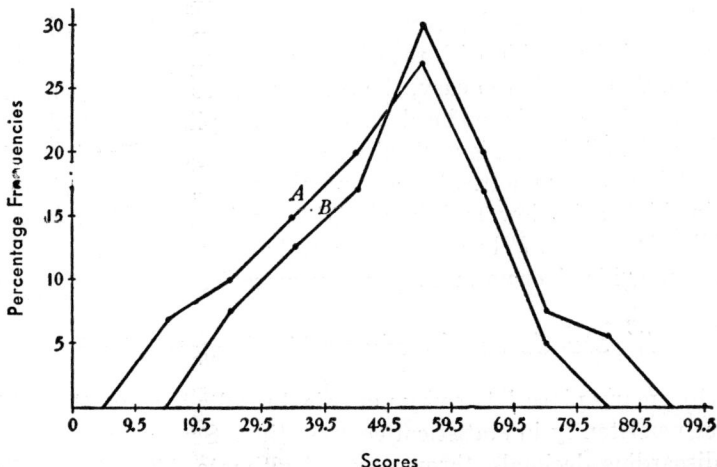

FIG. 6 Frequency polygons of the two distributions in Table 4. Scores are laid off on the X-axis, percentage frequencies on the Y-axis

Percentage frequencies are readily found by dividing each f by N and multiplying by 100. Thus $3/60 \times 100 = 5.0$. A simple method of finding percentage frequencies when a calculating machine is available is to divide 100 by N and, putting this figure in the machine, to multiply each f in turn by it.

For example: 1.667 (i.e., 100/60) $\times 3 = 5.0$; $1.667 \times 10 = 16.7$, etc.; .625 (i.e., 100/160) $\times 9 = 5.6$, $.625 \times 12 = 7.5$, etc. What percentage frequencies do, in effect, is to scale each distribution down to the same total N of 100, thus permitting a comparison of f's for each interval.

5. When to use the frequency polygon and when to use the histogram

The question of when to use the frequency polygon and when to use the histogram cannot be answered by a general rule which will cover all cases. The frequency polygon is less exact than the histogram in that it does not represent accurately, i.e., in terms of area, the number of measures within successive intervals. In comparing two or more graphs plotted on the same axes, however, the frequency polygon is the more useful, since the vertical and horizontal lines in the two histograms will often coincide. Both the histogram and the frequency polygon tell the same story and both are useful in enabling us to show in graphic form whether the scores of a group are distributed symmetrically or whether they are piled up at the low or at the high end of the scale. Not only information with regard to the group, but information with regard to the test, may be secured from a graph. If a test is too easy, the scores will crowd the high end of the scale; if the test is too hard, the scores will pile up at the low end of the scale. If the test is well suited to the group, scores will tend to be distributed symmetrically around the mean, a few individuals scoring high, a few low, and the majority scoring somewhere near the middle of the scale. When this happens, the frequency graph approximates the "ideal" or normal frequency curve described in Chapter 5.

IV. Standards of Accuracy in Computation*

"How many places" to carry numerical results is a question which arises persistently in statistical computation. Sometimes a student, by discarding decimals, throws away legitimate data. More often, however, he tends to retain too many decimals, a practice which may give a false appearance of great precision not always justified by the original material.

In this section are given some of the generally accepted principles which apply to statistical calculation. Observance of these rules will lead to greater uniformity in calculation. They should be followed carefully in solving the problems given in this book.

1. Rounded numbers

In calculation, numbers are usually "rounded" off to the standard of accuracy demanded by the problem. If we round off 8.6354 to two

---

* This section should be reviewed frequently, and referred to in solving the problems given in succeeding chapters.

decimals it becomes 8.64; to one decimal, 8.6; to the nearest integer, 9. Measures of central tendency and variability, coefficients of correlation, and other measures, are rarely reported to more than two decimal places. A mean of 52.6872, for example, is usually reported as 52.69; a standard deviation of 12.3841 as 12.38; and a coefficient of correlation of .6350 as .63, etc. It is very doubtful whether much of the work in mental measurement warrants accuracy beyond the second decimal. Convenient rules for rounding numbers to two decimals are as follows: When the third decimal is less than 5, drop it; when greater than 5, increase the preceding figure by 1; when exactly 5, compute the fourth decimal and correct back to the second place; when exactly 5 followed by zeros, drop it and make no correction.

2. Significant figures

The measurement 64.3 inches is assumed to be correct to the nearest tenth of an inch, its true value lying somewhere between 64.25 and 64.35 inches. Two places to the left of the decimal point, and one to the right are fixed, and hence 64.3 is said to contain *three* significant figures. The numbers 643 and .643 also contain three significant figures each.

In the number .003046 there are *four* significant figures, 3, 0, 4, and 6, the first two zeros serving merely to locate the decimal point. When used to locate a decimal point only, a zero is not considered to be a significant figure; .004, for example, has only *one* significant figure, the two zeros simply fixing the position of 4, the significant digit. The following illustrations should make clear the matter of significant figures:

   136 has *three* significant figures.
   136,000 has *three* significant figures also. The true value of this number lies
      between 136,500 and 135,500. Only the first three digits are definitely
      fixed, the zeros serving simply to locate the decimal point or fix the
      size of the number.
   1360. has *four* significant figures; the decimal indicates that the zero in the
      fourth place is known—and hence significant.
   .136 has *three* significant figures.
   .1360 has *four* significant figures; the zero fixes the fourth place.
   .00136 has *three* significant figures; the first two zeros merely locate the
      decimal point.
   2.00136 has *six* signifigcant figures; the integer, 2, makes the two zeros to the
      right of the decimal point significant.

3. Exact and approximate numbers

It is necessary in calculation to make a distinction between *exact* and *approximate* numbers. An exact number is one which is found by counting: ten children, 150 test scores, twenty desks are examples. Approximate numbers result from the measurement of variable quantities. Test scores and other measures, for example, are approximate since they are represented by intervals and not exact points on some scale. Thus a score of 61 may be any value from 60.5 up to 61.5 and a measured height of 47.5 inches may be any value from 47.45 up to 47.55 inches (see p. 3). Calculations with exact numbers may, in general, be carried to as many decimals as we please, since we may assume as many significant figures as we wish. For example, 110 test scores, which means that exactly 110 subjects were tested, could be written $N = 110.000 \ldots$ i.e., to n significant figures. Calculations based upon approximate numbers depend upon, and are limited by, the number of significant figures in the numbers which enter into the calculations. This will be made clearer in the following rules:

4. Rules for computation

(1) ACCURACY OF A PRODUCT

(a) The number of significant figures in the product of two or more approximate numbers will equal the number of significant figures in that one of the numbers which is the least accurate, i.e., which contains the smallest number of significant figures. To illustrate:

$125.5 \times 7.0 = 880$, not 878.5, because 7.0, the less accurate of the two numbers, contains only two significant figures. The number 125.5 contains four significant figures.

$125.5 \times 7.000 = 878.5$. Both numbers now contain four significant figures; hence their product also contains four significant figures.

(b) When multiplying an exact number by an approximate number, the number of significant figures in the product is determined by the number of significant figures in the approximate number. To illustrate:

If each of 12 children (12 is an exact number) has an M.A. of 8 years (8 is an approximate number) the product 12×8 must be written either as 90 or 100, since the approximate number has only *one* significant digit. If, however, each M.A. of 8 years can be written as 8.0, the product

THE FREQUENCY DISTRIBUTION · 23

12×8.0 can be written as 96, since 8.0 contains *two* significant digits.

(2) ACCURACY OF A QUOTIENT

(a) When dividing one approximate number by another approximate number, the significant figures in the quotient will equal the significant figures in that one of the two numbers (dividend or divisor) which is less accurate, i.e., which has the smaller number of significant digits. Illustrations:

$\dfrac{9.27}{41}$ should be written .23, not .22609, since 41 (the less accurate number) contains only two significant figures.

$\dfrac{16}{4724}$ should be written .0034, not .0033869, since 16 (the less accurate number) has two significant figures.

(b) In dividing an approximate number by an exact number, the number of significant figures in the quotient will equal the number of significant figures in the approximate number. Illustrations:

$\dfrac{9.27}{41}$ should be written .226, since 9.27, the approximate number, has three significant figures. The number 41 is an exact number.

$\dfrac{8541}{50}$ should be written 170.8, not 170.82 since 8541, the approximate number, contains only four significant figures.

(c) In dealing with exact numbers, quotients may be written to as many decimals as one wishes.

(3) ACCURACY OF A ROOT OR POWER

(a) The square root of an approximate number can contain no more significant figures than there are in the number itself. The number of significant figures retained in a square root is usually less than (often one-half) the number of significant figures in the number. For example, $\sqrt{159.5600}$ is usually written 12.63, and not 12.63176, although the original number, 159.5600, contains seven significant figures.

(b) The square, or higher power, of an approximate number contains as many significant figures as there are in the original number (and no more). For example, $(.034)^2 = .0012$ (two significant figures) and not .001156 (four significant figures).

(c) Roots and powers of exact numbers may be taken to as many decimal places as one wishes.

(4) ACCURACY OF A SUM OR DIFFERENCE

The number of decimal places to be retained in a sum or difference should be no greater than the *number of decimals* in the least accurate of the numbers added or substracted. Illustrations:

362.2 + 18.225 + 5.3062 = 385.7 not 385.7312, since the least accurate number (362.2) contains only one decimal
362.2 − 18.245 = 344.0, not 343.955, since the less accurate number (362.2) contains only one decimal.

PROBLEMS

1. Indicate which of the following variables fall into continuous and which into discrete series: (*a*) time; (*b*) salaries in a large business firm; (*c*) sizes of elementary school classes; (*d*) age; (*e*) census data; (*f*) distance traveled by car; (*g*) football scores; (*h*) weight; (*i*) numbers of pages in 100 books; (*j*) mental ages.
2. Write the exact upper and lower limits of the following scores in accordance with the two definitions of a score in continuous series, given on pages 3 and 4:

62	175	1
8	312	87

3. Suppose that sets of scores have the ranges given below. Indicate how large an interval, and how many intervals, you would suggest for use in drawing up a frequency distribution of each set.

Range	Size of Interval	Number of Intervals
16 to 87		
0 to 46		
110 to 212		
63 to 151		
4 to 12		

4. In each of the following write (*a*) the exact lower and upper limits of the class-intervals (following the first definition of a score, given on page 3), and (*b*) the midpoint of each interval.

45–47	162.5–167.5	63–67	0–9
1–4	80 up to 90	16–17	25–28

5. (*a*) Tabulate the following twenty-five scores into two frequency distributions, using (1) an interval of three, and (2) an interval of five units. Let the first interval begin with score 60.

72	75	77	67	72
81	78	65	86	73
67	82	76	76	70
83	71	63	72	72
61	67	84	69	64

THE FREQUENCY DISTRIBUTION • 25

(b) The following 100 scores were made on the Thorndike Intelligence Examination for High School Graduates by applicants for admission to college. Tabulate these scores into three frequency distributions, using class-intervals of three, five, and ten units. Let the first interval begin with score 45.

63	78	76	58	95
78	86	80	96	94
46	78	92	86	88
82	101	102	70	50
74	65	73	72	91
103	90	87	74	83
78	75	70	84	98
86	73	85	99	93
103	90	79	81	83
87	86	93	89	76
73	86	82	71	94
95	84	90	73	75
82	86	83	63	56
89	76	81	105	73
73	75	85	74	95
92	83	72	98	110
85	103	81	78	98
80	86	96	78	71
81	84	81	83	92
90	85	85	96	72

6. The following lists represent the final grades made by two sections of the same course in general psychology.

(a) Tabulate the grades into frequency distributions using an interval of 5. Begin with 45 in Section I and 50 in Section II.

(b) Represent these frequency distributions as frequency polygons on the same axes.

Section I ($N = 64$)

70	71	67	90	51	70	90
67	79	81	81	58	76	72
51	76	76	90	71	72	62
89	90	76	71	88	66	81
91	71	65	63	65	76	
79	80	71	76	54	80	
72	63	87	91	90	45	
69	66	80	79	71	75	
58	50	47	67	67	52	
64	88	54	70	80	92	

Section II ($N = 46$)

84	73	78	58	84
80	74	86	52	74
90	87	92	78	62
82	76	85	85	90
84	79	54	94	81
70	97	65	66	77
89	69	56	57	
77	78	71	63	
62	95	65	71	
79	85	70	71	

7. (a) Plot frequency polygons for the two distributions of 25 scores found in 5(a), using intervals of 3 and of 5 score units. Smooth both distributions (see p. 14) and plot the smoothed f's and the original scores on the same axes.

   (b) Plot a frequency polygon of the 100 scores in 5(b) using an interval of 10 score units. Superimpose a histogram upon the frequency polygon.

   (c) On the same axes, plot a frequency polygon and histogram of the 100 Thorndike scores using an interval of 5 score units. Smooth the frequency polygon and plot on the same diagram.

8. Reduce the distributions A and B below to percentage frequencies and plot them as frequency polygons on the same axes. Is your understanding of the achievement of these groups advanced by this treatment of the data?

Scores	Group A	Group B
52–55	1	8
48–51	0	5
44–47	5	12
40–43	10	58
36–39	20	40
32–35	12	22
28–31	8	10
24–27	2	15
20–23	3	5
16–19	4	0
	65	175

9. (a) Round off the following numbers to two decimals:

   3.5872   74.168   126.83500
   46.9223   25.193   81.72558

   (b) How many significant figures in each of the following:

   .00046   91.00   1.03
   46.02   18.365   15.0048

   (c) Write the answers to the following:

   $127.4 \times .0036 =$ (both numbers approximate)
   $200.0 \div 5.63 =$ "   "   "
   $62 \times .053 =$ (first number exact, second approximate)
   $364.2 + 61.596 =$
   $364.2 - 61.596 =$
   $\sqrt{47.86} =$
   $(18.6)^2 =$

ANSWERS

2. 61.5 to 62.5 and 62.0 to 63.0; 174.5 to 175.5 and 175.0 to 176.0;
   7.5 to 8.5 and 8.0 to 9.0; 311.5 to 312.5 and 312.0 to 313.0;
   .5 to 1.5 and 1.0 to 2.0
   86.5 to 87.5 and 87.0 to 88.0

3.
Size of Interval	No. of Intervals
5	15
3 or 4 or 5	16 or 12 or 10
10	11
5 or 10	18 or 9
1	9

4.
	Midpoint
44.5 to 47.5	46.0
.5 to 4.5	2.5
162.5 to 167.5	165.0
79.5 to 89.5	84.5
62.5 to 67.5	65.0
15.5 to 17.5	16.5
−.5 to 9.5	4.5
24.5 to 28.5	26.5

9. (a) 3.59   74.17   126.83
        46.92   25.19   81.73
   (b) 2   4   3
        4   5   6
   (c) .46
        35.5
        3.3
        425.8
        302.6
        6.918 or 6.92
        346

2

MEASURES OF CENTRAL TENDENCY

When scores or other measures have been tabulated into a frequency distribution, as shown in Chapter 1, usually the next task is to calculate one or more measures of *central tendency*. The value of a measure of central tendency is twofold. *First*, it is a single measure which represents *all* of the scores made by the group, and as such gives a concise description of the performance of the group as a whole; and *second*, it enables us to compare two or more groups in terms of typical performance. There are three "averages" or measures of central tendency in common use, (1) the *arithmetic mean*, (2) the *median*, and (3) the *mode*. Popularly, the *average* is used for the arithmetic mean. In statistical work, however, *average* is often used as a general term for any measure of central tendency.

I. Calculation of Measures of Central Tendency

1. The arithmetic mean or "average" (M)

(1) CALCULATION OF THE MEAN WHEN DATA ARE UNGROUPED

The arithemetic mean or simply the mean is the best known measure of central tendency. It may be defined as the sum of the separate scores or other measures divided by their number. To illustrate: if a man earns $3, $4, $3.50, $5, and $4.50 on five successive days his mean daily wage ($4.00) is obtained by dividing the sum of his daily earnings by the number of days he has worked. The formula for the arithmetic mean (M) of a series of ungrouped measures is

$$M = \frac{\Sigma X}{N} \qquad (1)$$

(*arithmetic mean calculated from ungrouped data*)

MEASURES OF CENTRAL TENDENCY • 29

in which N is the number of measures in the series, X stands for a score or other measure, and the symbol Σ means "sum of," here sum of scores.

(2) CALCULATION OF THE MEAN FROM DATA GROUPED INTO A FREQUENCY DISTRIBUTION

When measures have been grouped into a frequency distribution, the arithmetic mean is calculated by a slightly different method from the one given above. The two illustrations given in Table 5, page 30, will make the differences clear. The first example shows the calculation of the mean of the 50 Army Alpha scores which were tabulated into a frequency distribution in Table 1. First calculate the fX column by multiplying the midpoint (X) of each interval by the number of scores (f) on it; the mean (170.80) is then simply the sum of the fX (namely, 8450) divided by N (50). The use of the midpoint for all of the scores within an interval is made necessary by the fact that scores grouped into intervals lose their identity and must thereafter be represented by the midpoint of that particular interval in which they fall. Hence, we multiply the midpoint of each interval by the frequency upon that interval; add the fX and divide by N to obtain the mean. The formula may be written

$$M = \frac{\Sigma fX}{N} \qquad (2)$$

(*arithmetic mean calculated from scores grouped into a frequency distribution*)

The second example in Table 5 is another illustration of the calculation of the mean from grouped data. This frequency distribution represents 200 scores made by a group of adults upon a cancellation test. Scores have been classified by method (B), page 6, into 9 class-intervals; and since the intervals are 4 units, the midpoints are found by adding one-half of 4 to the lower limit of each. For example, in the first interval, $103.5 + 2.0 = 105.5$. The fX column totals 23,888.0; and N equals 200. Hence, applying formula (2), the arithmetic mean is found to be 119.44 (to two decimals).

In both of the illustrations in Table 5, the M of the scores made by the members of a *group* was found. We may, however, use either formula (1) or (2) to calculate the M of a number of measurements made upon the same individual. If an individual's reaction time to light is measured 100 times, and the measures tabulated into a fre-

TABLE 5 The calculation of the mean, median, and crude mode from data grouped into a frequency distribution

1. Data from Table 1, fifty Army Alpha scores
Class-interval = 5

Class-Intervals Scores	Midpoint X	f		fX
195–199	197	1		197
190–194	192	2		384
185–189	187	4	↓	748
180–184	182	5		910
175–179	177	8	20	1416
170–174	172	10		1720
165–169	167	6	20	1002
160–164	162	4	↑	648
155–159	157	4		628
150–154	152	2		304
145–149	147	3		441
140–144	142	1		142
		$N = 50$		8540
		$N/2 = 25$		

(1) Mean $= \dfrac{\Sigma fX}{N} = \dfrac{8540}{50} = 170.80$

(2) Median $= 169.5 + \tfrac{5}{10} \times 5 = 172.00$

(3) Crude Mode falls on class-interval 170–174 or at 172.00

2. Scores made by 200 adults upon a cancellation test
Class-interval = 4

Class-Intervals Scores	Midpoint X	f		fX
135.5 to 139.5	137.5	3		412.5
131.5 to 135.5	133.5	5		667.5
127.5 to 131.5	129.5	16	↓	2072.0
123.5 to 127.5	125.5	23		2886.5
119.5 to 123.5	121.5	52	99	6318.0
115.5 to 119.5	117.5	49		5757.5
111.5 to 115.5	113.5	27	52	3064.5
107.5 to 111.5	109.5	18	↑	1971.0
103.5 to 107.5	105.5	7		738.5
		$N = 200$		23888.0
		$N/2 = 100$		

(1) Mean $= \dfrac{\Sigma fX}{N} = \dfrac{23{,}888.0}{200} = 119.44$

(2) Median $= 115.5 + \tfrac{48}{49} \times 4 = 119.42$

(3) Crude Mode falls on class-interval 119.5 to 123.5 or at 121.50

quency distribution, the M is found in exactly the same way in which we compute the "average" reaction time to light of 100 *different* observers.

(3) THE MEAN FROM COMBINED SAMPLES OR GROUPS

Suppose that on a certain test the mean for a group of 10 children is 62, and that on the same test the mean for a group of 40 children is 66. Then the mean of the two groups combined is $\dfrac{62 \times 10 + 66 \times 40}{50}$ or 65.2. The formula for the weighted mean of n groups is

$$M_{\text{comb}} = \frac{N_1 M_1 + N_2 M_2 + \ldots\ldots + N_n M_n}{N_1 + N_2 + \ldots\ldots + N_n} \qquad (3)$$

(*weighted arithmetical mean obtained from combining n groups*)

When only two groups have been combined, the weighted mean is

$$M_{\text{comb}} = \frac{N_1 M_1 + N_2 M_2}{N_1 + N_2}$$

2. The median (Mdn) *

(1) CALCULATION OF THE MEDIAN WHEN DATA ARE UNGROUPED

When ungrouped scores or other measures are arranged in order of size, the median is the *midpoint* in the series. Two situations arise in the computation of the median from ungrouped data: (*a*) when N is *odd*, and (*b*) when N is *even*. To consider, first, the case where N is odd, suppose we have the following integral "mental ages": 7, 10, 8, 12, 9, 11, 7, calculated from seven performance tests. If we arrange these seven scores in order of size

7   7   8   (9)   10   11   12

the median is 9.0 since 9.0 is the midpoint of that score which lies midway in the series. Calculation is as follows: There are three scores above, and three below 9, and since a score of 9 covers the interval 8.5 to 9.5, its midpoint is 9.0. This is the median.

Now if we drop the first score of 7 our series contains six scores

                     9.5
7   8   9   ↑   10   11   12

and the median is 9.5. Counting three scores in from the beginning of the series, we *complete* score 9 (which is 8.5 to 9.5) to reach 9.5, the *upper* limit of score 9. In like manner, counting three scores in from the end of the series, we move *through* score 10 (10.5 to 9.5) reaching 9.5, the *lower* limit of score 10.

* The median is also designated as Md.

A formula for finding the median of a series of ungrouped scores is

$$\text{Median} = \text{the } \frac{(N+1)}{2}\text{th measure in order of size} \qquad (4)$$

(*median from ungrouped data*)

In our first illustration above, the median is on the $\frac{(7+1)}{2}$ or 4th score counting in from either end of the series, that is, 9.0 (midpoint 8.5 to 9.5). In our second illustration, the median is on the $\frac{(6+1)}{2}$ or 3.5th score in order of size, that is, 9.5 (upper limit of score 9, or lower limit of score 10).

(2) CALCULATION OF THE MEDIAN WHEN DATA ARE GROUPED INTO A FREQUENCY DISTRIBUTION

When scores in a continuous series are grouped into a frequency distribution, the median by definition is the 50% *point* in the distribution. To locate the median, therefore, we take 50% (i.e., $N/2$) of our scores, and count into the distribution until the 50% point is reached. The method is illustrated in the two examples in Table 5. Since there are 50 scores in the first distribution, $N/2 = 25$, and the median is that point in our distribution of Army Alpha scores which has 25 scores on each side of it. Beginning at the small-score end of the distribution, and adding up the scores in order, we find that intervals 140–144 to 165–169, inclusive, contain just 20 *f*'s—five scores short of the 25 necessary to locate the median. The next interval, 170–174, contains 10 scores assumed to be spread evenly over the interval (p. 7). In order to get the five extra scores needed to make exactly 25, we take 5/10 × 5 (the length of the interval) and add this increment (2.5) to 169.5, the beginning of the interval 170–174. This puts the *Mdn* at 169.5 + 2.5 or at 172.0. The student should note carefully that the median like the mean is a *point* and not a *score*.

A second illustration of the calculation of the median from data grouped into a frequency distribution is given in Table 5 (2). There are 200 scores in this distribution; hence, $N/2 = 100$, and the median must lie at a point 100 scores distant from either end of the distribution. If we begin at the small-score end of the distribution (103.5 to 107.5) and add the scores in order, 52 scores take us *through* the interval 111.5 to 115.5. The 49 scores on the next interval (115.5 to 119.5) plus the 52 already counted off total 101—*one* score too many to give us 100, the point at which the median falls. To get the scores needed to make *exactly* 100 we must take 48/49 × 4 (the length of the interval) and add this amount (3.92) to 115.5, the beginning of interval 115.5 to 119.5. This procedure takes us exactly 100 scores into the distribution, and locates the median at 119.42.

A formula for calculating the Mdn when the data have been classified into a frequency distribution is

$$Mdn = l + \left(\frac{\frac{N}{2} - F}{f_m}\right) i \qquad (5)$$

(*median computed from data grouped into a frequency distribution*)

where

l = lower limit of the class-interval upon which the median lies

$\frac{N}{2}$ = one-half the total number of scores

F = sum of the scores on all intervals *below* l

f_m = frequency (number of scores) *within* the interval upon which the median falls

i = length of the class-interval

To illustrate the use of formula (5), consider the first example in Table 5, page 30. Here $l = 169.5$, $N/2 = 25$, $F = 20$, $f_m = 10$, and $i = 5$. Hence, the median falls at $169.5 + \frac{(25 - 20)}{10} \times 5$ or at 172.0. In the second example, $l = 115.5$, $N/2 = 100$, $F = 52$, $f_m = 49$, and $i = 4$. The median, therefore, is $115.5 + \frac{(100 - 52)}{49} \times 4$ or 119.42.

The steps involved in computing the Mdn from data tabulated into a frequency distribution may be summarized as follows:

(1) Find $N/2$, that is, one-half of the cases in the distribution.
(2) Begin at the small-score end of the distribution and count off the scores in order up to the lower limit (l) of the interval which contains the median. The sum of these scores is F.
(3) Compute the number of scores necessary to fill out $N/2$, i.e., compute $N/2 - F$. Divide this quantity by the frequency (f_m) on the interval which contains the median; and multiply the result by the size of the class-interval (i).
(4) Add the amount obtained by the calculations in (3) to the lower

34 • STATISTICS IN PSYCHOLOGY AND EDUCATION

limit (l) of the interval which contains the Mdn. This will give the median of the distribution.

The median may also be computed by adding up one-half of the scores from the top down in a frequency distribution. The procedure is the same through step (3) in the summary above. When we count down from the top of the distribution, however, the quantity found in step (3) must be *subtracted* from the *upper* limit of the interval containing the median. To illustrate with the data of Table 5 (1), page 30, counting down in the f-column, 20 scores *complete* interval 175–179, and we reach 174.5, the upper limit of the interval 170–174. Five scores of the 10 on this interval are needed to make 25 ($N/2$). Hence we have $174.5 - \frac{5}{10} \times 5 = 172.0$, which checks our first calculation of the median. In Table 5 (2), the median found by counting down is $119.5 - \frac{1}{49} \times 4$ or 119.42.

(3) CALCULATION OF THE Mdn WHEN (a) THE FREQUENCY DISTRIBUTION CONTAINS GAPS; AND WHEN (b) THE FIRST OR LAST INTERVAL HAS INDETERMINATE LIMITS

(a) Difficulty arises when it becomes necessary to calculate the median from a distribution in which there are gaps or zero frequency upon one or more intervals. The method to be followed in such cases is shown in Table 6 below. Since $N = 10$, and $N/2 = 5$, we count *up*

TABLE 6 Computation of the median when there are gaps in the distribution

Class-Intervals Scores	f	
20–21	2	
18–19	1	
16–17	0	
14–15	0	
12–13	2	} 10–13
10–11	0	
8–9	0	} 6–9
6–7	2	
4–5	1	
2–3	1	
0–1	1	

$$N = \overline{10}$$
$$N/2 = 5$$
$$Mdn = 9.5 + \tfrac{2}{2} \times 2 = 9.5$$

the frequency column five scores through 6–7. Ordinarily, this would put the median at 7.5, the lower limit of interval 8–9. If we check this median, however, by counting *down* the frequency column five scores, the median falls at 11.5, the lower limit of 12–13. Obviously, the discrepancy between these two values of the median is due to the two intervals 8–9 and 10–11 (each of which has zero frequency) which lie between 6–7 and 12–13. In order to have the median come out at the same point, whether computed from the top or the bottom of the frequency distribution, the procedure usually followed in cases like this is to have interval 6–7 *include* 8–9, thus becoming 6–9; and to have interval 12–13 *include* 10–11, becoming 10–13. Lengthening these intervals from two to four units eliminates the zero frequency on the adjacent intervals by spreading the numerical frequency over them. If now we count off five scores, going *up* the frequency column through 6–9, the median falls at 9.5, the upper limit of this interval. Also, counting *down* the frequency column five scores, we arrive at a median value of 9.5, the *upper* limit of 6–9, *or* the *lower* limit of 10–13. Computation from the two ends of the series now gives consistent results—the median is 9.5 in both instances.

(b) When scores scatter widely, the last class-interval in a frequency distribution may be designated as "80 and above" or simply as 80 +. This means that *all* scores above 80 are thrown into this interval, the upper limit of which is indeterminate. The same lumping together of scores may also occur at the beginning of the distribution, when the first interval, for example, is designated "20 and below" or 20—. The lower limit of the beginning class-interval is now indeterminate. In irregular distributions like these, the median is readily computed since each score is simply counted as one frequency whether accurately classified or not. But it is impossible to calculate the mean exactly when the midpoint of one or more intervals is unknown. The mean depends upon the absolute size of the scores (or their midpoints) and is directly affected by indeterminate interval limits.

3. The mode

In a simple ungrouped series of measures the "crude" or "empirical" mode is that single measure or score which occurs most frequently. For example, in the series 10, 11, 11, 12, 12, 13, 13, 13, 14, 14, the most often recurring measure, namely 13, is the crude or empirical mode. When data are grouped into a frequency distribution, the crude mode is usually taken to be the midpoint of that interval which contains the largest frequency. In example 1, Table 5, page 30, the interval 170–174 contains the largest frequency and hence 172.0, its midpoint, is the crude mode. In example 2, Table 5, the largest frequency falls on 119.5 to 123.5 and the crude mode is at 121.5, the midpoint.

When calculating the mode from a frequency distribution, we distinguish between the "true" mode and the crude mode. The true mode is the point (or "peak") of greatest concentration in the distribution; that is, the point at which more measures fall than at any other point. When the scale is divided into finely graduated units, when scores are recorded exactly, and when N is large, the crude mode closely approaches the true mode. Ordinarily, however, the crude mode is only approximately equal to the true mode. A formula for approximating the true mode, when the frequency distribution is symmetrical, or at least not badly skewed (page 97) is

$$Mode = 3\,Mdn - 2\,Mean \qquad (6)$$

(*approximation to the true mode calculated from a frequency distribution*)

If we apply this formula to the data in Table 5, the mode is 174.40 for the first distribution, and 119.38 for the second. The first mode is somewhat larger and the second slightly smaller than the crude modes obtained from the same distributions.

The crude mode is often an unstable measure of central tendency. This instability is not, however, so serious a drawback as might seem at first glance. The crude mode is usually employed as a simple, inspectional "average," to indicate in a rough way the center of concentration in the distribution. For this purpose it need not be calculated as exactly as the median or mean.

II. Calculation of the Mean by the "Assumed Mean" or Short Method

In Table 5, page 30, the mean was calculated by multiplying the midpoint (X) of each interval by the frequency (number of scores) on the interval, summing up these values (the fX column) and dividing by N, the number of scores. This straightforward method (called the Long Method) gives accurate results but often requires the handling of large numbers and entails tedious calculation. Because of this, the "Assumed Mean" method, or simply the Short Method,

MEASURES OF CENTRAL TENDENCY · 37

has been devised for computing the mean. The Short Method does not apply to the calculation of the median or the mode. These measures are always found by the methods previously described.

The most important fact to remember in calculating the mean by the Short Method is that we "guess" or "assume" a mean at the outset, and later apply a correction to this assumed value (AM) in order to obtain the actual mean (M) (see Table 7, below). There

TABLE 7 The calculation of the mean by the short method

(Data from Table 1, 50 Army Alpha scores)

(1) Class-Intervals Scores	(2) Midpoint X	(3) f	(4) x'	(5) fx'
195–199	197	1	5	5
190–194	192	2	4	8
185–189	187	4	3	12
180–184	182	5	2	10
175–179	177	8	1	8
				$+43$
170–174	172	10	0	
165–169	167	6	-1	-6
160–164	162	4	-2	-8
155–159	157	4	-3	-12
150–154	152	2	-4	-8
145–149	147	3	-5	-15
140–144	142	1	-6	-6
		$N = 50$		-55

$AM = 172.00$ $c = -\frac{12}{50} = -.240$
$ci = -1.20$ $i = 5$
$M = 170.80$ $ci = -.240 \times 5 = -1.20$

is no set rule for assuming a mean.* The best plan is to take the midpoint of an interval somewhere near the *center* of the distribution; and if possible the midpoint of that interval which contains the largest *frequency*. In Table 7, the largest f is on interval 170–174, which also happens to be almost in the center of the distribution. Hence the AM is taken at 172.0, the middle of this interval. When the question of the AM is settled, we determine the correction which must be applied to the AM in order to get M. Steps are as follows:

(1) First, we fill in the x' column,† column (4). Here are entered the deviations of the midpoints of the different steps measured from

---

* The method outlined here gives consistent results no matter where the mean is tentatively placed or assumed.

† x' is regularly used to denote the deviation of a score X from the assumed mean (AM); x is the deviation of a score X from the actual mean (M) of the distribution.

38 • STATISTICS IN PSYCHOLOGY AND EDUCATION

the AM in *units of class-interval*. Thus 177, the midpoint of 175–179, deviates from 172, the AM, by *one* interval; and a "1" is placed in the x' column opposite 177. In like manner, 182 deviates *two* intervals from 172; and a "2" goes in the x' column opposite 182. Reading on up the x' column from 172, we find the succeeding entries to be 3, 4, and 5. The last entry, 5, is the interval-deviation of 197 from 172; the actual score-deviation, of course, is 25.

Returning to 172, we find that the x' of this midpoint measured from the AM (from itself) is zero; hence a zero is placed in the x' column opposite 170–174. Below 172, all of the x' entries are negative, since all of the midpoints are less than 172, the AM. So the x' of 167 from 172 is -1 interval; and the x' of 162 from 172 is -2 intervals. The other x's are -3, -4, -5, and -6 intervals.

(2) The x' column completed, we compute the fx' column, column (5) The fx' entries are found in exactly the same way as are the fX in Table 5, page 30. Each x' in column (4) is multiplied or "weighted" by the appropriate f in column (3). Note again that in the Short Method we multiply each x' by its deviation from the AM in *units of class-interval,* instead of by its actual deviation from the mean of the distribution. For this reason, the computation of the fx' column is much more simple than is the calculation of the fX column by the method given on page 29. All of the fx' on intervals *above* (greater than) the AM are *positive*; and all fx' on intervals *below* (smaller than) the AM are *negative*, since the signs of the fx' depend upon the signs of the x'.

(3) From the fx' column the correction is obtained as follows: The sum of the positive values in the fx' column is 43; and the sum of the negative values in the fx' column is -55. There are, therefore, 12 more *minus* fx' values than *plus* (the algebraic *sum* is -12); and -12 divided by 50 (N) gives $-.240$ which is the correction (c) in *units of class-interval.* If we multiply c ($-.240$) by i, the length of the interval (here 5), the result is ci (-1.20) the score correction, or the correction in *score units.* When -1.20 is added to 172.00, the AM, the result is the actual mean, 170.80.

The process of calculating the mean by the Short Method may be summarized as follows:

MEASURES OF CENTRAL TENDENCY • 39

(1) Tabulate the scores or measures into a frequency distribution.
(2) "Assume" a mean as near the center of the distribution as possible, and preferably on the interval containing the largest frequency.
(3) Find the deviation of the midpoint of each class-interval from the AM in units of interval.
(4) Multiply or weight each deviation (x') by its appropriate f— the f opposite it.
(5) Find the algebraic sum of the plus and minus fx' and divide this sum by N, the number of cases. This gives c, the correction in units of class-interval.
(6) Multiply c by the interval length (i) to get ci, the score correction.
(7) Add ci algebraically to the AM to get the actual mean. Some times ci will be positive and sometimes negative, depending upon where the mean has been assumed. The method works equally well in either case.

III. When To Use the Various Measures of Central Tendency

The beginning student of statistics is often puzzled to know which measure of central tendency to use in a given problem. The following will serve as a convenient summary.

1. Use the mean

   (1) When each score or measure should have *equal* weight in determining the central tendency. Since the mean is the sum of the scores divided by their number, each score has equal weight in its determination.
   (2) When the measure of central tendency having the highest reliability is desired (p. 194).
   (3) When standard deviations and product-moment coefficients of correlation are to be subsequently computed (p. 138).

2. Use the median

   (1) When a quick and easily computed measure of central tendency is wanted.
   (2) When there are extreme measures which would affect the mean disproportionately (p. 34).
   (3) When it is desired that certain scores should influence the

central tendency but all that is known about them is that they are above or below the median (p. 35).

3. *Use the mode*

   (1) When the most often recurring or "popular" score is sought.
   (2) When a quick approximate measure of concentration is all that is wanted.

PROBLEMS

1. Calculate the mean, median, and mode for the following frequency distributions. Use the Short Method in computing the mean.

(1) Scores	f	(2) Scores	f
70–71	2	90–94	2
68–69	2	85–89	2
66–67	3	80–84	4
64–65	4	75–79	8
62–63	6	70–74	6
60–61	7	65–69	11
58–59	5	60–64	9
56–57	4	55–59	7
54–55	2	50–54	5
52–53	3	45–49	0
50–51	1	40–44	2
	$N = 39$		$N = 56$

(3) Scores	f	(4) Scores	f
120–122	2	100–109	5
117–119	2	90–99	9
114–116	2	80–89	14
111–113	4	70–79	19
108–110	5	60–69	21
105–107	9	50–59	30
102–104	6	40–49	25
99–101	3	30–39	15
96–98	4	20–29	10
93–95	2	10–19	8
90–92	1	0–9	6
	$N = 40$		$N = 162$

(5) Scores	f	(6)	f
120–139	50	15	1
100–119	150	14	2
80–99	500	13	3
60–79	250	12	6
40–59	50	11	12
	$N = \overline{1000}$	10	15
		9	22
		8	31
		7	18
		6	6
		5	2
		4	2
			$N = \overline{120}$

2. Compute the mean and the median for each of the two distributions in problem 5(a), page 24, tabulated in 3- and 5-unit intervals. Compare the two means and the two medians, and explain any discrepancy found. (Let the first interval in the first distribution be 61–63; the first interval in the second distribution, 60–64.)

3. (a) The same test is given to the three sections of Grade VI. Results are: Section I, $M = 24$, $N = 32$; Section II, $M = 31$, $N = 54$; Section III, $M = 35$, $N = 16$. What is the general mean for the grade?
   (b) The mean score on AGCT in Camp A is 102, $N = 1500$; and in Camp B 106, $N = 450$. What is the mean for Camps A and B combined?

4. (a) Compute the median of the following 16 scores by the method of p. 34.

Scores	f
20 up to 22	2
18 up to 20	2
16 up to 18	0
14 up to 16	4
12 up to 14	0
10 up to 12	0
8 up to 10	4
6 up to 8	0
4 up to 6	0
2 up to 4	0
0 up to 2	4
	$N = \overline{16}$

(b) In a group of 50 children, the 8 children who took longer than 5 minutes to complete a performance test were marked D.N.C. (did not complete). In computing a measure of central tendency for this distribution of scores, what measure would you use, and why?

(c) Find the medians of the following arrays of ungrouped scores by formula (4) p. 32:
(1) 21, 24, 27, 29, 29, 30, 32, 33, 35, 38, 42, 45.
(2) 54, 59, 64, 67, 70, 72, 73, 75, 78, 83, 90.
(3) 7, 8, 9, 9, 10, 11.

5. The time by your watch is 10:31 o'clock. In checking with two friends, you find that their watches give the time as 10:25 and 10:34. Assuming that the three watches are equally good timepieces, what do you think is probably the "correct time"?

6. What is meant popularly by the "law of averages"?

7. (a) When one uses the term "in the mode" does he have reference to the mode of a distribution?

(b) What is approximately the modal time for each of the following meals: breakfast, lunch, dinner. Explain your answers.

(c) Why is the median usually the best measure of the typical contribution in a church collection?

ANSWERS

1. (1) Mean = 60.76   (2) Mean = 67.36
       Median = 60.79   Median = 66.77
       Mode = 60.85   Mode = 65.59

   (3) Mean = 106.00   (4) Mean = 55.43
       Median = 105.83   Median = 55.17
       Mode = 105.49   Mode = 54.65

   (5) Mean = 87.5   (6) Mean = 8.85
       Median = 87.5   Median = 8.55
       Mode = 87.5   Mode = 7.95

2. Class-interval = 3   Class-interval = 5
   Mean = 72.92   Mean = 73.00
   Median = 71.75   Median = 72.71

3. (a) 29.43   (b) 103 (to the nearest whole number)

4. (a) Median = 11.5
   (c) (1) Median = 31.0
       (2) Median = 72.0
       (3) Median = 9.0

5. Mean is 10:30.

3

MEASURES OF VARIABILITY

In Chapter 2 the calculation of three measures of central tendency —measures typical or representative of a set of scores as a whole— was described. Ordinarily, the next step is to find some measure of the *variability* of our scores, i.e., of the "scatter" or "spread" of the separate scores or measures around their central tendency. It will be the task of this chapter to show how measures of variability may be computed.

The usefulness of a measure of variability can be seen from a simple example. Suppose a test of controlled association has been administered to a group of 50 boys and to a group of 50 girls. The mean scores are, boys, 34.6 seconds, and girls, 34.5 seconds. So far as the means go there is no difference in the performance of the two groups. But suppose the boys' scores are found to range from 15 to 51 seconds and the girls' scores from 19 to 45 seconds. This difference in range shows that in a general way the boys "cover more territory," are more *variable*, than the girls; and this greater variability may be of more interest than the lack of a difference in the means. If a group is *homogeneous*, that is, made up of individuals of nearly the same ability, most of the scores will fall around the same point on the scale, the range will be relatively short, and the variability will be small. But if the group contains individuals of widely differing capacities, scores will be strung out from high to low, the range will be relatively wide, and the variability large.

This situation is represented graphically in Figure 7, which shows two frequency distributions of the same area (N) and same mean (50) but of very different variability. Group A ranges from 20 to 80, and Group B from 40 to 60. Group A is three times as variable as Group B—spreads over three times the distance on the scale of scores —though both distributions have the same central tendency.

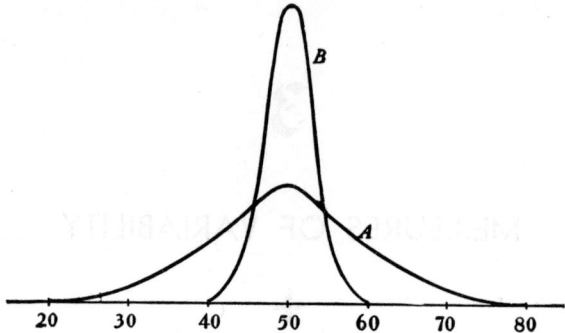

FIG. 7 Two distributions of the same area (N) and mean (50) but of very different variability

Four measures have been devised to indicate the variability or dispersion within a set of measures. These are (1) the *range*, (2) the *quartile deviation* or *Q*, (3) the *mean deviation* or *MD*, and (4) the *standard deviation* or *SD*.

I. Calculation of Measures of Variability

1. The range

In grouping the scores in Table 1 into a frequency distribution (p. 5) we have already had occasion to use the *range*. It may be redefined simply as the interval between the largest and the smallest scores. In the illustration above, the range of boys' scores was 51–15 or 36 seconds and the range of girls' scores 45–19 or 26 seconds. The range is the most general measure of spread or scatter, and is computed when we wish to make a rough comparison of two or more groups for variability. Since the range takes account of the extremes of the series only it is unreliable when *N* is small or when many or large gaps (i.e. zero *f*'s) occur in the frequency distribution.

2. The quartile deviation or Q

The *quartile deviation* or *Q* is one-half the distance between the 75th and 25th percentiles in a frequency distribution. The 25th percentile or Q_1 is the *first quartile* on the score-scale, the point below which lie 25% of the scores. The 75th percentile or Q_3 is the *third*

MEASURES OF VARIABILITY • 45

quartile on the score-scale, the point below which lie 75% of the scores.*

To find Q, we must first calculate the 75th and 25th percentiles. These values are found by exactly the same method employed in calculating the median. To find Q_1, count off 25% of the scores from the beginning of the distribution (low end); and to find Q_3 count off 75% of the scores from the low end of the distribution, or 25% from the high end.

Table 8 illustrates the calculation of Q for the distribution of fifty Alpha scores tabulated in Table 1. First, to find Q_1, count off 1/4 of N (12.5) from the *low*-score end of the distribution. When the scores (f) are added in order, the first four class-intervals (140–144 to 155–159, inclusive) are found to contain 10 scores. The next interval, 160–164, contains four scores, assumed to be spread evenly over the interval. Since we need only 2.5 additional scores to make up the necessary 12.5, take $2.5/4 \times 5$ (the interval) and add this amount, viz., 3.13, to 159.50, the beginning of the interval which contains Q_1. This calculation locates Q_1 at 162.63 (see Table 8).

Q_3 is found in the same way by counting off 3/4 of N (37.5) from the small-score end of the distribution. The f's on 140–144 to 170–174, inclusive, added in order, total 30. The next interval, 175–179, contains 8 scores. To make up the necessary 37.5, therefore, take $7.5/8 \times 5$ (interval) and add this amount (viz., 4.69) to 174.50. This puts Q_3 at 179.19 (see Table 8).

TABLE 8 The calculation of the Q, MD and SD from data grouped into a frequency distribution

1. Data from Table 1, page 5, 50 Army Alpha scores					
(1)	(2)	(3)	(4)	(5)	(6)
Class-Intervals Scores	Midpoint X	f	x	fx	fx^2
195–199	197	1	26.20	26.20	686.44
190–194	192	2	21.20	42.40	898.88
185–189	187	4	16.20	64.80	1049.76
180–184	182	5	11.20	56.00	627.20
175–179	177	8	6.20	49.60	307.52
170–174	172	10 30	1.20	12.00	14.40
165–169	167	6	− 3.80	− 22.80	86.64
160–164	162	4	− 8.80	− 35.20	309.76
155–159	157	4 10	− 13.80	− 55.20	761.76
150–154	152	2	− 18.80	− 37.60	706.88
145–149	147	3	− 23.80	− 71.40	1699.32
140–144	142	1	− 28.80	− 28.80	829.44
		$N = 50$		502.00	7978.00

*It may be noted that the second quartile, Q_2, is the median.

TABLE 8—(Continued)

Mean = 170.80 (Table 5, p. 30)

$\frac{N}{4} = 12.5$ and $\frac{3N}{4} = 37.5$

$Q_1 = 159.5 + \frac{2.5}{4} \times 5 = 162.63$ $Q_3 = 174.5 + \frac{7.5}{8} \times 5 = 179.19$

$Q = \frac{Q_3 - Q_1}{2} = \frac{179.19 - 162.63}{2} = 8.28$

$MD = \frac{\Sigma|fx|}{N} = \frac{502.00}{50} = 10.04$

$SD = \sqrt{\frac{\Sigma fx^2}{N}} = \sqrt{\frac{7978.00}{50}} = 12.63$

2. Data from Table 3, p. 13, 200 cancellation scores

(1) Class-Intervals Scores	(2) Midpoint X	(3) f		(4) x	(5) fx	(6) fx^2
135.5 to 139.5	137.5	3		18.06	54.18	978.49
131.5 to 135.5	133.5	5		14.06	70.30	988.42
127.5 to 131.5	129.5	16		10.06	160.96	1619.26
123.5 to 127.5	125.5	23		6.06	139.38	844.64
119.5 to 123.5	121.5	52		2.06	107.12	220.67
115.5 to 119.5	117.5	49	101	−1.94	−95.06	184.42
111.5 to 115.5	113.5	27		−5.94	−160.38	952.66
107.5 to 111.5	109.5	18	25	−9.94	−178.92	1778.46
103.5 to 107.5	105.5	7		−13.94	−97.58	1360.27
		$N = 200$			1063.88	8927.29

Mean = 119.44 (Table 5)

$\frac{N}{4} = 50$ and $\frac{3N}{4} = 150$

$Q_1 = 111.5 + \frac{23}{27} \times 4 = 115.20$ $Q_3 = 119.5 + \frac{49}{52} \times 4 = 123.27$

$Q = \frac{Q_3 - Q_1}{2} = \frac{123.27 - 115.20}{2} = 4.04$

$MD = \frac{\Sigma|fx|}{N} = \frac{1063.88}{200} = 5.32$

$SD = \sqrt{\frac{\Sigma fx^2}{N}} = \sqrt{\frac{8927.29}{200}} = 6.68$

When Q_1 and Q_3 are known, Q, the quartile deviation, is found from the formula

$$Q = \frac{Q_3 - Q_1}{2} \quad (7)$$

(*quartile deviation calculated from grouped data*)

In the present problem, $Q = \frac{179.19 - 162.63}{2}$ or 8.28.

MEASURES OF VARIABILITY • 47

A second illustration of the calculation of Q from a frequency distribution is given in Table 8, example 2. Since the N of this distribution is 200, 1/4 of N equals 50. The intervals 103.5 to 107.5 and 107.5 to 111.5 contain 25 scores; and the next interval, 111.5 to 115.5, contains 27 scores, which makes a total of 52—two more than the 50 wanted. To find the point reached by just 50 scores, take $25/27 \times 4$ (the interval) and add this amount (3.70) to 111.50, the lower limit of 111.5 to 115.5. This locates Q_1 at 115.20.

To find Q_3 count off 3/4 of N or 150 scores from the small-score end of the distribution. The first four intervals include 101 scores, and the next interval, 119.5 to 123.5, contains 52 scores. To fill out the required 150, take $49/52 \times 4$, the length of the interval, and add this increment (3.77) to 119.50, to locate Q_3 at 123.27. Substituting 115.20 for Q_1 and 123.27 for Q_3 in formula (7) we get a Q of 4.04.

The quartiles Q_1 and Q_3 mark off the limits of the *middle 50%* of scores in the distribution and the distance between these points is called the *interquartile range*. Q is one-half the range of the middle 50% or the *semi-interquartile range*. Since Q measures the average distance of the quartile points from the median, it is a good measure of score density around the middle of the distribution. If the scores of a distribution are packed closely together the quartiles will be near to one another and Q will be small; if the scores are widely scattered, the quartiles will be relatively far apart, and Q will be large (see Fig. 7, p. 44).

When the distribution is asymmetrical or "skewed," Q_1 and Q_3 are at unequal distances from the median, and the difference between $(Q_3 - Mdn)$ and $(Mdn - Q_1)$ gives a measure of the amount and direction of the skewness (p. 98). When the distribution is symmetrical or *normal*, Q marks off exactly the 25% of cases just above, and the 25% of cases just below, the median. The median then lies just halfway between the two quartiles Q_1 and Q_3. In a normal distribution Q becomes the PE (*probable error*). The terms Q and PE are often used interchangeably, but it is best to restrict the use of the term PE to the normal probability curve (p. 97).

Steps in calculating Q may be summarized as follows:

To find Q_1

(1) Divide N by 4.
(2) Begin at the low-score end of the distribution, and count off the scores up to the interval which contains Q_1.
(3) Divide the number of scores necessary to locate Q_1 (i.e., to complete

$N/4$) by the frequency in the interval reached in (2) above, and multiply the result by the class-interval.

(4) Add the amount obtained in (3) to the lower limit of the class-interval within which Q_1 lies. This gives Q_1.

To find Q_3

(1) Find 3/4 of N.
(2) Begin at the low-score * end of the distribution, and count up the scores until the interval which contains Q_3 is reached.
(3) Divide the number of scores required to locate Q_3 by the frequency within the interval reached in (2) and multiply the result by the class-interval.
(4) Add the amount obtained in (3) to the lower limit of the class-interval within which Q_3 lies. This gives Q_3.

To find Q

Substitute Q_3 and Q_1 in formula (7).

3. The Mean Deviation or MD

(1) CALCULATION OF MD FROM UNGROUPED DATA

The *mean deviation* or *MD* (also written *average deviation* or *AD* and *mean variation* or *MV*) is the mean of the deviations of all the separate measures in a series taken from their central tendency (usually the arithmetic mean; less frequently the median or mode). In averaging deviations to find the MD, no account is taken of signs, and all deviations whether positive or negative are treated as positive.

An example will make our definition clearer. If we have five scores, 6, 8, 10, 12, and 14, the mean is easily found to be 10. It is then a simple process to find the deviation of each measure from this mean by subtracting the mean from each measure. Thus 6, the first score, minus 10 equals -4; $8 - 10 = -2$; $10 - 10 = 0$; $12 - 10 = 2$; and $14 - 10 = 4$. The five deviations measured from the mean are $-4, -2, 0, 2,$ and 4. If we add these deviations *without regard to signs* the sum is 12; and dividing 12 by 5 (N), we get 2 4 as the *mean* of the five deviations from their mean, or the MD. The formula for the MD when scores are ungrouped may be written

$$MD = \frac{\Sigma |x|}{N} \qquad (8)$$

(*mean deviation for ungrouped measures*)

---

* Q_3 may also be found by counting in 25% from the high-score end of the distribution. To avoid confusion, the method given above is recommended to the beginner.

in which the $\Sigma \mid x \mid$ denotes the sum of the deviations from the mean and N is, as before, the number of cases or items. The bars $\mid\mid$ enclosing Σx indicate that signs are disregarded. The small letter x in the formula always represents the deviation of a score X from its mean M, i.e., $x = X - M$.

(2) CALCULATION OF MD FROM GROUPED DATA

In Table 8 the calculation of the MD for scores grouped into a frequency distribution is illustrated by two problems. The mean of the fifty Army Alpha scores in problem 1 has already been found in Table 5, page 30, to be 170.80. To compute the MD of the scores in this distribution we must take our deviations (x's) around this mean. However, since the scores have been grouped into class-intervals, we are unable to get the deviation of each *separate score* from the mean. In lieu of separate score deviations, therefore, we take the deviation of the *midpoint* of each interval from the mean. The substitution of the midpoint for all of the scores within an interval is the only difference between the computation of x's from grouped and from ungrouped data. The x of 195–199, for example, is 26.20, found by subtracting 170.80 (the mean) from 197.00 (the midpoint of the interval). All of the x's are positive as far down as 170–174, as in each case the midpoint is numerically larger than the mean. From the interval 165–169 on down to the beginning of the series, the x's are negative, as the midpoints of these intervals are all smaller than 170.80. Thus the x of interval 165–169 is -3.80; and the x of the lowest interval in the distribution, 140–144, is -28.80.

It will be helpful in calculating deviations from the mean to remember that the mean is *always* subtracted from the individual score or midpoint value. That is, x (deviation) $= X$ (score or midpoint) $- M$ (mean). The calculation is algebraic. When the score or midpoint is numerically *larger* than the mean the deviation is positive; when the score or midpoint is numerically *smaller* than the mean the deviation is negative.

Column (4) Table 8, page 45, gives the deviation of each class-interval, as represented by its midpoint, from the mean of the distribution. There are more scores on some intervals than on others; hence each midpoint deviation in column (4) must be "weighted" or multiplied by the number of scores (f) which it represents. This gives the fx column, column (5). The first fx is 26.20; for, since there is only one score on 195–199, we multiply the first x by 1. The next fx is 42.40, since each of the two scores on 190–194 has an x of 21.20. In the same way we obtain the other fx's by multiplying, in each case, the x in column (4) by its corresponding f in column (3). When all of the fx's have been calculated, the column is added without regard to sign, and the resulting sum is divided by N to give the MD. In the present problem the MD equals 502.00/50 or 10.04.

The formula for the MD when measures are grouped into a frequency distribution is as follows:

$$MD = \frac{\Sigma \mid fx \mid}{N} \qquad (9)$$

(*mean deviation for scores grouped into a frequency distribution*)

The second problem in Table 8 shows the calculation of the MD for 200 cancellation scores grouped into a frequency distribution in class-intervals of four. The mean of this distribution was found to be 119.44 (Table 5, page 30). Hence, the x of the topmost interval, 135.5 to 139.5 (midpoint 137.50), from the mean is 18.06. Since the class-interval is constant in size, the next x may be found by subtracting 4 (the interval) from 18.06; and each succeeding x may be found by subtracting 4 from the x just preceding it.

The fx's in column (5) are found, as shown in problem 1, by weighting each x by the f which it represents—by the f opposite it. The sum of the fx column is 1063.88; and, since N is equal to 200, from formula (9) we obtain 5.32 as the MD of the scores in this distribution around their mean of 119.44.

In a symmetrical or normal distribution the MD, when measured off on the scale above and below the mean, marks the limits of the middle 57.5% of the measures. The MD is always slightly larger, therefore, than the Q which marks off the limits of the middle 50%. A large MD means that the scores of the distribution tend to scatter widely around the central tendency; a small MD that they tend to be concentrated within a relatively narrow range.

4. The standard deviation or SD

The *standard* deviation or SD is the measure of variability customarily employed in research. The SD differs from the MD in several respects. In calculating the MD we disregard signs and treat all deviations as positive; in finding the SD we avoid this difficulty of signs by squaring the separate deviations. Again, the squared deviations used in computing the SD are always taken from the mean of the distribution, and never from the median or mode. The conventional symbol used to denote the SD is the Greek letter sigma (σ).

(1) CALCULATION OF *SD* FROM UNGROUPED DATA

The standard deviation or σ is the square root of the mean of the squared deviations taken from the arithmetical mean of the distribution. To illustrate the calculation of the *SD* in a simple ungrouped series, let us consider the example given on page 48, to illustrate the calculation of the *MD*, in which the deviations of the five measures, 6, 8, 10, 12, and 14 from their mean of 10 were found to be -4, -2, 0, 2, and 4, respectively. Squaring each of these deviations, we obtain 16, 4, 0, 4, and 16. Summing these five squares and dividing by five, we obtain the mean of the squares, and, extracting the square root, get 2.83, the *SD* of this series. The formula for the *SD* or σ when the series of scores is ungrouped is as follows:

$$\sigma = \sqrt{\frac{\Sigma x^2}{N}} \qquad (10)$$

(*standard deviation calculated from ungrouped data*)

(2) CALCULATION OF *SD* FROM GROUPED DATA

Table 8 illustrates the calculation of σ when scores are grouped into a frequency distribution. The process is identical with that used for ungrouped items, except that, in addition to squaring the x of each midpoint from the mean, we weight each of these squared deviations by the freqency which it represents—that is, by the frequency opposite it. This multiplication gives the fx^2 column. By simple algebra, $x \times fx = fx^2$; and accordingly the easiest way to obtain the entries in column fx^2 is to multiply the corresponding x's and fx's in columns (4) and (5). The first fx^2 entry, for example, is 686.44, the product of 26.20 times 26.20; the second entry is 898.88, the product of 42.40 times 21.20; and so on to the end of the column. All of the fx^2 are necessarily positive since each negative x is matched by a negative fx. The sum of the fx^2 column (7978.00) divided by N (50) gives the mean of the squared deviations as 159.56; and the square root of this result is 12.63, the *SD*. The formula for σ when data are grouped into a frequency distribution is:

$$\sigma = \sqrt{\frac{\Sigma fx^2}{N}} \qquad (11)$$

(*SD or σ for data grouped into a frequency distribution*)

Problem 2 of Table 8, page 46 furnishes another illustration of the calculation of σ from grouped data. In column (6), the fx^2 entries have been obtained, as in the previous problem, by multiplying each

52 • STATISTICS IN PSYCHOLOGY AND EDUCATION

x by its corresponding fx. The sum of the fx^2 column is 8927.29; and N is 200. Hence, applying formula (11) we get 6.68 as the SD.

The standard deviation is less affected by *sampling errors* (p. 194) than is the Q or the MD and is a more stable measure of dispersion. In a normal distribution the SD, when measured off above and below the mean, marks the limits of the middle 68.26% (roughly the middle two-thirds) of the distribution.* This is approximately true also of the σ in less symmetrical distributions. For example, in the first problem in Table 8 the middle 65% of the scores fall between score 183 (170.80 + 12.63) and score 158 (170.80 − 12.63).† The SD is larger than the MD which is, in turn, larger than Q. These relationships supply a rough check upon the accuracy of the measures of variability.

II. Calculation of the SD by the Short Method

1. Calculation of σ from grouped data

On page 37, the Short Method of calculating the mean was outlined. This method consisted essentially in "guessing" or assuming

TABLE 9 The calculation of the SD by the short method.‡ Data from Table I. Calculations by the long method given for comparison

		1. Short Method			
(1)	(2)	(3)	(4)	(5)	(6)
Scores	Midpoint X	f	x'	fx'	fx'^2
195–199	197	1	5	5	25
190–194	192	2	4	8	32
185–189	187	4	3	12	36
180–184	182	5	2	10	20
175–179	177	8	1	8 (+ 43)	8
170–174	172	10	0		
165–169	167	6	− 1	− 6	6
160–164	162	4	− 2	− 8	16
155–159	157	4	− 3	− 12	36
150–154	152	2	− 4	− 8	32
145–149	147	3	− 5	− 15	75
140–144	142	1	− 6	− 6 (− 55)	36
		$N = \overline{50}$		$\overline{98}$	$\overline{322}$

* See page 96.
† See page 71 for method of calculating the percentage of scores falling between two points in a frequency distribution.
‡ The calculation of the mean is repeated from Table 7.

TABLE 9—(Continued)

1. $AM = 172.00 \qquad c = -\frac{12}{50} = -.240 \qquad ci = -.240 \times 5 = -1.20$
   $\qquad\qquad\qquad c^2 = .0576$
   $ci = -1.20$
   $M = 170.80$

2. $SD = i\sqrt{\dfrac{\Sigma fx'^2}{N} - c^2} = 5\sqrt{\dfrac{322}{50} - .0576}$
   $\quad = 12.63$

2. Long Method

(1)	(2)	(3)	(4)	(5)	(6)	(7)
Scores	Midpoint X	f	fX	x	fx	fx^2
195–199	197	1	197	26.20	26.20	686.44
190–194	192	2	384	21.20	42.40	898.88
185–189	187	4	748	16.20	64.80	1049.76
180–184	182	5	910	11.20	56.00	627.20
175–179	177	8	1416	6.20	49.60	307.52
170–174	172	10	1720	1.20	12.00	14.40
165–169	167	6	1002	− 3.80	− 22.80	86.64
160–164	162	4	648	− 8.80	− 35.20	309.76
155–159	157	4	628	− 13.80	− 55.20	761.76
150–154	152	2	304	− 18.80	− 37.60	706.88
145–149	147	3	441	− 23.80	− 71.40	1699.32
140–144	142	1	142	− 28.80	− 28.80	829.44
		$N = 50$	8540		502.00	7978.00

1. $M = \dfrac{\Sigma fX}{N} = \dfrac{8540}{50} = 170.80$

2. $SD = \sqrt{\dfrac{\Sigma fx^2}{N}} = \sqrt{\dfrac{7978.00}{50}} = 12.63$

---

a mean, and later applying to this value a correction to give the actual mean. The Short Method may also be used to advantage in calculating the SD.* It is a decided time and labor saver in dealing with grouped data; and is well-nigh indispensable in the calculation of σ's in a correlation table (p. 134).

The Short Method of calculating the SD is illustrated in Table 9. The computation of the mean is repeated in the table, as is also the calculation of the mean and SD by the direct or Long Method. This procedure affords a readier comparison of the two techniques.

---

*The MD may also be calculated by the assumed mean or Short Method. The MD is so rarely used, however, that the Short Method of calculation (which is neither very short nor very satisfactory) is not given.

The formula for computing σ by the Short Method is

$$\sigma = i \sqrt{\frac{\Sigma f x'^2}{N} - c^2} \quad (12)$$

(SD *from a frequency distribution when deviations are taken from an assumed mean*)

in which $\Sigma f x'^2$ is the sum of the squared deviations in units of class-interval, taken from the assumed mean, c^2 is the squared correction in units of class-interval, and i is the class-interval.

The calculation of σ by the Short Method may be followed in detail from Table 9. Deviations are taken from the assumed mean (172.0) in units of class-interval and entered in column (4) as x'. In column (5) each x' is weighted or multiplied by its f to give the fx'; and in column (6) the fx'^2's are found by multiplying each x' in column (4) by the corresponding fx' in column (5). The process is identical with that used in the Long Method except that the x'''s are all expressed in units of class-interval. This considerably simplifies the multiplication. The calculation of c has already been described on page 38: c is the algebraic sum of column (5) divided by N. The sum of the fx'^2 column is 322, and c^2 is .0576. Applying formula (12) we get 2.525×5 (interval) or 12.63 as the σ of the distribution. Formula (12) for the calculation of σ by the Short Method holds good no matter what the size of c, the correction in units of class-interval, or where the mean has been assumed.

2. Calculation of σ from the original measures or scores

It will often save time and labor to apply the Short Method for computing σ directly to the ungrouped scores. The method is illustrated in Table 10. Note that the ten scores are ungrouped, and that it is not necessary even to arrange them in order of size. The assumed mean is taken at zero, and each score becomes at once a deviation (x') from this AM, that is, each score (X) is unchanged. The correction, c, is the difference between the actual mean (M) and the assumed mean (0), i.e., $c = M - 0$; hence c is simply M itself. The mean is calculated, as before, by summing the scores and dividing by N (see page 28). To find σ, we square the x'''s (or the X's which are the scores), sum them to get $\Sigma(x')^2$ or ΣX^2, divide by N, and

MEASURES OF VARIABILITY • 55

TABLE 10 To illustrate the calculation of the SD from original scores when the assumed mean is taken at zero, and data are ungrouped

Scores (X)	x' (or X)	$(x')^2$ or (X^2)
18	18	324
25	25	625
21	21	441
19	19	361
27	27	729
31	31	961
22	22	484
25	25	625
28	28	784
20	20	400
236	236	5734

$AM = 0$
$M = \frac{236}{10} = 23.6$ $N = 10$
$c = 23.6 - 0$
$ = 23.6$
$c^2 = 556.96$
$\sigma = \sqrt{\frac{5734}{10} - (23.6)^2} \times 1 \text{ (interval)}$
$ = \sqrt{16.44}$
$ = 4.05$

subtract M^2, the correction squared. The square root of the result gives σ. A convenient formula is

$$\sigma = \sqrt{\frac{\Sigma X^2}{N} - M^2} \qquad (13)$$

or replacing the M^2 by $\left(\frac{\Sigma X}{N}\right)^2$,

$$\sigma = \frac{\sqrt{N \Sigma X^2 - (\Sigma X)^2}}{N} \qquad (14)$$

(σ *calculated from original scores by the Short Method*)

This method of calculating σ is especially useful when there are relatively few scores, say fifty or less, and when the scores are expressed in not more than two digits,* so that the squares do not become unwieldy. A calculating machine and a table of squares will greatly facilitate computation. Simply sum the scores as they stand and divide by N to get M. Then enter the squares of the scores in

---

* For the application of this method to the calculation of coefficients of correlation, and a scheme for reducing the size of the original scores so as to eliminate the need for handling large numbers, see page 143.

the machine in order, sum, and substitute the result in formula (13) or formula (14).

3. Effect upon σ of (a) adding a constant to each score, or (b) multiplying each score by the same number

(a) If each score in a frequency distribution is increased by some set amount, say 5, the σ is unchanged. The table below provides a simple illustration. The mean of the original scores is 7 and σ is 1.41. When each score is increased by 5, the mean is 12 $(7+5)$, but σ is still 1.41. Adding a constant (e.g., 5, 10, 15) to each score simply moves the whole distribution up the scale 5, 10, or 15 points. The mean is increased by the amount of the constant added, but the variability (σ) is not affected. If a constant is subtracted from each score, the distribution is moved down the scale by that amount; the mean is decreased by the amount of the constant, and σ, again, is unchanged.

Original scores (X)	x	x^2	Original scores $X + 5$	x	x^2
9	2	4	14	2	4
8	1	1	13	1	1
7	0	0	12	0	0
6	−1	1	11	−1	1
5	−2	4	10	−2	4
5)35		10	5)60		10
M = 7			M = 12		

$$\sigma = \sqrt{\frac{10}{5}} = 1.41 \qquad \sigma = \sqrt{\frac{10}{5}} = 1.41$$

(b) What happens to the mean and σ when each score is multiplied by a constant is shown in the table below:

Original scores (X)	Original scores $X \times 10$	x	x^2
9	90	20	400
8	80	10	100
7	70	0	0
6	60	−10	100
5	50	−20	400
35	5)350		1000
M = 7	M = 70		
σ = 1.41			

$$\sigma = \sqrt{\frac{1000}{5}} = \sqrt{200} = 14.14$$

Each score in the list of five, shown above, has been multiplied by 10; and the net effect of this operation is to multiply the mean *and* the σ by 10.

4. The σ from combined distributions

When two sets of scores have been thrown together into a single distribution, it is possible to calculate the σ of the total distribution from the σ's of the two component distributions. The formula is

$$\sigma_{\text{comb}} = \sqrt{\frac{N_1(\sigma_1^2 + d_1^2) + N_2(\sigma_2^2 + d_2^2)}{N}} \quad (15)$$

(SD *of a distribution obtained by combining two frequency distributions*)

in which

$\sigma_1 = SD$ of distribution 1
$\sigma_2 = SD$ of distribution 2
$d_1 = (M_1 - M_{\text{comb}})$
$d_2 = (M_2 - M_{\text{comb}})$

N_1 and N_2 are the numbers of cases in component distributions 1 and 2, respectively, and $N = (N_1 + N_2)$. The M_{comb} is the mean of the combined distribution got from formula (3), page 31.

An example will illustrate the use of formula (15). Suppose that in a class of 25 children, the mean (M_1) of an achievement test is 80 and $\sigma_1 = 15$; and that in a second class of 75 children, the mean (M_2) on the same test is 70 and $\sigma_2 = 25$. What is the σ_{comb} of the total distribution of 100 cases? First, we find that M_{comb}

$= \dfrac{25 \times 80 + 75 \times 70}{100} = 72.50$. We have, then, that $d_1 = (80 - 72.5)$ and $d_1^2 = 56.25$; $d_2 = (70 - 72.5)$ and $d_2^2 = 6.25$. Substituting in formula (15) for $\sigma_1, \sigma_2, d_1, d_2, N_1$, and N_2 we find that

$$\sigma_{\text{comb}} = \sqrt{\frac{25(225 + 56.25) + 75(625 + 6.25)}{100}} = 23.32$$

Formula (15) may easily be extended to include more than two component distributions by adding N_3, σ_3, d_3, and so on.

III. The Coefficient of Variation, V

It is often desirable to compare the variability of a given group upon two or more *different* tests; or to compare the variabilities of two or more groups upon the *same* test. We may wish, for example, to know whether 8-year-old girls are more variable in height than

58 • STATISTICS IN PSYCHOLOGY AND EDUCATION

in weight; or whether 10-year-old boys are more variable than 10-year-old girls in vocabulary or in memory span. The Q, MD, and SD are not suitable, ordinarily, for such comparisons. These measures give the *absolute* spread or dispersion of test scores around their means in terms of the units of the test. But owing to differences in measuring units, we cannot compare the variability in height and the variability in weight of a given group directly; nor can we compare the relative variability in height of two groups, says boys and girls, unless the means of the two distributions are at least approximately equal. To enable us to tell whether one group is more variable than another, we need a measure which takes account *both* of the central tendency *and* of the variability of the group, and which is independent of the units in which ability is expressed. One such measure is the ratio σ/M, called the *coefficient of variation,* or V. The formula for V is

$$V = \frac{100 \times \sigma}{M} \qquad (16)$$

(*the coefficient of variation or coefficient of relative variability*) *

The following illustrations will make the use of the formula clear. Consider, first, the case where abilities are measured in different units. A group of 7-year-old boys has a mean height of 45 inches with a σ of 2.5 inches; and a mean weight of 50 pounds with a σ of 6.0 pounds. In which trait is the group more variable, height or weight? Since we cannot compare inches and pounds directly, it is impossible to answer this question by reference to the SD's of the height and weight distributions. But we can compare the relative variability of the two distributions in terms of their coefficients of variation. Thus,

$$V_{ht} = \frac{100 \times 2.5}{45} = 5.6 \qquad \text{by (16)}$$

and

$$V_{wt} = \frac{100 \times 6.0}{50} = 12 \qquad \text{by (16)}$$

from which it appears that these boys are 5.6/12 or 47% as variable in height as in weight.

Now let us consider the case where variability is measured in the same units, but around different points on the scale. At the end of five minutes, a group of 50 children had worked an average of 20.50 ex-

---

* The multiplier 100 is introduced for the purpose of avoiding small fractional results.

amples correctly, the σ being 5.24. At the end of ten minutes, the same group had worked an average of 34.80 examples correctly, the σ being 9.62. If we compared the σ's of the two distributions directly, we should probably be inclined to conclude that the group was nearly twice as variable at the end of the 10-minute period as it was at the end of the 5-minute period, since the σ has increased from 5.24 to 9.62. This conclusion is correct as far as the *absolute* spread or variability within the group is concerned. But to compare the *relative* dispersion of the group in the two periods, we must note that, with the increase in σ, the means have also increased from 20.50 to 34.80. The coefficients of variation give the following results:

$$\text{For the 5-minute period: } V = \frac{100 \times 5.24}{20.50} = 25.6$$

$$\text{For the 10-minute period: } V = \frac{100 \times 9.62}{34.80} = 27.6$$

Thus, instead of being about 50% as variable in the 5-minute period as in the 10, the group is 25.6/27.6 or 93% as variable, when the mean score is considered as well as the absolute variability.

Objection has been raised * to the use of V in comparing the relative variability of test scores because the "true" zero point of ability in mental and educational tests is unknown. This objection does not apply, of course, to physical and physiological measures since these have true zeros. How the lack of knowledge of the true zero in a mental test may affect V can be shown most readily, perhaps, by an example. Suppose that we have given a vocabulary test to a group of children, and have obtained a mean of 25 and a σ of 5. V will equal 20. Now suppose that we add 30 very easy items, say, to our vocabulary test. It is highly probable that every child will know all of the added words, and hence the mean score as well as every subject's score will be increased by 30. The absolute variability of the group (the σ) will, however, remain unchanged, as each subject occupies exactly the same relative position as before. An increase in the mean (from 25 to 55) without a corresponding increase in σ changes V from 20 to 9; and, since we could add 40 or 400 items as easily as 30, V appears to be a very unstable measure.

While theoretically correct, criticism of V because of the arbitrary

---

* Franzen, R., "Statistical Issues," *Journal of Educational Psychology*, 1924, 15, 367–382.
    Thurstone, L. L., "The Absolute Zero in Intelligence Measurement," *Psychological Review*, 1928, 35, 175–197.

nature of the zero point in mental and educational tests is not so generally destructive as it seems. Makers of standard psychological tests have been careful to begin their tests with items which, by experimental tryout, have been found to have minimal difficulty for the group for whom the test is designed. While admittedly arbitrary, such "zero" points are at least located at extremely low levels of difficulty in the ability measured by the test; hence it would be foolish to include additional easy items at the low end of the scale. The mean tells us how far the group has progressed, on the average, from the arbitrary zero point of the test. V shows, essentially, what percentage the variability is of this distance. Like M, V has a definite meaning for the test as it stands. If the range of difficulty in the test is altered, or the units changed, not only V, but M, is changed. V, therefore, is in a sense no more arbitrary than M, and the objections to this measure can be directed with equal force against M.

V is most useful, perhaps, in comparing the variability of a group upon the *same* test administered under different conditions, as, for example, when a group of students works at a task with and without distraction. The zero point here, at least, remains substantially constant. V may also be used to compare two or more groups on the *same* test, as when 10-year-old boys and 10-year-old girls are compared in tests of logical memory or picture completion. In both of these cases it is probably justifiable to assume that the "true" zero point of ability is sensibly the same for the groups compared.

It is, perhaps, most difficult to interpret V when the variability of a group upon *different* mental tests is a matter of interest. If we compare a group of girls for variability in paragraph reading and in arithmetic computation, it should be made plain that the V's refer *only* to the specific scales upon which performance has been measured. Other tests of reading and arithmetic may—and probably will —give different results because of difference in test units, range of difficulty covered by the test, and position of arbitrary zero points. But if one restricts his use of V to the particular measures which he has employed, this coefficient will furnish useful information.

IV. When To Use the Various Measures of Variability

1. *Use the range*
    (1) When the data are too scant or too scattered to justify the calculation of any other measure of variability.
    (2) When a knowledge of the total spread of scores is all that is wanted.

2. *Use the Q*
   (1) For a quick, inspectional measure of variability.
   (2) When there are scattered or extreme measures.
   (3) When the degree of concentration around the median is sought.

3. *Use the MD*
   (1) When it is desired to weight all deviations according to their size.
   (2) When extreme deviations should influence the measure of variability, but not influence it unduly.

4. *Use the SD*
   (1) When the measure having the highest degree of reliability is sought (p. 194).
   (2) When it is desired that extreme deviations have a proportionally greater influence upon the measure of variability.
   (3) When coefficients of correlation or measures of reliability are subsequently to be computed (p. 182).

PROBLEMS

1. Calculate the Q and σ for each of the four frequency distributions given on page 40 under problem 1, Chapter 2.

2. Calculate the σ of the 25 ungrouped scores given on page 24, problem 5(a), taking the AM at zero. Compare your result with the σ's calculated from the frequency distributions of the same scores which you tabulated in class-intervals of three and five units.

3. For the following list of test scores,
   $$52, 50, 56, 68, 65, 62, 57, 70$$
   (a) Find the M and σ by method on page 55.
   (b) Add 6 to each score and recalculate M and σ.
   (c) Subtract 50 from each score, and calculate M and σ.
   (d) Multiply each score by 5 and compute M and σ.

4. (a) In Sample A ($N = 150$), $M = 120$ and $\sigma = 20$; in Sample B ($N = 75$), $M = 126$ and $\sigma = 22$. What are the mean and SD of A and B when combined into one distribution of 225 cases?
   (b) What are the mean and SD obtained by combining the following three distributions?

Distribution	N	M	σ
I	20	60	8
II	120	50	20
III	60	40	12

62 • STATISTICS IN PSYCHOLOGY AND EDUCATION

5. Calculate coefficients of variation for the following traits:

Trait	Unit of measurement	Group	M	σ
Length of Head	mms.	802 males	190.52	5.90
Body Weight	pounds	868,445 males	141.54	17.82
Tapping Speed	M of 5 trials 30" each	68 adults, male and female	196.91	26.83
Memory Span	No. repeated correctly	263 males	6.60	1.13
General Intelligence (Otis Group Intell. Scale)	Points scored	1101 adults	153.3	23.6

Rank these traits in order for relative variability. Judged by their V's which trait is the most variable? which the least variable? which traits have true zeros?

6. (a) Why is the Q the best measure of variability when there are scattered or extreme scores?

(b) Why does the σ weight extreme deviations more than does the MD?

ANSWERS

1. (1) $Q = 3.38$ (2) $Q = 8.13$
      σ = 4.99   σ = 11.33

 (3) $Q = 4.50$ (4) $Q = 16.41$
      σ = 7.23   σ = 24.13

2. σ of ungrouped scores = 6.72
 σ of scores grouped in 3-unit intervals = 6.71
 σ of scores grouped in 5-unit intervals = 6.78

3. (a) $M = 60$ (b) $M = 66$ (c) $M = 10$ (d) $M = 300$
      σ = 6.91   σ = 6.91   σ = 6.91   σ = 34.55

4. (a) $M = 122.0$; σ = 20.9
 (b) $M = 48.00$; σ = 18.05

5. V's in order are 3.10; 12.59; 13.63; 17.12; 15.39. Ranked for relative variability from most to least: Memory Span; General Intelligence; Tapping Speed; Weight; Head Length. Last two traits have true zeros.

4

CUMULATIVE DISTRIBUTIONS, GRAPHIC METHODS, AND PERCENTILES

✦

In Chapter 1, we learned how to represent the frequency distribution by means of the polygon and the histogram. In the present chapter, other descriptive methods will be considered—the *cumulative frequency graph*, the *cumulative percentage curve* or *ogive*, and certain simple graphical devices. Also, methods will be given for calculating percentiles and percentile ranks from frequency distributions and directly from graphs.

I. The Cumulative Frequency Graph

1. Construction of the cumulative frequency graph

The cumulative frequency graph is another way of representing a frequency distribution by means of a diagram. Before we can plot a cumulative frequency graph, the scores of the distribution must be added serially or cumulated, as shown in Table 11, for the two distributions taken from Table 5, page 30. These two sets of scores have already been used to illustrate the frequency polygon and histogram in Figures 2, 4, and 5, pages 11, 17, and 18. The first two columns for each of the distributions in Table 11 repeat Table 5, page 30, exactly; but in the third column (Cum. f) scores have been "accumulated" progressively from the bottom of the distribution upward. To illustrate, in the distribution of Army Alpha scores the first "cumulative frequency" is 1; $1 + 3$, from the low end of the distribution gives 4 as the next entry; $4 + 2 = 6$; $6 + 4 = 10$, etc. The last cumulative frequency is, of course, equal to 50 or N, the total frequency.

TABLE 11 Cumulative frequencies for the two distributions given in Table 5, page 30

Army Alpha Scores	f	Cum. f	Cancellation Scores	f	Cum. f
195–199	1	50	135.5 to 139.5	3	200
190–194	2	49	131.5 to 135.5	5	197
185–189	4	47	127.5 to 131.5	16	192
180–184	5	43	123.5 to 127.5	23	176
175–179	8	38	119.5 to 123.5	52	153
170–174	10	30	115.5 to 119.5	49	101
165–169	6	20	111.5 to 115.5	27	52
160–164	4	14	107.5 to 111.5	18	25
155–159	4	10	103.5 to 107.5	7	7
150–154	2	6		$N = 200$	
145–149	3	4			
140–144	1	1			
	$N = 50$				

The two cumulative frequency graphs which represent the distributions of Table 11 are shown in Figures 8 and 9. Consider first the graph of the 50 Army Alpha scores in Figure 8. The class-intervals of the distribution have been laid off along the X-axis. There

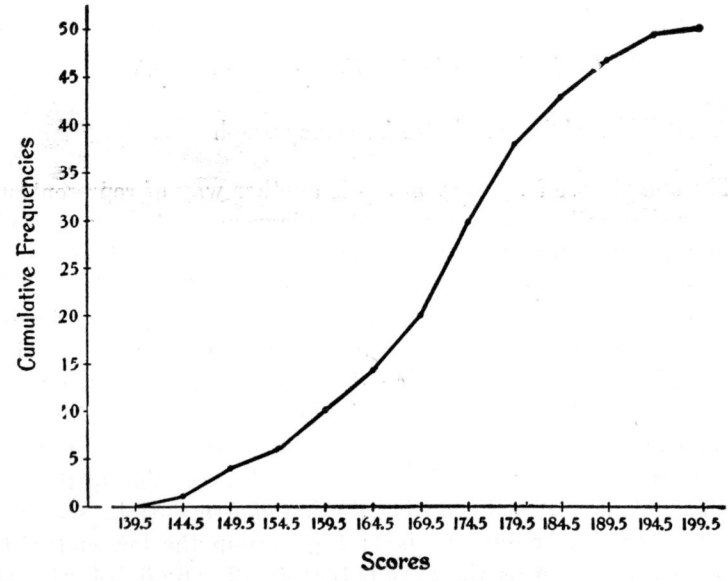

FIG. 8 Cumulative frequency graph

(Data from Table 11, above)

CUMULATIVE DISTRIBUTIONS, GRAPHIC METHODS, AND PERCENTILES • 65

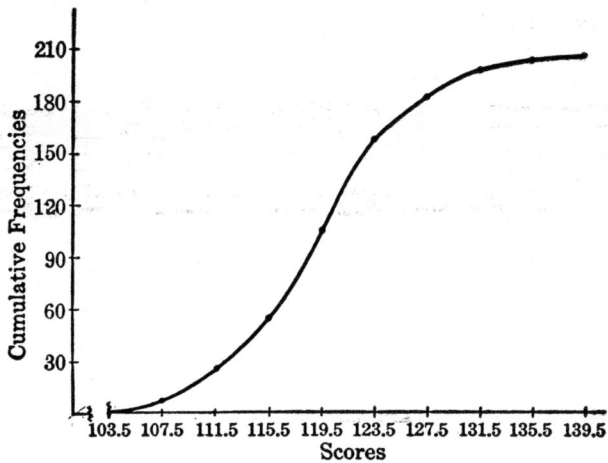

FIG. 9 Cumulative frequency graph

(Data from Table 11, p. 64)

are 12 intervals, and by the "75% rule" given on page 12 there should be about 9 unit distances (each equal to one class-interval) laid off on the Y-axis. Since the largest cumulative frequency is 50, each of these Y-units should represent 50/9 or 6 scores (approximately). Instead of dividing up the total Y-distance into 9 units each representing 6 scores, however, we have, for convenience in plotting, divided the total Y-distance into 10 units of 5 scores each. This does not change significantly the 3:4 relationship of height to width in the figure.

When plotting the frequency polygon the frequency on each interval is taken at the *midpoint* of the class-interval. But in constructing a cumulative frequency curve each cumulative frequency is plotted at the *upper limit* of the interval upon which it falls. This is because we are adding progressively from bottom up and hence each cumulative frequency carries through to the upper limit of the interval. The first point on the curve is one Y-unit (the cumulative frequency on 140–144) just above 144.5; the second point is 4 Y-units just above 149.5; the third, 6 Y-units just above 154.5, and so on to the last point which is 50 Y-units above 199.5. The plotted points are joined to give the S-shaped cumulative frequency graph. In order to have the curve begin on the X-axis it is started at 139.5 (upper limit of 134.5 to 139.5), the cumulative frequency of which is 0.

The cumulative frequency curve in Figure 9 has been plotted from the second distribution in Table 11 by the method just described. The curve begins at 103.5, the lower limit of the first class-interval,* and ends at 139.5, the upper limit of the last interval; and cumulative frequencies, 7, 25, 52, etc., are all plotted at the *upper limits* of their respective class-intervals. The height of this graph was determined by the "75% rule" as in the case of the curve in Figure 8. There are 9 class-intervals laid off on the X-axis; hence, since 75% of 9 is 7 (approximately), the height of the figure should be about seven class-interval units. To determine the score value of each Y-unit divide 200 (the largest cumulative frequency) by 7 to give 30 (approximately). Each of the 7 Y-units has been taken to represent 30 scores.

II. Percentiles and Percentile Ranks

1. Calculation of percentiles in a frequency distribution

We have learned (p. 31) that the median is that point in a frequency distribution below which lie 50% of the measures or scores; and that Q_1 and Q_3 mark points in the distribution below which lie, respectively, 25% and 75% of the measures or scores. In exactly the same way in which the median and quartiles are found, we may compute points below which lie 10%, 43%, 85%, or any percent of the scores. These points are called *percentiles*, and are designated, in general, by the symbol P_p, the p referring to the percentages of cases *below* the given value. P_{10}, for example, is the point below which lie 10% of the scores; P_{78}, the point below which lie 78% of the scores. It is evident that the median, expressed as a percentile, is P_{50}; also Q_1 is P_{25}, and Q_3 is P_{75}.

The method of calculating percentiles is essentially the same as that employed in finding the median. The formula is

$$P_p = l + \left(\frac{pN - F}{f_p}\right) \times i \text{ (interval)} \qquad (17)$$

(*percentiles in a frequency distribution, counting from below up*)
where

p = percentage of the distribution wanted, e.g., 10%, 33%, etc.

l = lower limit of the class-interval upon which P_p lies

* Or the upper limit of the interval just below, i.e., 99.5 to 103.5.

CUMULATIVE DISTRIBUTIONS, GRAPHIC METHODS, AND PERCENTILES • 67

pN = part of N to be counted off in order to reach P_p
F = sum of all scores upon intervals below l
f_p = number of scores within the interval upon which P_p falls
i = length of the class-interval

In Table 12, the percentile points, P_{10} to P_{90}, have been computed by formula (17) for the distribution of scores made by the fifty college students upon Army Alpha, shown in Table 1, page 5. The details of calculation are given in Table 12. We may illustrate

TABLE 12 Calculation of certain percentiles in a frequency distribution

(Data are fifty Army Alpha scores, see Table 1, p. 5)

Scores	f	Cum. f	Percentiles
195–199	1	50	$P_{100} = 199.5$
190–194	2	49	
185–189	4	47	$P_{90} = 187.0$
180–184	5	43	$P_{80} = 181.5$
175–179	8	38	$P_{70} = 177.6$
170–174	10	30	$P_{60} = 174.5$
165–169	6	20	$P_{50} = 172.0$
160–164	4	14	$P_{40} = 169.5$
155–159	4	10	$P_{30} = 165.3$
150–154	2	6	$P_{20} = 159.5$
145–149	3	4	$P_{10} = 152.0$
140–144	1	1	
	$N = \overline{50}$		$P_0 = 139.5$

CALCULATION OF PERCENTILE POINTS

10% of 50 = 5 $149.5 + \left(\dfrac{5-4}{2}\right) \times 5 = 152.0$

20% of 50 = 10 $159.5 + \left(\dfrac{10-10}{4}\right) \times 5 = 159.5$

30% of 50 = 15 $164.5 + \left(\dfrac{15-14}{6}\right) \times 5 = 165.3$

40% of 50 = 20 $169.5 + \left(\dfrac{20-20}{10}\right) \times 5 = 169.5$

50% of 50 = 25 $169.5 + \left(\dfrac{25-20}{10}\right) \times 5 = 172.0 \ (Mdn)$

60% of 50 = 30 $174.5 + \left(\dfrac{30-30}{8}\right) \times 5 = 174.5$

70% of 50 = 35 $174.5 + \left(\dfrac{35-30}{8}\right) \times 5 = 177.6$

80% of 50 = 40 $179.5 + \left(\dfrac{40-38}{5}\right) \times 5 = 181.5$

90% of 50 = 45 $184.5 + \left(\dfrac{45-43}{4}\right) \times 5 = 187.0$

68 • STATISTICS IN PSYCHOLOGY AND EDUCATION

the method with P_{70}. Here $pN = 35$ (70% of 50 = 35), and from the Cum. f we find that 30 scores take us through 170–174 up to 174.5, the *lower* limit of the interval next above. Hence, P_{70} falls upon 175–179, and, substituting $pN = 35$, $F = 30$, $f_p = 8$ (frequency upon 175–179), and $i = 5$ (class-interval) in formula (17), we find that $P_{70} = 177.6$ (for detailed calculation, see Table 12). This result means that 70% of the 50 students scored *below* 177.6 in the distribution of Army Alpha scores. The other percentile values are found in exactly the same way as P_{70}. The reader should verify the calculations of the P_p in Table 12 in order to become thoroughly familiar with the method.

It should be noted that P_0, which marks the lower limit of the first interval (namely, 139.5) lies at the beginning of the distribution. P_{100} marks the *upper limit* of the last interval, and lies at the end of the distribution. These two percentiles represent *limiting points*. Their principal value is to indicate the boundaries of the percentile scale.

2. Calculation of percentile ranks in a frequency distribution

We have seen in the last section how percentiles, e.g., P_{15} or P_{62}, may be calculated directly from a frequency distribution. To repeat what has been said above, percentiles are *points* in a continuous distribution below which lie given percentages of N. We shall now consider the problem of finding an individual's *percentile rank* (*PR*); or the position on a scale of 100 to which the subject's score entitles him. The distinction between *percentile* and *percentile rank* will be clear if the reader remembers that in calculating percentiles he *starts* with a certain percent of N, say 15% or 62%. He then counts into the distribution the given percent and the point reached is the required percentile, e.g., P_{15} or P_{62}. The procedure followed in computing percentile ranks is the reverse of this process. Here we begin with an individual *score*, and determine the percentage of scores which lies below it. If this percentage is 62, say, the score has a percentile rank or *PR* of 62 on a scale of 100.

We may illustrate with Table 12. What is the *PR* of a man who scores 163? Score 163 falls on interval 160–164. There are ten scores up to 159.5, lower limit of this interval (see column Cum. f), and four scores spread over this interval. Dividing 4 by 5 (interval length) gives us .8 score *per unit of interval*. The score of 163, which we are seeking, is 3.5 score units from 159.5, lower limit of the interval within which the score of 163 lies. Multiplying 3.5 by .8 we get 2.8 as the score-distance of 163 from 159.5; and adding 2.8 to 10 (number of scores below 159.5) we get 12.8 as the part of N lying *below* 163. Dividing 12.8 by 50 gives us 25.6% as that proportion of N below 163; hence the percentile rank of score 163 is 26. The diagram below will clarify the calculation:

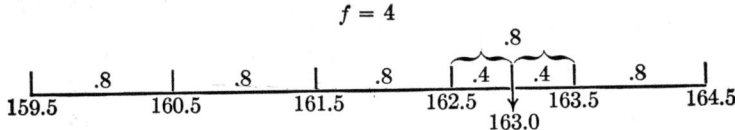

Ten scores lie below 159.5. Prorating the 4 scores on 160–164 over the interval of 5, we have .8 score per unit of interval. Score 163 is just .8 + .8 + .8 + .4 or 2.8 scores from 159.5; or score 163 lies 12.8 scores or 25.6% (12.8/50) into the distribution.

The PR of any score may be found in the same way. For example, the percentile rank of 181 is 79 (verify it). The reader should note that a score of 163 is taken as 163.0, midpoint of the score-interval 162.5 to 163.5. This means simply that the midpoint is assumed to be the most representative value in a score-interval. The percentile ranks for several scores may be read directly from Table 12. For instance, 152 has a PR of 10, 172 (median) a PR of 50, and 187 a PR of 90. If we take the percentile-points as representing *approximately* the score-intervals upon which they lie, the PR of 160 (upon which 159.5 lies) is approximately 20 (see Table 12); the PR of 165 (upon which 165.3 lies) is approximately 30; the PR of 170 is approximately 40; of 175, 60; of 178, 70; of 182, 80. These PR's are not strictly accurate, to be sure, but the error is slight.

III. The Cumulative Percentage Curve or Ogive

1. Construction of the ogive

The cumulative percentage curve or ogive differs from the cumulative frequency graph in that frequencies are expressed as cumulative *percents* of N on the Y-*axis* instead of as cumulative frequencies. Table 13 shows how cumulative frequencies can be turned into percentages of N. The distribution consists of scores made on a reading test by 125 seventh-grade pupils. In columns (1) and (2) class-intervals and frequencies are listed; and in column (3) the f's have

TABLE 13 Calculation of cumulative percentages to upper limits of class-intervals in a frequency distribution

(The data represent scores on a reading test achieved by 125 seventh-grade children)

(1) Scores	(2) f	(3) Cum. f	(4) Cum. Percent f
74.5 to 79.5	1	125	100.0
69.5 to 74.5	3	124	99.2
64.5 to 69.5	6	121	96.8
59.5 to 64.5	12	115	92.0
54.5 to 59.5	20	103	82.4
49.5 to 54.5	36	83	66.4
44.5 to 49.5	20	47	37.6
39.5 to 44.5	15	27	21.6
34.5 to 39.5	6	12	9.6
29.5 to 34.5	4	6	4.8
24.5 to 29.5	2	2	1.6
	$N = 125$		

$$\text{Rate} = \frac{1}{N} = \frac{1}{125} = .008$$

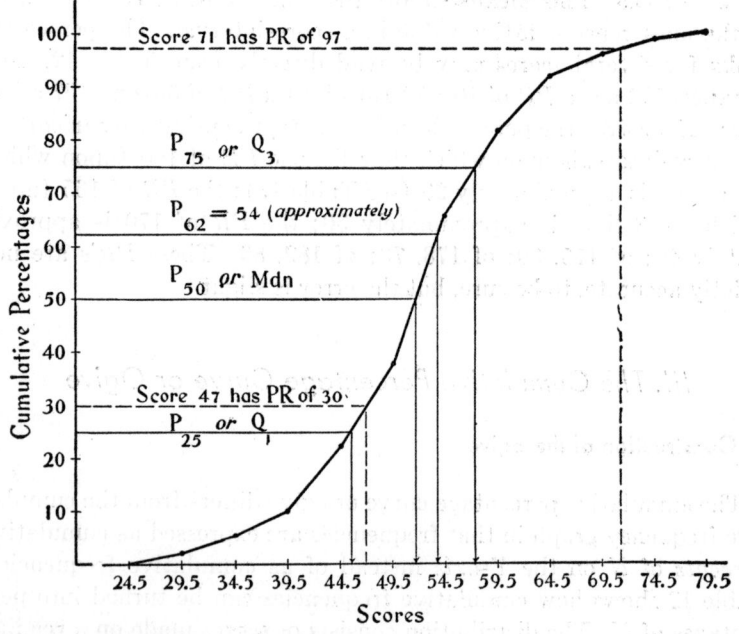

FIG. 10 Cumulative percentage curve or ogive plotted from the data of Table 13, above

CUMULATIVE DISTRIBUTIONS GRAPHIC METHODS, AND PERCENTILES • 71

been cumulated from the low end of the distribution upward as described before on page 63. These Cum. f's are expressed as percentages of N (125) in column (4). The conversion of Cum. f's into cumulative percents can be carried out by dividing each cumulative f by N; e.g., $2 \div 125 = .016$, $6 \div 125 = .048$, and so on. A better method—especially when a calculating machine is available—is to determine first the reciprocal, $1/N$, called the *Rate*, and multiply each cumulative f in order by this fraction. As shown in Table 13, the *Rate* is $1/125$ or .008. Hence, multiplying 2 by .008, we get .016 or 1.6%; $6 \times .008 = .048$ or 4.8%; $12 \times .008 = .096$ or 9.6%, etc.

The curve in Figure 10 represents an ogive plotted from the data in column (4), Table 13. Class-intervals have been laid off on the X-axis, and a scale consisting of 10 equal distances, each representing 10% of the distribution, has been marked off on the Y-axis. The first point on the ogive is placed 1.6 Y-units just above 29.5; the second point is 4.8 Y-units just above 34.5, etc. The last point is 100 Y-units above 79.5, upper limit of the highest class-interval.

2. Computing percentiles and percentile ranks from (a) the cumulative percentage distribution and from (b) the ogive

(a) Percentiles may be readily determined by direct interpolation in column (4), Table 13. We may illustrate by calculating the 71st percentile. Direct interpolation between the percentages in column (4) gives the following:

```
              66.4% of the distribution up to 54.5
71.0%    ----→-----------------------------------→ 55.9
(given)       82.4% of the distribution up to 59.5
              ─────                                ───
              16.0%                                5.0
```

The 71st percentile lies 4.6% above 66.4%. By simple proportion, $\frac{4.6}{16.0} = \frac{x}{5}$ or $x = \frac{4.6}{16.0} \times 5 = 1.4$ (x is the distance of the 71st percentile from 54.5). The 71st percentile, therefore, is $54.5 + 1.4$, or 55.9.

Certain percentiles can be read directly from column (4). We know, for instance, that the 5th percentile is approximately 34.5; that the 22nd percentile is approximately 44.5; that the 38th percentile is approximately 49.5; and that the 92nd percentile is exactly 64.5. Another way of expressing the same facts is to say that 21.6% of the seventh graders scored below 44.5, that 92% scored below 64.5, etc.

Percentile ranks may also be determined from Table 13 by interpolation. Suppose, for example, we wish to calculate the PR of score 43. From column (4) we find that 9.6% of the scores are *below* 39.5. Score 43 is 3.5 (43.0 − 39.5) from this point. There are 5 score-units on the interval 39.5 to 44.5 which correspond to 12.0% (21.6 − 9.6) of the distribution; hence, $3.5/5 \times 12.0$ or 8.4 is the percentage distance of score 43 from 39.5. Since 9.6% (up to 39.5) + 8.4% (from 39.5 to 43.0) comprise 18% of the distribution, this percentage of N lies *below* score 43. Hence, the PR of 43 is 18. See detailed calculation below.

```
                  9.6% of distribution up to 39.5
   18.0% ←---------------------------------←----score 43.0
                 21.6% of distribution up to 44.5     (given)
                 ─────                        ───
                 12.0%                        5.0
```

Score 43.0 is $3.5/5 \times 12.0\%$ or 8.4% from 39.5; hence score 43.0 is 9.6% + 8.4% or 18.0% into the distribution.

It should be noted that the cumulative percents in column (4) give the PR's of the *upper* limits of the class-intervals in which the scores have been tabulated. The PR of 74.5, for example, is 99.2; of 64.5, 92.0; of 44.5, 21.6, etc. These PR's are the ranks of given points in the distribution, and are not the PR's of scores.

(*b*) Percentiles and percentile ranks may also be determined quickly and fairly accurately from the ogive of the frequency distribution plotted in Figure 10. To obtain P_{50}, the median, for example, draw a line from 50 on the Y-scale parallel to the X-axis and where this line cuts the curve drop a perpendicular to the X-axis. This operation will locate the median at 51.5, approximately. The exact median, calculated from Table 13, page 70, is 51.65. Q_1 and Q_3 are found in the same way as the median. P_{25} or Q_1 falls approximately at 45.0 on the X-axis, and P_{75} or Q_3 falls at 57.0. These values may be compared with the calculated Q_1 and Q_3, which are 45.56 and 57.19, respectively. Other percentiles are read in the same way. To find P_{62}, for instance, begin with 62 on the Y-axis, go horizontally over to the curve, and drop a perpendicular to locate P_{62} approximately at 54.

In order to read the percentile rank of a given score from the ogive, we reverse the process followed in determining percentiles. Score 71, for example, has a PR of 97, approximately (see Figure 10). Calculation consists in starting with score 71 on the X-axis, going vertically up to the ogive, and horizontally across to the Y-axis to locate the PR at 97 on the cumulative percentage scale. The PR of score 47 is found in the same way to be approximately 30.

CUMULATIVE DISTRIBUTIONS, GRAPHIC METHODS, AND PERCENTILES • 73

It will be noted that percentiles and percentile ranks are usually slightly in error when read from an ogive. If the curve is carefully drawn, however, the diagram fairly large, and the scale divisions precisely marked, percentiles and PR's may be read to a degree of accuracy sufficient for most purposes.

3. Other uses of the ogive

(1) COMPARISON OF GROUPS

A useful over-all comparison of two or more groups is provided when ogives representing their scores on a given test are plotted upon the same coördinate axes. An illustration is given in Figure 11, page 74, which shows the ogives of the scores earned by two groups of children—200 ten-year-old boys and 200 ten-year-old girls—upon an arithmetic reasoning test of 60 items. Data from which these ogives were constructed are given in Table 14.

TABLE 14 Frequency distributions of the scores made by 200 ten-year-old boys and 200 ten-year-old girls on an arithmetic reasoning test

Scores	Boys f	Cum. f	Cum. % f	Smoothed Cum. Percent-age f	Girls f	Cum. f	Cum. % f	Smoothed Cum. Percent-age f
60–64	0	200	100.0	100.0	0	200	100.0	100.0
55–59	2	200	100.0	99.7	1	200	100.0	99.8
50–54	25	198	99.0	95.2	0	199	99.5	99.7
45–49	48	173	86.5	82.7	9	199	99.5	98.0
40–44	47	125	62.5	62.7	27	190	95.0	92.0
35–39	19	78	39.0	43.7	44	163	81.5	78.7
30–34	26	59	29.5	28.3	43	119	59.5	59.7
25–29	15	33	16.5	18.3	40	76	38.0	38.5
20–24	9	18	9.0	10.0	10	36	18.0	23.0
15–19	7	9	4.5	4.8	20	26	13.0	12.0
10–14	2	2	1.0	1.8	1	6	3.0	6.2
5–9	0	0	0	.3	2	5	2.5	2.3
0–4	0	0	0	0	3	3	1.5	1.3
	200				200		0	.5

$$\text{Rate} = \frac{1}{200} = .005$$

Several interesting observations can be made from Figure 11. The boys' ogive lies to the right of the girls' over the entire range, showing that the boys score consistently higher than the girls. Differences in achievement as between the two groups are shown by the distances

74 • STATISTICS IN PSYCHOLOGY AND EDUCATION

separating the two curves at various levels. It is clear that differences at the extremes—between the very high-scoring and the very low-scoring boys and girls—are not so great as are differences over the middle range. A more detailed analysis of the achievement of these two groups comes out in a comparison of certain points in the distribution. The boys' median is approximately 42, the girls' 32; and the difference between these measures is represented in Figure 11 by the line AB. The difference between the boys' Q_1 and the girls' Q_1 is represented by the line CD; and the difference between the two Q_3's is shown by the line EF. It is clear that the groups differ more at the median than at either quartile, and are farther separated at Q_3 than at Q_1.

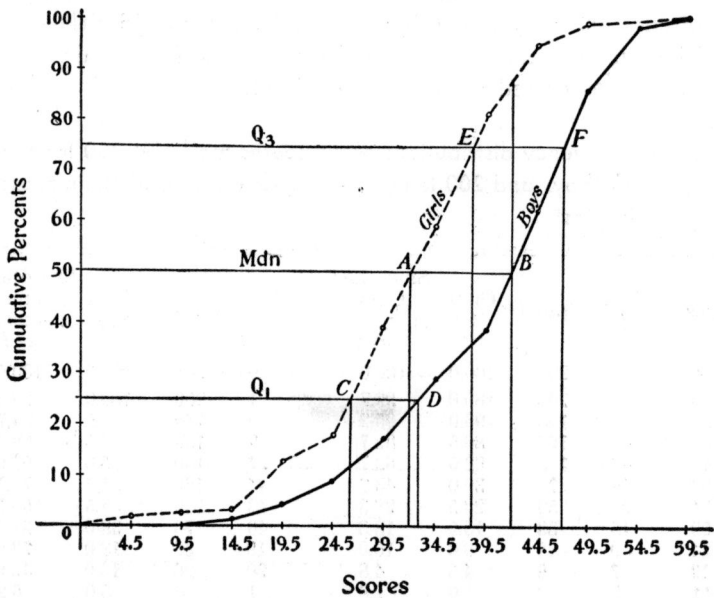

FIG. 11 Ogives representing scores made by 200 boys and 200 girls on an arithmetic reasoning test

(See Table 14, page 73)

The extent to which one distribution overlaps another, whether at the median or at other designated points, can be determined quite readily from their ogives. By extending the vertical line through B (the boys' median) up to the ogive of the girls' scores, it is clear that approximately 88% of the girls fall below the boys' median. Hence, approximately 12% of girls exceed the median of the boys in arithmetic reasoning. Computing overlap from boys to girls, we find that approximately 76% of the boys exceed the girls' median. The vertical line through A (girls' median) cuts the boys' ogive at approximately the 24th percentile. Therefore 24% of the boys fall below the girls' median, and 76% are above this point. Still another illustration may be helpful. Suppose the problem is to determine what percentage of the girls score at or above the boys' 60th percentile. The answer is found by locating first the point where the horizontal line through 60 cuts the boys' ogive. We then find the point on the girls' ogive directly above this value, and from here proceed horizontally across to locate the percentile rank of this point at 93. Since 93% of the girls fall below the boys' 60th percentile, about 7% score above this point.

(2) PERCENTILE NORMS

Norms are measures of achievement which represent the typical performance of a designated group or groups. The norm for 10-year-old boys in height, and the norm for seventh-grade pupils in City X in arithmetic is usually the mean or the median for the group. But norms may be much more detailed and may be reported for other points in the distribution as, for example, Q_1, Q_3, and various percentiles.

Percentile norms are especially useful in dealing with educational achievement examinations, when one wishes to evaluate and compare the achievement of a given student in a number of subject-matter tests. If the student earns a score of 63 on an achievement test in arithmetic, and a score of 143 on an achievement test in English, we have no way of knowing from the scores alone whether his achievement is good, medium, or poor, or how his standing in arithmetic and in English compare. If, however, we know that a score of 63 in arithmetic has a PR of 52, and a score of 143 in English a PR of 68, we may say at once that this student is average in arithmetic (52% of the students score lower than he) and good in English (68% score below him).

Percentile norms may be determined directly from the smoothed ogives of score distributions. Figure 12 represents the smoothed ogives of the two distributions of scores in arithmetic reasoning given in Table 14. Vertical lines drawn to the base line from points on the ogive locate the various percentile points. In Table 15 below, selected percentile norms in the arithmetic reasoning test have been tabulated

76 · STATISTICS IN PSYCHOLOGY AND EDUCATION

TABLE 15 Percentile norms for arithmetic reasoning test (Table 14) obtained from smoothed ogives in Figure 12

Cum. %'s	Girls Ogive	Girls Calculated	Boys Ogive	Boys Calculated
99	52.0	49.0	57.5	54.5
95	46.5	44.5	54.5	52.9
90	43.5	42.7	52.5	50.9
80	40.0	39.2	49.0	48.1
70	37.0	36.9	46.5	46.1
60	35.0	34.6	44.0	44.0
50	32.5	32.5	41.5	41.8
40	30.0	30.0	39.0	39.7
30	27.0	27.5	35.0	34.8
20	23.5	25.0	30.0	30.9
10	18.5	18.0	24.5	25.2
5	14.0	15.5	19.5	20.1
1	3.5	3.3	6.5	14.5

for boys and girls separately. This table of norms may, of course, be extended by the addition of other intermediate or extreme values. Calculated percentiles are included in the table for comparison with percentiles read from the smoothed ogives. These calculated values are useful as a check on the graphically determined points, but ordinarily need not be found.

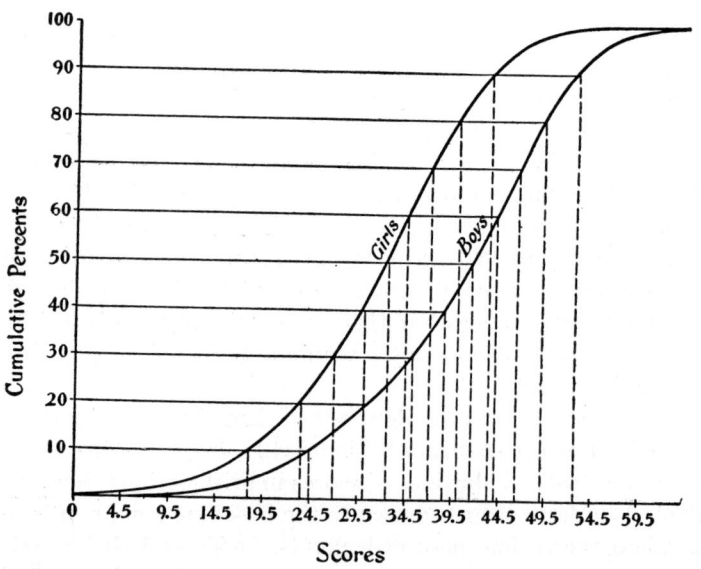

FIG. 12 Smoothed ogives of the scores in Table 14

CUMULATIVE DISTRIBUTIONS, GRAPHIC METHODS, AND PERCENTILES • 77

It is evident that percentile norms read from an ogive are not strictly accurate, but the error is slight except at the top and bottom of the distribution. Estimates of these extreme percentiles from smoothed ogives are probably more nearly true values than are the calculated points, since the smoothed curve represents what we might expect to get from larger groups or in additional samplings.

The ogives in Figure 12 were smoothed in order to iron out minor kinks and irregularities in the curves. Owing to the smoothing process, these curves are more regular and continuous than are the original ogives in Figure 11, page 74. The only difference between the process of smoothing an ogive and smoothing a frequency polygon (p. 14) is that we average cumulative percentage frequencies in the ogive instead of actual frequencies. Smoothed percentage frequencies are given in Table 14. The smoothed cumulative percent frequency to be plotted above 24.5, boys' distribution, is $\frac{16.5 + 9.0 + 4.5}{3}$ or 10.0; for the same point, girls' distribution, it is $\frac{38.0 + 18.0 + 13.0}{3}$ or 23.0. Care must be taken at the extremes of the distribution where the procedure is slightly different. In the boys' distribution, for example, the smoothed cumulative percent frequency at 9.5 is $\frac{1.0 + 0.0 + 0.0}{3}$ or .3%, and at 59.5, it is $\frac{99.0 + 100.0 + 100.0}{3}$ or 99.7. At 4.5 and 64.5, both of which lie outside the boys' distribution, the cumulative percentage frequencies are $\left[\frac{100 + 100 + 100}{3}\right]$ and $\left[\frac{0 + 0 + 0}{3}\right]$, respectively. Note that the smoothed ogive extends one interval beyond the original at both extremes of the distribution.

There is little justification for smoothing an ogive which is already quite regular or an ogive which is very jagged and irregular. In the first instance, smoothing accomplishes little if anything; in the second, it may seriously mislead. A smoothed curve shows what we might expect to get if the test or sampling, or both, were different (and perhaps better) than they actually were. Smoothing should never be a substitute for getting additional data or for constructing an improved test. It should certainly be avoided when the group is small and the ogive very irregular. Smoothing is perhaps most useful when the ogives show small irregularities here and there (see Figure 11) which may reasonably be assumed to have arisen from small and not very important factors.

IV. Other Graphical Methods

Data obtained from many problems in mental measurement, especially those which involve the study of changes attributable to growth, practice, learning, and fatigue, may be treated profitably by graphical methods. Two widely used devices are the *line graph*, frequently found in experimental psychology, and the *bar diagram* more often met with, perhaps, in education. These two methods will be described in this section.

1. The line graph

Figure 13 shows an age-progress curve. This graph represents the change in "logical memory for a connected passage" in boys and girls from 8 to 18 years old. Norms for adults are also included on the diagram. Age is represented on the horizontal or X-axis

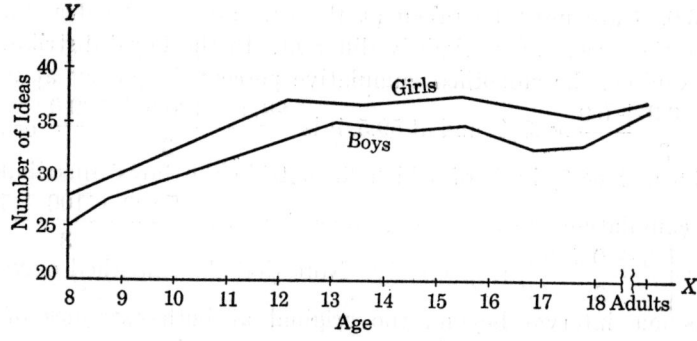

FIG. 13 Logical memory. Age is represented on X-line (horizontal); Score, i.e., number of ideas remembered, on Y-line (vertical)

(After Pyle)

and "average number of ideas reproduced" at each age level is marked off on the vertical or Y-axis. Memory ability as measured by this test rises to a peak at year 15 for both groups after which there is a slight decline followed by a rise at the adult level. There is a small but consistent sex difference throughout, the girls being higher on the average at each age.

Figure 14 illustrates the learning or practice curve. These curves

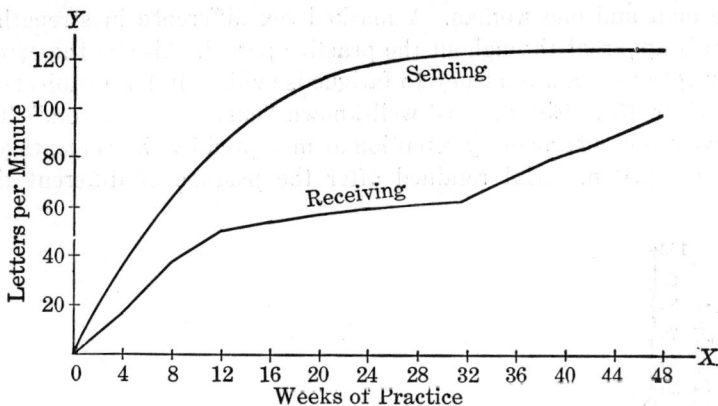

FIG. 14 Improvement in telegraphy. Weeks of practice on X-line; number of letters per minute on Y-line

(After Bryan and Harter)

show the improvement, in sending and receiving telegraphic messages, resulting from successive trials at the same task over a period of forty-eight weeks. Improvement as measured by the number of letters sent or received per minute is indicated along the Y-axis. Weeks of practice at the given task are represented by equal intervals on the X-axis.

Figure 15 is a performance or practice "curve." It represents twenty-five successive trials with the hand dynamometer made by

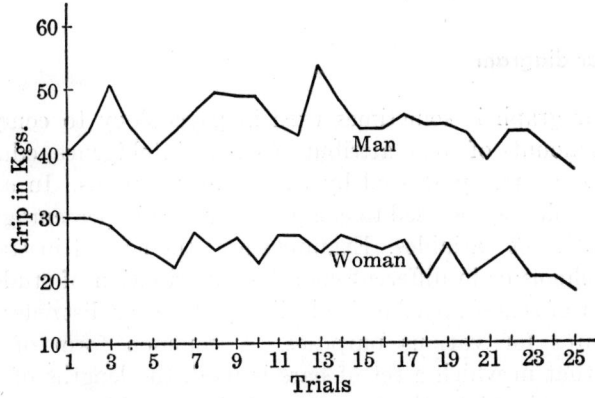

FIG. 15 Hand dynamometer readings in kilograms for 25 successive grips at intervals of ten seconds. Two subjects, a man and a woman

one man and one woman. A marked sex difference in strength of grip is apparent throughout the practice period. Also as the experiment progressed a tendency to fatigue is evident in both subjects.

Figure 16 is Ebbinghaus' well-known "curve of retention." This curve represents memory retention as measured by the percentage of the original material retained after the passage of different time

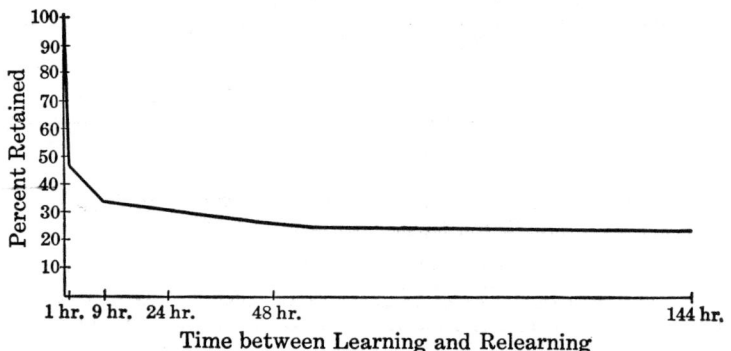

FIG. 16 Curve of retention. The numbers on the baseline give hours elapsed from time of learning; numbers along Y-axis give percent retained

intervals. The time intervals between learning and relearning are laid off on the X-axis; and the percent retained, as measured by relearning, on the Y-axis.

2. The bar diagram

The bar graph is sometimes used in psychology to compare the relative amounts of some attribute (height, intelligence, educational achievement, etc.) possessed by two or more groups. In education the bar graph may be used to compare (usually in percentage terms) several different variables. Examples are: the cost of instruction in various schools or in different counties; distribution of student time in and out of school; teachers' salaries by states or districts; relative expenditures for various purposes. A common form of the bar graph is that in which a set of bars is used, the lengths of the bars being proportional to the amounts of the variable possessed. For emphasis, a space is usually left between the bars, which are drawn side by side and may be either vertical or horizontal.

A horizontal bar graph is shown in Figure 17. These bars represent the percentage of officers in various branches of the military service during World War I who received grades of A and B or C upon the Army Alpha Examination. The bars are arranged in order, the group

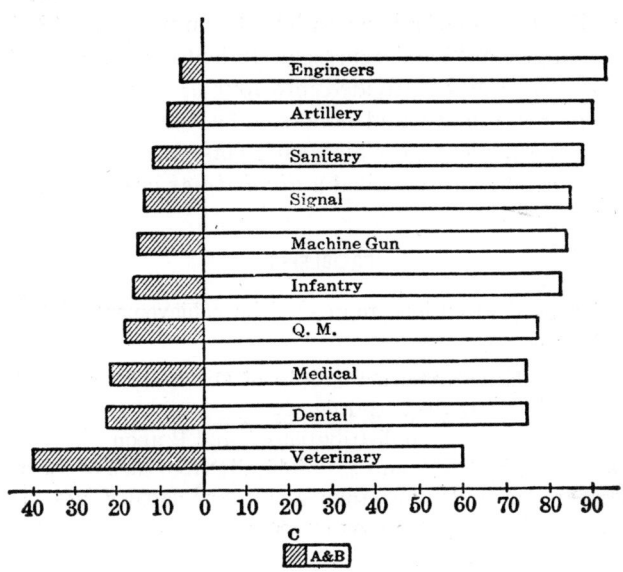

FIG. 17 Comparative bar graphs. The bars represent the percentage in each division of the military service receiving A's and B's or C's

School A

Freshmen	Sophomores	Juniors	Seniors
38%	31%	17%	14%

School B

Freshmen	Sophomores	Juniors	Seniors
45%	30%	16%	9%

FIG. 18 Divided bar graphs. The two bars represent student enrollment in two high schools. Each bar is divided into four divisions. The length of a division shows the proportion or percentage of students in that class

receiving the highest percent of A's and B's being placed at the top It is clear from the diagram that the Engineers, who ranked first, received about 95% A's and B's and about 5% C's. The Veterinary Corps, which ranked last, received about 60% A's and B's and 40% C's.

Another illustration of a bar graph is shown in Figure 18. The two parallel rectangles or "bars" represent student enrollment in two city high schools. Each bar is divided into four parts to represent freshmen, sophomores, juniors, and seniors. The size of a division is proportional to the percentage which each class is of the whole group. This type of graph is often called a *divided-bar graph*.

PROBLEMS

1. The following distributions represent the achievement of two groups, A and B, upon a memory test.

   (a) Plot cumulative frequency graphs of Group A's and of Group B's scores, observing the 75% rule.
   (b) Plot ogives of the two distributions A and B upon the same axes.
   (c) Determine P_{30}, P_{60}, and P_{90} graphically from each of the ogives and compare graphically determined with calculated values.
   (d) What is the percentile rank of score 55 in Group A's distribution? In Group B's distribution?
   (e) A percentile rank of 70 in Group A corresponds to what percentile rank in Group B?
   (f) What percent of Group A exceeds the median of Group B?

Scores	Group A	Group B
79–83	6	8
74–78	7	8
69–73	8	9
64–68	10	16
59–63	12	20
54–58	15	18
49–53	23	19
44–48	16	11
39–43	10	13
34–38	12	8
29–33	6	7
24–28	3	2
	$N = 128$	$N = 139$

CUMULATIVE DISTRIBUTIONS, GRAPHIC METHODS, AND PERCENTILES

2. Construct an ogive of the following distribution of scores.

Scores	f
159.5 to 169.5	1
149.5 to 159.5	5
139.5 to 149.5	13
129.5 to 139.5	45
119.5 to 129.5	40
109.5 to 119.5	30
99.5 to 109.5	51
89.5 to 99.5	48
79.5 to 89.5	36
69.5 to 79.5	10
59.5 to 69.5	5
49.5 to 59.5	1
	$N = \overline{285}$

Read off percentile norms for the cumulative percentages:

99, 95, 90, 80, 70, 60, 50, 40, 30, 20, 10, 5, and 1.

3. Given the following data from five cities in the United States, represent the facts graphically by means of a bar graph.

Percent of population which is

City	Native White	Foreign-born White	Negro
A	.65	.30	.05
B	.60	.10	.30
C	.50	.45	.05
D	.40	.20	.40
E	.30	.10	.60

ANSWERS

	Group A		Group B	
	Ogive	Cal.	Ogive	Cal.
1. (c) P_{30}	46.0	45.81	48.5	48.69
P_{60}	56.0	55.77	59.75	59.85
P_{90}	74.0	73.64	75.5	74.81

(d) 58; 47

(e) 62   (f) 39–40% of Group A exceed the median of Group B.

2. Read from ogive:

Cum. Percents:	99	95	90	80	70	60	50	40	30
Percentiles:	159	142.5	137.5	131.5	124.5	116.5	107	102	96.5
	20		10		5		1		
	91		82.5		79		64.5		

84 • STATISTICS IN PSYCHOLOGY AND EDUCATION

ADDITIONAL PROBLEMS AND QUESTIONS ON CHAPTERS 1–4

1. Describe the characteristics of those distributions for which the mean is not an adequate measure of central tendency.
2. When is it inadvisable to use the coefficient of variation?
3. What is a multimodal distribution?
4. A student writes in a theme that by the application of eugenics it would be possible to raise the intelligence of the race, so that more people would be above the median I.Q. of 100. Comment on this.
5. Why cannot the σ of one test usually be compared directly with the σ of another test?
6. What effect will an increase in N probably have upon Q?
7. What is the difference between a percentile and the ordinary percent grade used in school?
8. Does a percentile rank of 65 earned by a given pupil mean that 65% of the group make scores above him; that 65% make the same score; or that 65% make scores below him?
9. Calculate the mean, median, mode, Q, and SD for each of the following distributions:

(1) Scores	f	(2) Scores	f	(3) Scores	f
90–99	2	14–15	3	25	1
80–89	12	12–13	8	24	2
70–79	22	10–11	15	23	6
60–69	20	8–9	20	22	8
50–59	14	6–7	10	21	5
40–49	4	4–5	4	20	2
30–39	1			19	1
$N = 75$		$N = 60$		$N = 25$	

10. (a) Plot the distribution in 9 (1) as a frequency polygon and histogram upon the same coördinate axes.
    (b) Plot the distribution in 9 (2) as an ogive. Locate graphically the the median, Q_1, and Q_3. Determine the PR of score 9; of score 12.

ANSWERS

9. (1) Mean = 68.10 (2) Mean = 9.23 (3) Mean = 22.04
       Median = 68.75   Median = 9.10   Median = 22.06
       Mode = 70.05   Mode = 8.84   Mode = 22.10
       Q = 9.01 Q = 1.69 Q = .91
       SD = 12.50 SD = 2.48 SD = 1.34

10. (b) Median = 9.0; Q_1 = 7.5; Q_3 = 11.0 (Read from ogive)
        PR of 9 = 50; of 12 = 84.5

5

THE NORMAL PROBABILITY CURVE

I. The Meaning and Importance of the Normal Probability Distribution

1. Introduction

In Figure 19 are four diagrams, two polygons and two histograms, which represent frequency distributions of data drawn from anthropometry, psychology, and meteorology. It is apparent, even upon superficial examination, that all of these graphs have the same general form—the measures are concentrated closely around the center and taper off from this central high point or crest to the left and right. There are relatively few measures at the "low-score" end of the scale; an increasing number up to a maximum at the middle position; and a progressive falling-off toward the "high-score" end of the

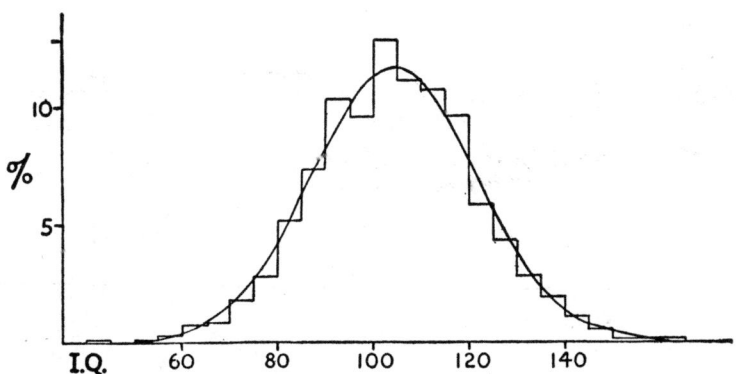

1. Form L I.Q. distribution and best-fitting normal curve, ages 2½ to 18. (*from* McNemar, Quinn, *The Revision of the Stanford-Binet Scale*, p. 19)

86 • STATISTICS IN PSYCHOLOGY AND EDUCATION

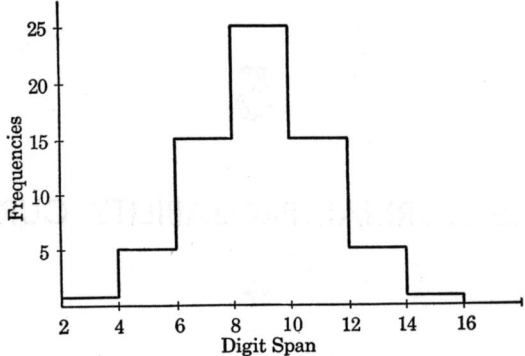

2. Memory span for digits, 123 adult women students. (After Thorndike.)

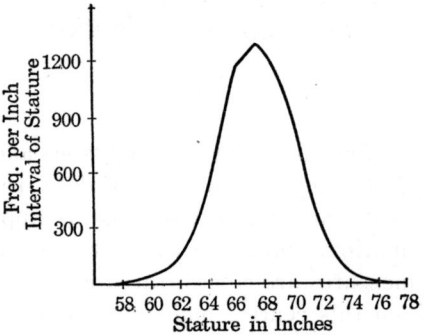

3. Statures of 8585 adult males born in the British Isles. (After Yule.)

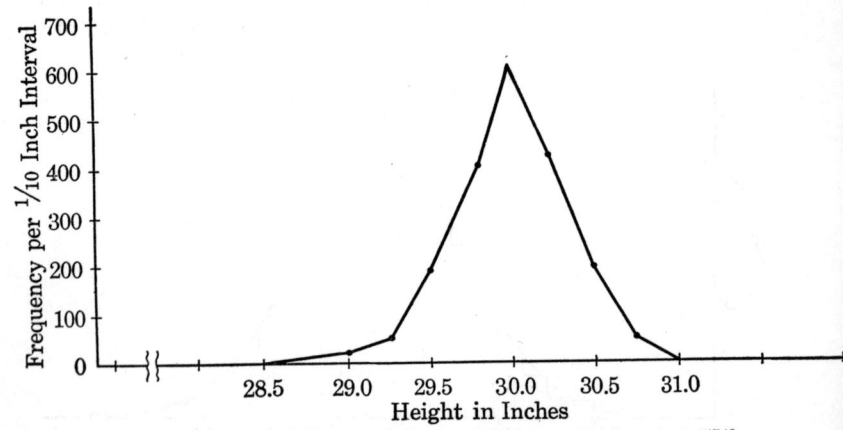

4. Frequency distribution of barometer heights at Southampton: 4748 observations. (After Yule.)

FIG. 19 Frequency distributions drawn from different fields

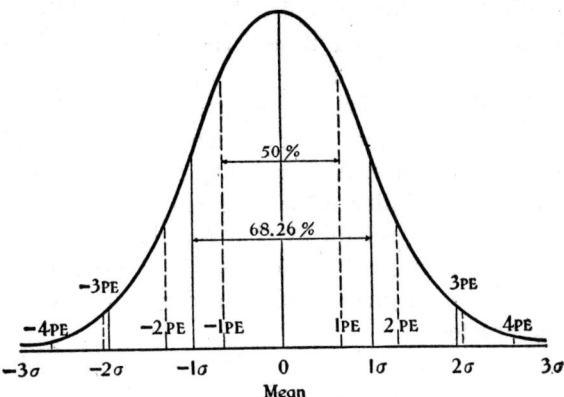

FIG. 20 Normal probability curve

scale. If we divide the area *under* each curve (the area between the curve and the *X-axis*) by a line drawn perpendicularly through the central high point to the baseline, the two parts thus formed will be similar in shape and very nearly equal in area. It is clear, therefore, that each figure exhibits almost perfect bilateral symmetry. The perfectly symmetrical curve, or frequency surface, to which all of the graphs in Figure 19 approximate, is shown in Figure 20. This bell-shaped figure is called the *normal probability curve,* or simply the *normal curve,* and is of great value in mental measurement. An understanding of the characteristics of the frequency distribution represented by the normal curve is essential to the student of experimental psychology and mental measurement. This chapter, therefore, will be concerned with the normal distribution, and its frequency polygon, the normal probability curve.

2. Elementary principles of probability

Perhaps the simplest approach to an understanding of the normal probability curve is through a consideration of the elementary principles of probability. As used in statistics, the "probability" of a given event is defined as the expected frequency of occurrence of this event among events of a like sort. This expected frequency of occurrence may be based upon a knowledge of the conditions determining the occurrence of the phenomenon, as in dice-throwing or coin-tossing, or upon empirical data, as in mental and social measurements.

The probability of an event may be stated most simply, perhaps, as a ratio. We know, for example, that the probability of an unbiased coin falling heads is 1/2, and that the probability of a die showing a two-spot is 1/6. These ratios, called *probability ratios*, are defined by that fraction the numerator of which equals the desired outcome or outcomes and the denominator of which equals the total possible outcomes. A probability ratio always falls between the limits .00 (impossibility of occurrence) and 1.00 (certainty of occurrence). Thus the probability that the sky will fall is .00; that an individual now living will some day die is 1.00. Between these limits are all possible degrees of likelihood which may be expressed by appropriate ratios.

Let us now apply these simple principles of probability to the specific case of what happens when we toss coins.* If we toss one coin, obviously it must fall either heads (H) or tails (T) 100% of the time; and furthermore, since there are only two possible outcomes in a given throw, a head or a tail is *equally probable*. Expressed as a ratio, therefore, the probability of H is 1/2; of T 1/2; and

$$(H + T) = 1/2 + 1/2 = 1.00$$

If we toss two coins, (a) and (b), at the same time, there are four possible arrangements which the coins may take:

(1)	(2)	(3)	(4)
a b	a b	a b	a b
H H	H T	T H	T T

Both coins (a) and (b) may fall H; (a) may fall H and (b) T; (b) may fall H and (a) T; or both coins may fall T. Expressed as ratios, the probability of *two* heads is 1/4 and the probability of *two* tails 1/4. Also, the probability of an HT combination is 1/4, and of a TH combination 1/4. And since it ordinarily makes no difference which coin falls H or which falls T, we may add these two ratios (or double the one) to obtain 1/2 as the probability of an HT combination. The sum of our probability ratios is $1/4 + 1/2 + 1/4$ or 1.00.

Let us go a step farther and increase the number of coins to three. If we toss three coins (a), (b), and (c) simultaneously, there are eight possible outcomes:

(1)	(2)	(3)	(4)	(5)	(6)	(7)	(8)
a b c	a b c	a b c	a b c	a b c	a b c	a b c	a b c
H H H	H H T	H T H	T H H	H T T	T H T	T T H	T T T

Expressed as ratios, the probability of *three* heads is 1/8 (combination 1); of *two* heads and *one* tail 3/8 (combinations 2, 3, and 4);

---

*Coin-tossing and dice-throwing furnish easily understood and often used illustrations of the so-called "laws of chance."

THE NORMAL PROBABILITY CURVE • 89

of *one* head and *two* tails 3/8 (combinations 5, 6, and 7) ; and of *three* tails 1/8 (combination 8). The sum of these probability ratios is 1/8 + 3/8 + 3/8 + 1/8, or 1.00.

By exactly the same method used above for two and for three coins, we can determine the probability of different combinations of heads and tails when we have four, five, or any number of coins. These various outcomes may be obtained in a somewhat more direct way, however, than by writing down all of the different combinations which may occur. If there are n independent factors, the probability of the presence or absence of each being the same, the "compound" probabilities of the appearance of various combinations of factors will be expressed by expansion of the binomial $(p+q)^n$. In this expression p equals the probability that a given event will happen, q the probability that the event will not happen, and the exponent n indicates the number of factors (e.g., coins) operating to produce the final result.* If we substitute H for p and T for q (tails = nonheads), we have for two coins $(H+T)^2$; and squaring, the binomial $(H+T)^2 = H^2 + 2HT + T^2$. This expansion may be written,

1 H^2 1 chance in 4 of 2 heads; *probability ratio* = 1/4
2 HT 2 chances in 4 of 1 head and 1 tail; *probability ratio* = 1/2
1 T^2 1 chance in 4 of two tails; *probability ratio* = 1/4

Total = $\overline{4}$

These outcomes are identical with those obtained above by listing the three different combinations possible when two coins are tossed.

If we have three independent factors operating, the expression $(p+q)^n$ becomes for three coins $(H+T)^3$. Expanding this binomial, we get $H^3 + 3H^2T + 3HT^2 + T^3$, which may be written,

1 H^3 1 chance in 8 of 3 heads; *probability ratio* = 1/8
3 H^2T 3 chances in 8 of 2 heads and 1 tail; *probability ratio* = 3/8
3 HT^2 3 chances in 8 of 1 head and 2 tails; *probability ratio* = 3/8
1 T^3 1 chance in 8 of 3 tails; *probability ratio* = 1/8

Total = $\overline{8}$

Again these results are identical with those got by listing the four different combinations possible when three coins are tossed.

---

* We may, for example, consider our coins to be independent factors, the occurrence of a head to be the *presence* of a factor and the occurrence of a tail the *absence* of a factor. Factors will then be "present" or "absent" in the various heads-tails combinations.

The binomial expansion may be applied still more generally to those cases in which there are a larger number of independent factors operating. If we toss ten coins simultaneously, for instance, we have by analogy with the above, $(p + q)^{10}$. This expression may be written $(H + T)^{10}$, H standing for the probability of a head, T for the probability of a non-head (tail), and 10 for the number of coins tossed. When the binomial $(H + T)^{10}$ is expanded, the terms are

$$H^{10} + 10H^9T + 45H^8T^2 + 120H^7T^3 + 210H^6T^4 + 252H^5T^5 + 210H^4T^6$$
$$+ 120H^3T^7 + 45H^2T^8 + 10HT^9 + T^{10}$$

which may be summarized as follows:

		Probability Ratio
1 H^{10}	1 chance in 1024 of all coins falling heads	$\frac{1}{1024}$
10 H^9T^1	10 chances in 1024 of 9 heads and 1 tail...	$\frac{10}{1024}$
45 H^8T^2	45 chances in 1024 of 8 heads and 2 tails..	$\frac{45}{1024}$
120 H^7T^3	120 chances in 1024 of 7 heads and 3 tails..	$\frac{120}{1024}$
210 H^6T^4	210 chances in 1024 of 6 heads and 4 tails..	$\frac{210}{1024}$
252 H^5T^5	252 chances in 1024 of 5 heads and 5 tails..	$\frac{252}{1024}$
210 H^4T^6	210 chances in 1024 of 4 heads and 6 tails..	$\frac{210}{1024}$
120 H^3T^7	120 chances in 1024 of 3 heads and 7 tails..	$\frac{120}{1024}$
45 H^2T^8	45 chances in 1024 of 2 heads and 8 tails..	$\frac{45}{1024}$
10 HT^9	10 chances in 1024 of 1 head and 9 tails...	$\frac{10}{1024}$
1 T^{10}	1 chance in 1024 of all coins falling tails..	$\frac{1}{1024}$

Total = 1024

These data are represented graphically in Figure 21 by a histogram and frequency polygon plotted on the same axes. The eleven terms of the expansion have been laid off at equal distances along the X-axis, and the "chances" of the occurrence of each combination of H's and T's are plotted as frequencies on the Y-axis. The result is a symmetrical frequency polygon with the greatest concentration in the center and the "scores" falling away by corresponding decrements above and below the central high point. Figure 21 represents the results to be expected *theoretically* when ten coins are tossed 1024 times.

Many experiments have been conducted in which coins were tossed or dice thrown a great many times, with the idea of checking theoretical against actual results. In one well-known experiment,* twelve dice were thrown 4096 times. Each four-, five-, and six-spot

---

* Weldon's experiment; see Yule, G. U., *An Introduction to the Theory of Statistics* (London: C. Griffin and Co., 1932), 10th ed., p. 258.

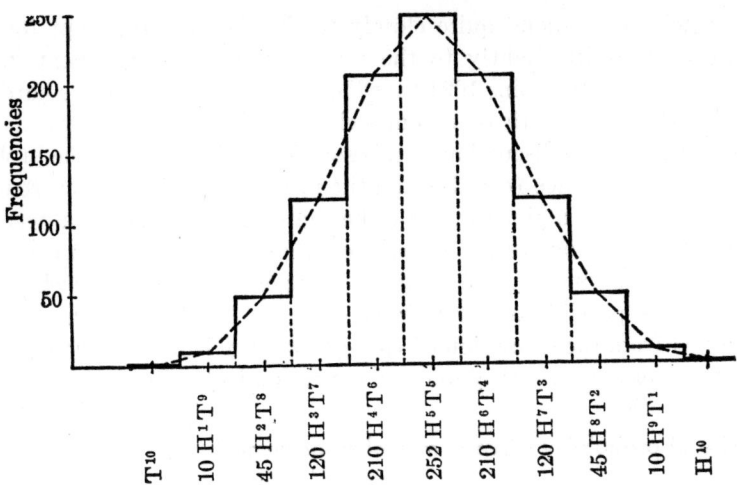

FIG. 21 Probability surface obtained from the expansion of $(H + T)^{10}$

combination was taken as a "success" and each one-, two-, and three-spot combination as a "failure." Hence the probability of success and the probability of failure were the same. In a throw showing the faces 3, 1, 2, 6, 4, 6, 3, 4, 1, 5, 2, and 3, there would be five successes and seven failures. The *observed* frequency of the different numbers of successes and the *theoretical* outcomes obtained from the expansion of the binomial expression $(p + q)^{12}$ have been plotted on the same axes in Figure 22. The student will note that the observed

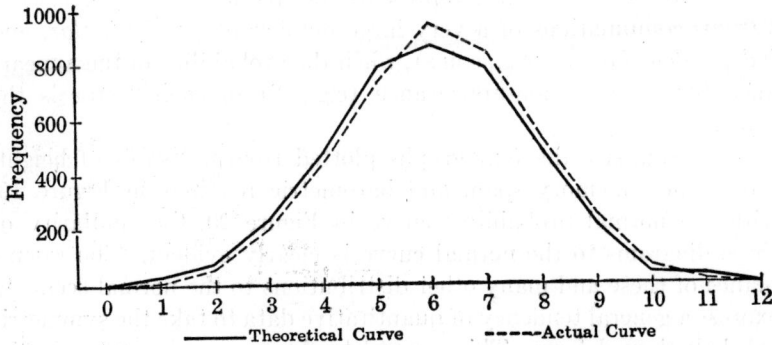

FIG. 22 Comparison of observed and theoretical results in throwing twelve dice 4096 times

(After Yule.)

frequencies correspond quite closely to the theoretical except for a tendency to shift slightly to the right. If, as an experiment, the reader will toss ten coins 1024 times his results will be in close agreement with the theoretical outcomes shown in Figure 21.

Throughout the discussion in this section, we have taken the probability of occurrence (e.g., H) and the probability of non-occurrence (non-H or T) of a given factor to be the same. This is not a necessary condition, however. For instance, the probability of an event's happening may be only 1/5; of its not happening, 4/5. Any probability ratio is possible as long as $(p + q) = 1.00$. But distributions obtained from the expansion of $(p + q)^n$ when p is not equal to q are "skewed" or asymmetrical and are not normal (p. 116).

3. Use of probability curve in mental measurement

The frequency curve plotted in Figure 21 from the expansion of the expression $(H + T)^{10}$ is a symmetrical many-sided polygon. If the number of factors (e.g., coins) determining this polygon were increased from 10 to 20, to 30, and then to 100, say (the baseline extent remaining the same), the faces of the polygon would increase regularly in number. With each increase in the number of factors, the faces of the figure would become shorter, and the points on the frequency surface would move closer together. Finally, when the number of factors became very large—when n in the expression $(p + q)^n$ became infinite—the polygon would exhibit a perfectly smooth surface like that of the curve in Figure 20. This "ideal" polygon or "normal" curve represents the frequency of occurrence of various combinations of a very large number of *equal, similar,* and *independent* factors (e.g., coins), when the probability of the appearance (e.g., H) or non-appearance (e.g., T) of each factor is the same.

If we compare the four graphs plotted from measures of height, intelligence, memory span, and barometric readings in Figure 19, with the normal probability curve in Figure 20, the similarity of these diagrams to the normal curve is clearly evident. The resemblance of these and many other distributions to the normal seems to express a general tendency of quantitative data to take the symmetrical, bell-shaped form. This general tendency may be stated in the form of a "principle" as follows: measurements of many natural phenomena and of many mental and social traits under certain conditions *tend* to be distributed symmetrically about their means in

THE NORMAL PROBABILITY CURVE • 93

proportions which approximate those of the normal probability distribution.

Much evidence has accumulated to show that the normal distribution serves to describe the frequency of occurrence of many variable facts with a relatively high degree of accuracy. Various phenomena which follow the normal probability curve (at least approximately) may be classified as follows:

1. *Biological statistics:* the proportion of male to female births for the same country or community over a period of years; the proportion of different types of plants and animals in cross-fertilization (the Mendelian ratios).
2. *Anthropometrical data:* height, weight, cephalic index, etc., for large groups of the same age and sex.
3. *Social and economic data:* rates of birth, marriage, or death under certain constant conditions; wages and output of large numbers of workers in the same occupation under comparable conditions.
4. *Psychological measurements:* intelligence as measured by standard tests; speed of association, perception-span, reaction-time; educational test scores, e.g., in spelling, arithmetic, reading.
5. *Errors of observation:* measures of height, speed of movement, linear magnitudes, physical and mental traits, and the like, contain errors which are as likely to cause them to deviate above as below their true values. Chance errors of this sort vary in magnitude and sign and occur in frequencies which follow closely the normal probability curve.*

It is an interesting speculation that many frequency distributions of scores and other measures are similar to those obtained by tossing coins or throwing dice because the former, like the latter, are actually probability distributions. The symmetrical normal distribution, as we have seen, represents the probability of occurrence of the various possible combinations of a great many factors (e.g., coins). In a normal distribution all of the n factors are taken to be *similar, independent,* and *equal in strength*; and the probability that each will be present (e.g., show an H) or absent (e.g., show a T) is the same. The appearance on a coin of a head or a tail is undoubtedly determined by a large number of small (or "chance") influences as liable to work one way as another. The twist with which the coin is spun may be important, as well as the height from which it is thrown, the weight of the coin, the kind of surface upon which it falls, and many

* This topic is treated in Chapter 8.

other circumstances of a like sort. By analogy, the presence or absence of each one of the large number of genetic factors which determine the shape of a man's head, or his intelligence, or his personality, may depend upon a host of adventitious influences whose net effect we call "chance."

But the striking similarity of obtained and probability distributions should not lead us to conclude that *all* distributions of mental and physical traits which exhibit the bell-shaped form have *necessarily* arisen through the operation of those principles which govern the appearance of dice or coin combinations. The factors which determine musical ability, let us say, or mechanical skill are too little known to justify the assumption, *a priori*, that they combine in the same proportions as do the head and tail combinations in "chance" distributions of coins. Moreover, the psychologist usually constructs his tests with the normal hypothesis definitely in mind. The resulting symmetrical distribution is to be taken, then, as evidence of the success of his efforts rather than as conclusive proof of the "normality" of the trait being measured.*

The selection of the normal rather than some other type curve is sufficiently warranted by the fact that this distribution generally does fit the data better, and is more useful. But the "theoretical justification and the empirical use of the normal curve are two quite different matters." †

II. Properties of the Normal Probability Distribution

1. The equation of the normal curve

The equation of the normal probability curve reads

$$y = \frac{N}{\sigma\sqrt{2\pi}} e^{-\frac{x^2}{2\sigma^2}} \tag{18}$$

(*equation of the normal probability curve*)

in which

$x =$ scores (expressed as deviations from the mean) laid off along the baseline or X-*axis*.

---

* McNemar, Q., *The Revision of the Stanford-Binet Scale* (Boston: Houghton Mifflin Co., 1942), Chapter II.

† Jones, D. C., *A First Course in Statistics* (London: G. Bell and Sons, 1921), p. 233.

THE NORMAL PROBABILITY CURVE • 95

y = the height of the curve above the X-axis, i.e., the frequency of a given x-value or the number achieving a certain score.

The other terms in the equation are constants:—

N = number of cases.

σ = standard deviation of the distribution.

π = 3.1416 (the ratio of the circumference of a circle to its diameter).

e = 2.7183 (base of the Napierian system of logarithms).

When N and σ are known, it is possible from equation (18) to compute (1) the frequency (or y) of a given value x, i.e., the *number* of individuals making a certain *score*; and (2) the number, or percentage, of individuals scoring between two points, or above or below a given point in the distribution. But these calculations are rarely necessary, as tables are available from which this information may be readily obtained. A knowledge of these tables (Table A, p. 424) is extremely valuable in the solution of a number of problems. For this reason it is very desirable that the construction and use of Table A be clearly understood.

2. Table of areas under the normal curve

Table A gives the fractional parts of the total area under the normal curve found between the mean and ordinates (y's) erected at various distances from the mean. In Table A distances along the X-axis are measured in σ units (see Fig. 20). The total area under the curve (the number of scores in the distribution) is taken arbitrarily to be 10,000, because of the greater ease with which fractional parts of the total area may then be calculated.

The first column of the table, x/σ, gives distances in tenths of σ measured off on the baseline of the normal curve from the mean as origin. We have already learned that $x = X - M$, i.e., that x measures the deviation of a score X from M. If x is divided by σ, deviation from the mean is expressed in σ-units. Such σ-deviation scores are often called *standard scores*, or *z*-scores ($z = x/\sigma$). Distances from the mean in hundredths of σ are given by the headings of the columns. To find the number of cases in a normal distribution between the mean and the ordinate erected at a distance of 1σ from the mean, go down the x/σ column until 1.0 is reached, and in the next column under .00 take the entry opposite 1.0, viz., 3413. This figure means that 3413 cases in 10,000, or 34.13% of the entire area of the curve, lie between the mean and 1σ. Put more exactly, 34.13% of the cases in a normal distribution fall within the area bounded by the baseline of the curve, the ordinate erected at the mean, the ordinate erected at a distance of 1σ from the mean, and the curve itself (see Fig. 20, p. 87). To find the percentage of the distribution between the mean and 1.57σ, say, go down the x/σ column to 1.5, then across horizontally to the column headed .07, and take the entry 4418. This means that in a normal distribution, 44.18% of the area (N) lie between the mean and 1.57σ.

We have so far considered only σ-distances measured in the *positive* direction from the mean; that is, we have taken account only of the *right* half—the high-score end—of the normal curve. Since the curve is bilaterally symmetrical, the entries in Table A apply to σ-distances measured in the *negative* direction (to the *left*) as well as to those measured in the positive direction. To find the percentage of the distribution between the mean and −1.26σ, for instance, take the entry in the column headed .06, opposite 1.2 in the x/σ column. This entry (3962) tells us that 39.62% of the cases in the normal distribution fall between the mean and −1.26σ. The percentage of cases between the mean and −1σ is 34.13; and the student will now be able to verify the statement made on page 52 that between the mean and ±1σ are 68.26% of the cases in a normal distribution (see also Fig. 20).

While the normal curve does not actually meet the baseline until we are at infinite distances to the right and left of the mean, for practical purposes the curve may be taken to end at points −3σ and +3σ distant from the mean. Table A shows that 4986.5 cases in the total 10,000 fall between the mean and +3σ; and 4986.5 cases will, of course, fall between the mean and −3σ. Therefore, 9973 cases in 10,000, or 99.73% of the entire distribution, lie within the limits −3σ and +3σ. By cutting off the curve at these two points, therefore, we disregard only .27 of 1% of the distribution, a negligible amount except in very large samples.

3. Relationships among the constants of the normal probability curve

In the normal probability curve, the mean, the median, and the mode all fall exactly at the midpoint of the distribution and are numerically equal. Since the normal curve is bilaterally symmetrical, all of the measures of central tendency must coincide at the center of the distribution.

THE NORMAL PROBABILITY CURVE • 97

The measures of variability include certain constant fractions of the total area of the normal curve, which may be read from Table A. Between the mean and $\pm 1\sigma$ lie the middle two-thirds (approximately) of the cases in the normal distribution. Between the mean and $\pm 2\sigma$ are found 95% (approximately) of the distribution; and between the mean and $\pm 3\sigma$ are found 99.7% (approximately 100%) of the distribution. There are 68 chances (approximately) in 100 that a score will lie within $\pm 1\sigma$ from the mean in the normal distribution; there are 95 chances in 100 that it will lie within $\pm 2\sigma$ from the mean; and 99.7 chances in 100 that it will lie within $\pm 3\sigma$ from the mean.

Instead of σ the Q may be used as the unit of measurement in determining areas within given parts of the normal curve. In the normal curve the Q (p. 46) is generally called the probable error or PE. The relationships between PE and σ are given in the following equations:

$$PE = .6745\sigma$$
$$\sigma = 1.4826\, PE$$

from which it is seen that σ is always about 50% larger than the PE (p. 52).

By interpolation in Table A we find that $\pm .6745\sigma$ or $\pm 1\ PE$ include the 25% just above and the 25% just below the mean. This part of the normal curve, sometimes called the "middle 50," is important because it is often taken to define the range of "normal" performance. The upper 25% is considerably better, and the lowest 25% considerably poorer in performance than the typical middle or average group. From Table A we find also that $\pm 2\, PE$ (or $\pm 1.3490\sigma$) from the mean include 82.26% of the measures in the normal curve; that $\pm 3\ PE$ (or $\pm 2.0235\sigma$) include 95.70%; and that $\pm 4\ PE$ (or $\pm 2.6980\sigma$) include 99.30%.

III. Measuring Divergence from Normality

1. Skewness

In a frequency polygon or histogram, usually the first thing which strikes the eye is the degree of symmetry in the figure. In the normal curve the mean, the median, and the mode all coincide and there is perfect balance between the right and left halves of the figure. A distribution is said to be "skewed" when the mean, the median, and the mode fall at different points in the distribution, and the balance (or center of gravity) is shifted to one side or the other, to right or left. It is important to know (1) whether the skewness which often occurs in distributions of test scores and other measures represents a real divergence from the normal form; or (2) whether such divergence is the result of chance fluctuations, arising from temporary causes, and is not significant of real discrepancy. The degree of displacement or skewness in a frequency distribution may be determined by the formula

$$Sk = \frac{3(\text{mean} - \text{median})}{\sigma} \qquad (19)$$

(*a measure of skewness in a frequency distribution*)

In a normal distribution the mean equals the median and the skewness is 0. The more nearly the distribution approaches the normal form, the closer together are the mean and the median, and the less the skewness. Distributions are said to be skewed *negatively*, or to the *left*, when the scores are massed at the high end of the scale (the right end), and spread out gradually at the low or left end, as shown

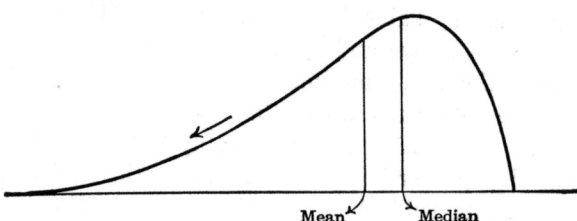

FIG. 23 Negative skewness: to the left

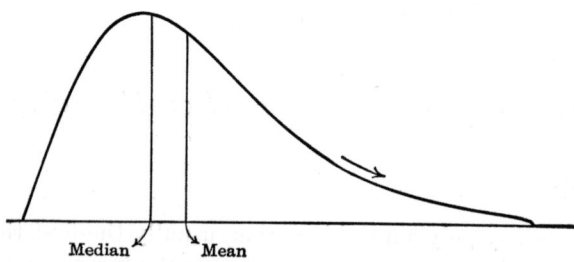

FIG. 24 Positive skewness: to the right

THE NORMAL PROBABILITY CURVE · 99

in Figure 23. Distributions are skewed *positively*, or to the *right*, when the scores are massed at the low (the left) end of the scale, and spread out gradually toward the high or right end as shown in Figure 24.

If we apply formula (19) to the distribution of 50 Army Alpha scores in Table 1, page 5, —.28 is obtained as a measure of skewness. This result points to a slight negative skewness in the data, which may be seen by reference to Figure 2, page 11. Formula (19) gives the measure of skewness for the distribution of the 200 cancellation scores (Table 3, page 13) as .009. This negligible degree of positive skewness shows how closely this distribution approaches the symmetrical probability form.

Another measure of skewness is given by the formula

$$Sk = \frac{(P_{90} + P_{10})}{2} - P_{50} \qquad (20)$$

(*a measure of skewness in terms of percentiles*) *

For the normal distribution Sk by formula (20) is zero: P_{50} lies just midway between P_{90} and P_{10}.

Applying this formula to the distributions of 50 Army Alpha scores and 200 cancellation scores, we obtain for the first $Sk = -2.50$; and for the second $Sk = .03$. These results are numerically different from the measures of skewness obtained from formula (19), because the two measures of skewness are computed from different reference values in the distribution, and hence are not directly comparable. The two formulas agree, however, in indicating some negative skewness for the distribution of 50 Alpha scores, and an insignificant degree of positive skewness for the 200 cancellation scores. In comparing the skewness of two distributions we should use either formula (19) or (20); not first the one and then the other.

The important question of how much skewness a distribution must exhibit before it may be said to be *significantly* skewed cannot be answered until we have calculated a "standard error" of our measure of skewness. A formula for the standard error of Sk, when determined by formula (20), and a method of testing whether the skewness of a given distribution is significant are discussed in Chapter 9, page 241.

* Kelley, T. L., *Statistical Method* (New York: Macmillan, 1923), p. 77. The terms in this formula, as given by Kelley, have been reversed so that the sign of Sk will agree with the conventional notion of positive and negative skewness.

2. Kurtosis

The term kurtosis refers to the "peakedness" or flatness of a frequency distribution as compared with the normal. A frequency distribution more peaked than the normal is said to be *leptokurtic*; one flatter than the normal, *platykurtic*. Figure 25 shows a leptokurtic

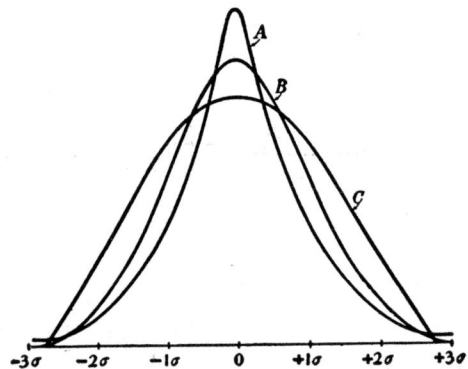

FIG. 25 Leptokurtic (A), normal or mesokurtic (B), and platykurtic (C) curves

distribution and a platykurtic distribution plotted on the same diagram around the same mean. A normal curve (called *mesokurtic*) has also been drawn in on the diagram to bring out the contrast in the figures, and to make comparison easier. A formula for measuring kurtosis is

$$Ku = \frac{Q}{(P_{90} - P_{10})} \qquad (21)$$

(*a measure of kurtosis in terms of percentiles*)

For the normal curve, formula (21) gives $Ku = .263$.* If Ku is *greater* than .263 the distribution is platykurtic; if *less* than .263 the distribution is leptokurtic. Calculating the kurtosis of the distributions of fifty Alpha scores and 200 cancellation scores, discussed above, we obtain $Ku = .237$ for the first distribution, and $Ku = .223$

* From Table A, $PE(Q) = .6745\sigma$, $P_{90} = 1.28\sigma$, and $P_{10} = -1.28\sigma$. Hence by formula (21)

$$Ku = \frac{.6745}{[1.28 - (-1.28)]} = .263$$

THE NORMAL PROBABILITY CURVE • 101

for the second. Both distributions, therefore, are slightly leptokurtic. To determine whether the kurtosis in a distribution is significant, that is, whether the curve is too high or too flat to be treated as sensibly normal, we must evaluate Ku in terms of its standard error. A formula for the standard error of Ku, and a method of determining the significance of an obtained measure of Ku will be given in Chapter 9, page 242.

3. Comparing a given histogram or frequency polygon with a normal curve of the same area, M and σ

In this section methods will be described for superimposing on a given histogram or frequency polygon a normal curve of the same N, M, and σ as the actual distribution. Such a normal curve is the "best fitting" normal distribution for the given data. The research worker often wishes to compare his distribution "by eye" with that normal curve which "best fits" the data, and such a comparison may profitably be made even if no measures of divergence from normality are computed. In fact, the direction and extent of asymmetry often strike us more convincingly when seen in a graph than when expressed by measures of skewness and kurtosis. It may be noted that a normal curve can always be readily constructed by following the procedures given here, provided the area (N) and variability (σ) are known.

TABLE 16 Frequency distribution of the scores made by 206 freshmen on the Thorndike Intelligence Examination

Scores	f	
115–119	1	
110–114	2	
105–109	4	
100–104	10	Mean = 81.59
95–99	13	Median = 81.00
90–94	18	σ = 12.14
85–89	34	
80–84	30	
75–79	37	
70–74	27	
65–69	15	
60–64	10	
55–59	2	
50–54	2	
45–49	1	
	$N = \overline{206}$	

Table 16 shows the frequency distribution of scores made on the Thorndike Intelligence Examination by 206 college freshmen. The mean is 81.59, the median 81.00, and the σ 12.14. This frequency distribution has been plotted in Figure 26, and over it, on the same axes has been drawn in the best-fitting normal curve, i.e., the normal curve which best describes these data. The Thorndike scores are represented by a histogram instead of by a frequency polygon in order to prevent coincidence of the surface outlines and to bring out more clearly agreement and disagreement at different points. To plot a normal curve over this histogram, we first compute the height of the maximum ordinate (y_o) or the frequency at the middle of the distribution. The maximum ordinate (y_o) can be determined from the equation of the normal curve given on page 94. When x in this equation is put equal to zero (the x at the mean of the normal curve is 0), the term $e^{-\frac{x^2}{2\sigma^2}}$ equals 1.00, and $y_o = \dfrac{N}{\sigma\sqrt{2\pi}}$. In the present problem, $N = 206$; $\sigma = 2.43$ * (in units of class-interval), and $\sqrt{2\pi} = 2.51$; hence $y_o = 33.8$ (see Fig. 26 for calculations). Knowing y_o, we are

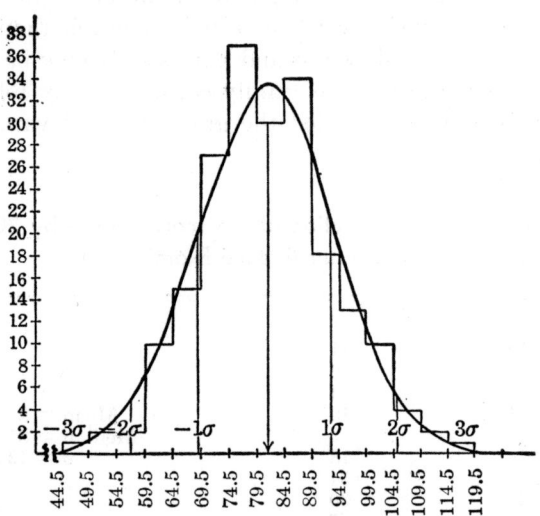

FIG. 26 Frequency distribution of the scores of 206 freshmen on the Thorndike Intelligence Examination, compared with best-fitting normal curve for same data

(For data, see Table 16.)

* $\sigma = 2.43 \times 5$ (interval). The σ in interval units is used in the equation, since the units on the X-*axis* are in terms of class-intervals.

NORMAL CURVE ORDINATES AT MEAN, $\pm 1\sigma$, $\pm 2\sigma$, $\pm 3\sigma$

$$y_o = \frac{N}{\sigma\sqrt{2\pi}} = \frac{206}{2.43 \times 2.51} = 33.8$$

$\pm 1\sigma = .60653 \times 33.8 = 20.5$
$\pm 2\sigma = .13534 \times 33.8 = 4.6$
$\pm 3\sigma = .01111 \times 33.8 = .4$

able to compute from Table B the heights of ordinates at given distances from the mean. The entries in Table B give the heights of the ordinates in the normal probability curve, at various σ-distances from the mean, expressed as fractions of the maximum or middle ordinate taken equal to 1.00000. To find, for example, the height of the ordinate at $\pm 1\sigma$, we take the entry .60653 from the table opposite $x/\sigma = 1.0$. This means that when the maximum central ordinate (y_o) is 1.00000, the ordinate (i.e., frequency) $\pm 1\sigma$ removed from M is .60653; or the frequency at $\pm 1\sigma$ is about 61% of the maximum frequency at the middle of the distribution. In Figure 26 the ordinates $\pm 1\sigma$ from M are $.60653 \times 33.8$ (y_o) or 20.5 The ordinates $\pm 2\sigma$ from M are $.13534 \times 33.8$ or 4.6; and the ordinates $\pm 3\sigma$ from M are $.01111 \times 33.8$ or .4.

The normal curve may be sketched in without much difficulty through the ordinates at these seven points. Somewhat greater accuracy may be obtained if various intermediate ordinates, for example, at $\pm .5\sigma$, $\pm 1.5\sigma$, etc., are also plotted. The ordinates for the curve in Figure 26 at $\pm .5\sigma$ are $.88250 \times 33.8$ or 29.3; at $\pm 1.5\sigma$, $.32465 \times 33.8$ or 11.0, etc.

From formula (20) the skewness of our distribution of 206 scores is found to be 1.25. This small value indicates a low degree of positive skewness in the data. The kurtosis of the distribution by formula (21) is .244, and the distribution appears to be slightly leptokurtic (this is shown by the "peak" rising above the normal curve). Neither measure of divergence, however, is significant of a "real" discrepancy between our data and those of the normal distribution (see p. 212). On the whole, then, the normal curve plotted in Figure 26 fits the obtained distribution well enough to warrant our treating these data as sensibly normal.

IV. Applications of the Normal Probability Curve

This section will consider a number of problems which may readily be solved if one can assume that the distributions of scores may be treated as normal, or at least as approximately normal. Each general

104 • STATISTICS IN PSYCHOLOGY AND EDUCATION

problem will be illustrated by several examples. These examples are intended to present the issues concretely, and should be carefully worked through by the student. Constant reference will be made to Table A; and a knowledge of how to use this table is essential.

1. To determine the percentage of cases in a normal distribution which fall within given limits

Example (1) Given a normal distribution with a mean of 12, and a σ of 4. (a) What percentage of the cases fall between 8 and 16? (b) What percentage of the cases lie above 18? (c) Below 6?

(a) A score of 16 * is four points above the mean, and a score of 8 is four points below the mean. If we divide this scale distance of four score units by the σ of the distribution (i.e., by 4) it is clear that 16 is 1σ above the mean, and that 8 is 1σ below the mean (see Fig. 27, below). There are 68.26% of the cases in a normal distribution between the mean and ±1σ (Table A). Hence, 68.26% of the scores

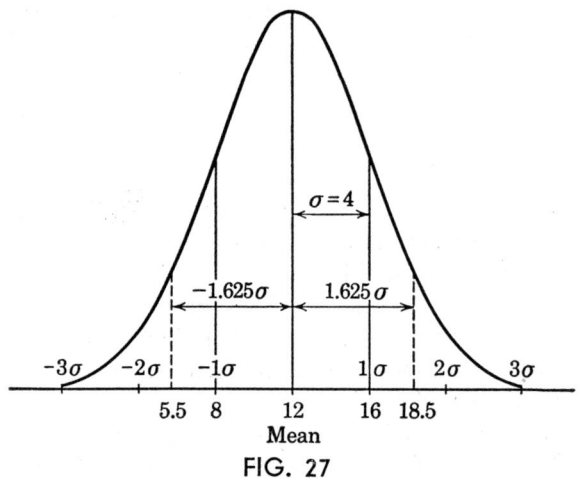

FIG. 27

in this distribution, or approximately the middle two-thirds, fall between 8 and 16. This result may also be stated in terms of "chances." Since 68.26% of the cases in the given distribution fall between 8 and 16, the chances are about 68 in 100 that any score in the distribution will be found between these points.

(b) The *upper limit* of a score of 18, namely, 18.5, is 6.5 score units

* A score of 16 is the midpoint of the interval 15.5 to 16.5

THE NORMAL PROBABILITY CURVE • 105

or 1.625σ above the mean (6.5/4 = 1.625). From Table A we find that 44.79% of the cases in the entire distribution fall between the mean and 1.625σ. Accordingly, 5.21% of the cases (50.00 − 44.79) must lie *above* the upper limit of 18 (viz., 18.5) in order to fill out the 50% of cases in the upper half of the normal curve (Fig. 27). In terms of chances, there are about 5 chances in 100 that any score in the distribution will be larger than 18.

(c) The *lower limit* of a score of 6, namely 5.5, is −1.625σ from the mean. Between the mean and 5.5 (−1.625σ) are 44.79% of the cases in the whole distribution. Hence, about 5% of the cases in the distribution lie below 5.5—fill out the 50% below the mean—and the chances are about 5 in 100 that any score in the distribution will be less than 6, i.e., below the lower limit of score 6.

Example (2) Given a normal distribution with a mean of 29.75 and a σ of 6.75. What percentage of the distribution will lie between 22 and 26? What are the chances that a score will be between these two points?

A score of 22 * is 7.75 score units or −1.15σ (7.75/6.75 = 1.15) from the mean; and a score of 26 is 3.75 or −.56σ from the mean

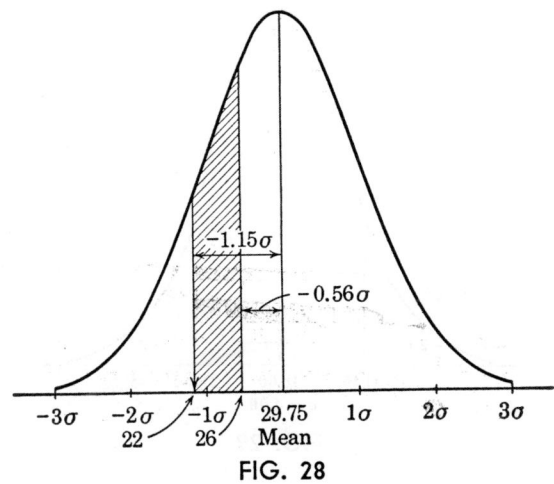

FIG. 28

(Fig. 28, above). We know from Table A that 37.49% of the cases in a normal distribution lie between the mean and −1.15σ; and that 21.23% of the cases lie between the mean and −.56σ. By simple subtraction, therefore, 16.26% of the cases fall between −1.15σ and

* A score of 22 is the midpoint of the interval 21.5 − 22.5.

—.56σ or between the scores 22 and 26. The chances are 16 in 100 that any score in the distribution will lie between these two points.

2. To find the limits in any normal distribution which will include a given percentage of the cases

Example (1) Given a normal distribution with a mean of 16.00 and a σ of 4.00. What limits will include the middle 75% of the cases?

The middle 75% of the cases in a normal distribution must include the 37.5% just above, and the 37.5% just below the mean. From Table A we find that 3749 cases in 10,000, or 37.5% of the distribution, fall between the mean and 1.15σ; and, of course, 37.5% of the distribution also fall between the mean and −1.15σ. The middle 75% of the cases, therefore, lie between the mean and ±1.15σ; or, since σ = 4.00, between the mean and ±4.60 score units. Adding ±4.60 to the mean (to 16.00), we find that the middle 75% of the scores in the given distribution lie between 20.60 and 11.40 (see Fig. 29, below).

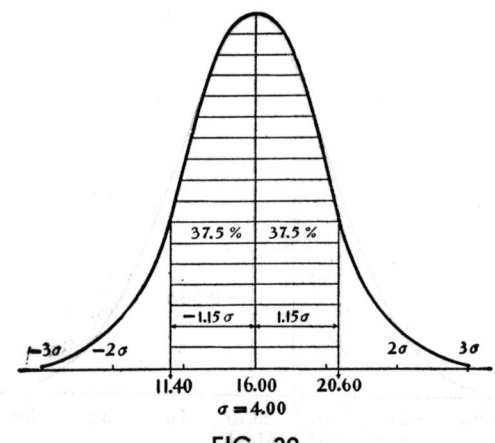

FIG. 29

Example (2) Given a normal distribution with a median of 150.00 and a $PE(Q)$ of 17. What limits will include the *highest* 20% of the distribution? the *lowest* 10%?

We know from page 97 that σ = 1.4826 PE; hence the σ of this distribution is 25.20 (1.4826 × 17). The highest 20% of a normally distributed group will have 30% of the cases between its lower limit and the median, since 50% of the cases lie in the right half of the distribution. From Table A we know that 2995 cases in 10,000 or 30% of the distribution are between the median and .84σ. Since the σ of the given distribution is 25.20, .84σ will be .84 × 25.20 or 21.17 score units *above* the median, or at 171.17. The lower limit of the highest 20% of the given group, therefore, is 171.17; and the upper limit is the highest score in the distribution, whatever that may be.

The lowest 10% of a normally distributed group will have 40% of the cases between the median and its upper limit. Almost exactly 40% of the distribution fall between the median and −1.38σ. Hence, since σ = 25.20, −1.38σ must lie at −1.38 × 25.20 or 34.78 score units *below* the median, that is, at 115.22. The upper limit of the lowest 10% of scores in the group, accordingly, is 115.22; and the lower limit is the lowest score in the distribution.

3. To compare two distributions in terms of "overlapping"

Example (*1*) Given the distributions of the scores made on a logical memory test by 300 boys and 250 girls (Table 17). The boys' mean score is 21.49 with a σ of 3.63. The girls' mean score is 23.68 with a σ of 5.12. The medians are: boys, 21.41, and girls, 23.66. What percentage of boys exceed the median of the girls' distribution?

On the assumption that these distributions are sensibly normal, we may solve this problem by means of Table A. The girls' *median* is 23.66 − 21.49 or 2.17 score units above the boys' *mean*. Dividing 2.17 by 3.63 (the σ of the boys' distribution), we find that the girls' median is .60σ above the mean of the boys' distribution. Table A shows that 23% of a normal distribution lie between the mean and .60σ; hence 27% of the boys (50% − 23%) exceed the girls' median.

This problem may also be solved by direct calculation from the distributions of boys' and girls' scores without any assumption as to normality of distribution. The calculations are shown in Table 17; and it will be interesting to compare the result found by direct calculation with that obtained by use of the probability tables. The problem is to find the *number* of boys whose scores exceed 23.66, the girls' median, and then turn this number into a percentage. There are 217 boys who score up to 23.5 (lower limit of 23.5 to 27.5). The class-interval 23.5 to 27.5 contains 68 scores; hence there are 68/4 or 17 scores *per scale unit* on this interval. We wish to reach 23.66 in the boys' distribution. This point is .16 of a score $(23.66 - 23.50 = .16)$ above 23.5, or 2.72 (i.e., $17 \times .16$) score units above 23.5. Adding 2.72 to 217, we find that 219.72 of the boys' scores fall *below* 23.66, the girls' median. Since $300 - 219.72 = 80.28$, it is clear that

TABLE 17 To illustrate the method of determining overlapping by direct calculation from the distribution

Boys		Girls	
Scores	f	Scores	f
27.5 to 31.5	15	31.5 to 35.5	20
23.5 to 27.5	68	27.5 to 31.5	35
19.5 to 23.5	128	23.5 to 27.5	73
15.5 to 19.5	79	19.5 to 23.5	68
11.5 to 15.5	10	15.5 to 19.5	41
	$N = \overline{300}$	11.5 to 15.5	13
	$N/2 = 150$		$N = \overline{250}$
			$N/2 = 125$
$Mdn = 19.5 + \frac{61}{128} \times 4$		$Mdn = 23.5 + \frac{3}{73} \times 4$	
$= 21.41$		$= 23.66$	
$M = 21.49$		$M = 23.68$	
$\sigma = 3.63$		$\sigma = 5.12$	

What percent of the boys exceed 23.66, the median of the girls? First, 217 boys make scores *below* 23.5. The class-interval 23.5–27.5 contains 68 scores; hence, there are 68/4 or 17 scores *per scale unit* on this interval. The girls' median, 23.66, is .16 *above* 23.5, lower limit of interval 23.5–27.5. If we multiply 17 (number of scores per scale unit) by .16 we obtain 2.72 which is the distance we must go into interval 23.5–27.5 to reach 23.66. Adding 217 and 2.72, we obtain 219.72 as that part of the boys' distribution which falls *below* the point 23.66 (girls' median). N is 300; hence 300–219.72 gives 80.28 as that part of the boys' distribution which lies *above* 23.66. Dividing 80.28 by 300, we find that .2676, or approximately 27%, of the boys exceed the girls' median.

$80.28 \div 300$ or 26.76% (approximately 27%) of the boys exceed the girls' median. This result is in almost perfect agreement with that obtained above. Apparently the assumption of normality of distribution for the boys' scores was justified.

The agreement between the percentage of overlapping found by direct calculation from the distribution and that found by use of the probability tables will nearly always be close, especially if the groups are large and the distributions fairly symmetrical. When the overlapping distributions are small and not very regular in outline, it is safer to use the method of direct calculation, since no assumption as to form of distribution is then made.

4. To determine the relative difficulty of test questions, problems, and other test items

Example (1) Given a test question or problem solved by 10% of a large unselected group; a second problem solved by 20% of the same group; and a third problem solved by 30%. If we assume the capacity measured by the test problems to be distributed normally, what is the relative difficulty of questions 1, 2, and 3?

Our first task is to find for Question 1 a position in the distribution, such that 10% of the entire group (the percent passing) lie above, and 90% (the percent failing) lie below the given point. The highest 10% in a normally distributed group has 40% of the cases between

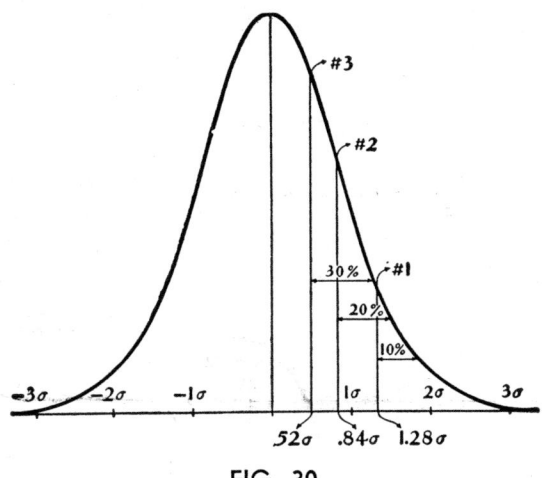

FIG. 30

its lower limit and the mean (see Fig. 30, above). From Table A we find that 39.97% (i.e., 40%) of a normal distribution fall between the mean and 1.28σ. Hence, Question 1 belongs at a point on the baseline of the curve, a distance of 1.28σ from the mean; and, accordingly, 1.28σ may be set down as the difficulty value of this question.

Question 2, passed by 20% of the group, falls at a point in the distribution 30% above the mean. From Table A it is found that 29.95% (i.e., 30%) of the group fall between the mean and .84σ; hence, Question 2 has a difficulty value of .84σ. Question 3, which lies at a point in the distribution 20% above the mean, has a difficulty value of .52σ, since 19.85% of the distribution fall between the mean and .52σ. To summarize our results:

Question	Passed by	σ-value	σ-difference
1	10%	1.28	—
2	20%	.84	.44
3	30%	.52	.32

The σ-difference in difficulty between Questions 2 and 3 is .32, which is roughly 3/4 of the σ-difference in difficulty between Questions 1 and 2. Since the percentage difference is the same in the two comparisons, it is evident that when ability is assumed to follow the normal distribution, σ and not percentage differences are the better indices of differences in difficulty.

Example (2) Given three test items, 1, 2, and 3, passed by 50%, 40%, and 30%, respectively, of a large group. On the assumption of normality of distribution, what percentage of this group must pass test item 4, in order for it to be as much more difficult than 3, as 2 is more difficult than 1?

An item passed by 50% of a group is, of course, failed by 50%; and, accordingly, such an item falls exactly in the middle of a normal distribution of "difficulty." Test item 1, therefore, has a σ-value of .00, since it falls exactly at the mean (Fig. 31). Test item 2 lies at a

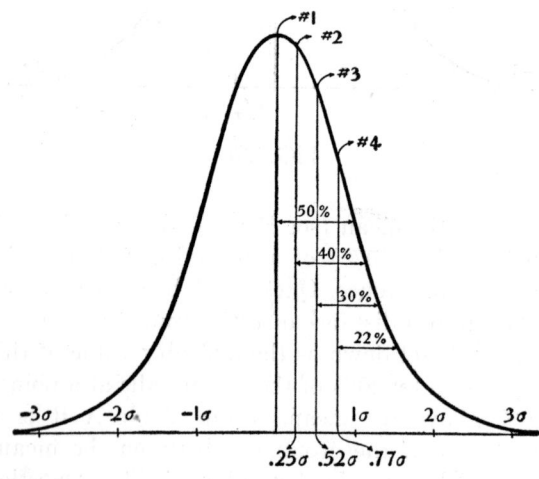

FIG. 31

point in the distribution 10% above the mean, since 40% of the group passed and 60% failed this item. Accordingly, the σ-value of item 2 is .25, since from Table A we find that 9.87% (roughly 10%) of the cases lie between the mean and .25σ. Test item 3, passed by 30% of the group, lies at a point 20% above the mean, and this item has a difficulty value of .52σ, as 19.85% (20%) of the normal distribution fall between the mean and .52σ.

Since item 2 is .25σ farther along on the difficulty scale (toward the high-score end of the curve) than item 1, it is clear that item 4 must be .25σ above item 3, if it is to be as much harder than item 3 as item 2 is harder than item 1. Item 4, therefore, must have a value of .52σ + .25σ or .77σ; and from Table A we find that 27.94% (28%) of the distribution fall between the mean and this point. This means that 50% − 28% or 22% of the group must *pass* item 4. To summarize:

Test Item	Passed by	σ-value	σ-difference
1	50%	.00	—
2	40%	.25	.25
3	30%	.52	—
4	22%	.77	.25

A test item, therefore, must be passed by 22% of the group in order for it to be as much more difficult than an item passed by 30%, as an item passed by 40% is more difficult than one passed by 50%. Note again that percentage differences are not reliable indices of differences in difficulty when the capacity measured is distributed normally.

5. To separate a given group into sub-groups according to capacity, when the trait is normally distributed

Example (1) Suppose that we have administered a certain examination to 100 college students. We wish to classify our group into five sub-groups A, B, C, D, and E according to ability, the *range* of ability to be equal in each sub-group. On the assumption that the trait measured by our examination is normally distributed, how many students should be placed in groups A, B, C, D, and E?

Let us first represent the positions of the five sub-groups diagrammatically on a normal curve as shown in Figure 32, below. If the baseline of the curve is considered to extend from -3σ to $+3\sigma$, that is, over a range of 6σ, dividing this range by 5 (the number of subgroups) gives 1.2σ as the baseline extent to be allotted to each group. These five intervals may be laid off on the baseline as shown in the figure, and perpendiculars erected to demarcate the various subgroups. Group A covers the upper 1.2σ; group B the next 1.2σ; group C lies $.6\sigma$ to the *right* and $.6\sigma$ to the *left* of the mean; groups D and E occupy the same relative positions in the lower half of the curve that B and A occupy in the upper half.

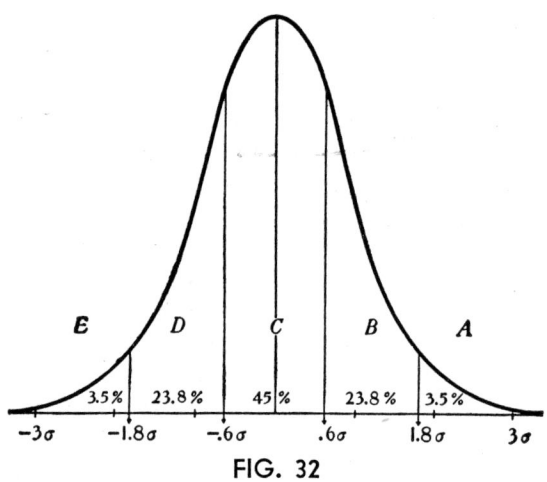

FIG. 32

To find what percentage of the whole group belongs in A we must find what percentage of a normal distribution lies between 3σ (upper limit of the A group) and 1.8σ (lower limit of the A group). From Table A 49.86% of a normal distribution is found to lie between the mean and 3σ; and 46.41% between the mean and 1.8σ. Hence, 3.5% of the total area under the normal curve (49.86% − 46.41%) lie between 3σ and 1.8σ; and, accordingly, group A comprises 3.5% of the whole group.

The percentages in the other groups are calculated in the same way. Thus, 46.41% of the normal distribution fall between the mean and 1.8σ (upper limit of group B) and 22.57% fall between the mean and $.6\sigma$ (lower limit of group B). Subtracting, we find that 46.41% − 22.57% or 23.84% of our distribution belong in subgroup B. Group C lies from $.6\sigma$ above to $-.6\sigma$ below the mean. Between the mean and $.6\sigma$ are 22.57% of the normal distribution, and the same percent lies between the mean and $-.6\sigma$. Group C, therefore, includes 45.14% (22.57 × 2) of the distribution. Finally, sub-group D, which lies between $-.6\sigma$ and -1.8σ, contains exactly the same percentage of the distribution as sub-group B; and group E, which lies between -1.8σ and -3σ, contains the same percent of the whole distribution as group A. The percentage and number of men in each group are given in the following table:

	Groups				
	A	B	C	D	E
Percent of total in each group	3.5	23.8	45	23.8	3.5
Number in each group (100 men in all)	4 or 3	24	45	24	4 or 3

On the assumption that the capacity measured follows the normal curve, it is clear that three to four men in our group of 100 should be placed in group A, the "marked" ability group; twenty-four in group B, the "high average" ability group; forty-five in group C, the "average" ability group; twenty-four in group D, the "low average" ability group; and three or four in group E, the "very low" or "inferior" group.

The above procedure may be used to determine how many students in a class should be assigned to each of any given number of grade-groups. It must be remembered that the assumption is made that performance in the subject matter upon which the individuals are being marked is represented by the normal curve. The larger and more unselected the group the more nearly is this assumption justified.

V. Why Frequency Distributions Deviate from the Normal Form

It is often important for the research worker to know why his distributions diverge from the normal form, and this is especially true when the deviation from normality is large and significant (p. 212). The reasons why distributions exhibit skewness and kurtosis are numerous and often complex, but a careful analysis of the data will often permit the setting up of hypotheses concerning non-normality which may be tested experimentally. Common causes of asymmetry, all of which must be taken into consideration by the careful experimenter, will be summarized in the present section.

1. Unrepresentative or biased sampling

Selection is a potent cause of skewness. We should hardly expect the distribution of I.Q.'s obtained from a group of twenty-five ten-year-old boys (all superior students) to be normal; nor would we look for symmetry in the distribution of I.Q.'s got from a special class of dull-normal ten-year-old boys, even though the group were fairly large. Neither of these groups is an unbiased selection (i.e., a cross-section) from the population of ten-year-old boys; and in addition, the first group is quite small. A small sample is not *necessarily* unrepresentative, but more often than not it is apt to be.

Selection will produce skewness and kurtosis in distributions even when the test has been adequately constructed and carefully administered. For example, a group of elementary school pupils which contains (a) a large proportion of bilinguals, (b) many children of very low or very high socio-economic status, (c) a large number of pupils over-age for grade or accelerated, will almost surely return skewed distributions of test scores even upon standard intelligence and educational achievement examinations.

Scores made by small and homogeneous groups are likely to yield leptokurtic distributions; while scores from large and heterogeneous groups are more likely to be platykurtic. The distribution of scores achieved upon an educational examination by pupils throughout the elementary grades, as well as the distribution of chronological ages for these same pupils, will probably be somewhat flattened owing to the considerable overlap from grade to grade.

Distributions of physical traits, such as height, weight, and strength, are also affected by selection. Measurements of physical traits in large groups of the same age, sex, and race will closely approximate the normal form (p. 85). But the distribution of height for fourteen-year-old girls in the high school of a small city, or the distribution of weight for freshmen in a midwestern college, will probably be skewed, as these groups are subject to selection in various traits related to height and weight.

2. Use of unsuitable or poorly made tests

If a test is too easy, scores will pile up at the high-score end of the distribution, while if the test is too hard scores will pile up at the low-score end. Imagine, for example, that an examination in arithmetic

THE NORMAL PROBABILITY CURVE • 115

which requires only addition, subtraction, multiplication, and division, has been given to 1000 seventh graders. The resulting distribution will almost certainly be badly skewed to the left (see Fig. 23). On the other hand, if the examination contains only problems in complex fractions, interest, square root, and the like, the score distribution is likely to be positively skewed—low scores will be more numerous than intermediate or high scores. It is probable also that both distributions will be somewhat more "peaked" (leptokurtic) than the normal.

Asymmetry in cases like these may be explained in terms of those small positive and negative factors which determine the normal distribution. Too easy a test excludes from operation some of the factors which would make for an extension of the curve at the upper end, such as knowledge of more advanced arithmetical processes which the brighter child would know. Too hard a test excludes from operation factors which make for the extension of the distribution at the low end, such as knowledge of those very simple facts which would have permitted the answering of a few at least of the easier questions had these been included. In the first case we have a number of perfect scores and little discrimination; in the second case a number of zero scores and equally poor differentiation. Besides the matter of difficulty in the test, asymmetry may be brought about by ambiguous or poorly made items and by other technical faults.*

3. The measurement of traits the distributions of which are not normal

Skewness or kurtosis or both may also appear owing to a real lack of normality in the trait being measured.† Non-normality of distribution will arise, for instance, when some of the hypothetical factors determining performance in a trait are dominant or prepotent over the others, and hence are present more often than chance will allow. Illustrations may be found in distributions resulting from the throwing of loaded dice. When off-center or biased dice are cast the

---

* Hawkes, Lindquist and Mann, *The Construction and Use of Achievement Examinations* (Boston: Houghton Mifflin Co., 1936), Chapters II and III.
† There is no reason why all distributions should approach the normal form. Thorndike has written: "There is nothing arbitrary or mysterious about variability which makes the so-called normal type of distribution a necessity, or any more rational than any other sort, or even more to be expected on *a priori* grounds. Nature does not abhor irregular distributions."—*Theory of Mental and Social Measurement* (New York: Teachers College, 1913), pp. 88–89.

resulting distribution will certainly be skewed and probably peaked, owing to the greater likelihood of combinations of faces yielding extreme scores. The same is true of biased coins. Suppose, for example, that the probability of "success" (appearance of H) is four times the probability of failure (non-occurrence of H, or presence of T), so that $p = 4/5$, $q = 1/5$, and $(p+q) = 1.00$. If we think of the factors making for success or failure as 3 in number, we may expand $(p+q)^3$ to find the incidence of success and failure in varying degree. Thus, $(p+q)^3 = p^3 + 3p^2q + 3pq^2 + q^3$, and substituting $p = 4/5$ and $q = 1/5$, we have

(1) $p^3 = (4/5)^3 = \dfrac{64}{125}$

$3p^2q = 3(4/5)^2 \cdot (1/5) = \dfrac{48}{125}$

$3pq^2 = 3(4/5) \cdot (1/5)^2 = \dfrac{12}{125}$

$q^3 = (1/5)^3 = \dfrac{1}{125}$

(2) Expressed as a frequency distribution:

"Successes"	f
3	64
2	48
1	12
0	1
	$N = 125$

The numerators of the probability ratios (frequency of success) may be plotted in the form of a histogram to give Figure 33.

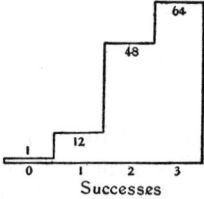

FIG. 33 Histogram of the expansion $(p+q)^3$, where $p = \frac{4}{5}$, $q = \frac{1}{5}$. p is the probability of success, q the probability of failure

FIG. 34 U-shaped frequency curve

Note that this distribution is negatively skewed (to the *left*); that the incidence of three "successes" is 64, of two 48, of one 12, and of none 1. J-shaped distributions like these are essentially non-normal. Such curves have been most often found by psychologists to describe certain forms of social behavior. For example, suppose that we tabulate the number of students who appear at a lecture "on time"; and the number who come in five, ten, and fifteen-plus minutes late. If frequency of arrival is plotted against time, the distribution will be highest at zero ("on time") on the Y-axis and will fall off rapidly as we go to the right, i.e., will be positively skewed and J-shaped (see Fig. 24). If only the early-comers are tallied, up to the "on time" group, the curve will be negatively skewed like those in Figures 23 and 33. J-curves describe behavior which is essentially non-normal in occurrence because the causes of the behavior differ greatly in strength. But J-curves may also represent frequency distributions badly skewed for other reasons. We have seen in (1) and (2) above that selection and poorly chosen tests can produce distributions which closely resemble J-curves.

Skewed curves often occur in medical statistics. The frequency of death due to degenerative disease, for instance, is highest during maturity and old age and minimal during the early years. If age is laid off on the baseline and frequency of death plotted on the Y-axis the curve will be negatively skewed and will resemble Figure 23 closely. Factors making for death are prepotent over those making for survival as age increases, and hence the curve is essentially asymmetrical. In the case of a childhood disease, the occurrence of death will be positively skewed when plotted against age as the probability of death becomes less with increase in age.

Another type of non-normal distribution, which may be briefly described, is the U-shaped curve shown in Figure 34. U-shaped distributions, like J-curves, are rarely encountered in mental and physical measurement. They are sometimes found in the measurement of social and personality traits, if the group is extremely heterogeneous with respect to some attribute, or if the test measures a trait that is likely to be present or absent in an all-or-none manner. Thus, in a group composed about equally of normals and mentally ill persons, the normals will tend to make low scores on a Neurotic Inventory while the abnormals will tend to make high scores—with considerable overlapping, of course. Again, in tests of suggestibility, if a subject yields to suggestion in the first trial he is likely to be suggestible in all trials—thus earning a high score. On the other hand, if he resists suggestion on the first trial, he is likely to resist in all subsequent trials—thus earning a zero (or a very low) score.* This all-or-none feature of the score makes for a U-shaped distribution.

* See Hull, C. L., *Hypnosis and Suggestibility* (New York: Appleton-Century-Crofts, 1938), p. 68.

4. The influence upon distribution form of errors made in the construction and administration of tests

Other factors besides those already mentioned make for distortions in score distributions. Differences in the size of the units in which a trait has been measured, for example, will lead to skewness. Thus, if the test items are very easy at the beginning and very hard later on, an increment of one point of score at the upper end of the test scale will be much greater than an increment of one point at the low end of the scale. The effect of such unequal or "rubbery" units is the same as that encountered when the test is too easy—scores tend to pile up toward the high end of the scale and be stretched out or skewed toward the low end.

Errors in administration of a test as in timing or giving instructions; errors in the use of scoring stencils; large differences in practice or in motivation among the subjects—all of these factors, if they cause many students to score higher or lower than they normally would, will make for skewness in the distribution.

PROBLEMS

1. In two throws of a coin, what is the probability of throwing at least one head?
2. What is the probability of throwing exactly one head in three throws of a coin?
3. Five coins are thrown. What is the probability that exactly two of them will be heads?
4. A box contains 10 red, 20 white and 30 blue marbles. After a thorough shaking, a blindfolded person draws out 1 marble. What is the probability that
   (a) it is blue?
   (b) red or blue?
   (c) neither red nor blue?
5. If the probability of answering a certain question correctly is four times the probability of answering it incorrectly, what is the probability of answering it correctly?
6. (a) If two unbiased dice are thrown what is the probability that the number of spots showing will total 7?
   (b) Draw up a frequency distribution showing the occurrence of combinations of from 2 to 12 spots when two dice are thrown.

7. (a) In an attitude questionnaire containing 10 statements, each to be marked as True or False, what is the probability of getting a perfect score by sheer guesswork?
    (b) Suppose you know 5 statements to be True and 5 False. What is the probability that you will mark the right ones True (select the right five)?

8. A rat has five choices to make of alternate routes in order to reach the food-box. If it is true that for each choice the odds are two to one in favor of the correct pathway, what is the probability that the rat will make all of its choices correctly?

9. Assuming that trait X is completely determined by 6 factors—all similar and independent, and each as likely to be present as absent—plot the distribution which one might expect to get from the measurement of trait X in an unselected group of 1000 people.

10. Toss five pennies thirty-two times, and record the number of heads and tails after each throw. Plot frequency polygons of obtained and expected occurrences on the same axes. Compare the M's and σ's of obtained and expected distributions.

11. What percentage of a normal distribution is included between the
    (a) mean and 1.54σ
    (b) mean and $-2.7PE$
    (c) -1.73σ and $.56\sigma$
    (d) $-3.5PE$ and $1.0PE$
    (e) $.66\sigma$ and 1.78σ
    (f) $-1.8PE$ and $-2.5PE$

12. In a normal distribution
    (a) Determine P_{27}, P_{46}, P_{54}, and P_{81} in σ-units.
    (b) What are the percentile ranks of scores at -1.23σ, $-.50\sigma$, $+.84\sigma$?

13. (a) Compute measures of skewness and of kurtosis for the first two frequency distributions in Chapter 2, Problem 1, page 40.
    (b) Fit normal probability curves to these same distributions, using the method given on page 102.
    (c) For each distribution, compare the percentage of cases lying between $\pm 1\sigma$ with the 68.26% found in the normal distribution.

14. Suppose that the height of the maximum ordinate (y_o) in a normal curve is 50. What is the height to the nearest integer of the ordinate at the x/σ point which cuts off the top 11% of the distribution? top 30%? bottom 5%? (Use Tables A and B.)

15. In a sample of 1000 cases the mean of a certain test is 14.40 and σ is 2.50. Assuming normality of distribution
    (a) How many individuals score between 12 and 16?
    (b) How many score *above* 18? *below* 8?
    (c) What are the chances that any individual selected at random will score *above* 15?

16. In the Army General Classification Test the distribution is essentially normal with a $M = 100$ and $SD = 20$.
    (a) What percent of scores lie between 85 and 125?
    (b) The middle 60% fall between what two scores?
    (c) On what score does Q_3 fall?

17. In a certain achievement test, the seventh-grade mean is 28.00 and SD is 4.80; and the eighth-grade mean is 31.60 and SD is 4.00. What percent of the seventh grade is above the mean of the eighth grade? What percent of the eighth grade is below the mean of the seventh grade?

18. Two years ago a group of twelve-year-olds had a reading ability expressed by a mean score of 40.00 and a σ of 3.60; and a composition ability expressed by a mean of 62.00 and a σ of 9.60. Today the group has gained 12 points in reading and 10.8 points in composition. How many times greater is the gain in reading than the gain in composition?

19. In Problem 1, Chapter 4, we computed directly from the distribution the percent of Group A which exceeds the median of Group B. Compare this value with the percentage of overlapping obtained on the assumption of normality in Group A.

20. Four problems, A, B, C, and D, have been solved by 50%, 60%, 70%, and 80%, respectively, of a large group. Compare the difference in difficulty between A and B with the difference in difficulty between C and D.

21. In a certain college, ten grades, A+, A, A−; B+, B, B−; C+, C, C−; and D, are assigned. If ability in mathematics is distributed normally, how many students in a group of 500 freshmen should receive each grade?

22. Assume that the distribution of grades in a class of 500 freshmen is normal with $M = 72$ and $SD = 10$. The instructor wants to give letter grades as follows: 10% A's; 30% B's; 40% C's; 15% D's; and 5% F's. Compute to the closest score the *divisions* between A's and B's; B's and C's; C's and D's; D's and F's.

ANSWERS

1. 3/4   2. 3/8   3. 10/32
4. (a) 1/2
   (b) 2/3
   (c) 1/3
5. 4/5   6. (a) 1/6

7. (a) 1/1024
   (b) 1/252

8. 32/243

10. For expected distribution
    $M = 2.5$, $\sigma = 1.12$

11. (a) .4383   (d) .7409
    (b) .4657   (e) .2171
    (c) .6705   (f) .0665

12. (a) $-.61\sigma, -.10\sigma, .10\sigma, .88\sigma$
    (b) 11, 31, 80

13. (a)

	Skewness			Kurtosis	
	By formula	(19)	By formula (20)	By formula	(21)
(1)	$-.018$		$-.27$	.239	
(2)	.156		1.03	.277	

   (c) 66%, 67%

14. 23, 44, 12

15. (a) 570
    (b) 50; 3
    (c) 33 in 100 or 1 in 3

16. (a) 67%
    (b) 83 and 117
    (c) 113

17. 23%; 18%

18. Three times as great.

19. 39% as compared with 42%.

20. Difference between A and B is $.25\sigma$; between C and D, $.32\sigma$.

21.
Grades:	A+	A	A−	B+	B	B−	C+	C	C−	D
Students Receiving:	3	14	40	80	113	113	80	40	14	3

22. 85; 75; 64; 56

6

LINEAR CORRELATION

I. The Meaning of Correlation

1. Correlation as a measure of relationship

In previous chapters we have been concerned primarily with methods of computing statistical measures designed to represent in a reliable way the performance of an individual or a group in some defined trait. Frequently, however, it is of more importance to examine the *relationship* of one ability to another than to measure performance in either alone. Are certain abilities closely related, and others relatively independent? Is it true that good pitch discrimination accompanies musical achievement; or that bright children tend to be less neurotic than average children? If we know the general intelligence of a child, as measured by a standard test, can we say anything about his probable scholastic achievement as represented by grades? Problems like these and many others which involve the relations among abilities can be studied by the method of correlation.

When the relationship between two sets of measures is "linear," i.e., can be described by a straight line,* the correlation between scores may be expressed by the "product-moment" coefficient of correlation, designated by the letter r. The method of calculating r will be outlined in Section III. Before taking up the details of calculation, let us make clear what correlation means, and how r measures relationship.

Consider, first, a situation in which relationship is fixed and unchanging. The circumference of a circle is always 3.1416 times its

---

* See pages 154–158 for a further discussion of "linear" relationship.

diameter ($C = 3.1416D$), and this equation holds no matter how large or how small the circle, or in what part of the world we find it. Each time the diameter of a circle is increased or decreased, the circumference is increased or decreased by just 3.1416 times the same amount. In short, the dependence of circumference upon diameter is absolute; the correlation between the two dimensions is said to be perfect, and $r = 1.00$. In theory, at least, the relationship between two abilities, as represented by test scores, may also be perfect. Suppose that a hundred students have exactly the same standing in two tests—the student who scores first in the one test scores first in the other, the student who ranks second in the first test ranks second in the other, and this one-to-one correspondence holds throughout the entire list. The relationship is perfect, since the relative position of each subject is exactly the same in one test as in the other; and the coefficient of correlation is 1.00.

Now let us consider the case in which there is just *no* correlation present. Suppose that we have administered to 100 college seniors the Army General Classification Test and a simple "tapping test" in which the number of separate taps made in thirty seconds is recorded. Let the mean AGCT score for the group be 120, and the mean tapping rate be 185 taps in thirty seconds. Now suppose that when we divide our group into three sub-groups in accordance with the size of their AGCT scores, the mean tapping rate of the superior or "high" group (whose mean AGCT score is 130) is 184 taps in thirty seconds; the mean tapping rate of the "middle" group (whose mean AGCT score is 110) is 186 taps in thirty seconds; and the mean tapping rate of the "low" group (whose mean AGCT score is 100) is 185 taps in thirty seconds. Since tapping rate is almost identical in all three groups, it is clear that from tapping rate alone we should be unable to draw any conclusion as to a student's probable performance upon AGCT. A tapping rate of 185 is as likely to be found with an AGCT score of 100 as with one of 120 or even 160. In other words, there is no correspondence between the scores made by the members of our group upon the two tests, and r, the coefficient of correlation, is zero.*

Perfect relationship, then, is expressed by a coefficient of 1.00, and just no relationship by a coefficient of .00. Between these two limits, increasing degrees of relationship are indicated by such coefficients as

---

* It may be noted that the number of groups (here 3) is unimportant: any convenient set may be used. The important point is that when the correlation is zero, there is no systematic relationship between two sets of scores.

.33, or .65, or .92. A coefficient of correlation falling between .00 and 1.00 always implies *some* degree of positive association, the degree of correspondence depending upon the size of the coefficient.

Relationship may also be negative; that is, a *high* degree of one trait may be associated with a *low* degree of another. When negative or inverse relationship is perfect, $r = -1.00$. To illustrate, suppose that in a small class of ten schoolboys, the boy who stands first in Latin ranks lowest (tenth) in shop work; the boy who stands second in Latin ranks next to the bottom (ninth) in shop work; and that each boy stands just as far from the top of the list in Latin as from the bottom of the list in shop work. Here the correspondence between achievement in Latin and performance in shop work is one-to-one and definite enough, but the *direction* of relationship is inverse and $r = -1.00$. Negative coefficients may range from -1.00 up to .00, just as positive coefficients may range from .00 up to 1.00. Coefficients of $-.20$, $-.50$, or $-.80$ indicate increasing degrees of negative or inverse relationship, just as positive coefficients of .20, .50, and .80 indicate increasing degrees of positive relationship.

2. Correlation expressed as agreement between ranks

The notion underlying correlation can often be most readily comprehended from a simple graphic treatment. Three examples will be given to illustrate values of r of 1.00, -1.00, and approximately .00. Correlation is rarely computed when the number of cases is less than 25, so that the examples here presented must be considered to have illustrative value only.

Suppose that four tests, A, B, C, and D, have been administered to a group of five children. The children have been arranged in order of merit on Test A and their scores are then compared separately with Tests B, C, and D to give the following three cases:

	Case 1			Case 2			Case 3	
Pupil	A	B	Pupil	A	C	Pupil	A	D
a	15	53	a	15	64	a	15	102
b	14	52	b	14	65	b	14	100
c	13	51	c	13	66	c	13	104
d	12	50	d	12	67	d	12	103
e	11	49	e	11	68	e	11	101

Now if the *second* series of scores under each case (i.e., B, C, and D) is arranged in order of merit from the highest score down, and the two scores earned by each child are connected by a straight line, we have the following graphs:

Case 1	Case 2	Case 3
A B	A C	A D
15——53	15 68	15 104
14——52	14 67	14 103
13——51	13 ╳ 66	13 ╳ 102
12——50	12 65	12 101
11——49	11 64	11 100

| All connecting lines are horizontal and parallel, and the correlation is positive and perfect. $r = 1.00$ | All connecting lines intersect in one point. The correlation is negative and perfect, and $r = -1.00$ | No system is exhibited by the connecting lines, but the resemblance is closer to Case 2 than to Case 1. Correlation low and negative |

The more nearly the lines connecting the paired scores are horizontal and parallel, the higher the positive correlation. The more nearly the connecting lines tend to intersect in one point, the larger the negative correlation. When the connecting lines show no systematic trend, the correlation approaches zero.

3. Summary

To summarize our discussion up to this point, coefficients of correlation range over a scale which extends from -1.00 through .00 to 1.00. A positive correlation indicates that *large* amounts of the one variable tend to accompany *large* amounts of the other; a negative correlation indicates that *small* amounts of the one variable tend to accompany *large* amounts of the other. A zero correlation indicates no consistent relationship. We have illustrated above only perfect positive, perfect negative, and approximately zero correlation in order to bring out the meaning of correlation in a striking way. Only rarely, if ever, however, will a coefficient fall at either extreme of the scale, i.e., at 1.00 or -1.00. In most actual problems, calculated r's fall at intermediate points, such as .72, $-.26$, .50, etc. Such r's are to be interpreted as "high" or "low" depending in general upon how close they are to ± 1.00. Interpretation of the degree of relationship expressed by r in terms of various criteria will be discussed later on pages 173–178.

II. The Coefficient of Correlation*

1. The coefficient of correlation as a ratio

The product-moment coefficient of correlation may be thought of essentially as that *ratio* which expresses the extent to which changes in one variable are accompanied by—or are dependent upon—changes in a second variable. As an illustration, consider the following simple example which gives the paired heights and weights of five college seniors:

(1)	(2)	(3)	(4)	(5)	(6)	(7)	(8)	(9)
Student	Ht. in inches	Wt. in lbs.						
	X	Y	x	y	xy	$\dfrac{x}{\sigma_x}$	$\dfrac{y}{\sigma_y}$	$\left(\dfrac{x}{\sigma_x} \cdot \dfrac{y}{\sigma_y}\right)$
a	72	170	3	0	0	1.34	.00	.00
b	69	165	0	−5	0	.00	−.37	.00
c	66	150	−3	−20	60	−1.34	−1.46	1.96
d	70	180	1	10	10	.44	.73	.32
e	68	185	−1	15	−15	−.44	1.10	−.48
					55			1.80

$M_X = 69$ in. $\sigma_x = 2.24$ in.
$M_Y = 170$ lbs. $\sigma_y = 13.69$ lbs.   correlation $= \dfrac{\Sigma\left(\dfrac{x}{\sigma_x} \cdot \dfrac{y}{\sigma_y}\right)}{N} = \dfrac{1.80}{5} = .36$

From the X and Y columns it is evident that tall students tend to be somewhat heavier than short students, and hence the correlation between height and weight is almost certainly positive. The mean height is 69 inches, the mean weight 170 pounds, and the σ's are 2.24 inches and 13.69 pounds, respectively. In column (4) are given the deviations (x's) of each man's height from the mean height, and in column (5) the deviations (y's) of each man's weight from the mean weight. The product of these paired deviations (xy's) is a measure of the agreement between individual heights and weights, and the larger the sum of the xy column the higher the degree of correspondence. When agreement is perfect (and $r = 1.00$) the Σxy column has its maximum value. One may wonder why the sum of $\dfrac{xy\text{'s}}{N}\left(\text{i.e., } \dfrac{55}{5}\right)$ would not yield a suitable measure of relationship between x and y. The answer is that such an average is *not* a stable measure of relationship, as it depends upon the *units* in which height

* This section may be taken up after Section III.

LINEAR CORRELATION • 127

and weight have been expressed, and consequently will vary if centimeters and kilograms, say (as shown in the example below), are employed instead of inches and pounds. One way to avoid the troublesome matter of differences in units is to divide each x and each y by its own σ, i.e., express each deviation as a σ-score. The sum of the products of the σ-scores—column (9)—divided by N yields a ratio which, as we shall see later, *is* a stable expression of relationship. This ratio is the "product-moment"* coefficient of correlation. Its value of .36 indicates a fairly high positive correlation between height and weight in this small sample. The student should note that our ratio or coefficient is simply the *average product* of the σ-scores of corresponding X and Y measures.

Let us now investigate the effect upon our ratio of changing the units in terms of which X and Y have been expressed. In the example below, the heights and weights of the same five students are expressed (to the nearest whole number) in centimeters and kilograms instead of in inches and pounds:

(1)	(2)	(3)	(4)	(5)	(6)	(7)	(8)	(9)
Student	Ht. in cms.	Wt. in kgs.						
	X	Y	x	y	xy	$\dfrac{x}{\sigma_x}$	$\dfrac{y}{\sigma_y}$	$\left(\dfrac{x}{\sigma_x} \cdot \dfrac{y}{\sigma_y}\right)$
a	183	77	8	0	0	1.43	.00	.00
b	175	75	0	−2	0	.00	−.32	.00
c	168	68	−7	−9	63	−1.25	−1.43	1.79
d	178	82	3	5	15	.53	.80	.42
e	173	84	−2	7	−14	−.36	1.11	−.40
					64			1.81

$M_X = 175$ cms. $\sigma_x = 5.61$ cms.
$M_Y = 77$ kgs. $\sigma_y = 6.30$ kgs.   correlation $= \dfrac{\Sigma\left(\dfrac{x}{\sigma_x} \cdot \dfrac{y}{\sigma_y}\right)}{N} = \dfrac{1.81}{5} = .36$

The mean height of our group is now 175 cms. and the mean weight 77 kgs.; the σ's are 5.61 cms. and 6.30 kgs., respectively. Note that the sum of the xy column, namely, 64, differs by 9 from the sum of the xy's in the example above, in which inches and pounds were the units of measurement. However, when deviations are expressed as σ-scores, the sum of their products $\left(\dfrac{x}{\sigma_x} \cdot \dfrac{y}{\sigma_y}\right)$ divided by N equals .36 as before.

---
* The sum of the deviations from the mean (raised to some power) and divided by N is called a "moment." When corresponding deviations in x and y are multiplied together, summed, and divided by N $\left(\text{to give } \dfrac{\Sigma xy}{N}\right)$ the term "product-moment" is used.

The quotient

$$\frac{\Sigma\left(\dfrac{x}{\sigma_x} \cdot \dfrac{y}{\sigma_y}\right)}{N}$$

is a measure of relationship which remains constant for a given set of data, no matter in what units X and Y are expressed. When this ratio is written $\dfrac{\Sigma xy}{N\sigma_x\sigma_y}$ it becomes the well-known expression for r, the product-moment coefficient of correlation.*

2. The scatter diagram and the correlation table

When N is small, the ratio method described in the preceding section may be employed for computing the coefficient of correlation between two sets of data. But when N is large, much time and labor may be saved by first arranging the data in the form of a diagram or chart, and then calculating deviations from assumed, instead of from actual, means. Let us consider the diagram in Figure 35. This chart, which is called a "scatter diagram" or "scattergram," represents the paired heights and weights of 120 college students. The construction of a scattergram is relatively simple. Along the left-hand margin from bottom to top are laid off the class-intervals of the height distribution, measurement expressed in inches; and along the top of the diagram from left to right are laid off the class-intervals of the weight distribution, measurement expressed in pounds. Each of the 120 men is represented on the diagram with respect to height and weight. Suppose that a man weighs 150 pounds and is 69 inches tall. His weight locates him in the sixth column from the left, and his height in the third row from the top. Accordingly, a "tally" is placed in the third cell of the sixth column. There are three tallies in all in this cell, that is, there are three men who weight from 150 to 159 pounds, and are 68–69 inches tall. Each of the 120 men is represented by a tally in a cell or square of the table in accordance with the two characteristics, height and weight. Along the bottom of the diagram in the f_x row is tabulated the number of men who fall in each weight-interval; while along the right-hand margin in the f_y column is tabu-

---

* The coefficient of correlation, r, is often called the "Pearson r" after Professor Karl Pearson who developed the product-moment method, following the earlier work of Galton and Bravais. See Walker, H. M., *Studies in the History of Statistical Method* (Baltimore: Williams and Wilkins Co., 1929), Chapter 5, pp. 96–111.

LINEAR CORRELATION • 129

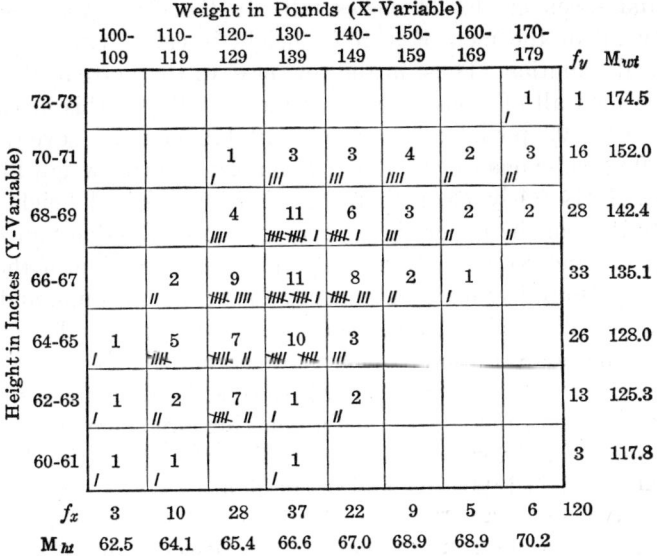

FIG. 35 A scattergram and correlation table showing the paired heights and weights of 120 students

lated the number of men who fall in each height-interval. The f_y column and f_x row must each total 120, the number of men in all. After all of the tallies have been listed, the frequency in each cell is added and entered on the diagram. The scattergram is then a *correlation table*.

Several interesting facts may be gleaned from the correlation table as it stands. For example, all of the men of a given weight-interval may be studied with respect to the distribution of their heights. In the third column there are twenty-eight men all of whom weigh 120–129 pounds. One of the twenty-eight is 70–71 inches tall; four are 68–69 inches tall; nine or 66–67 inches tall; seven are 64–65 inches tall; and seven are 62–63 inches tall. In the same way, we may classify all of the men of a given height-interval with respect to weight distribution. Thus, in the row next to the bottom, there are thirteen men all of whom are 62–63 inches tall. Of this group one weighs 100–109 pounds; two weigh 110–119 pounds; seven weigh 120–129 pounds; one weighs 130-139 pounds; and two weigh 140–149 pounds. It is fairly clear that the "drift" of paired heights and weights is from the upper right-hand section of the diagram to the lower left-hand section. Even a superficial examination of the diagram reveals a fairly marked tendency for heavy, medium, and light men to be tall, medium, and short, respectively; and this general relationship holds in spite of the scatter of heights and weights within any given "array" (an array is the distribution of cases within a given column or row). Even before making any calculations, then, we should probably be willing to guess that the correlation between height and weight is positive and fairly high.

Let us now go a step further and calculate the mean height of the three men who weigh 100–109 pounds, the men in column one. The mean height of this group (using the assumed mean method described in Chapter 2, p. 36) is 62.5 inches, and this figure has been written in at the bottom of the correlation table. In the same way, the mean heights of the men who fall in each of the succeeding weight-intervals have been written in at the bottom of the diagram. These data have been tabulated in a somewhat more convenient form below the diagram. From this summary, it appears that an actual weight increase of approximately 70 pounds (104.5–174.5) corresponds to an increase in mean height of 7.7 inches; that is, the increase from the lightest to the heaviest man is paralleled by an increase of approximately eight inches in height. It seems clear, therefore, that the correlation between height and weight is positive.

Let us now shift from height to weight, and applying the method used above, find the change in *mean weight* which corresponds to the given change in height.* The mean weight of the three men in the bottom row of the diagram is 117.8 pounds. The mean weight of the thirteen men in the next row from the bottom (who are 62–63 inches tall) is 125.3 pounds. The mean weights of the men who fall in the other rows have been written in their appropriate places in the M_{wt} column. In the summary of results we find that in this group of 120 men an increase of about 12 inches in height is accompanied by an

---

* This change corresponds to the *second* regression line in the correlation diagram (see p. 153).

increase of about 56.7 pounds in mean weight. Thus it appears that the taller the man the heavier he tends to be, and again the correlation between height and weight is seen to be positive.

3. The graphic representation of the correlation coefficient

It is often helpful in understanding how the correlation coefficient measures relationship to see how a correlation of .00 or .50, say, looks graphically. Figure 36 (1) pictures a correlation of .50. The data

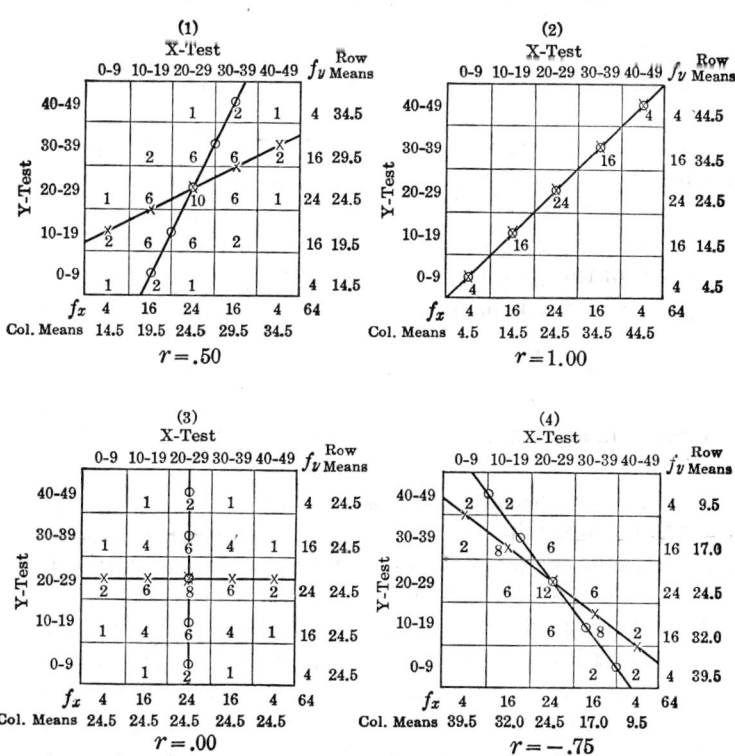

FIG. 36 The graphical representation of the correlation coefficient

in the table are artificial, and were selected to bring out the relationship in as unequivocal a fashion as possible. The scores laid off along the top of the correlation table from left to right will be referred to simply as the X-test "scores," and the scores laid off at the left of the table from bottom to top as the Y-test "scores." As was done in

Figure 35, the mean of each Y-row is entered on the chart, and the means of the X-columns are entered at the bottom of the diagram.

The means of each Y-array, that is, the means of the "scores" falling in each X-column, are indicated on the chart by small crosses. Through these crosses a line, called a *regression* line,* has been drawn. This line represents the change in the *mean* value of Y over the given range of X. In similar fashion, the means of each X-array, i.e., the means of the scores in each Y-row, are designated on the chart by small circles, through which another line has been drawn. This second regression line shows the change in the *mean* value of X over the given range of Y. These two lines together represent the linear or straight-line relationship between the variables X and Y.

The closeness of association or degree of correspondence between the X- and Y-tests is indicated by the relative positions of these two regression lines. When the correlation is positive and perfect, the two regression lines close up like a pair of scissors to form one line. Chart (2) in Figure 36 shows how the two regression lines look when $r = 1.00$, and the correlation is perfect. Note that the entries in Chart (2) are concentrated along the diagonal from the upper right- to the lower left-hand section of the diagram. There is no "scatter" of scores in the successive columns or rows, all of the scores in a given array being concentrated within one cell. If Chart (2) represented a correlation table of height and weight, we should know that the tallest man was the heaviest, the next tallest man the next heaviest, and that throughout the group the correspondence of height and weight was perfect.

A very different picture from that of perfect correlation is presented in Chart (3) where the correlation is .00. Here the two regression lines, through the means of the columns and rows, have spread out until they are perpendicular to each other. There is no change in the *mean* Y-score over the whole range of X, and no change in the *mean* X-score over the whole range of Y. This is analogous to the situation described on page 123, in which the mean tapping rate of a group of students was the same for those with "high," "middle," and "low" AGCT scores. When the correlation is zero, there is no way of telling from a subject's performance in one test what his performance will be in the other test. The best one can do is to select the *mean* as the most probable value of the unknown score.

---

* Regression lines have important properties; they will be defined and discussed more fully in Chapter 7.

LINEAR CORRELATION · 133

Chart (4) in Figure 36 represents a correlation coefficient of —.75. Negative relationship is shown by the fact that the regression lines, through the means of the columns and rows, run from the upper left- to the lower right-hand section of the diagram. The regression lines are closer together than in Chart (1) where the correlation is .50, but are still separated. If this chart represented a correlation table of height and weight, we should know that the tendency was strong for tall men to be light, and for short men to be heavy.

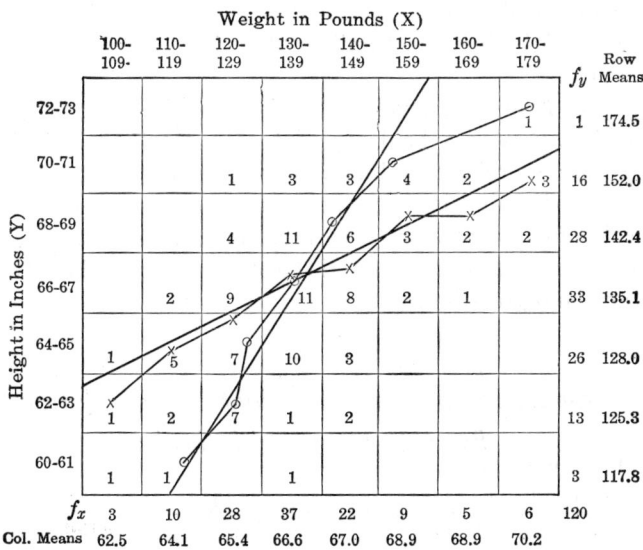

FIG. 37 Graphical representation of the correlation between height and weight in a group of 120 college students (Fig. 35)

The charts in Figure 36 represent, as was stated above, a linear relationship between sets of artificial test scores. The data were selected so as to be symmetrical around the means of each column and row, and hence the regression lines go through *all* of the crosses and through *all* of the circles in the successive columns and rows. It is rarely if ever true, however, that the regression lines pass through all of the means of the columns and rows in a correlation table which represents actual test scores or other real measures. Figure 37, which reproduces the correlation table of heights and weights given on page 129, illustrates this fact. The mean heights of the men in the weight (X) columns are indicated by crosses, and the mean weights of the men in the height (Y) rows by circles, as in Figure 36. Note that the series of short lines joining the successive crosses or circles presents a decidedly jagged appearance. Two straight lines have been drawn in to describe the general trend of these irregular lines. These two lines go through, or as close as possible to, the crosses or the circles, more consideration being given to those points near the middle of the chart (because they are based upon more data) than to those at the extremes (which are based upon few scores). Regression lines are called lines of "best fit" because they satisfy certain mathematical criteria to be given later (p. 154). Such lines describe better than any other *straight* lines the "run" or "drift" of the crosses and circles across the chart.

In Chapter 7 we shall develop equations for the "best fitting" lines and show how they may be drawn in to describe the trend of irregular points on a correlation table. For the present, the important fact to get clearly in mind is that when correlation is linear, the means of the columns and rows in a correlation table can be adequately described by two straight lines and the closer together these two lines, the higher the correlation.

III. The Calculation of the Coefficient of Correlation by the Product-Moment Method

1. The calculation of *r* from a correlation table

Having discussed the meaning of correlation in the last sections, we shall now proceed to the calculation of the coefficient of correlation by the product-moment method. Figure 38 will serve as an illustration of the computations required. This correlation table gives the paired heights and weights of 120 college students, and is derived from the scattergram for the same data shown in Figure 35. The following outline of the steps in the process of calculating r will be best understood if the student will constantly refer to Figure 38 as he reads through each step.

Step 1

Construct a scattergram for the two variables to be correlated, and from it draw up a correlation table as described on page 128.

Weight in Pounds (X-Variable); Height in Inches (Y-Variable)

Height in Inches (Y-Variable)	100-109	110-119	120-129	130-139	140-149	150-159	160-169	170-179	f_y	y'	fy'	fy'^2	$\Sigma x'y'$ +	$\Sigma x'y'$ −	$\Sigma x'$	$\Sigma x'y'$
72-73								(12) 1 12	1	3	3	9	12		4	12
70-71			(-2) 1 -2	0 3 0	(2) 3 6	(4) 4 16	(6) 2 12	(8) 3 24	16	2	32	64	58	2	28	56
68-69			(-1) 4 -4	0 11 0	(1) 6 6	(2) 3 6	(3) 2 6	(4) 2 8	28	1	28(63)	28	26	4	22	22
66-67		0 2 0	0 9 0	0 11 0	0 8 0	0 2 0	0 1 0		33	0					2	0
64-65	(3) 1 3	(2) 5 10	(1) 7 7	0 10 0	(-1) 3 -3				26	−1	−26	26	20	3	−17	17
62-63	(6) 1 6	(4) 2 8	(2) 7 14	0 1 0	(-2) 2 -4				13	−2	−26	52	28	4	−12	24
60-61	(9) 1 9	(6) 1 6		0 1 0					3	−3	−9(−61)	27	15		−5	15
f_x	3	10	28	37	22	9	5	6	120		2	206	159	−13	22	146
x'	−3	−2	−1	0	1	2	3	4					(146)			
fx'	−9	−20	−28(−57)		22	18	15	24(79)	= 22							
fx'^2	27	40	28		22	36	45	96	= 294							
$\Sigma y'$	−6	−12	−15	2	5	11	6	11	= 2							
$\Sigma x'y'$	18	24	15	0	5	22	18	44	= 146							

check check check

$c_y = \frac{2}{120} = .02$ $\qquad c_x = \frac{22}{120} = .18$

$c_y^2 = .0004$ $\qquad c_x^2 = .0324$

$$\sigma_y = \sqrt{\frac{206}{120} - .0004} \times 2 \qquad \sigma_x = \sqrt{\frac{294}{120} - .0324} \times 10 \qquad r = \frac{\frac{146}{120} - .02 \times .18}{1.31 \times 1.55}$$

$$= 1.31 \times 2 = 2.62 \qquad = 1.554 \times 10 = 15.54 \qquad r = .60$$

FIG. 38 Calculation of the product-moment coefficient of correlation between the heights and weights of 120 college students

Step 2

The distribution of heights for the 120 men is in the f_y column at the right of the diagram. Assume a mean for the height distribution, using the rules given in Chapter 2, page 37, and draw double lines to mark off the *row* in which the assumed mean (ht) falls. The mean for the height distribution has been taken at 66.5 in. (midpoint of interval 66–67) and the y's have been taken from this point. The prime (') of the x'''s and y'''s indicates that these deviations are taken from the *assumed* means of the X and Y distributions (see p. 37). Now fill in the fy' and fy'^2 columns. From the first column c_y, the correction in units of interval, is obtained; and this correction together with the sum of the fy'^2 will give the σ of the height distribution, σ_y. As shown by the calculations in Figure 38, the value of σ_y is 2.62 inches.

The distribution of the weights of the 120 men is in the f_x row at the bottom of the diagram. Assume a mean for the weight distribution, and draw double lines to designate the *column* under the assumed mean (wt). The mean for the weight distribution is taken at 134.5 pounds (midpoint of interval 130–139), and the x'''s are taken from this point. Fill in the fx' and the fx'^2 rows; from the first calculate c_x, the correction in units of interval, and from the second calculate σ_x, the σ of the entire weight distribution. In Figure 38, the value of σ_x is found to be 15.54 pounds.

Step 3

The calculations in *Step 2* simply repeat the now familiar process of calculating σ by the Assumed Mean method. Our first *new* task is to fill in the $\Sigma x'y'$ column at the right of the chart. Since the entries in this column may be either $+$ or $-$, two columns are provided under $\Sigma x'y'$. Calculation of the entries in the $\Sigma x'y'$ column may be illustrated by considering, first, the single entry in the only occupied cell in the topmost row. The deviation of this cell from the AM of the weight distribution, that is, its x', is four *intervals*, and its deviation from the AM of the height distribution, that is, its y', is three *intervals*. Hence, the product of the deviations of this cell from the two AM's is 4×3 or 12; and a small figure (12) is placed in the upper right-hand corner of the cell.* The "product-deviation" of the

---

*We may consider the coördinates of this cell to be $x' = 4$, $y' = 3$. The x' is obtained by counting over four intervals from the *vertical column* containing the AM (wt), and the y' by counting up three intervals from the *horizontal row* containing the AM (ht). The unit of measurement is the class-interval.

one entry in this cell is $1(4 \times 3)$ or 12 also, and hence a figure 12 is placed in the lower left-hand corner of the cell. This figure shows the product of the deviations of this single entry from the AM's of the two distributions. Since there are no other entries in the cells of this row, 12 is placed at once under the $+$ sign in the $\Sigma x'y'$ column.

Consider now the next row from the top, taking the cells in order from right to left. The cell immediately below the one for which we have just found the product-deviation also deviates four intervals from the AM (wt) (its x' is 4), but its deviation from the AM (ht) is only two intervals (its y' is 2). The product-deviation of this cell, therefore, is 4×2 or 8, as shown by the small figure (8) in the upper right-hand corner of the cell. There are three entries in this cell, and since each has a product-deviation of 8, the final entry in the lower left-hand corner of the cell is $3(4 \times 2)$ or 24. The product-deviation of the second cell in this row is 6 (its x' is 3 and its y' is 2) and since there are two entries in the cell, the final entry is $2(3 \times 2)$ or 12. Each of the four entries in the third cell over has a product-deviation of 4 (since $x' = 2$ and $y' = 2$) and the final entry is 16. In the fourth cell, each of the three entries has a product-deviation of $2(x' = 1$ and $y' = 2)$ and the cell entry is 6. The entry in the fifth cell over, the cell in the AM (wt) column, is 0, since x' is 0, and accordingly $3(2 \times 0)$ must be 0. Note carefully the entry (-2) in the last cell of the row. Since the deviations of this cell are $x' = -1$, and $y' = 2$, the product $1(-1 \times 2) = -2$, and the final entry is negative. Now we may total up the plus and minus entries in this row and enter the results, 58 and -2, in the $\Sigma x'y'$ column under the appropriate signs.

The final entries in the cells for the other rows of the table and the sums of the product-deviations of each row are obtained as illustrated for the two rows above. The reader should bear in mind in calculating $x'y'$'s that the product-deviations of *all* entries in the cells in the *first* and *third* quadrants of the table are positive, while the product-deviations of *all* entries in the *second* and *fourth* quadrants are negative (p. 10). It should be remembered, too, that all entries either in the column headed by the AM_X or the row headed by the AM_Y have zero product-deviations, since in the one case the x' and in the other the y' equals zero.

Since all entries in a given row have the same y', the arithmetic of calculating $x'y'$'s may often be considerably reduced if each entry in a row-cell is first multiplied by its x', and the sum of these deviations ($\Sigma x'$) multiplied once for all by the common y', viz., the y' of the row. The last two columns $\Sigma x'$ and $\Sigma x'y'$ contain the entries for the rows. To illustrate the method of calculation, in the second row from the bottom, taking the cells in order from right to left, and multiplying the entry in each cell by its x', we have $(2 \times 1) + (1 \times 0) + (7 \times -1) + (2 \times -2) + (1 \times -3)$ or -12. If we multiply this "deviation-sum" by the y' of the whole row (i.e., by -2) the result is 24 which is the final entry in the $\Sigma x'y'$ column. Note that this entry checks the 28 and -4 entered separately in the $\Sigma x'y'$ column by the longer method. This shorter method is often employed in printed correlation charts and is recommended for use as soon as the student understands fully how the cell entries are obtained.

Step 4 (Checks)

The $\Sigma x'y'$ may be checked by computing the product-deviations and summing for columns instead of rows. The two rows at the bottom of the diagram, $\Sigma y'$ and $\Sigma x'y'$, show how this is done. We may illustrate with the first column on the left, taking the cells from top to bottom. Multiplying the entry in each cell by its appropriate y', we have $(1 \times -1) + (1 \times -2) + (1 \times -3)$ or -6. When this entry in the $\Sigma y'$ row is multiplied by the common x' of the column (i.e., by -3) the final entry in the $\Sigma x'y'$ row is 18. The sum of the $x'y'$ computed from the rows should check the sum of the $x'y'$ computed from the columns.

Two other useful checks are shown in Figure 38. The fy' will equal the $\Sigma y'$ and the fx' will equal the $\Sigma x'$ if no error has been made. The fy' and the fx' are the same as the $\Sigma y'$ and $\Sigma x'$; although these columns and rows are designated differently, they denote in each case the sum of deviations around their AM.

Step 5

When all of the entries in the $\Sigma x'y'$ column have been made, and the column totaled, the coefficient of correlation may be calculated by the formula

$$r = \frac{\dfrac{\Sigma x'y'}{N} - c_x c_y}{\sigma_x \sigma_y} \qquad (22)$$

(*coefficient of correlation when deviations are taken from the assumed means of the two distributions*) *

---

* This formula for r differs slightly from the ratio formula developed on page 128). The fact that deviations are taken from assumed rather than from actual means makes it necessary to correct $\Sigma x'y'$ by subtracting the product of the two corrections c_x and c_y.

Substituting 146 for $x'y'$; .02 for c_y; .18 for c_x; 1.31 for σ_y; 1.55 for σ_x; and 120 for N, r is found to be .60. (See Fig. 38.)

It is very important to remember that c_x, c_y, σ_x, and σ_y are all left in *units of class-interval* in formula (22). This is done because all product-deviations ($x'y'$'s) are in interval-units, and it is desirable therefore to keep *all* of the terms in the formula in interval-units. Leaving the corrections and the two σ's in units of class-interval facilitates computation, and does not change the result (i.e., the value of the coefficient of correlation).

2. The calculation of *r* from ungrouped data

(1) THE FORMULA FOR r WHEN DEVIATIONS ARE TAKEN FROM THE MEANS OF THE TWO DISTRIBUTIONS X AND Y

In formula (22) x' and y' deviations are taken from assumed means; and hence it is necessary to correct $\dfrac{\Sigma x'y'}{N}$ by the product of the two corrections, c_x and c_y (p. 138). When deviations have been taken from the actual means of the two distributions, instead of from assumed means, no correction is needed, as both c_x and c_y are zero. Under these conditions, formula (22) becomes

$$r = \frac{\Sigma xy}{N\sigma_x\sigma_y} \qquad (23)$$

(*coefficient of correlation when deviations are taken from the means of the two distributions*)

which is the ratio for measuring correlation developed on page 128. If we write $\sqrt{\dfrac{\Sigma x^2}{N}}$ for σ_x and $\sqrt{\dfrac{\Sigma y^2}{N}}$ for σ_y, the N's cancel and formula (23) becomes

$$r = \frac{\Sigma xy}{\sqrt{\Sigma x^2 \times \Sigma y^2}} \qquad (24)$$

(*coefficient of correlation when deviations are taken from the means of the two distributions*)

in which x and y are deviations from the actual means as in (23) and Σx^2 and Σy^2 are the sums of the squared deviations in x and y taken from the two means.

When N is fairly large, so that the data can be grouped into a correlation table, formula (22) is always used in preference to formulas (23) or (24) as it entails much less calculation. Formulas (23) and (24) may be used to good advantage, however, in finding the correla-

140 • STATISTICS IN PSYCHOLOGY AND EDUCATION

tion between short, ungrouped series (say, twenty-five cases or so). It is not necessary to tabulate the scores into a frequency distribution. An illustration of the use of formula (24) is given in Table 18, below. The problem is to find the correlation between the scores made by twelve adults on two tests of "controlled association."

The steps in computing r may be outlined as follows:

Step 1

Find the mean of Test 1 (X) and the mean of Test 2 (Y). The means in Table 18 are 62.5 and 30.4, respectively.

Step 2

Find the deviation of each score on Test 1 from its mean, 62.5, and enter it in column x. Next find the deviation of each score in Test 2 from its mean, 30.4, and enter it in column y.

Step 3

Square all of the x's and all of the y's and enter these squares in columns x^2 and y^2, respectively. Total these columns to obtain Σx^2 and Σy^2.

TABLE 18 To illustrate the calculation of r from ungrouped scores when deviations are taken from the means of the series

Subject	Test 1 X	Test 2 Y	x	y	x^2	y^2	xy
A	50	22	−12.5	−8.4	156.25	70.56	105.00
B	54	25	−8.5	−5.4	72.25	29.16	45.90
C	56	34	−6.5	3.6	42.25	12.96	−23.40
D	59	28	−3.5	−2.4	12.25	5.76	8.40
E	60	26	−2.5	−4.4	6.25	19.36	11.00
F	62	30	−.5	−.4	.25	.16	.20
G	61	32	−1.5	1.6	2.25	2.56	−2.40
H	65	30	2.5	−.4	6.25	.16	−1.00
I	67	28	4.5	−2.4	20.25	5.76	−10.80
J	71	34	8.5	3.6	72.25	12.96	30.60
K	71	36	8.5	5.6	72.25	31.36	47.60
L	74	40	11.5	9.6	132.25	92.16	110.40
	750	365			595.00 (Σx^2)	282.92 (Σy^2)	321.50 (Σxy)

$M_X = 62.5 \qquad M_Y = 30.4$

$$r = \frac{\Sigma xy}{\sqrt{\Sigma x^2 \times \Sigma y^2}} = \frac{321.50}{\sqrt{595 \times 282.92}} = .78 \qquad (24)$$

Step 4

Multiply the x's and y's in the same rows, and enter these products (with due regard for sign) in the xy column. Total the xy column, taking account of sign, to get Σxy.

Step 5

Substitute for Σxy, 321.50; for Σx^2, 595; and for Σy^2, 282.92 in formula (24), as shown in Table 18, and solve for r.

While formula (24) is useful in calculating r directly from two ungrouped series of scores, it has the same disadvantage as the "long method" of calculating means and σ's described in Chapters 2 and 3. The deviations x and y when taken from the actual means are usually decimals and the multiplication and squaring of these values is often a tedious task. For this reason—even when working with short ungrouped series—it is often easier to assume means, calculate deviations from these AM's, and apply formula (22). The procedure is illustrated in Table 19 with the same data given in Table 18. Note

TABLE 19 To illustrate the calculation of r from ungrouped scores when deviations are taken from the assumed means of the series

Subject	Test 1 X	Test 2 Y	x'	y'	x'^2	y'^2	$x'y'$
A	50	22	−10	−8	100	64	80
B	54	25	−6	−5	36	25	30
C	56	34	−4	4	16	16	−16
D	59	28	−1	−2	1	4	2
E	60	26	0	−4	0	16	0
F	62	30	2	0	4	0	0
G	61	32	1	2	1	4	2
H	65	30	5	0	25	0	0
I	67	28	7	−2	49	4	−14
J	71	34	11	4	121	16	44
K	71	36	11	6	121	36	66
L	74	40	14	10	196	100	140
	750	365			670 ($\Sigma x'^2$)	285 ($\Sigma y'^2$)	334 ($\Sigma x'y'$)

$AM_X = 60.0$
$M_X = 62.5$
$c_x = 2.5$
$c^2_x = 6.25$

$AM_Y = 30.0$
$M_Y = 30.4$
$c_y = .4$
$c^2_y = .16$

$$r = \frac{\frac{334}{12} - 1.00}{7.04 \times 4.86} \quad (22)$$

$\sigma_x = \sqrt{\frac{670}{12} - 6.25}$
$\quad = 7.04$

$\sigma_y = \sqrt{\frac{285}{12} - .16}$
$\quad = 4.86$

$r = .78$

142 · STATISTICS IN PSYCHOLOGY AND EDUCATION

that the two means, M_X and M_Y, are first calculated. The corrections, c_x and c_y, are found by subtracting AM_X from M_X and AM_Y from M_Y (p. 38). Since deviations are taken from assumed means, fractions are avoided; and the calculations of $\Sigma x'^2$, $\Sigma y'^2$, $\Sigma x'y'$ are readily made. Substitution in formula (22) then gives r.

(2) THE CALCULATION OF r FROM RAW SCORES, I.E., WHEN DEVIATIONS ARE TAKEN FROM ZERO

The calculation of r may often be carried out most readily—especially when a calculating machine is available—by means of the following formula which is based upon "raw" or obtained scores:

$$r = \frac{\Sigma XY - NM_XM_Y}{\sqrt{[\Sigma X^2 - NM^2_X][\Sigma Y^2 - NM^2_Y]}} \qquad (25)$$

(*coefficient of correlation calculated from raw or obtained scores*)

In this formula, X and Y are obtained scores, and M_X and M_Y are the means of the X and Y series, respectively. ΣX^2 and ΣY^2 are the sums of the squared X and Y values, and N is the number of cases.

Formula (25) is derived directly from formula (22) by assuming the means of the X and Y tests to be zero. If AM_X and AM_Y are zero, each X and Y score is a deviation from its AM as it stands, and hence we work with the scores themselves. Since the correction, c, always equals $M - AM$, it follows that when the AM equals 0, $c_x = M_X$, $c_y = M_Y$ and $c_xc_y = M_XM_Y$. Furthermore, when $c_x = M_X$ and $c_y = M_Y$ and the "scores" are "deviations," the formula

$$\sigma_x = \sqrt{\frac{\Sigma fx'^2}{N} - c^2_x} \times \text{interval}$$

(see p. 54) becomes

$$\sigma_x = \sqrt{\frac{\Sigma X^2}{N} - M^2_X}$$

and σ_y for the same reason equals $\sqrt{\frac{\Sigma Y^2}{N} - M^2_Y}$. If we substitute these equivalents for c_xc_y, σ_x, and σ_y in formula (22), the formula for r in terms of raw scores given in (25) is obtained.

An alternate form of (25) is often more useful in practice. This is

$$r = \frac{N\Sigma XY - \Sigma X \times \Sigma Y}{\sqrt{[N\Sigma X^2 - (\Sigma X)^2][N\Sigma Y^2 - (\Sigma Y)^2]}} \qquad (26)$$

(*coefficient of correlation calculated from raw or obtained scores*)

LINEAR CORRELATION • 143

This formula is obtained from (25) by substituting $\frac{\Sigma X}{N}$ for M_X, and $\frac{\Sigma Y}{N}$ for M_Y in numerator and denominator, and canceling the N's.

The calculation of r from original scores is shown in Table 20. The data are again the two sets of twelve scores obtained on the "controlled association" tests, the correlation for which was found to be .78 in Table 18. This short example is for the purpose of illustrating the arithmetic and must not be taken as a recommendation that formula (25) be used only with short series. As a matter of fact, formula (25) or (26) is most useful, perhaps, with long series, especially if one is working with a calculating machine.

TABLE 20 To illustrate the calculation of *r* from ungrouped data when deviations are original scores (AM's = 0)

Subject	Test 1 X	Test 2 Y	X^2	Y^2	XY
A	50	22	2500	484	1100
B	54	25	2916	625	1350
C	56	34	3136	1156	1904
D	59	28	3481	784	1652
E	60	26	3600	676	1560
F	62	30	3844	900	1860
G	61	32	3721	1024	1952
H	65	30	4225	900	1950
I	67	28	4489	784	1876
J	71	34	5041	1156	2414
K	71	36	5041	1296	2556
L	74	40	5476	1600	2960
	750	365	47470	11385	23134

$M_X = 62.50$
$M_Y = 30.42$ (means to two decimals)

$$r = \frac{23134 - 12 \times 62.50 \times 30.42}{\sqrt{[47470 - 12 \times (62.50)^2][11385 - 12 \times (30.42)^2]}} \quad (25)$$

$r = .78$

The computation by formula (26) is straightforward and the method easy to follow, but the calculations become tedious if the scores are expressed in more than two digits. When using formula (26), therefore, it will often greatly lessen the arithmetical work, if we first "reduce" the original scores by subtracting a constant quantity from each of the original X and Y scores. In Table 21, the same two series of twelve scores have been reduced by subtracting 65 from each of the X scores, and 25 from each of the Y scores. The reduced scores, entered in the table under X' and Y', are first squared to give

144 • STATISTICS IN PSYCHOLOGY AND EDUCATION

TABLE 21 To illustrate the calculation of r from ungrouped data when deviations are original scores (AM's = 0)

Scores are "reduced" by the subtraction of 65 from each X, and 25 from each Y to give X' and Y'.

Subject	Test 1 X	Test 2 Y	X'	Y'	X'^2	Y'^2	$X'Y'$
A	50	22	−15	−3	225	9	45
B	54	25	−11	0	121	0	0
C	56	34	−9	9	81	81	−81
D	59	28	−6	3	36	9	−18
E	60	26	−5	1	25	1	−5
F	62	30	−3	5	9	25	−15
G	61	32	−4	7	16	49	−28
H	65	30	0	5	0	25	0
I	67	28	2	3	4	9	6
J	71	34	6	9	36	81	54
K	71	36	6	11	36	121	66
L	74	40	9	15	81	225	135
	750	365	−30($\Sigma X'$)	65($\Sigma Y'$)	670($\Sigma X'^2$)	635($\Sigma Y'^2$)	159($\Sigma X'Y'$)

$$M_X = \frac{\Sigma X'}{N} + 65 \qquad M_Y = \frac{\Sigma Y'}{N} + 25$$

$$= -\frac{30}{12} + 65 \qquad\qquad = \frac{65}{12} + 25$$

$$= 62.5 \qquad\qquad\qquad = 30.$$

$$r = \frac{(12 \times 159) - (-30 \times 65)}{\sqrt{[12 \times 670 - (-30)^2][12 \times 635 - (65)^2]}} \qquad (26)$$

$$= \frac{3858}{4923}$$

$$= .78$$

$\Sigma X'^2$ and $\Sigma Y'^2$, and then multiplied by rows to give $\Sigma X'Y'$. Substitution of these values in formula (26) gives the coefficient of correlation r. If the means of the two series are wanted, these may readily be found by adding to $\frac{\Sigma X'}{N}$ and $\frac{\Sigma Y'}{N}$ the amounts by which the X and Y scores were reduced (see computations in Table 21).

The method of computing r by first reducing the scores is usually superior to the method of applying formula (25) or (26) directly to the raw scores. This is because we deal with smaller whole numbers, and much of the arithmetic can be done mentally. When raw scores have more than two digits, they are cumbersome to square and multiply unless reduced. The student should note that instead of 65 and

25 other constants might have been used to reduce the X and Y scores. If the smallest X and Y scores had been subtracted, namely, 50 and 22, all of the X' and Y' would, of course, have been positive. This is an advantage in machine calculation but these reduced scores would have been somewhat larger numerically than are the reduced scores in Table 21. In general, the best plan in reducing scores is to subtract constants which are close to the means. The reduced scores are then both plus and minus, but are numerically about as small as we can make them.

(3) THE CALCULATION OF r BY THE DIFFERENCE-FORMULA

It is apparent from the preceding sections that the product-moment formula for r may be written in several ways, depending upon whether deviations are taken from actual or assumed means and upon whether raw scores or deviations are employed. The present section contributes still another formula for calculating r—namely, the difference-formula. This formula will complete our list of expressions for r, as it is believed that the student who understands the meaning and use of the correlation formulas given in this chapter will have no difficulty with other variations which he may encounter.*

The formula for r by the difference method is

$$r = \frac{\Sigma x^2 + \Sigma y^2 - \Sigma d^2}{2\sqrt{\Sigma x^2 \times \Sigma y^2}} \qquad (27)$$

(*coefficient of correlation by difference-formula, deviations from the means of the distributions*)

in which $\Sigma d^2 = \Sigma (x - y)^2$.

The principal advantage of the difference-formula is that no cross products (xy's) need be computed. For this reason, this formula is employed in several of the printed correlation charts. Formula (27) is illustrated in Table 22 with the same data used in Table 19 and elsewhere in this chapter. Note that the x, y, x^2, and y^2 columns repeat Table 19. The d or $(x - y)$ column is found by subtracting algebraically each y-deviation from its corresponding x-deviation. These differences are then squared and entered in the d^2 or $(x - y)^2$ column. Substitution of Σx^2, Σy^2, and Σd^2 in formula (27) gives $r = .78$.

* See the following article which lists fifty-two variations of the r-formula: Symonds, P. M., "Variations of the Product-Moment (Pearson) Cofficient of Correlation," *Journal of Educ. Psych.*, 1926, 17, 458–469.

TABLE 22 To illustrate the calculation of *r* from ungrouped data by the difference-formula, deviations from the means

Subject	Test 1 X	Test 2 Y	x	y	d (x − y)	x²	y²	d² (x − y)²
A	50	22	− 12.5	− 8.4	− 4.1	156.25	70.56	16.81
B	54	25	− 8.5	− 5.4	− 3.1	72.25	29.16	9.61
C	56	34	− 6.5	3.6	− 10.1	42.25	12.96	102.01
D	59	28	− 3.5	− 2.4	− 1.1	12.25	5.76	1.21
E	60	26	− 2.5	− 4.4	1.9	6.25	19.36	3.61
F	62	30	− .5	− .4	− .1	.25	.16	.01
G	61	32	− 1.5	1.6	− 3.1	2.25	2.56	9.61
H	65	30	2.5	− .4	2.9	6.25	.16	8.41
I	67	28	4.5	− 2.4	6.9	20.25	5.76	47.61
J	71	34	8.5	3.6	4.9	72.25	12.96	24.01
K	71	36	8.5	5.6	2.9	72.25	31.36	8.41
L	74	40	11.5	9.6	1.9	132.25	92.16	3.61
						595.00	282.92	234.92

$M_X = 62.5$

$M_Y = 30.4$

$$r = \frac{595.00 + 282.92 - 234.92}{2\sqrt{595 \times 282.92}} \qquad (27)$$

$$= .78$$

Another form of the difference-formula is often useful, especially in machine calculation. This version makes use of raw or obtained scores:

$$r = \frac{N[\Sigma X^2 + \Sigma Y^2 - \Sigma(X-Y)^2] - 2(\Sigma X) \times (\Sigma Y)}{2\sqrt{[N\Sigma X^2 - (\Sigma X)^2][N\Sigma Y^2 - (\Sigma Y)^2]}} \qquad (28)$$

(*coefficient of correlation by difference-formula, calculation from raw or obtained scores*)

in which $\Sigma(X-Y)^2$ is the sum of the squared differences between the two sets of scores.

3. Averaging coefficients of correlation

It has been a fairly common practice to average correlation coefficients computed from tests given to comparable groups in order to obtain a generalized picture of the relationship between the two variables. The averaging of *r*'s is, however, a dubious and often an incorrect procedure. In the first place, *r*'s do not vary along a linear scale so that the increase from .40 to .50 does not mean the same increase in relationship as does an increase from .80 to .90. Secondly, when +*r*'s and −*r*'s are averaged, they tend to cancel each other out.

If r's do not differ greatly in size, their arithmetic mean will yield a useful result; but this is not true when r's differ widely in size or in sign. Averaging an r of .70 and an r of .60 to obtain .65 is permissible; but averaging an r of .90 and an r of .10 to obtain .50 is not.

The safest plan is not to average r's at all. When for various reasons averaging seems to be demanded by the problem, the best method is to transform the r's into Fisher's z-function (p. 426), and take the arithmetic mean of the z's. The mean z may then be converted into an equivalent r. An example will illustrate the procedure to be followed in converting r's to z's.

Example (*1*) In 5 parallel experiments the following r's are obtained between the same two variables: .50, .90, .40, .30, and .70. What is the mean of these coefficients?

By Table C we may convert these r's into the following z's: .55, 1.47, .42, .31, and .87. The mean of these z's is .72, which is equivalent to an r of .62. Comparison of this mean r with .56, the average of the r's as they stand, gives an idea of the correction effected in using z.

PROBLEMS

1. Find the correlation between the two sets of scores given below, using the ratio method (p. 126).

Subjects	X	Y
a	15	40
b	18	42
c	22	50
d	17	45
e	19	43
f	20	46
g	16	41
h	21	41

2. The scores given below were achieved upon Army Alpha and Typewriting Tests by 100 students in a typewriting class. The typewriting scores are in number of words written per minute, with certain penalties. Find the coefficient of correlation. Use an interval of 5 units for Y and an interval of 10 units for X.

Typing (Y)	Alpha (X)	Typing (Y)	Alpha (X)	Typing (Y)	Alpha (X)
46	152	26	164	40	120
31	96	33	127	36	140
46	171	44	144	43	141
40	172	35	160	48	143
42	138	49	106	45	138
41	154	40	95	58	149
39	127	57	146	23	142
46	156	23	175	45	166
34	156	51	126	44	138
48	133	35	120	47	150
48	173	41	154	29	148
38	134	28	146	46	166
26	179	32	154	46	146
37	159	50	159	39	167
34	167	29	175	49	139
51	136	41	164	34	183
47	153	32	111	41	150
39	145	49	164	49	179
32	134	58	119	31	138
37	184	35	160	47	136
26	154	48	149	40	172
40	90	40	149	30	145
53	143	43	143	40	109
46	173	38	159	38	158
39	168	37	157	29	115
52	187	41	153	43	93
47	166	51	149	55	163
31	172	40	163	37	147
33	189	35	175	52	169
22	147	31	133	38	75
46	150	23	178	39	152
44	150	37	168	32	159
37	143	46	156	42	150
31	133				

3. In the correlation table given below compute the coefficient of correlation.

Boys: Ages 4.5 to 5.5 Years

Weight in Pounds (X)

Height in Inches (Y)	24–28	29–33	34–38	39–43	44–48	49–53	Totals
45–47			1		2		3
42–44			4	35	21	5	65
39–41		5	87	90	7	1	190
36–38	1	18	72	8			99
33–35	5	15	5				25
30–32	2						2
Totals	8	38	169	133	30	6	384

4. In the following correlation table compute the coefficient of correlation.

Army Alpha I.Q.'s

School Marks	84 and lower	85–89	90–94	95–99	100–104	105–109	110–114	115–119	120–124	125 over	Totals
90 and over				3	3	15	12	9	9	5	56
85–89				8	17	15	24	13	6	6	89
80–84			4	6	22	21	20	10	5	1	89
75–79			7	25	33	23	10	7	4		109
70–74		4	10	18	14	22	12	1	1		82
65–69	1	3	3	12	7	8	8	1			43
60–64			2	5	3	1	1				12
Totals	1	7	26	77	99	105	87	41	25	12	480

150 • STATISTICS IN PSYCHOLOGY AND EDUCATION

5. Compute the coefficient of correlation between the Algebra Test scores and I.Q.'s shown in the table below.

ALGEBRA TEST SCORES

		30–34	35–39	40–44	45–49	50–54	55–59	60–64	65–69	Totals
I.Q.'s	130–139				1		1		1	3
	120–129			1		1	2	1		5
	110–119	1	2	5	6	11	6	3	2	36
	100–109	3	7	9	17	13	5	1	1	56
	90–99	4	10	16	12	5	1			48
	80–89	4	9	8	2	2				25
	Totals	12	28	39	38	32	15	5	4	173

6. Compute the correlation between the two sets of scores given below

   (a) when deviations are taken from the means of the two series [use formula (24)];

   (b) when the means are taken at zero. First reduce the scores by subtracting 150 from each of the scores in Test 1, and 40 from each of the scores in Test 2.

Test 1	Test 2	Test 1	Test 2
150	60	139	41
126	40	155	43
135	45	147	37
176	50	162	58
138	56	156	48
142	43	146	39
151	57	133	31
163	38	168	46
137	41	153	52
178	55	150	57

7. Find the correlation between the two sets of memory-span scores given below (the first series is arranged in order of size) (a) when deviations are taken from assumed means [formula (22)], (b) by the difference-method given on page 145.

Test 1 (digit span)	Test 2 (letter span)
15	12
14	14
13	10
12	8
11	12
11	9
11	12
10	8
10	10
10	9
9	8
9	7
8	7
7	8
7	6

ANSWERS

1. $r = .65$
2. $r = -.05$
3. $r = .71$
4. $r = .46$
5. $r = .52$
6. $r = .41$
7. $r = .78$

7

REGRESSION AND PREDICTION

I. The Regression Equations

1. The problem of predicting one variable from another

Suppose that in a group of 120 college students (p. 129), we wish to estimate a certain man's height knowing his weight to be 153 pounds. The best possible "guess" that we can make of this man's height is the mean height of all of the men who fall in the 150–159 weight-interval. In Figure 39 the mean height of the nine men in this column is 68.9 inches, which is, therefore, the most *likely* height of a man who weighs 153 pounds. In the same way, the most probable height of a man who weighs 136 pounds is 66.6 inches, the mean height of the thirty-seven men who fall in weight-column 130–139 pounds. And, in general, the most probable height of any man in the group is the *mean* of the heights of *all* of the men who weigh the same (or approximately the same) as he, i.e., who fall within the same weight-column.

Turning to weight, we can make the same kind of estimates. Thus, the best possible "guess" that we can make of a man's weight knowing his height to be 66.5 inches is 135.1 pounds, viz., the mean weight of the thirty-three men who fall in the height-interval 66–67 inches. Again, in general, the most probable weight of any man in the group is the *mean* weight of *all* of the men who are of the same (or approximately the same) height.

Our illustration shows that from the scatter diagram alone it is possible to "predict" one variable from another. But the prediction is rough, and is obviously subject to a large "error of estimate." *

---

* See page 161.

REGRESSION AND PREDICTION • 153

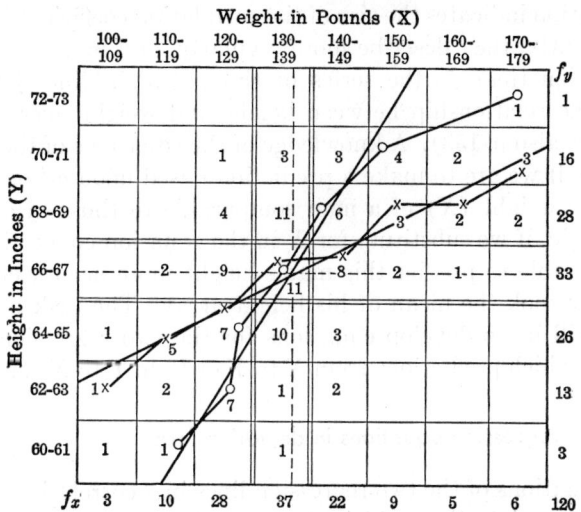

FIG. 39 Illustrating positions of regression lines and calculation of the regression equations (See Fig. 38, p. 135.)

$r = .60$
$M_X = 136.3$ pounds
$M_Y = 66.5$ inches

For plotting on the chart, regression equations are written with σ_x and σ_y in class-interval units, viz.—
$\bar{y} = .51x$ } see
$\bar{x} = .71y$ } p. 154.

Calculation of Regression Equations

I. Deviation Form

(1) $\qquad \bar{y} = .60 \times \dfrac{2.62}{15.54} x = .10x \qquad$ (29)

(2) $\qquad \bar{x} = .60 \times \dfrac{15.54}{2.62} y = 3.56y \qquad$ (30)

II. Score Form
(1) $Y - 66.5 = .10(X - 136.3)$ or $\bar{Y} = .10X + 52.9 \qquad$ (31)
(2) $X - 136.3 = 3.56(Y - 66.5)$ or $\bar{X} = 3.56Y - 100.4 \qquad$ (32)

Calculation of Standard Errors of Estimate

$\sigma_{(est.\ Y)} = 2.62\sqrt{1 - .60^2} = 2.10$ inches $\qquad$ (33)

$\sigma_{(est.\ X)} = 15.54\sqrt{1 - .60^2} = 12.43$ pounds $\qquad$ (34)

Moreover, while we have made use of the fact that the means are the most probable points in our arrays (columns or rows), we have made no use of our knowledge concerning the over-all relationship between the two variables. The two regression lines in Figure 39 are determined by the correlation between height and weight and their degree of separation indicates the size of the correlation coefficient * (p. 131). Consequently, they describe more regularly, and in a more generalized fashion than do the series of short straight lines joining the means, the relationship between height and weight *over the whole range* (see also p. 153). A knowledge of the equations of these lines is necessary if we are to make a prediction based upon *all* of our data. Given the weight (X) of a man comparable to those in our group, for example, if we substitute for X in the equation connecting Y and X we are able to predict this man's height more accurately than if we simply took the mean of his height array. The task of the next section will be to develop equations for the two regression lines by means of which predictions from X to Y or from Y to X can be made.

2. The two regression equations in deviation form

The equations of the two regression lines in a correlation table represent the straight lines which "best fit" the means of the successive columns and rows in the table. Using as a definition of "best fit" the criterion of "least squares," † Pearson worked out the equation of the line which goes through, or as close as possible to, more of the column-means than any other straight line; and the equation of the line which goes through, or as close as possible to, more of the row-means than any other straight line. These two lines are "best fitting" in a mathematical sense, the one to the observations of the columns and the other to the observations of the rows.

The equation of the first regression line, the line drawn to represent the trend of the crosses in Figure 39, is as follows:

$$\bar{y} = r\frac{\sigma_y}{\sigma_x} \times x \qquad (29)$$

(*regression equation of* y *on* x, *deviations taken from the means of* Y *and* X)

The factor $r\frac{\sigma_y}{\sigma_x}$ is called the *regression coefficient*, and is often re-

* The term "regression" was first used by Francis Galton with reference to the inheritance of stature. Galton found that children of tall parents tend to be less tall, and children of short parents less short, than their parents. In other words, the heights of the offspring tend to "move back" toward the mean height of the general population. This tendency toward maintaining the "mean height" Galton called the principle of regression, and the line describing the relationship of height in parent and offspring was called a "regression line." The term is still employed, although its original meaning of "stepping back" to some stationary average is not necessarily implied (see p. 171).

† For an elementary mathematical treatment of the method of least squares as applied to the problem of fitting regression lines, see Walker, H. M., *Elementary Statistical Method* (New York: Henry Holt and Co., 1943), pp. 308–310.

placed in (29) by the term b_{yx} or b_{12} so that formula (29) may be written $\bar{y} = b_{yx} \times x$, or $\bar{y} = b_{12} \times x$. The bar over the ($\bar{y}$) means that our estimate is an average value.

If we substitute in formula (29) the values of r, σ_y, and σ_x, obtained from Figure 39, we have

$$\bar{y} = .60 \times \frac{2.62}{15.54} x, \text{ or } \bar{y} = .10x$$

This equation gives the relationship of deviations from mean height to deviations from mean weight. When $x = \pm 1.00$, $\bar{y} = \pm .10$; and a deviation of one pound from the mean of the X's (weight) is accompanied by a deviation of .10 inch from the mean of the Y's (height). The man who stands one pound *above* the mean weight of the group, therefore, is most probably .10 inch *above* the mean height. Since this man's weight is 137.3 pounds ($136.3 + 1.00$), his height is most probably 66.6 inches ($66.5 + .10$). Again, the man who weighs 120 pounds, i.e., is 16.3 pounds *below* the mean of the group, is most probably 64.9 inches tall—or about 1.6 inches *below* the mean height of the group. To get this last value, substitute $x = -16.3$ in the equation above to get $\bar{y} = -1.63$, and refer this value to its mean. The regression equation is a generalized expression of relationship. It tells us that the most probable deviation of an individual in our group from the M_{ht} is just .10 of his deviation from the M_{wt}.

The equation $\bar{y} = r\frac{\sigma_y}{\sigma_x} \times x$ gives the relationship between Y and X in *deviation form*. This designation is appropriate since the two variables are expressed as deviations from their respective means (i.e., as x and y); hence, for a given *deviation* from M_X the equation gives the most probable accompanying *deviation* from M_Y.

The equation of the second regression line, the line drawn through the circles (i.e., the means) of the rows in Figure 39, is

$$\bar{x} = r\frac{\sigma_x}{\sigma_y} \times y \qquad (30)$$

(*regression equation of* x *on* y, *deviations taken from the means of* X *and* Y)

As in the first regression equation, the regression coefficient $r\frac{\sigma_x}{\sigma_y}$ is often replaced by the expression b_{xy} or b_{21} and formula (30) written $\bar{x} = b_{xy} \times y$ or $\bar{x} = b_{21} \times y$.

If we substitute for r, σ_x, and σ_y, in formula (30), we have

$$\bar{x} = .60 \times \frac{15.54}{2.62} y \text{ or } \bar{x} = 3.56y$$

from which it is evident that a deviation of 1 inch from the M_{ht}, or from 66.5 inches, is accompanied by a deviation of 3.56 pounds from the M_{wt}, or from 136.3 pounds. Expressed generally, the most probable deviation of *any man* from the mean weight is just 3.56 times his deviation from the mean height. Accordingly, a man 67 inches tall or .5 inch *above* the mean height ($66.5 + .5 = 67$) most probably weighs 138.1 pounds, or is 1.8 pounds *above* the mean weight ($136.3 + 1.8$). (Substitute $y = .5$ in the equation and $\bar{x} = 1.8$).

Equation $\bar{x} = r\dfrac{\sigma_x}{\sigma_y} \times y$ gives the relationship between X and Y in *deviation form*. That is to say, it gives the most probable *deviation* of an X-measure from M_X corresponding to a known *deviation* in the Y-measure from M_Y.

Although both regression equations given above involve x and y, the two equations cannot be used interchangeably—neither can be used to predict *both* x and y. This is an important fact which the student must understand clearly and constantly bear in mind. The first regression equation $\bar{y} = r\dfrac{\sigma_y}{\sigma_x} \times x$ can be used *only* when y is to be predicted from a given x (when y is the "dependent" variable)*; while the second equation $\bar{x} = r\dfrac{\sigma_x}{\sigma_y} \times y$ can be used only when x is to be predicted from a known y (when x is the "dependent" variable).

There are always *two* regression equations in a correlation table, the one through the means of the columns and the other through the means of the rows, unless the correlation is 1.00 or -1.00. When $r = 1.00$, $\bar{y} = r\dfrac{\sigma_y}{\sigma_x} \times x$ becomes $\bar{y} = \dfrac{\sigma_y}{\sigma_x} \times x$ or $\bar{y}\sigma_x = x\sigma_y$. Also, when $r = 1.00$, $\bar{x} = r\dfrac{\sigma_x}{\sigma_y} \times y$ becomes $\bar{x} = \dfrac{\sigma_x}{\sigma_y} \times y$ or $\bar{x}\sigma_y = y\sigma_x$. In short, when the correlation is perfect (± 1.00), the two equations are identical and the two regression lines coincide. To illustrate this situation, suppose that the correlation between height and weight in Figure 39 were perfect. The first regression equation would then be $\bar{y} = 1.00 \times \dfrac{2.62}{15.54} x$ or $\bar{y} = .17x$, and the second, $\bar{x} = 1.00 \times \dfrac{15.54}{2.62} y$, or $\bar{x} = 5.93y$. Algebraically, the equation $x = 5.93y$ is equal to $y = .17x$; for if we put $x = \dfrac{y}{.17}$, $x = 5.93y$. When $r = \pm 1.00$ there is only *one*

---

* The dependent variable takes its value from the other (independent) variable in the equation. For example, in the equation $y = 5x - 10$, y "depends" for its value upon x; hence y is the dependent variable.

REGRESSION AND PREDICTION • 157

equation and a *single* regression line. Moreover, if $r = \pm 1.00$, and in addition $\sigma_x = \sigma_y$, the single regression line makes an angle of 45° or 135° with the horizontal axis, since $y = \pm x$.

3. Plotting the regression lines in a correlation table *

In Figure 39, the coördinate axes have been drawn in on the correlation table through the means of the X- and Y-distributions. The

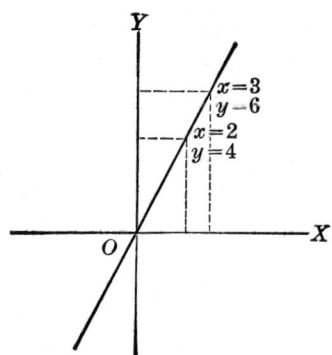

FIG. 40 Plot of the straight line, y = 2x

---

* A brief review of the equation of a straight line, and of the method of plotting a simple linear equation is given here in order to simplify the plotting of the regression equations.

In Figure 40, let X and Y be coördinate axes, or axes of reference. Now suppose that we are given the equation $y = 2x$ and are required to represent the relation between x and y graphically. To do this we assign values to x in the equation and compute the corresponding values of y. When $x = 2$, for example, $y = 2 \times 2$ or 4; when $x = 3$, $y = 2 \times 3$ or 6. In the same way, given any x-value we can compute the value of y which will "satisfy" the equation, that is, make the left side equal to the right. If the series of x and y values found from the equation are plotted on the diagram with respect to the X- and Y-coördinates (as in Fig. 40) they will be found to fall along a straight line. This straight line pictures the relation $y = 2x$. It goes through the origin, since when $x = 0$, $y = 0$. The equation $y = 2x$ represents, then, a straight line which passes through the origin; and the relation of its coördinates (points lying along the line) is such that $\frac{y}{x}$, called the *slope* of the line, is always equal to 2.

The general equation of any straight line which passes through the origin may be written $y = mx$, where m is the slope of the line. If we replace m in the general formula by $r\frac{\sigma_y}{\sigma_x}$ it is clear that the regression line in *deviation form*, namely, $y = r\frac{\sigma_y}{\sigma_x}x$, is simply the equation of a straight line which goes through the origin. For the same reason, when the general equation of a straight line through the origin is written $x = my$, $x = r\frac{\sigma_x}{\sigma_y}y$ is also seen to be a straight line through the origin, its slope being $r\frac{\sigma_x}{\sigma_y}$.

vertical axis is drawn through 136.3 pounds (M_{wt}), and the horizontal axis through 66.5 inches (M_{ht}). These axes intersect close to the center of the chart. Equations (29) and (30) define straight lines which pass through the origin or point of intersection of these coordinate axes. It is a comparatively simple task to plot in our regression lines on the correlation chart with reference to the given coördinate axes.

Correlation charts are usually laid out with equal distances representing the X and Y class-intervals (the printed correlation charts are always so constructed) although the intervals expressed in terms of the variables themselves may be, and often are, unequal and incommensurable. This is true in Figure 39. In this diagram, the intervals in X and Y appear to be equal, although the actual interval for height is 2 inches, and the actual interval for weight is 10 pounds. Because of this difference in interval-length in the two variables it is very important that we express σ_x and σ_y in our regression equations in *class-interval units* before plotting the regression lines on the chart. Otherwise we must equate our X and Y intervals by laying out our diagram in such a way as to make the X-interval five times the Y-interval. This latter method of equating intervals is impractical, and is rarely used, since all we need do in order to use correlation charts drawn up with equal intervals is to express σ_x and σ_y in formulas (29) and (30) in units of interval. When this is done, and the interval, *not* the score, is the unit, the first regression equation becomes

$$y = .60 \frac{1.31}{1.55} x \text{ or } \bar{y} = .51x$$

and the second

$$\bar{x} = .60 \frac{1.55}{1.31} y \text{ or } \bar{x} = .71y$$

Since each regression line goes through the origin, only one other point (besides the origin) is needed in order to determine its course. In the first regression equation, if $x = 10$, $y = 5.1$; and the two points (0, 0) and (10, 5.1) locate the line. In the second regression equation, if $y = 10$, $x = 7.1$; and the two points (0, 0) and (7.1, 10) determine the second line. In plotting points on a diagram any convenient scale may be employed. A millimeter rule is useful.

It is important for the student to remember that when the two σ's are expressed in interval units, regression equations do *not* give the relationship between the X and Y score deviations. These special forms of the regression equations should not be used except when plotting the equations on a correlation chart. Whenever the most probable deviation in the one variable corresponding to a known deviation in the other is wanted, formulas (29) and (30), in which the σ's are expressed in *score units,* must be employed.

4. The regression equations in score form

In the last sections it was pointed out that formulas (29) and (30) give the equations of the regression lines in deviation form—that values of x and y substituted in these equations are deviations from the means of the X and Y distributions, and are not scores. While the equations in *deviation form* are actually all that one needs in order to pass from one variable to another, it is decidedly convenient to be able to estimate an individual's *actual score* in Y, say, directly from the score in X without first converting the X-score into a deviation from M_X. This can be done by using the *score form* of the regression equation. The conversion of deviation form to score form is made as follows: Denoting the mean of the Y's by M_Y and any Y-score simply by Y, we may write the deviation of any individual from the mean as $Y - M_Y$ or, in general, $y = Y - M_Y$. In the same way, $x = X - M_X$ when x is the deviation of any X-score from the mean X. If we substitute $Y - M_Y$ for y, and $X - M_X$ for x, in formulas (29) and (30), the two regression equations become

$$Y - M_Y = r\frac{\sigma_y}{\sigma_x}(X - M_X) \text{ or}$$

$$\overline{Y} = r\frac{\sigma_y}{\sigma_x}(X - M_X) + M_Y \tag{31}$$

and

$$X - M_X = r\frac{\sigma_x}{\sigma_y}(Y - M_Y) \text{ or}$$

$$\overline{X} = r\frac{\sigma_x}{\sigma_y}(Y - M_Y) + M_X \tag{32}$$

(*regression equations of* Y *on* X *and* X *on* Y *in score form*)

These two equations are said to be in *score form*, since the X and Y in both equations represent *actual scores, and not deviations from the means* of the two distributions.

If we substitute in (31) the values of M_Y, r, σ_y, σ_x, and M_X obtained from Figure 39, the regression of height on weight in score form becomes

$$\overline{Y} = .60 \times \frac{2.62}{15.54}(X - 136.3) + 66.5$$

or upon reduction

$$\overline{Y} = .10X + 52.9$$

To illustrate the use of this equation, suppose that a man in our groups weighs 160 pounds and we wish to estimate his most probable height. Substituting 160 for X in the equation, $\overline{Y} = 69$ inches; and accordingly, the most probable height of a man who weighs 160 pounds is 69 inches.

If the problem is to predict weight instead of height, we must use the second regression equation, formula (32). Substituting for M_X, r, σ_x, σ_y, and M_Y in (32) we have

$$\overline{X} = .60 \times \frac{15.54}{2.62}(Y - 66.5) + 136.3$$

or

$$\overline{X} = 3.56Y - 100.4$$

Now if a man is 71 inches tall, we find, on replacing Y by 71 in the equation, that $\overline{X} = 152.4$. Hence the most probable weight of a man who is 71 inches tall is about 152½ pounds.

5. The meaning of a "prediction" from the regression equation

It may seem strange, perhaps, to talk of "predicting" a man's height from his weight, when the heights and weights of the 120 men in our group are already known. When we have measures of both height and weight it is unnecessary, of course, to estimate one from the other. But suppose that all we know about a given individual is his weight and the fact that he falls within the age-range of our group of 120 men. Since we know the correlation between height and weight to be .60, it is possible from the regression equation to predict the most probable height of our subject in lieu of actually measuring him. Furthermore, the regression equation may be employed to estimate the height of *any* man in the population from which our group is chosen, provided our sample is an unbiased selection from the larger group. A regression equation holds, of course, only for the population from which the sample group was drawn. We cannot estimate the heights of children or of women from a regression equation which describes the relationship between height and weight in men between the ages of eighteen and twenty-five years (the age-range of the students in our group). Conversely, we cannot expect a regression equation established for elementary-school children to hold for older groups.

Height and weight, since they are both easily measured, perhaps do not demonstrate the value of the regression equation so clearly as do other and more complex traits. These variables were chosen for our "model" problem because they are objective and observable and their meaning is definite. Let us now consider a problem of more direct psychological interest. Suppose that in a group of 300 high-school children of nearly the same age, the correlation between a group intelligence test given at the beginning of the school year and average grades made in the first year of high school is .60. Now if we administer the group test to a child who enters school the next year, it is possible from his score to estimate his probable scholastic performance by means of the regression equation between test score and grades obtained from the previous years' class. Forecasts of this sort are useful in educational prognosis and guidance.* The same is true of vocational guidance; we are often able to predict from a test battery the probable success of an individual who contemplates entering a certain trade or profession.† Advice on such a basis is measurably better than subjective judgment.

II. The Reliability of Predictions ‡

1. The standard error of estimate

The values of X and Y "predicted" from regression equations have been constantly referred to as being the "most probable" values of the one variable accompanying the given value of the other. In order to show just how probable such estimates are it is necessary that we calculate their standard errors of estimate. The accuracy with which we are able to predict Y-scores from equation (31) is given by the formula

---

* Edgerton, H. A., *Academic Prognosis in the University*, Educational Psychology Monographs, 1930, 27.
† Stead, W. H., and Shartle, C. L., *Occupational Counseling Techniques* (New York: American Book Co., 1940).
‡ This section may be omitted until after Chapter 8.

162 • STATISTICS IN PSYCHOLOGY AND EDUCATION

$$\sigma_{(\text{est. }Y)} = \sigma_y\sqrt{1-r^2} \qquad (33)$$

[*standard error of a Y-score predicted from equation* (31)]

in which σ_y is the σ of the Y distribution, and r is the coefficient of correlation. The subscript "est." is used to distinguish this standard error from the σ of the distribution.

From formula (31) we have calculated the most probable height of a man weighing 160 pounds to be 69 inches. The reliability of this prediction is obtained by substituting $\sigma_{(ht)}$ and r in formula (33) to find

$$\sigma_{(\text{est. }Y)} = 2.62\sqrt{1-.60^2} = 2.1 \text{ inches}$$

We now say that the most probable height of a man weighing 160 pounds is 69 inches with a $\sigma_{(\text{est.})}$ of 2.1 inches; and that the chances are about two in three that our prediction does not miss the man's actual height by more than ±2.1 inches. We may feel quite certain that the estimated height of this man does not miss his true height by more than ±3$\sigma_{(\text{est.})}$ or by more than ±6.3 inches (p. 185).

The degree of accuracy with which X-scores can be predicted from (32) is given by the formula

$$\sigma_{(\text{est. }X)} = \sigma_x\sqrt{1-r^2} \qquad (34)$$

[*standard error of an X-score predicted from equation* (32)]

in which σ_x is the σ of the X distribution, and r is the coefficient of correlation.

We found on page 160 that the most probable weight of a man in our group who is 71 inches tall is 152.4 pounds. The $\sigma_{(\text{est.})}$ of this prediction from (34) is

$$\sigma_{(\text{est. }X)} = 15.54\sqrt{1-.60^2} = 12.4 \text{ pounds}$$

and the most probable weight of *any* man 71 inches tall, in our group or in the population from which our sample was drawn, is 152.4 pounds with a $\sigma_{(\text{est.})}$ of 12.4 pounds. The chances, therefore, are about two in three that our prediction does not miss our man's true weight by more than ±12.4 pounds.

2. The accuracy of individual predictions from regression equations

The formulas for $\sigma_{(\text{est.})}$ measure the error made in taking predicted, instead of actual, X and Y measures. If $r = 1.00$, $\sqrt{1-r^2}$ is

0, and $\sigma_{(est.)}$ is zero—there is *no* error of estimate and each person's measurement is predicted exactly. On the other hand, when $r = .00$, $\sqrt{1 - r^2} = 1.00$, and the error of estimate is equal to the σ of the distribution into which prediction is made. When this last situation occurs, the regression equation is of no value in enabling us the better to predict scores, as each person's most probable score (e.g., X) is simply the mean (i.e., M_X). When $r = .00$ all that we can say definitely is that a subject's score lies *somewhere* in the distribution of Y's or X's. But just where we cannot tell, since our SE * of estimate equals the SD of the test.

It is clear from formulas (33) and (34) that the accuracy of prediction from a regression equation depends directly upon the σ of the distribution (σ_y or σ_x) and upon the degree of correlation between the two sets of measures. If the variability (σ_y) of Y is small, and the correlation between Y and X high (e.g., .90), values of Y can be predicted from known values of X with a comparatively high degree of accuracy. However, when the variability of a test is large, or the correlation low (or when both conditions exist), prediction from regression equations becomes so unreliable as to be almost valueless. Even when the correlation is fairly high, forecasts will often have an uncomfortably large error of estimate. Thus we have seen that in spite of the $r = .60$ between height and weight (Fig. 39), our forecast of a man's weight, knowing his height, has a $\sigma_{(est. X)}$ of about 12 pounds (p. 162). Predicted heights will, in two-thirds of the cases, be in error by not more than 2 inches. An example in which high correlation offsets fairly large variability, permitting reasonably accurate forecasts, is given later in Figure 41, page 169.

When an investigator uses the regression equations for purposes of prediction, he should always give the $\sigma_{(est.)}$ of his estimated scores. The value of a forecast depends, first of all, upon the size of the error of estimate; but it also depends upon the units of measurement, and upon the purposes for which the prediction is made (p. 186).

3. The accuracy of group predictions

We have seen that the standard error of a predicted score $\sigma_{(est.)}$ may often be uncomfortably large. Only when $r = 1.00$ is $\sqrt{1 - r^2} = .00$, and only then can an estimate be made without error. The correlation coefficient must be .87 before $\sqrt{1 - r^2}$ is .50, i.e., before the standard error of estimate is reduced 50% below the σ of

* SE = standard error.

the test. Obviously, unless r is quite large (larger than we usually get in practice) the regression equation is of little aid in forecasting with reasonable accuracy what a given individual may be expected to do (p. 162). This fact has led many to discount unwisely the value of correlation in prediction and to conclude that the calculation of r is not worth the trouble.

Fortunately correlation makes out better in forecasting the performance of *groups* than in predicting the most likely achievement of a given *individual*. In forecasting achievement the psychologist is in much the same position as the insurance statistician or actuary. The actuary cannot tell how long John Smith, aged twenty, will live. But from his tables, he can tell quite accurately how many of 10,000 men now aged twenty will live to be thirty, forty, or fifty years old. In the same way, the psychologist may be quite uncertain concerning the performance of a given individual. But knowing the correlation between a test (or test battery) and some criterion of performance, he can forecast, often with considerable accuracy, the probable performance of various groups chosen from his distribution of test scores. The degree of accuracy in such predictions depends upon the size of the correlation coefficient.

To illustrate "actuarial" prediction in psychology, suppose that 70% of a freshman class of 400 men achieve grades in their college work above the minimum passing mark and hence are regarded as "satisfactory" students. Suppose, further, that the correlation between a standard intelligence test and freshman performance is .50. Now if we had selected the *upper half* of our group (i.e., the 200 students who performed *best* on the intelligence test) at the beginning of the term, how many of these 200 would have been "satisfactory," i.e., in the upper 70% of the grades distribution? From Table 23 it can easily be read that 84% of our 200 selected freshmen (i.e., 168) should be found in the satisfactory group with respect to grades. The entry .84 is found in column .50 (percentage of test distribution chosen) opposite the correlation of .50. This result should be compared with the 70% (i.e., 140) who might be expected to fall in the satisfactory group when selection is by "guess," without knowledge of the correlation. This entry is in column .50 opposite the r of .00.

The probable performance of other and smaller groups chosen from our test distribution can be estimated with much greater accuracy from Table 23. We know, for example, that 91% of the best 20% of our students (roughly, seventy-three in the first eighty) can be expected to prove satisfactory in terms of our criterion (i.e.,

TABLE 23 * Proportion of students considered satisfactory in terms of grades = .70

Selection Ratio: Proportion Selected on Basis of Tests

r	.05	.10	.20	.30	.40	.50	.60	.70	.80	.90	.95
.00	.70	.70	.70	.70	.70	.70	.70	.70	.70	.70	.70
.05	.73	.73	.72	.72	.72	.71	.71	.71	.71	.70	.70
.10	.77	.76	.75	.74	.73	.73	.72	.72	.71	.71	.70
.15	.80	.79	.77	.76	.75	.74	.73	.73	.72	.71	.71
.20	.83	.81	.79	.78	.77	.76	.75	.74	.73	.71	.71
.25	.86	.84	.81	.80	.78	.77	.76	.75	.73	.72	.71
.30	.88	.86	.84	.82	.80	.78	.77	.75	.74	.72	.71
.35	.91	.89	.86	.83	.82	.80	.78	.76	.75	.73	.71
.40	.93	.91	.88	.85	.83	.81	.79	.77	.75	.73	.72
.45	.94	.93	.90	.87	.85	.83	.81	.78	.76	.73	.72
.50	.96	.94	.91	.89	.87	.84	.82	.80	.77	.74	.72
.55	.97	.96	.93	.91	.88	.86	.83	.81	.78	.74	.72
.60	.98	.97	.95	.92	.90	.87	.85	.82	.79	.75	.73
.65	.99	.98	.96	.94	.92	.89	.86	.83	.80	.75	.73
.70	1.00	.99	.97	.96	.93	.91	.88	.84	.80	.76	.73
.75	1.00	1.00	.98	.97	.95	.92	.89	.86	.81	.76	.73
.80	1.00	1.00	.99	.98	.97	.94	.91	.87	.82	.77	.73
.85	1.00	1.00	1.00	.99	.98	.96	.93	.89	.84	.77	.74
.90	1.00	1.00	1.00	1.00	.99	.98	.95	.91	.85	.78	.74
.95	1.00	1.00	1.00	1.00	1.00	.99	.98	.94	.86	.78	.74
1.00	1.00	1.00	1.00	1.00	1.00	1.00	1.00	1.00	.88	.78	.74

being located in the upper 70% of the grade distribution). Read the entry .91 in column 20 opposite $r = .50$. If the correlation of the intelligence test and school grades had been .60 instead of .50, 87% (174 in 200) of the "best half" according to the test would have been satisfactory students; and 95% of the "best" 20% on the test should be satisfactory students. These forecasts are to be compared with 70%, the estimate when $r = .00$. It is clear that a knowledge of the correlation greatly improves the estimate, and the larger the r the better the forecast.

Table 23 is a small part of a larger table in which "proportions considered satisfactory in achievement" range from .05 to .95. The correlation between test score and performance ranges from .00 to 1.00. These tables are strictly accurate only when the distributions are normal both in the test and in the criterion of performance. They may be used with considerable confidence when the distributions are approximately normal, especially when the N's are large; and in any case they furnish useful information.

* Taylor, H. C., and Russell, J. T., "The Relationships of Validity Coefficients to the Practical Effectiveness of Tests in Selection: Discussion and Tables," *Journal of Applied Psychology*, 1939, 23, 565–578.

Forecasting tables have considerable value in selecting personnel for business or other vocations. First, we must determine what proportion of a given group of workers is to be considered "successful." With this information in hand and knowing the correlation between our test battery and performance in the given activity, we may forecast the probable success of groups of new applicants from their test scores. Assume, for example, that 70% of a group of factory workers are regarded as "acceptable workers," acceptability having been determined from ratings by foremen, number of pieces done in a given time, or time taken to complete certain standard jobs. Assume, further, that a test battery has a correlation of .45 with worker-performance. Then if we select the best twenty out of 100 applicants ("best" according to our tests), we find from Table 23 that 90% of this number or eighteen should be acceptable workers. If we had had no test and had simply selected the *first* twenty applicants to appear —or *any* twenty—70% or fourteen should be acceptable. Use of the tests improves our forecast 30%; and the more stringent the criterion of acceptability the greater the improvement in forecast made by the tests.

III. The Effect of Variability of Scores upon the Size of r

Suppose that the correlation between two tests in a group of 50 sixth-grade children has been found to be .50. How will this correlation compare with that between the same tests in a group of greater range, e.g., a group of 200 children spread over grades 6, 7, and 8? More generally, knowing the correlation between two tests in a group of narrow range of talent, can we predict the probable correlation in a group of wider range of talent?

The problem of the effect upon r of the "range of talent" (size of σ_x and σ_y) within the group being studied often arises in correlational work. It becomes important, for example, when one wishes to go beyond the correlation obtained in the sample with which one is working and to generalize (estimate the r) for a group of wider range; or when r's between the same tests obtained in different ranges are to be compared. A formula for estimating the correlation between two tests in a heterogeneous group when we know the correlation between the tests in a homogeneous group may be developed in the following way: Let $\sigma_{(\text{est. } Y_n)}$ be the standard error of estimate in a group somewhat curtailed in variability or in range of talent;

REGRESSION AND PREDICTION • 167

and $\sigma_{(\text{est. } Y_w)}$ be the standard error of estimate in a larger group less restricted in variability. (Y is the *dependent* variable, p. 156.) Then, on the assumption that our tests are as effective in the *wide* as in the *narrow* range, $\sigma_{(\text{est. } Y_w)} = \sigma_{(\text{est. } Y_n)}$, or, by formula (33), p. 162,

$$\sigma_{y_n}\sqrt{1 - r^2_{x_n y_n}} = \sigma_{y_w}\sqrt{1 - r^2_{x_w y_w}}$$

and

$$\frac{\sigma_{y_n}}{\sigma_{y_w}} = \frac{\sqrt{1 - r^2_{x_w y_w}}}{\sqrt{1 - r^2_{x_n y_n}}} \qquad (35)$$

(formula for estimating correlation in a wide *range from a knowledge of the correlation in a* narrow *range)*

in which σ_{y_n} is the standard deviation of Y in the group of curtailed range; σ_{y_w} is the standard deviation of Y in the group of uncurtailed range; $r_{x_n y_n}$ = the correlation in the curtailed group, and $r_{x_w y_w}$ = the correlation in the uncurtailed group.

To illustrate formula (35), suppose that in one group $\sigma_{y_n} = 10$ and $r_{x_n y_n}$ is .50. What would the r between the same two tests probably be in a group in which $\sigma_{y_w} = 15$: in which σ_{y_w} is 50% larger than σ_{y_n}? Substituting $\sigma_{y_n} = 10$, $\sigma_{y_w} = 15$, and $r_{x_n y_n} = .50$ in (35), we have

$$\frac{10}{15} = \frac{\sqrt{1 - r^2_{x_w y_w}}}{\sqrt{1 - .25}}$$

Squaring both sides of this equation, and solving, we have $r_{x_w y_w} = .82$. The r of .50 in the narrow range becomes an r of .82 in the wide range. It is clear from this example that direct comparison of r's is not valid when the variabilities (σ's) within the groups from which the r's were computed are quite different.

If X and not Y is the dependent variable, formula (35) becomes

$$\frac{\sigma_{x_n}}{\sigma_{x_w}} = \frac{\sqrt{1 - r^2_{x_w y_w}}}{\sqrt{1 - r^2_{x_n y_n}}} \qquad (36)$$

(formula for estimating correlation in a wide *range from a knowledge of the correlation in a* narrow *range)*

Formulas (35) and (36) are open to the objection that each takes account of only *one* distribution in estimating the probable increase in r with increase in range of talent. If, however, the increase in σ_y as the group becomes more heterogeneous is accompanied by a proportional increase in σ_x (or vice versa), formulas (35) and (36) will give accurate estimates. Experimental trial of these formulas has yielded results closely in accord with theoretical expectation.*

IV. The Solution of a Second Correlation Problem

The solution of a second correlation problem will be found in Figure 41. The purpose of another "model" is to strengthen the reader's grasp of correlational techniques by having him work straight through the process of calculating r and the regression equations upon a new set of data. A student often fails to relate the various aspects of a correlational problem when these are presented in piecemeal fashion.

1. Calculation of r

Our first problem in Figure 41 is to find the correlation between the I.Q.'s achieved by 190 children of the same—or approximately the same—chronological age who have taken an intelligence examination upon two occasions separated by a six-month interval. The correlation table has been constructed from a scattergram, as described on page 129. The test given first is the X-variable, and the test given second is the Y-variable. The calculation of the two means, and of c_x, c_y, σ_x, and σ_y covers familiar ground, is given in detail on the chart, and need not be repeated here.

The product-deviations in the $\Sigma x'y'$ column have been taken from column 100–104 (column containing the AM_X) and from row 105–109 (row containing the AM_Y). The entries in the $\Sigma x'y'$ column have been calculated by the shorter method described on page 137; that is, each cell entry in a given row has been multiplied *first* by its x-deviation (x') and the sum of these deviations entered in the column $\Sigma x'$. The $\Sigma x'$ entries were then "weighted" once for all by the y' of the whole row. To illustrate, in the first row reading from left to right $(1 \times 5) + (1 \times 6)$ or 11 is the $\Sigma x'$ entry. The x''s are 5 and 6, respectively, and may be read from the x' row at the bottom of the correlation table. Since the common y' is 5, the final $\Sigma x'y'$ entry is 55. Again in the seventh row reading down from the top of the diagram $(5 \times -3) + (3 \times -2) + (7 \times -1) + (16 \times 0) + (2 \times 1)$

*Peters, C. C., and Van Voorhis, W. R., *Statistical Procedures and Their Mathematical Bases* (New York: McGraw-Hill, 1940), pp. 208–212.

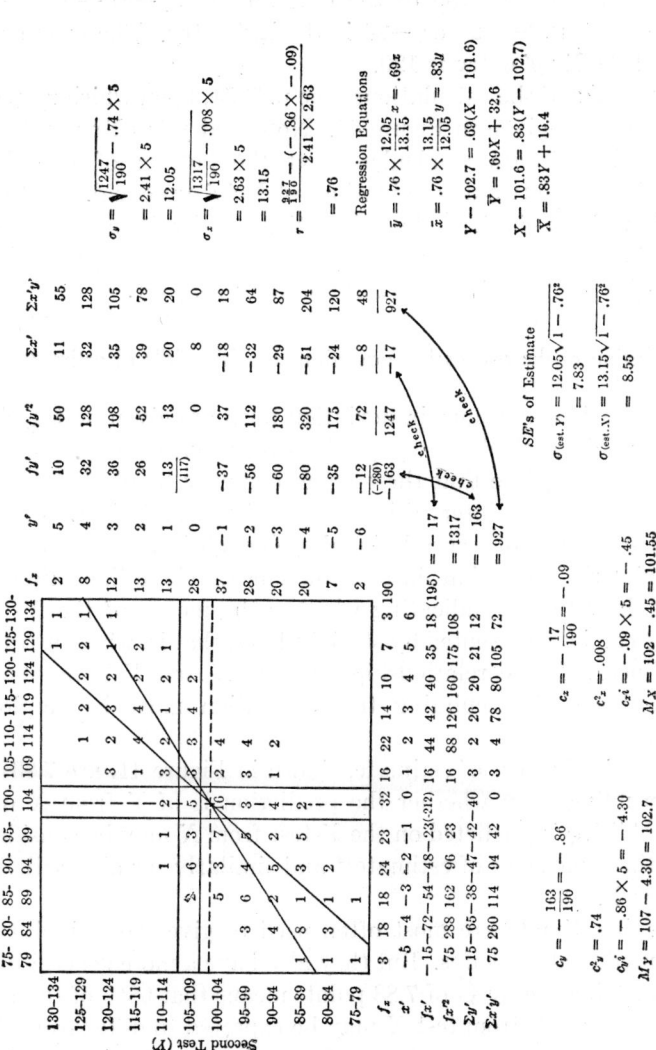

FIG. 41 Calculation of the correlation between the I.Q.'s achieved by 190 children of the same C.A. upon two forms of an individual intelligence examination

$+ (4 \times 2)$ or -18 makes up the $\Sigma x'$ entry. The y' of this row is -1, and the final $\Sigma x'y'$ entry is 18. To take still a third example, in the eleventh row from the top of the diagram, $(1 \times -5) + (3 \times -4) + (1 \times -3) + (2 \times -2)$ or -24 is the $\Sigma x'$ entry. The common y' is -5 and the $\Sigma x'y'$ entry is 120.

Three checks of the calculations (see p. 135), upon which r, σ_x and σ_y are based, are given in Figure 41. Note that $fx' = \Sigma x'$; and that, when the $\Sigma x'y''$s are recalculated, at the bottom of the chart, $fy' = \Sigma y'$, and the two determinations of $\Sigma x'y'$ are equal. When the $\Sigma x'y''$s have been checked, the calculation of r by formula (22) is a matter of substitution. Note carefully that c_x, c_y, σ_x, σ_y are all left in *units of class-interval* in the formula for r (p. 139).

2. Calculation of the regression equations and the SE's of estimate

The regression equations in deviation form are given on the chart and the two lines which these equations represent have been plotted on the diagram. Note that these equations may be plotted as they stand, since the class-interval is the same for X and Y (p. 158). In the routine solution of a correlational problem it is not strictly necessary to plot the regression lines on the chart. These lines are often of value, however, in indicating whether the means of the X- and Y-arrays can be represented by straight lines, that is, whether regression is linear. If the relationship between X and Y is not linear, other methods of calculating the correlation must be employed (p. 371).

The standard errors of estimate, shown in Figure 41, are 7.83 and 8.55, depending upon whether the prediction is of Y from X or X from Y. All I.Q.'s predicted on the Y-test from X may be considered to have the same error of estimate,* and similarly for all predictions of X from Y.

Errors of estimate are most often used to give the reliability of specific predicted measures. But they also have a more general interpretation. Thus a $\sigma_{(est. Y)}$ of 7.83 points means that 68% of the I.Q.'s predicted on test Y from test X may be expected to differ from their actual values by not more than ±7.83 points, while the remaining 32% may be expected to differ from their actual values by more than ±7.83 points.

---

* See, however, Terman, L. M., and Merrill, M. A., *Measuring Intelligence* (Boston: Houghton Mifflin Co., 1937), pp. 44–47, where the SE's of estimate have been computed for various I.Q. levels.

3. The "regression effect" in prediction

Predicted scores tend to "move in" toward the mean of the distribution into which prediction is made (p. 154). This so-called regression effect has often been noted by investigators and is always present when correlation is less than ± 1.00.* The regression phenomenon can be clearly seen in the following illustrations: From the regression equation $\overline{Y} = .69X + 32.6$ (Fig. 41) it is clear that a child who earns an I.Q. of 130 on the first test (X) will most probably earn an I.Q. of 122 on the second test (Y); while a child who earns an I.Q. of 120 in X will most probably score 115 in Y. In both of these illustrations the predicted Y-test I.Q. is lower than the first or X-test I.Q. Put differently, the second I.Q. has *regressed* or moved down toward the mean of test Y, i.e., toward 102.7 The opposite effect occurs when the I.Q. on the X-test is *below* its mean: the tendency now is for the predicted score in Y to move *up* toward its mean. Thus from the equation $\overline{Y} = .69X + 32.6$, we find that if a child earns an I.Q. of 70 on the X-test his most likely score on the second test (Y) is 81; while an I.Q. of 80 on the first test forecasts an I.Q. of 88 on the second. Both of these predicted I.Q.'s have moved up nearer to the mean 102.7 (i.e., M_y).

The tendency for all scores predicted from a regression equation to pull in—down or up—toward the mean can be seen as a general phenomenon if the regression equation is written in standard-score form. Given

$$\overline{y} = r\frac{\sigma_y}{\sigma_x} \times x \qquad (29) \text{ p. 154}$$

if we divide both sides of this equation by σ_y and write σ_x under x, we have

$$\frac{\overline{y}}{\sigma_y} = r\frac{x}{\sigma_x} \text{ or } \overline{z}_y = rz_x \qquad (37)$$

(*regression equation when scores in* X *and* Y *are expressed as* z *or* σ-*scores*)

In the problem in Figure 41, $\overline{z}_y = .76z_x$. If z_x is $\pm 1.00\sigma$, or $\pm 2.00\sigma$, or $\pm 3.00\sigma$ from M_x, $\overline{z}_y$ will be $\pm .76\sigma$, $\pm 1.52\sigma$, or $\pm 2.28\sigma$ from M_y. That is to say, *any* score above or below the mean of X forecasts a Y-score somewhat *closer* to the mean of Y.

* Thorndike, R. L., "Regression Fallacies in the Matched Groups Experiment," *Psychometrika*, 1942, 7, 85–102.

In studying the relation of height in parent and offspring, Galton (p. 154) interpreted the phenomenon of regression to the mean to be a provision of nature designed to protect the race from extremes. This same effect occurs, however, in any correlation table in which r is less than ± 1.00, and need not be explained in biological terms. The I.Q.'s of a group of very bright children, for instance, will tend upon retest to move *downward* toward 100, the mean of the group; while the I.Q.'s of a group of dull children will tend upon retest to move *upward* toward 100.

V. The Interpretation of the Coefficient of Correlation

When should a coefficient of correlation be called "high," when "medium," and when "low"? Does an r of .40 between two tests indicate "marked" or "low" relationship? How high should an r be in order to permit accurate prediction from one variable to another? Can an r of .50, say, be interpreted with respect to "overlap" of determining factors in the two variables correlated? Questions like these, all of which are concerned with the *significance* or *meaning* of the relationship expressed by a correlation coefficient constantly arise in problems involving mental measurement, and their implications must be understood before we can effectively employ the correlational method.

The value of r as a measure of correspondence may be profitably considered from two points of view. In the first place, r's are computed in order to determine whether there is *any* correlation (over and above chance) between two variables; and in the second place, r's are computed in order to determine the *degree* or closeness of relationship when some association is known, or is assumed, to exist. The question, "Is there *any* correlation between brain weight and intelligence?", voices the first objective. And the question, "*How significant* is the correlation between high-school grades and first-year performance in college?", expresses the second. The problem of when an obtained r denotes significant relationship will be considered later, on page **197**. This section is concerned mainly with the second problem, namely, the evaluation—with respect to degree of relationship—of an obtained coefficient. The questions at the beginning of the paragraph above all bear upon this topic.

1. The interpretation of r in terms of verbal description

It is customary in mental measurement to describe the correlation between two tests in a general way as high, marked or substantial, low or negligible. While the descriptive label applied will vary somewhat in meaning with the author using it, there is fairly good agreement among workers with psychological and educational tests that an

r from .00 to ± .20 denotes indifferent or negligible relationship;
r from ± .20 to ± .40 denotes low correlation; present but slight;
r from ± .40 to ± .70 denotes substantial or marked relationship;
r from ± .70 to ± 1.00 denotes high to very high relationship.

This classification is broad and somewhat tentative, and can only be accepted as a general guide with certain reservations. Thus a coefficient of correlation must always be judged with regard to

(1) the nature of variables with which we are dealing;
(2) the significance of the coefficient;
(3) the size and variability of the group (p. 166);
(4) the reliability coefficients of the tests used (p. 342);
(5) the purpose for which the r was computed.

To consider, first, the matter of the variables being correlated, an r of .30 between height and intelligence, or between head measurements and mechanical ability would be regarded as important although it is rather low, since correlations between physical and mental functions are usually much lower—often zero. On the other hand, the correlation must be .70 or more between measures of general intelligence and school grades or between achievement in English and in history to be considered high, since r's in this field usually run from .40 to .60. Resemblances of parents and offspring with respect to physical and mental traits are expressed by r's of .35 to .55; and, accordingly, an r of .60 would be high.* By contrast, the reliability of a standard intelligence test is ordinarily much higher than .60, and the self-correlation of such a test must be .85 to .95 to be regarded as high. In the field of vocational testing, the r's between test batteries and measures of aptitude represented by various criteria rarely rise above .50; and r's above this figure would be considered exceptionally promising.

* Jones, H. E., *A First Study of Parent-Child Resemblance in Intelligence*, 27th Yearbook of the N.S.S.E., 1928, Part I, 61–72.

Correlation coefficients must be evaluated also with due regard to the reliabilities (p. 332) of the two tests concerned. Because of chance errors, an obtained r is always less than its "corrected" value (p. 346) and hence, in a sense, is a minimum measure of the relationship present. The effect upon an r of the size and variability of the group is discussed elsewhere (p. 167), and a formula for estimating such effect provided. The *purpose* for which the correlation has been computed is important.* The r which is to be employed in predicting the scores of *individuals* from one test to another, for instance, should be much higher than the r the purpose of which is to provide forecasts of the achievement of selected groups (p. 344).

In summary, a correlation coefficient is always to be judged with reference to the circumstances under which it was obtained. There is no such thing as *the* correlation between mechanical aptitude and abstract intelligence, for instance, but only *a* correlation between certain tests of mechanical aptitude and intelligence given to certain groups under definite conditions. Correlation coefficients are always to be thought of as *relative* and never as *absolute* indices of relationship.

2. The interpretation of r in terms of $\sigma_{(est.)}$ and the coefficient of alienation

One of the most practical ways of evaluating the effectiveness of a coefficient of correlation is through the standard error of estimate, $\sigma_{(est.)}$. We have found (p. 161) that $\sigma_{(est.\ Y)}$—which equals $\sigma_y \sqrt{1 - r^2}$—enables us to tell how accurately we can estimate (by means of the regression equation) an individual's score in Test Y when we know his score is Test X. The size of $\sigma_{(est.\ Y)}$ depends directly upon σ_y and upon the correlation between the two tests. When $r = 1.00$, $\sigma_{(est.\ Y)} = .00$, and we can predict a person's score in Y, knowing his score in X, with 100% accuracy—no error. On the other hand, when $r = .00$, $\sigma_{(est.\ Y)} = \sigma_y$, and we can only be certain that the predicted score lies *somewhere* within the limits of the Y-distribution, i.e., within the limits Mean Score $\pm 3\sigma_y$. In other words, when $r = .00$ our estimate of a person's Y-score is not aided at all by a knowledge of his score in X. As r decreases from 1.00 to .00, the standard error of estimate increases so markedly that predictions from the regression equation range all the way from cer-

---

*Stead. W. H., and Shartle, C. L., *Occupational Counseling Techniques*, op. cit., Chapters 7 and 8.

tainty to what is virtually a "guess." * The significance of an r, with respect to predictive value, therefore, may be accurately gauged by the extent to which r improves our prediction over a "mere guess."

The following problem will serve as an illustration: Suppose that the correlation between two tests Y and X is .60, and that $\sigma_y = 5.00$. Then $\sigma_{(est.\ Y)}$ is $5 \times \sqrt{1 - .60^2}$ or 4.00. This SE is 20% less than 5.00, the $\sigma_{(est.\ Y)}$ when $r = .00$, i.e., when $\sigma_{(est.\ Y)}$ has minimum predictive value. The amount of reduction in $\sigma_{(est.\ Y)}$ as r varies from .00 to 1.00 is given by the expression $\sqrt{1 - r^2}$, and hence it is possible from $\sqrt{1 - r^2}$ alone to gauge the predictive value of an r. The expression $\sqrt{1 - r^2}$ is often called the *coefficient of alienation* and is denoted by the letter k. The coefficient of alienation may be thought of as measuring the *absence* of relationship between two variables X and Y in the same sense in which r measures the *presence* of relationship. When $k = 1.00$, $r = .00$, and when $k = .00$, $r = 1.00$: the *larger* the coefficient of alienation the *smaller* the degree of relationship, and the less precise the prediction from X to Y. In order to show how the estimate improves as r increases, the k's for certain values of r from .00 to 1.00 are tabulated in Table 24.

TABLE 24 Coefficients of alienation (k) for values of r from .00 to 1.00

r	$k = \sqrt{1 - r^2}$	r	$k = \sqrt{1 - r^2}$
.0000	1.0000	.8000	.6000
.1000	.9950	(.8660)	(.5000)
.2000	.9798	.9000	.4359
.3000	.9539	.9500	.3122
.4000	.9165	.9800	.1990
.5000	.8660	.9900	.1411
.6000	.8000	1.0000	.0000
.7000	.7141		
(.7071)	(.7071)		

Note that r must be .866 before k lies *halfway* between 1.00 and .00, before the standard error of estimate is reduced to one-half of its value where $r = .00$. For r's of .80 or less, the coefficients of alienation are clearly so large that predictions of individual scores based upon the regression equation are little better than "guesses." †

* The term "guess" as here used does not imply an estimate which is based upon no information whatsoever—a shot in the dark, so to speak. When $r = .00$, the most probable Y-score predicted for every individual in the X-distribution is M_Y, and $\sigma_{(est.\ Y)} = \sigma_y$. Hence, our Y-estimates are "guesses" in the sense that they may lie anywhere in the Y-distribution—but not anywhere at all!

† An r is more efficient in forecasting the probable success of a *group* (see p. 163).

Even when $r = .99$, the standard error of estimate is still 1/7 as large as when $r = .00$. In contrast to actuarial prediction, therefore, the estimation of an individual's score in one test from his score in another is not often warranted unless r is at least .90.

The coefficient E given by the formula below is often useful in providing a quick estimate of the predictive efficiency of an obtained r. E, which is called the "coefficient of forecasting efficiency" or the coefficient of dependability, is derived from k as follows:

$$E = 1 - \sqrt{1 - r^2} \qquad (38)$$

or

$$E = 1 - k$$

("coefficient of forecasting efficiency" or coefficient of dependability) *

To illustrate the application of E, suppose that the correlation of a test (or of a test battery) with some criterion of performance is .50. From formula (38) $E = 1 - .87$ or .13; and the test's efficiency in predicting criterion scores may be put at 13%. When $r = .90$, $E = .56$ and the test is 56% efficient; when $r = .98$, $E = .80$ and the tests is 80% efficient, and so on. Obviously, the correlation must be above .87 for the test's forecasting efficiency to be greater than 50%.

E gives essentially the same information as $\sigma_{(est. Y)}$ or k. Thus, if $r = .50$, $k = .87$ and $\sigma_{(est. Y)}$ is 87% of σ_y, which is its value when $r = .00$. Accordingly, an r of .50 reduces the $\sigma_{(est. Y)}$ by 13%.

3. The interpretation of r in terms of the coefficient of determination (r^2)

The interpretation of r in terms of "overlapping" factors in the tests being correlated may be generalized through an analysis of the *variance* (σ^2) of the dependent variable—usually the Y test. In studying the variability among individuals upon a given test, the variance of the test scores is often a more useful measure of "spread" than is the standard deviation. The object in analyzing the variance of Test Y is to determine from the correlation between Y and X what part of Test Y's variance is associated with, or dependent upon, the variance of Test X, and what part is determined by the variance of factors not in Test X.

When we have computed the correlation between Tests X and Y,

* See Conrad, H. S., and Martin, G. B., "The Index of Forecasting Efficiency, for the Case of a 'True' Criterion," *Journal of Experimental Education*, 1935, 4, 231–244.

σ^2_y provides a measure of the *total* variance of the Y-scores; and $\sigma^2_{(\text{est. }Y)}$ which equals $\sigma^2_y(1 - r^2_{xy})$ gives a measure of the variance *left* in Test Y when that part of the variance caused by Test X has been ruled out or made constant. Instead of $\sigma_{(\text{est. }Y)}$ the designation $\sigma_{y.x}$ is often used to denote that variability in X—insofar as it affects Y—is ruled out. What is meant by the term "X constant" or "ruled out" may be seen in Figure 39 where the variability within *any* column ("140–149," for instance) is given by $\sigma_y\sqrt{1 - r^2_{xy}}$. X has a constant value for *each* column ($X = 144.5$ in column 140–149, for example) and accordingly $\sigma_{y.x}$ becomes a measure of the variability of Y for a constant X. In Figure 39, $\sigma_{y.x}$ is 2.10 in the column 140–149 as compared with a "total" σ_y of 2.62.

The relationship between σ_y and $\sigma_{y.x}$ may be seen in the following illustration. If we have the correlation between height and weight in a group of school children, σ^2_{ht} will be reduced to $\sigma^2_{ht.wt}$ when the variance in weight is zero—when *all* of the children in the group have the *same* weight. If $\sigma^2_{y.x}$ is subtracted from σ^2_y there remains that part of the variance of Test Y which *is* associated with X; and if this is divided by σ^2_y we obtain that fraction of the variance of Y attributable to or associated with X. Carrying out these operations, we have

$$\frac{\sigma^2_y - \sigma^2_{y.x}}{\sigma^2_y} = \frac{\sigma^2_y - \sigma^2_y + \sigma^2_y r^2_{xy}}{\sigma^2_y} = r^2_{xy}$$

from which it is clear that r^2_{xy} gives the *proportion* of the variance of Test Y which is associated with Test X. When used in this way, r^2 is called the *coefficient of determination*. If the correlation between Tests Y and X is .707, r^2 is .50. Hence, an r of .707 means that 50% of the variance of Test Y is associated with the variability in Test X. Since $r^2 + k^2 = 1.00$, the proportion of the variance in Test Y which is *not* associated with Test X is given by k^2. In the present case, since r^2 is .50, k^2 is also .50.

The coefficient of determination tells us what part of the variance of Test Y is determined by Test X. But r alone gives us no information as to the character of the association and we cannot assume a causal relationship unless we have evidence beyond the correlation. Inspection of the squares of small coefficients of correlation emphasizes the slight degree of association, in terms of related changes in variability, indicated by low r's. An r of .10, for example, or .20, or .30, between Tests X and Y, indicates that only 1%, 4%, and 9%, respectively, of the variance of Y is associated with X. On the other hand, when r is .95, about 90% ($r^2 = .90$) of the variance of Test Y is associated with Test X, only 10% being unrelated. Valuable insight into the part played by one or more variables in determining the total variance of a criterion may be obtained through the coefficient of determination.

4. Summary

It may be helpful to summarize the main points brought out in this section.

(1) Whether an obtained r is to be regarded as "high," "medium," or "low" will depend upon the variables being studied, the reliability coefficients of the two tests, the size of the group and its variability, and the purpose for which the r is being computed. Correlation coefficients are never *absolute* indices of relationship.

(2) The accuracy with which an r enables us to predict (through the regression equation) *individual* scores in Test Y from given scores in Test X may be determined from $\sigma_{(est.\ Y)}$, from E, and from k, *the coefficient of alienation*.

(3) The *coefficient of determination* provides a method of determining what proportion of the total variance (σ^2) of Test Y is associated with Test X; and what proportion is independent of Test X. This method of analysis may be extended to problems employing partial and multiple correlation (p. 396).

PROBLEMS

1. Write out the regression equations in score form for the correlation table in example 3, page 149.
   (a) Compute $\sigma_{(est.\ Y)}$ and $\sigma_{(est.\ X)}$.
   (b) What is the most probable height of a boy who weighs 30 pounds? 45 pounds? What is the most probable weight of a boy who is 36 inches tall? 40 inches tall?

2. In example 4, page 149, find the most probable grade made by a child whose score on Army Alpha is 120. What is the $\sigma_{(est.)}$ of this grade?

3. What is the most probable algebra grade of a child whose I.Q. is 100 (data from example 5, p. 150)? What is the $\sigma_{(est.)}$ of this grade?

4. Given the following data for two tests:

   History (X) English (Y)
   $M_X = 75.00$ $M_Y = 70.00$
   $\sigma_x = 6.00$ $\sigma_y = 8.00$
   $r_{xy} = .72$

   (a) Work out the regression equations in score form.
   (b) Predict the probable grade in English of a student whose history mark is 65. Find the $\sigma_{(\text{est.})}$ of this prediction.
   (c) If r_{xy} had been .84 (σ's and means remaining the same) how much would $\sigma_{(\text{est. }Y)}$ be reduced?

5. The correlation of a test battery with worker efficiency in a large factory is .40, and 70% of the workers are regarded as "satisfactory."

   (a) From seventy-five applicants you select the best twenty-five in terms of test score. How many of these should be satisfactory workers?
   (b) How many of the best ten should be satisfactory?
   (c) How many in the two groups should be satisfactory if selected at random, i.e., without using the test battery?

6. Plot the regression lines in on the correlation diagram given in example 5, page 150. Calculate the means of the Y-arrays (successive Y-columns), plot as points on the diagram, and join these points with straight lines. Plot, also, the means of the X-arrays and join them with straight lines. Compare these two "lines-through-means" with the two fitted regression lines (see Fig. 39, p. 153).

7. In a group of 115 freshmen, the r between reaction time to light and substitution learning is .30. The σ of the reaction times is 20 ms. What would you estimate the correlation between these two tests to be in a group in which the σ of the reaction times is 25 ms.?

8. Show the regression effect in example 4, page 149, by calculating the regression equation in standard-score form. For I.Q.'s $\pm 1.00\sigma$ and $\pm 2.00\sigma$ from the mean I. Q., find the corresponding school marks in standard-score form.

9. Basing your answer upon your experience and general knowledge of psychology, decide whether the correlation between the following pairs of variables is most probably (1) positive or negative; (2) high, medium, or low.

   (a) Intelligence of husbands and wives.
   (b) Brain weight and intelligence.
   (c) High-school grades in history and physics.
   (d) Age and radicalism.
   (e) Extroversion and college grades.

STATISTICS IN PSYCHOLOGY AND EDUCATION

10. How much more will an r of .80 reduce a given $\sigma_{(est.)}$ than an r of .40? An r of .90 than an r of .40?

11. (a) Determine k and E for the following r's: .35; —.50; .70; .95. Interpret your results.
    (b) What is the "forecasting efficiency" of an r of .45? an r of .99?

12. The correlation of a criterion with a test battery is .75. What percent of the variance of the criterion is associated with variability in the battery? What percent is independent of the battery?

ANSWERS

1. $\overline{Y} = .40X + 24.12$; $\overline{X} = 1.26Y - 11.52$
   (a) $\sigma_{(est.\ Y)} = 1.78$; $\sigma_{(est.\ X)} = 3.16$
   (b) 36.12 inches; 42.12 inches; 33.84 pounds; 38.88 pounds

2. 85.2; $\sigma_{(est.\ Y)} = 7.0$

3. $\overline{X} = .37Y + 8.16$. When Y(I.Q.) is 100, $\overline{X}$ (algebra) is 45.2 $\sigma_{(est.\ X)} = 6.8$

4. (a) $\overline{Y} = .96X - 2$; $\overline{X} = .54Y + 37.2$
   (b) 60.4; $\sigma_{(est.\ Y)} = 5.5$
   (c) 22%

5. (a) 21
   (b) 9
   (c) 17.5 and 7 (i.e., 70%)

7. $r = .65$

8. $\pm.46$ and $\pm.92$

10. Five times as much; seven times as much.

11. (a)

r	k	E
.35	.94	.06
—.50	.87	.13
.70	.71	.29
.95	.31	.69

   (b) 11%; 86%

12. 56%; 44%

8

THE RELIABILITY OF THE MEAN AND OF OTHER STATISTICS

1. The Meaning of Reliability

The true mean or the true σ of any set of measurements (of height, mechanical aptitude or intelligence, for example) is that hypothetical value obtained by taking into account the scores made by *all* of the members of some defined group called the *population*. Since it is rarely if ever possible to measure all of the members of a population, we must usually be content with "samples"; and owing to slight differences in the composition of these samples, computed means and σ's may be somewhat larger or somewhat smaller than their true values. Population measures are called *parameters,* and are to be thought of as fixed reference points. Measurements obtained from samples are called *statistics.* Statistics are always *estimates* of their parameters; and the accuracy of the estimate is a measure of the *reliability* of the statistic.

While we cannot determine the parameters themselves, we can estimate them by computing the amount by which our statistics probably diverge from these parameters. This amount, which may be large or small, serves as an index of the dependability or trustworthiness of the statistic. Whenever we have calculated a statistic, therefore, we should ask ourselves this question: "How accurate an estimate is this statistic (mean or *SD*, say) of the parameter which I would get by taking into account the entire population from which this sample was drawn?" The purpose of this chapter is to outline methods which will enable us to answer this question. The reliability of the mean and the median will first be considered; following this the reliability of the σ and *Q* and of certain other useful statistics.

II. The Reliability of the Mean and of the Median

1. The reliability of the mean

(1) THE STANDARD ERROR (SE) OF THE MEAN (σ_M)

What is meant by the reliability of the mean can best be understood by examining the factors upon which the stability of this measure depends. Suppose that we wish to know the mean ability of college freshmen in the United States as shown by their scores upon the American Council Psychological Examination. To measure the achievement of college freshmen *in general* would require in strict logic that we test *all* of the freshmen in the United States. But this is obviously a stupendous if not an impossible task, and we must perforce be satisfied with taking the records of a sample as large and as randomly drawn as possible. The definition of a random sample is given on page 202. Suffice it to say here that we cannot use freshmen from only a single institution or from only one section of the country; and that we must guard against selecting only those with high, or only those with low, scholastic records. The more successful we are in getting an "unselected" group, the more nearly representative this group will be of all freshmen in the country. Evidently, therefore, the reliability of a mean depends for one thing upon how impartially we have chosen our sample.

Given an adequate sample, the reliability of a mean can be shown to depend mathematically upon *two* characteristics of the distribution: (1) the number of cases and (2) the variability or spread of the measures. The formula for the standard error of the mean is

$$SE_{\text{mean}} \text{ or } \sigma_M = \frac{\sigma}{\sqrt{N}} \tag{39}$$

(*standard error of the arithmetic mean*)

where σ = standard deviation of the population and
N = number of cases in the sample.

In this formula for the SE of the mean the σ in the numerator is really the population and not the sample standard deviation. As we rarely have the population σ we must of necessity use an estimate of it (p. 190), and our best estimate is the SD of the sample. Modern writers on statistics often make a distinction between the standard deviation of the population and the standard deviation of a sample drawn from this population, designating the population SD by σ and the sample SD by s. While this distinction is helpful, σ as a symbol for the standard deviation of a sample has been so widely used in the psychological literature (σ-scaling, σ-units, and the like) that in this chapter we shall continue to use only σ (or SD) and not s. We shall designate the standard deviation as population σ or sample σ when the meaning is not evident from the context.

It is clear that the number of cases influences the mean, since the addition of even one extra measure to a series will change the mean unless the additional case happens to coincide with the mean exactly. Moreover, the addition of 1 score to a set of 10 scores will effect a greater change in the obtained mean than the addition of 1 score to a set of 1000 scores, as each case counts for less in the larger group. It has been shown mathematically that the reliability of a sample mean increases, not in proportion to the number of scores upon which it is based, but in proportion to the *square root* of the number of scores. The mean obtained from 25 scores is not 25 times, but $\sqrt{25}$ or 5 times, as reliable as a single score. And a mean based upon an N of 36 is not 4 times as reliable as a mean based upon an N of 9, but only 2 times as reliable—since $\sqrt{36}$ divided by $\sqrt{9}$ equals 2.

The reliability of a mean depends also upon the variability of the separate measures around the obtained mean. If the σ of the sample is large, we are unable to say where the means of other samples which we have not drawn will most probably fall—whether they will be close to, or far from, the given obtained mean. On the other hand, if the σ is small, we may be fairly certain that other sample means will fall reasonably close to the mean of our sample. The reliability of a sample mean, therefore, will vary with the size of the σ; as σ increases, reliability decreases.

The SE of the mean is an important and much-used formula. It measures the extent to which this statistic is affected by (a) errors of measurement as well as by (b) sampling errors—differences occasioned by fluctuation from sample to sample. A decrease in σ or an increase in N will cause the standard error to become smaller numerically. A decrease in σ_M means that the amount by which the obtained mean *probably* misses the mean of the population is just so much less. In short, the reliability of a sample mean *increases* as σ_M decreases.

184 • STATISTICS IN PSYCHOLOGY AND EDUCATION

(2) APPLICATION AND USE OF THE SE OF THE MEAN

A problem will serve to illustrate the use and interpretation of the SE of the mean.

Example (1) In 1883, the Anthropometric Committee of the British Association found the mean height of 8585 adult males in the British Isles to be 67.46 inches, with a SD of 2.57 inches. How reliable is this measure of mean height? Specifically, how much does it probably diverge from the true mean (parameter) which might have been obtained had *all* adult males in the British Isles been measured?

We cannot answer this question precisely as the value of the true mean is, of course, unknown. But we can give an estimate of reliability in terms of the *probable divergence* of our mean from the TM (true mean). Applying formula (39), we find the SE_M to be

$$\sigma_M = \frac{2.57}{\sqrt{8585}} = .028 \text{ inch}$$

This SE * approximates to the SD of a distribution of means which like our mean of 67.46 inches are all derived from samples drawn from the common population. The normal curve in Figure 42 repre-

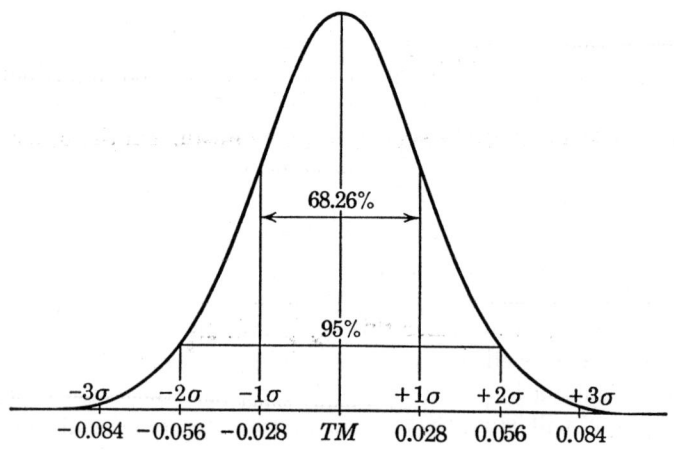

FIG. 42 Sampling distribution of means showing variability of obtained means around the true or population mean (TM) in terms of σ_M (.028)

---

* Our σ of 2.57 inches is our best *estimate* of the population σ (see p. 190) and hence is used as our closest approximation to it.

sents this distribution of sample means: it is centered at the hypothetical true mean (TM) and its SD (σ_M) is .028 inch. Sample means fall equally often on the plus and minus sides of the TM. About two-thirds of such means (actually 68.26%) lie within $\pm 1.0\sigma_M$ of the TM, that is, within a range of $\pm$ .028 inch. Also, 95 out of 100 sample means lie within $\pm$ 2.0 σ_M (more exactly $\pm$ 1.96 σ_M) of the true mean; and accordingly miss the TM by not more than $\pm$ .055 inch ($\pm$ 1.96 $\times$ .028).

Our mean of 67.46 inches is, of course, *one* of the sample means represented in the sampling distribution of Figure 42. Hence the probability is high ($P = .95$) that 67.46 inches (or *any* sample mean) does *not* miss the population mean (the parameter) by more than $\pm$ .055 inch. And conversely, the probability is .05 (one chance in 20) that 67.46 inches *does* miss the TM by *more* than $\pm$ .055 inch. Both of these statements are estimates of the reliability of our sample mean in terms of its probable divergence from the population mean. Deviations from the TM which are less likely of occurrence than those listed above may be computed by taking into account more of the sampling distribution of means in Figure 42.

Discussion

How the standard error measures the reliaoility or stability of an obtained mean may be more clearly shown perhaps in the following way: Suppose that we have calculated the mean height of each of 100 groups of men; that each group contains 8585 subjects; and that the groups or samples are drawn at random from the general population. The 100 means obtained from these samples will tend to differ slightly from one another owing to "errors of sampling," or sampling fluctuations. Hence, not all samples will represent with equal fidelity the population from which they have been drawn. It can be shown mathematically that the frequency distribution of these sample means will fall into a normal distribution around the "true" or population mean as their measure of central tendency. Even when the *samples* are themselves skewed, the *means* from such samples will be normally distributed. This "sampling distribution" of means measures the errors of sampling or fluctuations in mean values from sample to sample. In this hypothetical normal distribution of means we find relatively few *large* plus or minus deviations; and many *small* plus, *small* minus, and *zero* deviations. In short, the obtained means will hit very near to the true mean, or fairly close to it, more often than they will miss it by large amounts.

The mean of our distribution of 100 means is our best estimate of the "true" or population mean. And our best estimate of the σ of this distribution of means is the standard error of the mean which we have calculated. In other words, σ_M measures the spread of sample means around the true or population mean. It is because of this fact that the standard error of the mean becomes a measure of the amount by which *any* sample mean *probably diverges* from the population mean.

The results of our hypothetical experiment are represented graphically in Figure 42, page 184. The 100 sample means are represented by a normal frequency distribution around the TM (true mean) and σ_M is put equal to .028. The heights of the different ordinates (y's) represent the frequency of the various sample means. The σ of a normal distribution when measured off in the plus and minus directions from the mean includes the middle 68.26% of the cases. About 68 of our 100 obtained means, therefore, may be expected to miss the TM by not *more* than $\pm 1\sigma_M$ ($\pm .028$ inch); and about 95 of our obtained means may be expected to miss the TM by not more than $\pm 2\sigma_M$ ($\pm .056$ inch). Since our mean of 67.46 inches is *one* of these sample means the probability is approximately .95 that 67.46 inches does not miss the true mean by more than $\pm .056$ inch.

(3) DEFINING RELIABILITY IN TERMS OF LEVELS OF CONFIDENCE

The definition of reliability in terms of the "probable divergence of statistic from parameter" is straightforward and reasonable as it is evident that confidence can be placed in an obtained mean if there is small likelihood of its having missed its true value by a large amount. An obvious difficulty with probability statements concerning reliability, however, arises from our inability to say how far the sample mean must miss the TM before the expected deviation is to be judged "large." The sampling error allowable in a mean will always depend upon the purpose of the experiment, the standards of accuracy demanded, the units of measurement employed and other factors.* An experimenter can never say categorically that a computed mean is—or is not—reliable, as reliability is a relative, not an absolute, concept. But he can set up *accuracy limits* which will mark off for a given degree of probability the deviation of computed mean from TM. Degree of confidence in the stability of a given statistic will then depend upon the accuracy limits imposed.

Two sets of accuracy limits are in general use and have been accepted as standard by most investigators. These limits define what are called the .05 and .01 *levels of confidence*. How level of confidence in a mean or other statistic is dependent upon the accuracy limits chosen may be shown in the following way. The sampling distribution of a mean computed from any fairly large random sample will be normal or nearly normal (see Fig. 42). In a normal distribution, 95% of the cases (Table A) fall between $\pm$ 1.96 σ_M so

* Garrett, H. E., "Mean Differences and Individual Differences," *Human Biology*, 1943, 15. 155–170.

that the odds are 19:1 that *any* sample mean will lie within these limits. Furthermore, 99% of the cases in a normal distribution fall between $\pm 2.58\ \sigma_M$ and the odds are 99:1 that any sample mean will lie within these limits. Conversely, 5% of the means can be expected to lie outside the limits $\pm 1.96\ \sigma_M$ and 1% outside of the limits $\pm 2.58\ \sigma_M$.

These two intervals ($\pm 1.96\ \sigma_M$ and $\pm 2.58\ \sigma_M$) constitute, then, ranges or accuracy limits within which, for a known probability, our sample mean will fall. Our faith in these limits is expressed by saying that we may be "confident at the .05 level" that our M lies in the range $TM \pm 1.96\ \sigma_M$; and "confident at the .01 level" that our mean lies in the range $TM \pm 2.58\ \sigma_M$. We can expect to be wrong 5% of the time if we take the .05 level and 1% of the time if we take the .01 level. These levels .05 and .01 reflect degrees of assurance, therefore, the .01 level deserving greater respect than the .05.

We may illustrate the concept of confidence levels by reference to Example (1), p. 184. Taking the $\pm 2.58\ \sigma_M$ accuracy limits, we may be confident at the .01 level that 67.46 inches does not deviate from the TM by more than $\pm .07$ inch ($\pm 2.58 \times .028$). The expectation of an error of $\pm .07$ inch or more in our sample mean is expressed by a probability of .01. It is extremely doubtful whether our measuring instrument for height could detect an error of the order $\pm .07$ inch. Therefore, an experimenter would be clearly justified in taking the sample mean of 67.46 inches (with an SE of .028 inch) as highly stable and deserving of great confidence.

(4) ESTABLISHING CONFIDENCE-INTERVALS FOR THE TM

So far we have discussed reliability in terms of the probable divergence of sample mean from TM. Another approach to the problem of how best to describe the reliability of a statistic is through the setting up of limits which for a given level of confidence will embrace the TM. Such limits are said to define <u>confidence-intervals</u>. The method of establishing such intervals is as follows. It is clear from Figure 43 that in our sampling distribution of mean heights, $TM \pm 3\sigma_M$ provides reasonable limits within which nearly *all* (actually 99.97%) of our sample means can be expected to lie. Since the TM itself is unknown, all that we can infer with respect to this parameter is that it could take a range of values—one of which is the given sample mean. Suppose we take $\pm 3\sigma_M$ as a fairly inclusive working range (Fig. 43). Then if our M falls at the tentative upper limit of the sampling distribution, $TM = M - 3\ \sigma_M$; while if

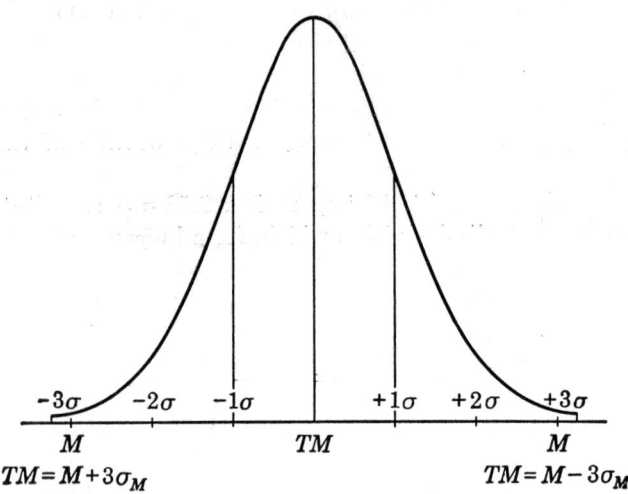

FIG. 43 When M falls at $+3\sigma_M$, $TM = M - 3\sigma_M$; when M falls at $-3\sigma_M$, $TM = M + 3\sigma_M$

M falls at the tentative lower limit of the sampling distribution, $TM = M + 3\sigma_M$. These relations are shown graphically in Figure 43. Since $\pm 3 \sigma_M$ in a normal distribution include 99.97% of the cases, the limits specified by $M \pm 3 \sigma_M$ are said to define the 99.97% confidence-interval. Evidently, we may feel confident to a degree approaching certainty that the TM lies within this range.

Intervals which portray other degrees of confidence can be set up in the same way. We know that 95% of the cases in a normal distribution fall within the limits $\pm 1.96 \sigma_M$ and that 99% fall within the limits $\pm 2.58 \sigma_M$ (Table A). If we take the limits specified by $M \pm 1.96 \sigma_M$, we define the 95% confidence-interval for the TM. Basing our judgment on these limits, in a long series of experiments we stand to be right 95% of the time and wrong 5%. For still greater assurance, we may take the limits $M \pm 2.58 \sigma_M$, which define the 99% confidence-interval for the TM.

Let us apply the concept of confidence-intervals to the problem of heights on page 184. Taking as our limits $M \pm 1.96 \sigma_M$, we have $67.46 \pm 1.96 \times .028$ or a confidence-interval limited by the points 67.41 and 67.51. If we say that this interval contains the TM the probability of our being right is .95, of our being wrong .05. If we desire a higher degree of assurance, we can take the 99% confidence-interval. Here the limiting points are 67.39 and 67.53 (i.e., 67.46 ± 2.58 × .028). Our faith that these limits contain the TM is expressed by a probability of .99.

It may seem to many students that use of the confidence-interval is an exceedingly roundabout way of making an inference concerning the population mean; that it would be much more straightforward to say "the chances are 95 in 100 that the TM lies between 67.41 and 67.51." Such probability statements concerning the value of the TM are often made and lead to what appears to be virtually the same result as that given above in terms of confidence-intervals. Theoretically, however, such inferences regarding the TM are definitely incorrect, as the TM is *not* a variable which can take several values but is a fixed point. The TM has only *one* value and the probability that it equals some given figure is always either 100% or zero—right or wrong. Our probability figures (e.g., .95 or .99) do not relate to our confidence that the TM itself could take one of several values within the given range. Rather, the probability used in specifying confidence-intervals is an expression of our confidence in the *inference*, namely, of our confidence that the *given interval* includes the TM. This is a subtle point, but a valid one.

The limits of the confidence-interval of a parameter (TM) have been called by Fisher * *fiduciary limits*, and the confidence to be placed in the fiducial limits as containing the given parameter is called *fiduciary probability*. In terms of fiduciary probability, the reliability of an obtained mean could be stated as follows: "The fiduciary probability is .95 that the true mean lies in the interval $M \pm 1.96\ \sigma_M$, .05 that it lies outside these limits."

(5) THE SE OF THE MEAN IN SMALL SAMPLES

It can be shown mathematically that the SD of a sample systematically underestimates (is *smaller* than) the population σ, although this underestimation is not severe unless the samples are quite small.† To correct this tendency toward negative bias, we must compute the standard deviation of a small sample by the formula $\sigma' = \sqrt{\dfrac{\Sigma x^2}{(N-1)}}$ rather than by the usual formula, $\sigma = \sqrt{\dfrac{\Sigma x^2}{N}}$ (p. 51).

---

* Fisher, R. A., *The Design of Experiments* (London: Oliver and Boyd, 1935), pp. 200 f.
† Holtzman, W. H., "The Unbiased Estimate of the Population Variance and Standard Deviation," *Amer. Jour. Psychol.*, 1950, 63, 615–617.

When N is less than 50 or so (some statisticians say 30) the formula for the SE of the mean should read

$$\sigma_M = \frac{\sigma'}{\sqrt{N}} \qquad (40)\ *$$

(*standard error of the mean in small samples*)

where $\sigma' = \sqrt{\dfrac{\Sigma x^2}{(N-1)}}$ and $N =$ number of cases in the sample.

Formula (40) *always* provides the best estimate of the SE of the mean, i.e., of the SD of the sampling distributions of means (Fig. 42, p. 184), no matter what the size of N. In very large samples, however, the correction effected by using (40) is so slight as to be negligible and formula (39) may be safely used. When N is less than 50 it is advisable to use the more exact formula, and it is imperative that we do so when N is quite small—less than 10, say.

When we are dealing with small samples, the normal distribution

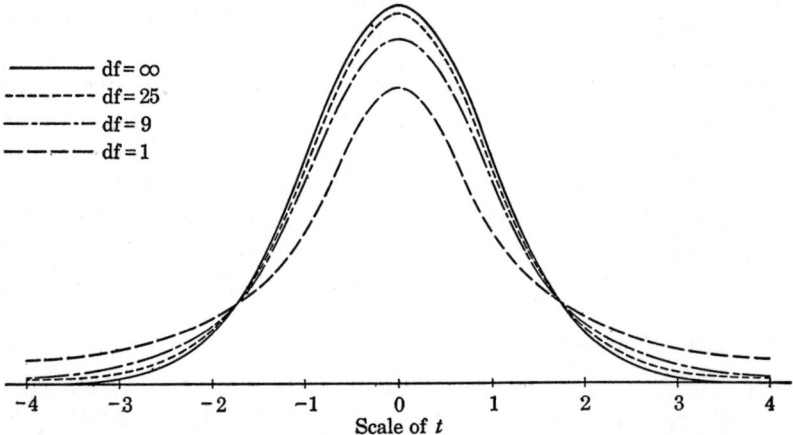

FIG. 44 Distribution of *t* for degrees of freedom from 1 to ∞. When *df* is very large, the distribution of *t* is virtually normal

[After Lewis, D., *Quantitative Methods in Psychology* (Iowa City, 1948), p. 188.]

* If the SD of the sample has been computed by the formula $\sigma = \sqrt{\dfrac{\Sigma x^2}{N}}$, we can make the same correction in σ_M as that given in formula (40) by using the formula $\sigma_M = \dfrac{\sigma}{\sqrt{(N-1)}}$.

no longer tells us accurately the amount by which a statistic probably diverges from its parameter. The sampling distribution to be used when N is small is not as tall as the normal curve and the "tails" or ends are somewhat higher. Figure 44 shows graphically how this distribution—called the t-distribution or "Student's"[*] distribution—compares with the normal. The student should note that the t-distribution does not differ greatly from the normal unless N is quite small; and that as N increases in size the t-distribution approaches more and more closely to the normal form. In the case of the sampling distribution of the mean, $t = \dfrac{(M - TM)}{SE_M}$ or $\pm \dfrac{x}{\sigma_M}$; that is, t is essentially a σ-score (p. 305).

Selected points in the t-distribution are given in Table D. For N's increasing in size, this table gives $\pm t$ distances *beyond* which (i.e., to the left *and* right) certain percentages of the sampling distribution lie. These percents are .10, .05, .02, and .01. An illustration will make clear the use of Table D in small samples and will introduce the new concept "degrees of freedom" (see p. 193).

Example (2) Ten measures of reaction time to a light stimulus are taken from one practiced Observer. The mean is 175.50 ms and the σ′ is 5.82 ms. How reliable is this mean?

From formula (40) we find that $\sigma_M = \dfrac{5.82}{\sqrt{10}}$ or 1.84 ms. By definition, $t = \dfrac{(M - TM)}{SE_M}$ or in the present case, $t = \dfrac{175.50 - TM}{1.84}$. We do not know, of course, the value of the TM in the t-equation; but if we know the proper number of degrees of freedom we can determine the value of t at selected points in the t-distribution. The df (degrees of freedom) available for evaluating the given t are $(N - 1)$ or 9. Entering Table D with 9 df we read that $t = 2.26$ at the .05 point and 3.25 at the .01. From the first t we know that 95% of sample means like 175.50 ms, the mean we have, lie between the TM and $\pm 2.26\sigma_M$ and that 5% fall outside these limits. From the second t we know that 99% of our sample means lie between the population mean and $\pm 3.25\sigma_M$ and that 1% falls outside these limits. We may be confident at the .05 level, therefore, that our mean of 175.50 ms does not differ from its parameter (TM) by more than ± 4.16 ms

---

[*] "Student" was the pseudonym of W. S. Gosset who developed the t-distribution. See Walker, Helen M., *Elementary Statistical Method* (New York: **Henry Holt and Co.**, 1943), p. 159.

($\pm 2.26 \times 1.84$); and we may be confident at the .01 level that our mean does not miss the TM by more than ± 5.98 ms ($\pm 3.25 \times 1.84$).

Confidence-intervals may also be established for the TM in this problem by the methods of page 187. Taking as our limits $M \pm 2.26\sigma_M$, we have 175.50 ± 4.16 or 171.34–179.66 as indicating the limits of our .95 confidence-interval. Or taking $M \pm 3.25\sigma_M$ as broader limits, we have 175.50 ± 5.98 or 169.52–181.48 as marking off our .99 confidence-interval. If we infer that the population mean lies within the latter interval, in a long series of experiments we stand to be right 99% and wrong 1% of the time. The width of the .99 confidence-interval (11.96) shows clearly the high unreliability likely to exist in a mean when our estimate is based upon a very small sample.

Several points in the solution of this problem deserve further comment as they illustrate clearly the difference between confidence levels in large and small samples. Had we used formula (39) in Example (2) instead of the correct formula (40), the SE of our mean would have been 1.75 ms instead of 1.84 ms, 5% too small. Again, the .05 and .01 confidence levels in the normal curve are ± 1.96 and ± 2.58 (p. 187). These limits are 15% and 20% smaller than the correct t-limits of ± 2.26 and ± 3.25 read from Table D for 9 df. It is clear, therefore, that when N is quite small, use of formula (39) will cause a calculated mean to appear more accurate than it actually is.

The SE of the mean in the height problem on page 184 was $\dfrac{2.57}{\sqrt{8585}}$ or .028 inch. The student should note that had formula (40) and Table D been used in determining the reliability of the obtained mean of 67.46 inches, results would not have differed to the third decimal from those got with formula (39) and Table A. This is true, of course, because the N of 8585 is very large. As N increases (see Fig. 44), t-entries in Table D approach more and more closely the corresponding normal curve deviates in Table A. In the normal curve, for instance (see Table A), 10% of the distribution lie *beyond* the limits ± 1.65, 5% beyond the limits ± 1.96, and 1% beyond the limits ± 2.58. In Table D the corresponding t-limits for $(N-1) = 50$, are ± 1.68, ± 2.01, ± 2.68. For $(N-1) = 100$, these limits are ± 1.66, ± 1.98, ± 2.63. When N is very large (see last entry in Table D) the t-distribution becomes a normal curve. It is only when N is less than about 50, say, that the t-distribution diverges markedly from the normal. As research workers in the social sciences rarely use groups smaller than 50, small-sample statistics are not as generally useful in psychology and education as they are in biology and agriculture.*

(6) DEGREES OF FREEDOM

The concept of "degrees of freedom" which we have encountered on pages 191–192 is highly important in small-sample statistics. It is crucial, too, in analysis of variance and will appear increasingly often in later chapters. The degrees of freedom (df) available for evaluating a statistic depend upon the number of restrictions placed upon the observations—one df being lost for each restriction imposed. Where one restriction comes from can best be shown by a simple example. If we have five scores, 5, 6, 7, 8, and 9, the M is 7; and the deviations of these scores around 7 are $-2, -1, 0, 1$, and 2. The sum of these deviations is zero.† While there are 5 deviations, only 4 of these $[(N-1)]$ can be freely selected as the condition that the sum of the deviations equals zero immediately fixes the fifth deviation. When there are N independent scores, there are N degress of freedom for computing the M, but only $(N-1)$ df available for the SD since this statistic is computed from deviations taken around the M. In Example (2), page 191, the df available for determining the reliability of the M were given as $(N-1)$ or 9: one less than the number of observations (i.e., 10). Since one df was lost in computing the M only $(N-1)$ are left for estimating the reliability of the M by way of the SD and the t-ratio.

Our best estimate of the true (or population) σ (see p. 190) is obtained by using $(N-1)$ instead of N in the formula for the σ; that is, by taking due account of the restriction imposed through calculation of the M. It is quite important that we take df into account when N is small; unimportant practically that we do so when N is large (p. 192). In general the number of degrees of freedom available at any given time equals N minus the number of parameters already estimated from the N observations (each parameter adds a restriction). M is the only parameter estimated before computing the SD, and accordingly the df available in Example (2) were $(N-1)$. The number of df is not always $(N-1)$, however, but will vary with the statistic. In determining confidence levels for r, for example, the available df are $(N-2)$. Two df are lost, one restriction being im-

---

* Snedecor, George W., *Statistical Methods* (4th ed.; Ames, Iowa: Iowa State College Press, 1946), Chaps. 3 and 8.
† $\Sigma(X-M)$ or Σx (calculation algebraic) is always zero.

posed for the M of Y (the dependent variable) and another for the regression coefficient b, which describes the relation between Y and X.* Rules for determining the df available in the Chi-square test and in analysis of variance tables are given in appropriate places in later chapters.

2. The reliability of the median

The standard error of the median is roughly 5/4 times σ_M. In terms of σ and Q, the SE's of the median are

$$\sigma_{Mdn} = \frac{1.253\sigma}{\sqrt{N}} \tag{41}$$

$$\sigma_{Mdn} = \frac{1.858Q}{\sqrt{N}} \tag{42}$$

(*standard error of the median in terms of σ and of Q*)

An example will illustrate the use of formula (42).

Example (3) On the Trabue Language Scale A, 801 twelve-year-old boys made the following record: Median $= 21.40$; $Q = 4.9$. How reliable is this median? How well does it represent the median of twelve-year-old boys in general on the given scale?

By formula (42) the $\sigma_{Mdn} = \dfrac{1.858 \times 4.9}{\sqrt{801}}$ or .32. Since N is quite large, accuracy limits may be taken at ± 1.96 and ± 2.58 (last line of Table D). We may be confident at the .05 level that the median of 21.40 does not miss the population median by more than $\pm 1.96 \times .32$ or $\pm .63$; and confident at the .01 level that 21.40 does not differ from the true median by more than $\pm 2.58 \times .32$ or by $\pm .83$. The .99 confidence-interval for the true median is $21.40 \pm .83$ or from 20.57 to 22.23. This very narrow range (for which the $P = .99$) indicates high stability in the computed median.

III. The Reliability of Measures of Variability

1. The reliability of the standard deviation

The reliability of the SD, like the reliability of the mean and median, is determined by calculating the probable discrepancy be-

* See page 154.

tween the obtained SD and its parameter (true or population SD). The formula for the SE of the σ is

$$SE_\sigma \text{ or } \sigma_\sigma = \frac{.71\sigma}{\sqrt{N}} \qquad (43)$$

(*standard error of a standard deviation*)

The sampling distribution of σ is skewed for small samples (N less than 25, say). When samples are large, however (greater than 100), and have been drawn at random from a normal population, formula (43) may be applied and interpreted in the same way as SE_M. To illustrate, we found on page 184 that for 8585 British males, the SD around the M of 67.46 inches was 2.57 inches. By formula (43) $\sigma_\sigma = \frac{2.57 \times .71}{\sqrt{8585}}$ or .02 inch. Since N is large, the .99 confidence-interval for the true or population SD can be taken as $\sigma \pm 2.58\sigma_\sigma$. Substituting for σ and σ_σ we have $2.57 \pm 2.58 \times .02$ or 2.52—2.62 as our .99 confidence-interval. If we proceed on the assumption that the true SD lies within this range we will—in a long series of experiments—be right 99% and wrong 1% of the time.

It is not often that we are called upon to compute the SE of σ in small samples. This is fortunate, as there is no very efficient way of estimating the reliability of σ when the sample is small.

2. The reliability of the quartile deviation or Q

The reliability of Q may be found from the formulas

$$\sigma_Q = \frac{.786\sigma}{\sqrt{N}} \qquad (44)$$

and

$$\sigma_Q = \frac{1.17Q}{\sqrt{N}} \qquad (45)$$

(*standard error of Q in terms of σ and of Q*)

These formulas are applied and interpreted as are the other SE formulas. On page 194, for example, the median of the 801 twelve-year-old boys who took the Trabue Completion Test was 21.40 with a Q of 4.9. The SE of this Q by (45) is $\frac{1.17 \times 4.9}{\sqrt{801}}$ or .20. The .95 confidence-interval for the true or population Q may be taken as 4.5 to 5.3, i.e., $4.9 \pm 1.96 \times .20$. The narrow range of the .95 confidence-interval indicates high stability.

IV. The Reliability of Percentages and Correlation Coefficients

This section will consider the computation and use of the SE's of a percentage and a correlation coefficient. For the SE's of other statistics the student should go to the more advanced references. *The Handbook of Statistical Nomographs, Tables and Formulas*, by Dunlap and Kurtz (World Book Co., 1932), contains many formulas helpful in research.

1. The reliability of a percentage

It is often feasible to find the percentage of a given group which exhibits certain behaviors or possesses certain definite attitudes or other characteristics when it is difficult or impossible to measure these attributes directly. Given the percentage occurrence of a behavior the question often arises of how much confidence we can place in our figure. How reliable an index is it of the incidence of the behavior in which we are interested? To answer this question, we must go to the SE of the percentage given by the formula

$$\sigma_\% = \sqrt{\frac{PQ}{N}} \qquad (46)$$

(SE *of a percentage*)

in which P = the percentage occurrence of the behavior, $Q = 1 - P$, and N is the number of cases.

We may illustrate formula (46) with the following problem.

Example (1) In a study of cheating among elementary school children, 144 or 41.4% of 348 children from homes of good socio-economic status were found to have cheated on the various tests. Assuming our sample to be representative of children from "good" social levels, how much confidence can be put in this percentage? How well does it represent the population or true percentage?

Applying formula (46) we get that $\sigma_\% = \sqrt{\dfrac{41.4\% \times 58.6\%}{348}}$ = 2.7%. The sampling distribution of percents can be taken as normal when N is large (larger than 50, say) and when P is not too close to 0% or 100%. The SE is interpreted like σ_M. Thus in the present problem the .99 confidence-interval for the population percentage is

THE RELIABILITY OF THE MEAN AND OF OTHER STATISTICS • 197

41.4% ± 2.58 × 2.7 or from 34.4% to 48.4%. We may feel sure, therefore, that the percentage of children who will cheat in samples of this sort is at least as large as 34.4 and not larger than 48.4. The *SE* of a percentage finds its chief use in problems in which the significance of the difference between two percentages is to be determined (p. 236).

2. The reliability of the coefficient of correlation (*r*)

(1) THE *SE* OF *r*

The classical * formula for the *SE* of *r* is

$$\sigma_r = \frac{(1 - r^2)}{\sqrt{N}} \qquad (47)$$

(SE *of a coefficient of correlation* r *when* N *is large*)

In the height-weight problem on page 129, $r = .60$ and $N = 120$. The *SE* of *r* by formula (47), therefore, is $\frac{(1 - .60^2)}{\sqrt{120}}$ or .06 (to two decimals). To test the reliability of *r* in terms of its *SE*, we assume the sampling distribution of *r* to be normal, place the "true r" at the center (Fig. 45) of the distribution, and take .06 (i.e., SE_r) to be the

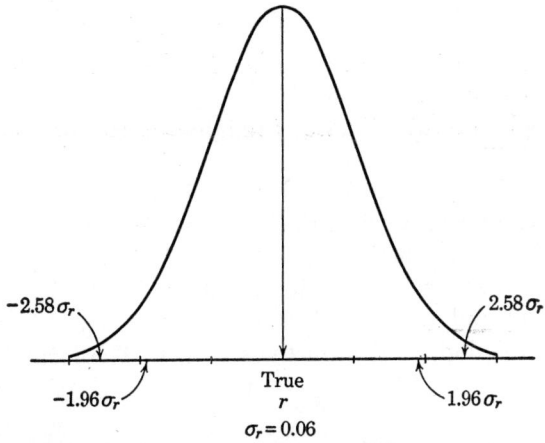

FIG. 45 There are 95 chances in 100 that the obtained *r* does not miss the true *r* by more than $\pm.12 (\pm 1.96\sigma_r)$. The .99 confidence-interval for the true *r* is $r \pm 2.58\sigma_r$ or $.60 \pm .15$, i.e., .45 to .75

* Yule, G. Udny, *An Introduction to the Theory of Statistics* (10th ed.; London: Charles Griffin and Co., 1932), p. 352.

SD of this sampling distribution of r's. Since the probability is .05 of an error exceeding $\pm 1.96\sigma_r$, there is only one chance in 20 that an error of $\pm.12$ or more exists in our r. Again, the .99 confidence interval for the true r can be taken as $r \pm 2.58\sigma_r$. Substituting for r and SE, we get .45 and .75 as the limits of our .99 confidence-interval. It would seem reasonably certain, therefore, that r is at least as large as .45.

There are two serious objections to the use of formula (47). In the first place, the r in the formula is really the true or population r. Since we do not have the true r, we must substitute the calculated or sample r in the formula in order to get an estimate of the standard error. If the obtained r is in error, our estimate will also be in error; and at best it is approximate.

In the second place, the sampling distribution of r is not normal except when the population r is .00 and N is large. When r is high (.80 or more, say) and N is small, the sampling distribution of r is skewed and the SE from (47) is decidedly misleading. Skewness in the sampling distribution of high r's grows out of the fact that the range of r is from $+1.00$ to -1.00. If $r = .80$ and $N = 20$, the probability of an r less than .80 in a new sample of 20 cases is much greater than the probability of an r greater than .80 because of the obtained r's nearness to unity. The distribution of r's obtained from successive samples of 20 cases will be skewed negatively (p. 98) and the skewness will increase as r increases. For values of r, between $\pm.50$, and for N's of 100 or more, the distribution of r in successive samples will conform fairly closely to the normal curve and formula (47) will yield a useful estimate of reliability. But unless used with caution, SE_r is likely to be misleading.

A mathematically more defensible method of testing the significance of an r, especially when the coefficient is high, is to convert r into R. A. Fisher's z-function * and find the SE of z. The function z has two advantages over r: (1) its sampling distribution is approximately normal and (2) its SE depends only upon the size of the sample N, and is independent of the size of r. The formula for σ_z is

$$\sigma_z = \frac{1}{\sqrt{N-3}} \qquad (48)$$

(SE *of Fisher's function* z)

Suppose that $r = .85$, and $N = 52$. Then from Table C we read

* Fisher, R. A., *Statistical Methods for Research Workers* (8th ed.; London: Oliver and Boyd, 1941), pp. 190–203.

that an r of .85 corresponds to a z of 1.26. SE_z from (48) is $\dfrac{1}{\sqrt{52-3}}$ or .14. The .95 confidence-interval for the true z is now .99 to 1.53 (i.e., $1.26 \pm 1.96 \times .14$ or $1.26 \pm .27$). Converting these z's back into r's we get a confidence-interval of from .76 to .91. The fiduciary probability is .95 that this interval contains the true r (p. 189).

The coefficient of correlation .60 in the height-weight problem above is not large enough for the conversion into z to make much difference in our reliability estimates. An r of .60 is equivalent to a z of .69 (Table C), and the SE_z is $\dfrac{1}{\sqrt{120-3}}$ or .09 (to two decimals). The .99 confidence-interval for the true z, therefore, is .46 to .92 (i.e., $.69 \pm 2.58 \times .09$ or $.69 \pm .23$). When we convert these z's back into r's the .99 confidence-interval for the true r becomes .43 to .73. This range is almost identical with that on page 198 obtained when we used r and SE_r.

(2) TESTING r AGAINST THE NULL HYPOTHESIS

The reliability of an obtained r may be tested also against the

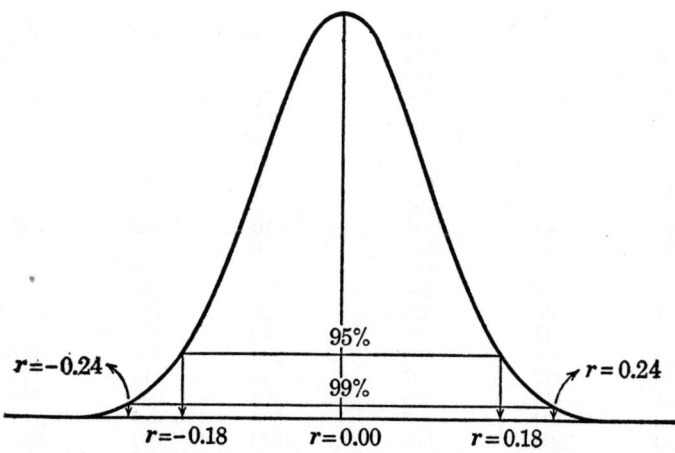

FIG. 46 When the population r is zero, and $df = 118$, 5% of the sample r's exceed $\pm.18$, and 1% exceeds $\pm.24$

hypothesis that the population r is in fact zero.* If the computed r is large enough to invalidate or cast serious doubt upon this null hypothesis we accept r as indicating the presence of at least some

* See page 213 for definition of null hypothesis.

degree of correlation. To make the test, enter Table 25 with $(N-2)$ degrees of freedom * and compare the obtained r with the tabulated entries. Two significance levels, .05 and .01, are given in Table 25, which is read as follows when, for example, $r = .60$ and $N = 120$. For 118 df the entries at .05 and .01 are by linear interpolation .18 and .24, respectively (to two decimals). This means that only 5 times in 100 trials would an r as large as $\pm.18$ arise from fluctuations of sampling, *if* the population r were actually .00; and only once in 100 trials would an r of $\pm.24$ appear if the population r were in fact .00 (Fig. 46). It is clear that the obtained r of .60, since it is much larger than .24, is significant at the .01 level.

TABLE 25 † Correlation coefficients at the 5% and 1% levels of significance

Example: When N is 52 and df is 50, an r must be .273 to be significant at .05 level, and .354 to be significant at .01 level.

Degrees of freedom $(N-2)$	.05	.01	Degrees of freedom $(N-2)$	.05	.01
1	.997	1.000	24	.388	.496
2	.950	.990	25	.381	.487
3	.878	.959	26	.374	.478
4	.811	.917	27	.367	.470
5	.754	.874	28	.361	.463
6	.707	.834	29	.355	.456
7	.666	.798	30	.349	.449
8	.632	.765	35	.325	.418
9	.602	.735	40	.304	.393
10	.576	.708	45	.288	.372
11	.553	.684	50	.273	.354
12	.532	.661	60	.250	.325
13	.514	.641	70	.232	.302
14	.497	.623	80	.217	.283
15	.482	.606	90	.205	.267
16	.468	.590	100	.195	.254
17	.456	.575	125	.174	.228
18	.444	.561	150	.159	.208
19	.433	.549	200	.138	.181
20	.423	.537	300	.113	.148
21	.413	.526	400	.098	.128
22	.404	.515	500	.088	.115
23	.396	.505	1000	.062	.081

Table 25 takes account of *both* ends of the sampling distribution—does not consider the sign of r. When $N = 120$, the probability $(P/2)$ of an r of .18 or more arising on the null hypothesis is .025; and the

* Page 193.
† This table is abstracted from the column for 2 variables in Table J, page 437.

probability of an r of $-.18$ or less is, of course, .025 also. For a $P/2$ of .01 (or P of .02) the r by linear interpolation between .05 (.18) and .01 (.24) is .21. On the hypothesis of a population r of zero, therefore, only once in 100 trials would a *positive* r of .21 or larger arise through accidents of sampling.

The .05 and .01 levels in Table 25 are the only ones needed ordinarily in evaluating the significance of an obtained r. Several illustrations of the use of Table 25 in determining significance are given below:

Size of Sample (N)	Degrees of Freedom ($N-2$)	Calculated r	Interpretation
10	8	.70	significant at .05, not at .01 level
152	150	$-.12$	not significant
27	25	.50	significant at .05, barely at .01 level
500	498	.20	very significant
100	98	$-.30$	very significant

It is clear from these examples that even a small r may be significant if computed from a very large sample, and that an r as high as .70 may not be significant if N is quite small. Table 25 is especially useful when N is small. Suppose that we have found an r of .55 from a sample of 12 cases. Entering Table 25 with $(N-2)$ or 10 df we find that r must be .71 to be significant at the .01 level and .58 to be significant at the .05 level. In this small sample, therefore, even an r as high as .55 cannot be taken as indicative of any real correlation.

V. Sampling and the Use of Reliability Formulas

All of the reliability formulas given in this chapter depend upon N, the size of the sample, and most of them require some measure of variability (usually σ). It is unfortunate, perhaps, that there is nothing in the *statement* of an *SE* formula which might deter the uncritical worker from applying it to the statistics calculated from any set of test scores. But the general and indiscriminate computation of *SE*'s will inevitably lead to erroneous conclusions and false interpretations. Hence, it is highly important that the research worker in experimental psychology and in educational research have clearly in mind (1) the conditions under which reliability formulas are (and are not) applicable; and that he know (2) what his reliability formulas may be reasonably expected to do. Some of the limitations to reliability formulas have been given in this chapter. These statements will now be amplified and further cautions to be observed in the use of SE's will be indicated.

1. Methods of sampling

Various techniques have been devised for obtaining a sample which will be representative of its population. The adequacy of a sample (i.e., its lack of bias) will depend upon our knowledge of the population or supply * as well as upon the method used in drawing the sample. Commonly used sampling methods will be described in this section under four headings: *random, stratified* or *quota, incidental,* and *purposive.*

(1) RANDOM SAMPLING

The descriptive term "random" is often misunderstood. It does not imply that the sample has been chosen in an offhand, careless or haphazard fashion. Instead it means that we rely upon a certain method of selection (called "random") to provide an unbiased cross section of the larger group or population. The criteria for randomness in a sample are met when (1) every individual (or animal or thing) in the population or supply has the same chance of being chosen for the sample; and (2) when the selection of one individual or thing in no way influences the choice of another. Randomness in a sample is assured when we draw similar and well shaken-up slips out of a hat; or numbers in a lottery (provided it is honest); or a hand from a carefully shuffled deck of cards. In each of these cases selection is made in terms of some mechanical process and is not subject to the whims or biases (if any) of the experimenter.

A clear distinction should be made between representative and random samples. A representative sample is one in which the distribution of scores in the sample closely parallels that of the population. Experience has shown that if one is asked to get representative samples from a population he will for various reasons (some not recognized) often draw samples which exhibit consistent biases of one sort or another. The most trustworthy way of securing representativeness, therefore, is to make sure that the sampling is random. If we draw samples at random from the population we know at least

* A supply usually means a population of objects or things.

that (a) there will be no *consistent* biases; (b) *on the average* these samples will be representative; (c) the degree of discrepancy likely to occur in any given sample can be determined by probability methods. The SE formulas given in this chapter apply *only* to random samples.

In research problems in psychology and in education three situations arise in connection with the drawing of a random sample: (a) the members of the population or supply are on file or have been catalogued in some way; (b) the form of the distribution of the trait in the population is known to be (or can reasonably be assumed to be) normal; (c) the population is known only in general terms. These situations will be discussed in order.

(a) *Members of population are on file or are catalogued.* If the population has been accurately listed, a type of systematic selection will provide what is approximately a random sample. Thus we may take every fifth or tenth name (depending upon the size of the sample wanted) in a long list, provided names have been put in alphabetical order and are not arranged with respect to some differential factor, such as age, income or education. (A better plan in such cases is to assign numbers to the members of the population and draw a sample as described below.) By this method an approximately random sample of telephone users may be obtained by reference to the telephone directory; of sixth grade children from attendance rolls; of automobile owners from the licensing bureau; of workers in a factory from payroll lists. Random samples of the population with respect to a variety of characteristics may be drawn in the same way from census data.

Systematic selection from a catalogued population is often used in determining the acceptance rate of industrial products. Thus in sampling machine-produced articles for defectives, a random sample may be obtained by taking every tenth article, say, as it comes from the machine. Sampling of this sort is justified if the manufactured articles are taken just as they come from the machine, so that systematic selection provides an approximately random sample from the supply.

When the subjects in a group are to be assigned at random to one or more experimental and control sub-groups, tables of random numbers may be used to good purpose.* In such tables, numbers arranged

---

* Fisher, R. A., and Yates, F., *Statistical Tables* (New York: Hafner Publishing Co., 1948), Table 33.

204 • STATISTICS IN PSYCHOLOGY AND EDUCATION

by a chance procedure are printed in sequence. The tenth block of 25 numbers taken from Fisher's and Yates' Table and reproduced below will serve as an example.

34	50	57	74	37
85	22	04	39	43
09	79	13	77	48
88	75	80	18	14
90	96	23	70	00

The Fisher-Yates table is made up of 300 similar blocks of 25 numbers, printed on 6 pages of 10 rows and 5 columns each. To read from the table one may begin at any point on any page and read in any direction, up or down, right or left. When all of the individuals in the entire group or population have been numbered in 1, 2, 3 order, a random sample of any size can be drawn by following in order the numbers read from the table. Suppose, for example, that a random sample of 25 is to be drawn from a larger "population" of 100. Then if we have decided beforehand to start with the second column in the block above and read down, individuals numbered 50, 22, 79, 75, and 96 will be included. Other blocks chosen in advance may be used to provide the additional 20 subjects. If the same number occurs twice, the second draw is disregarded.

(b) *Distribution of trait in population known.* As result of much research in individual differences many physical and mental traits are believed to be normally distributed (at least approximately) in the population. If we are justified in assuming that the trait or ability in which we are interested is normally distributed in the general population, a sample drawn at random from this population will itself tend toward normality, so that symmetry of distribution becomes an excellent criterion of sample adequacy.

(c) *Population known only in general terms.* In many problems in psychology and in education the population is (1) not clearly defined, (2) not readily accessible for sampling (for example, the population of a state), and (3) very expensive to sample extensively. Under conditions such as these a useful test of the adequacy of a sample consists in drawing several samples at random and in succession from the population, such samples to be of approximately the same size as the sample with which we are working. Random samples of ten-year-old school boys in a large school system, for instance, must be drawn without bias as to able, mediocre, or poor individuals;

they cannot be drawn exclusively from poor neighborhoods, from expensive private schools, or from any larger group in which special factors are likely to make for systematic differences.

When the means and σ's of these presumably random samples are closely alike we may feel reasonably sure that our samples are representative of their population. If the correspondence among samples is not close we must re-examine each sample for bias. This test has been criticized on the grounds that (1) the correspondence of two or more samples may reflect nothing more than a common bias, and (2) consistency is not a sufficient criterion of randomness. While this is true and the test is admittedly rough, it may be argued that a reasonable consistency among samples is a necessary first condition of randomness. If samples are fairly consistent, therefore, they are presumably random unless subsequent examination reveals a common bias. If samples differ widely, we cannot be sure that *any* is random.

(2) STRATIFIED OR QUOTA SAMPLING

Stratified or quota sampling (also called "controlled" sampling) is a technique designed to insure representativeness and avoid bias by use of a modified random sampling method. This scheme is applicable when the population is composed of sub-groups or *strata* of different sizes, so that a representative sample must contain individuals drawn from each category or stratum in accordance with the sizes of the sub-groups. Within each stratum or sub-group the sampling is random—or as nearly so as possible. Stratified sampling is illustrated in the standardization of the 1937 Stanford-Binet Scale in the course of which approximately 3000 children were tested. To insure an adequate selection of American youth, the occupational levels of the parents of the children in the standard group were checked against the six occupational levels of employed males in the general population as shown by the U.S. Census of 1930. Differing proportions of men were found in the groups classified as professionals, semi-professionals, businessmen, farmers, skilled laborer, slightly skilled and unskilled laborers. Only 4% of employed males were found in the professional group, while 31% were in the skilled labor group. Accordingly, only 4% of the children in the Stanford-Binet standardization group could have fathers in the professional category, while 31% could have fathers in the skilled labor group. In public opinion polling, the investigator must see that his sample takes account of various strata or criteria such as age, sex, political affiliation, urban and rural residence, etc.

When sampling is stratified, the SE formula for the mean differs slightly from the SE_M formula when sampling is strictly random. The new formula is

$$\sigma_M = \sqrt{\frac{\sigma^2 - \sigma_s^2}{N}} \qquad (49)$$

(SE of M *when sampling has been stratified*)

in which $\sigma = SD$ of the entire sample

$\sigma_s = SD$ of the means of the various strata around the mean of the entire sample.

A convenient formula for σ_s is

$$\sigma_s = \sqrt{\frac{[N_1(M_1-M)^2 + N_2(M_2-M)^2 + \ldots + N_k(M_k-M)^2]}{N}} \quad (50)$$

(*standard deviation of the means of strata around the mean of the entire group*)

in which $N_1, N_2 \ldots N_k =$ number of cases in strata 1 to k; and N and M are the size and mean of the whole sample.

To illustrate formula (49), suppose that in a sample of 400 cases, there are 8 sub-groups or strata which vary in size from 70 to 25. The M of the whole sample is 80 and σ is 15. The SD of the means of the 8 strata [by (50)] around the general mean of 80 is known to be 5. Substituting in (49) we have

$$\sigma_M = \sqrt{\frac{225 - 25}{400}} = \sqrt{\frac{200}{400}} = .71$$

Had no account been taken of the variation in the sub-groups, σ_M would have been $\sqrt{\frac{225}{400}}$ or .75. Unless the various strata introduce considerable variation, it is obvious that the correction got by using (49) instead of (39) is fairly small.

(3) INCIDENTAL SAMPLING

The term incidental sampling (also called "accidental" sampling) should be applied to those groups which are used chiefly because they are easily or readily obtainable. School children, college sophomores enrolled in psychology classes, and laboratory animals are available at times, in numbers, and under conditions none of which may be of the experimenter's choosing. Such casual groups rarely constitute random samples of any definable population. Reliability formulas apply with a high degree of approximation —if at all—to incidental samples. And generalizations based upon such data are often misleading.

(4) PURPOSIVE SAMPLING

A sample may be expressly chosen because, in the light of available evidence, it mirrors some larger group with reference to a given characteristic. Newspaper editors are believed to reflect accurately public opinion upon various social and economic questions in their sections of the country. A sample of housewives may represent accurately the buyers of canned goods; a sample of brokers, the opinion of financiers on a new stock issue. If the saying "As Maine goes, so goes the Nation" is accepted as correct, then Maine becomes an important barometer (a purposive sample) of political thinking. Random sampling formulas apply more or less accurately to purposive samples.

2. Size of sample

The reliability of M or σ depends (p. 182) upon the *size* of the sample upon which the SE is based. SE's vary inversely as the square root of sample size so that the larger the N in general the smaller the SE. A small sample is often satisfactory in an intensive laboratory study in which many measurements are taken upon each subject. But if N is less than 25, say, there is often little reason for believing such a small group of persons to be adequately descriptive of *any* population.

The larger the N the larger the SD of the sample and the more inclusive (and presumably representative) our sample becomes of the general population. The range covered by samples of different sizes—when all are drawn from a normal population—will be approximately as follows:

$N = 10$ Range $\pm 2.0\sigma$
$N = 50$ Range $\pm 2.5\sigma$
$N = 200$ Range $\pm 3.0\sigma$
$N = 1000$ Range $\pm 3.5\sigma$

A range of $\pm 3.5\sigma$ from the mean includes 9995 cases in 10,000 in a normally distributed population. In a sample of 10,000 only 5 cases lie outside of this range; in a sample of 100 cases none lies outside of this range. The more extreme the score, large or small, the less the probability of its occurrence in a small sample. In fact, in very small samples widely deviant scores will rarely appear in a random sample drawn from a normal group.

A fairly simple and practical method of deciding when a sample is "sufficiently large" is to increase N until the addition of extra cases, drawn at random, fails to produce any appreciable change (more than $\pm 1 SE_M$, say) in the M and σ. When this point is reached, the sample is probably large enough to be taken as adequately descriptive of its population. But the corollary must be recognized that mere numbers in and of themselves do not guarantee a random sample. (See also p. 114.)

3. Sampling fluctuations and errors of measurement

SE's measure (1) errors of sampling *and* (2) errors of measurement. We have already considered the question of sampling errors on page 185. The investigator in establishing generalizations from his data regarding individual differences, say, must perforce make his observations upon limited groups or samples drawn at random from the population. Owing to differences among individuals and groups, plus chance factors (errors of measurement), neither the sample in hand nor another similarly drawn and approximately of the same size will describe the population exactly. Hence it is unlikely that M's and σ's from successive samples will equal each other. Variations from sample to sample—the so-called "errors" of sampling—are not to be thought of as mistakes, failures and the like, but as fluctuations arising from the fact that no two samples are ever quite alike. Means and σ's from random samples are, then, *estimates* of their parameters, and the SE formulas measure the goodness of this estimate.

The term errors of measurement includes all of those variable factors which affect test scores, sometimes in the plus and sometimes in the minus direction. If the SE_M is large, it does not follow *necessarily* that the mean is affected by a large sampling error, as much of the variation may be due to errors of measurement. When errors of measurement are low, however (reliability of tests high, see p. 348), a large SE_M indicates considerable sampling error.

4. Bias in sampling and constant errors

Errors which arise from inadequate sampling or from bias of any sort are neither detected nor measured by reliability formulas. The mean score on an aptitude test achieved by 200 male college freshmen in a college of high admission standards will not be representative of the aptitude of the general male population between the ages of 18 and 21, say, and for this reason the SE_M for this group is not an adequate measure of sampling fluctuations. College freshmen usually constitute an incidental—and often a highly biased—sample. In consequence, other samples of young men 18–25, drawn at random from the male population, will return very different means and σ's from those in our group. Differences like these are not sampling fluctuations but are errors due to inadequate or biased selection. Reliability formulas do not apply.

SE's do not detect constant errors. Such errors work in only one direction and are always plus or minus. They arise from many sources—familiarity with test materials prior to examination, cheating, fatigue, faulty techniques in administering and in scoring tests, in fact from a consistent bias of any sort. SE's are of doubtful value when computed from scores subject to large constant errors. The careful study of successive samples, rechecks when possible, care in controlling conditions, and the use of objective tests will reduce many of these troublesome sources of error. The research worker cannot learn too early that even the best statistical techniques are unable to make bad data yield valid results.

PROBLEMS

1. Given $M = 26.40$; $\sigma = 5.20$; $N = 100$
   (a) What is the probable divergence of this M from its parameter (true mean) at the .01 level of confidence?
   (b) What is the probable divergence of σ from its true (population) value at the .05 level of confidence?
   (c) Find the .99 confidence-interval for the true mean.

2. The mean of 16 independent observations of a certain magnitude is 100 and the SD is 24.
   (a) At the .05 confidence level what are the fiduciary limits of the true mean? (p. 189)
   (b) Taking the .99 confidence-interval as our standard, we may be assured that the true mean is at least as large as what value?

210 • STATISTICS IN PSYCHOLOGY AND EDUCATION

3. For a given group of 500 soldiers the mean AGCT score is 95.00 and the SD is 25.
   (a) Determine the .99 confidence-interval for the true mean.
   (b) It is unlikely that the true mean is larger than what value?

4. The mean of a large sample is K and σ_K is 2.50. What are the chances that the sample mean misses the true mean by more than (a) ± 1.00; (b) ± 3.00; (c) ± 10.00?

5. The following measures of perception span for unrelated words are obtained from 5 children: 5 6 4 7 5
   (a) Find the .99 confidence-interval for the true mean of these scores.
   (b) Compare the fiduciary limits (.99 confidence-interval) when calculated by large sample methods with the result in (a).

6. Suppose it is known that the SD of the scores in a certain population is 20. How many cases would we need in a sample in order that the SE
   (a) of the sample M be 2?
   (b) of the sample SD be 1?

7. In a sample of 400 voters, 50% favor the Democratic candidate for president. How often can we expect polls based on random samples of 400 to return percents of 55 or more in favor of the Democrats?

8. Opinion upon an issue seems about equally divided. How large a sample (N) would you need to be sure (at .01 level) that a deviation of 3% in a sample is not accidental (due to chance)?

9. Given an r of .45 based upon 60 cases,
   (a) Using formula (47), p. 197, find the SE_r. Determine the limits of the .99 confidence-interval for the population r.
   (b) Convert the given r into z, and find σ_z by formula (48). Check the limits of the .99 confidence-interval determined from σ_z against those found in (a) above.
   (c) Is the given r significant at the .01 level? (Use Table 25.)

10. An r of .81 is obtained from a random sample of 37 cases.
    (a) Establish the fiduciary limits of the true r at the .01 level, using the z-conversion.
    (b) Check the significance of r from Table 25.

11. Given a sample of 500 cases in which there are six sub-groups or strata. The means of the six sub-groups are 50 ($N = 100$), 54 ($N = 50$), 46 ($N = 100$), 50 ($N = 120$), 58 ($N = 80$), 42 ($N = 50$). The SD for the entire sample is 12.
    (a) Find the mean of the whole sample of 500 (p. 272).
    (b) Compute the σ_M by formula (49) (p. 206).
    (c) Compare σ_M by formula (39) with the result found in (b).

THE RELIABILITY OF THE MEAN AND OF OTHER STATISTICS • 211

12. Fill in the following table:

	Size of Sample (N)	df ($N-2$)	r	Significance
(a)	50	13	−.68	
(b)	30	28	.22	
(c)	82	80	−.40	
(d)	225	223	.05	

ANSWERS

1. (a) We may be confident at the .01 level that the obtained M does not miss the TM by more than ± 1.34 ($TM \pm 1.34$).
   (b) $\pm .73$ ($T\sigma \pm 1.96 \times .37$).
   (c) 27.74 to 25.06.
2. (a) 112.78 and 87.22
   (b) 82.3
3. (a) 97.89 to 92.11
   (b) 97.89
4. 69 in 100; 23 in 100; less than 1 in 100
5. (a) 7.75 to 3.05
   (b) By large sample methods ($\pm 2.58\sigma_M$) fiducial limits are 6.72 to 4.08.
6. (a) 100   (b) 202
7. About once in 50 trials
8. 1850
9. (a) .72 to .18   (b) .67 to .15   (c) Yes
10. (a) .91 to .60
    (b) Significant at .01 level
11. (a) 52.08   (b) .487   (c) .539 vs. .487
12. (a) Significant at .01 level
    (b) Not significant
    (c) Significant at .01 level
    (d) Not significant

9

THE RELIABILITY OF THE DIFFERENCE BETWEEN MEANS AND OTHER MEASURES

1. The Significance of Differences between Means and Medians

Suppose that we wish to discover whether ten-year-old boys and ten-year-old girls differ in mechanical aptitude. In attacking this problem, ordinarily we would first secure as large and as representative a sample of ten-year-old boys and ten-year-old girls as possible, administer our mechanical aptitude tests, compute means and σ's, and find the difference between the two means. A *large* mean difference in favor of the boys would offer strong evidence that boys of ten are mechanically more apt than are girls of ten. Contrariwise, a *small* difference (not more than 2–3 points, for example) would clearly be unimpressive, and would suggest that further comparative tests might well show no difference at all between the two groups.

When can we feel reasonably sure that a difference is large enough to be taken as real and dependable? This question involves the reliability of the measures compared, and its answer can rarely be stated in unequivocal terms. Reliability, as we found in Chapter 8, is always relative and can be stated only in terms of probability. A given difference is called reliable or *significant* when the probability is high that it cannot be explained away as temporary or accidental. And a difference is called *non-significant* when it appears to be reasonably certain that it could easily have arisen from sampling fluctuations (or sampling accidents) and hence implies no "real" or true difference.

1. The null hypothesis

Experimenters have found the *null hypothesis* a useful tool in testing the reliability of differences. In its simplest form (see p. 247), this hypothesis asserts that there is no true difference between two population means, and that the difference found between sample means is, therefore, accidental and unimportant. The null hypothesis is akin to the legal principle that a man is innocent until he is proved guilty. It constitutes a challenge; and the function of an experiment is to give the facts a chance to refute (or fail to refute) this challenge. To illustrate, suppose it is claimed that Eskimos have keener vision than Americans. This hypothesis is vaguely stated and cannot be tested precisely as we do not know how *much* better the Eskimo's vision must be before it can be adjudged "keener." If, however, we assert that Eskimos do not possess keener vision than Americans, or that the differences are trifling and unimportant (the true difference being zero), this null hypothesis is *exact* and can be tested. If our null hypothesis is untenable it must be rejected. And in discarding our null hypothesis, what we are saying is that differences in visual acuity as between Eskimos and Americans cannot be fully explained as temporary and occasional.

2. The reliability of the difference between two independent means

In order to discover whether two groups differ sufficiently in mean performance to enable us to say with confidence that a difference will persist upon repetition of the experiment, we need a standard error of the difference between the two means. Two situations with respect to mean differences arise: those in which the means are uncorrelated and those in which the means are correlated.

(1) THE SE OF THE DIFFERENCE (σ_D) WHEN MEANS ARE UNCORRELATED

The formula for the SE of the difference between uncorrelated or independent means is

$$\sigma_D \text{ or } \sigma_{M_1 - M_2} = \sqrt{\sigma^2_{M_1} + \sigma^2_{M_2}}$$

or (51)

$$\sigma_D \text{ or } \sigma_{M_1 - M_2} = \sqrt{\frac{\sigma_1^2}{N_1} + \frac{\sigma_2^2}{N_2}}$$

(*standard error of the difference between two uncorrelated means*) in which σ_{M_1} is the *SE* of the mean of the first group; σ_{M_2} is the *SE* of the mean of the second group; and σ_D is the *SE* of the difference between the two means. Means are uncorrelated when calculated from *different* groups, or from uncorrelated tests administered to the *same* group. From formula (51) it is clear that one way to find the *SE* of the difference between two means is first to compute the *SE*'s of the two means themselves. Another way is to calculate σ_D directly if σ_{M_1} and σ_{M_2} are not wanted.

Application of formula (51) is illustrated by the following example:

> *Example (1)* In a study of the intelligence of the foreign-born white draft during World War I, a sample of 611 native-born Norwegians and a sample of 129 native-born Belgians were found to test as follows on the "combined scale." *

Country of Birth	Number of Cases	Mean Score	σ
Norway	611	12.98	2.47
Belgium	129	12.79	2.42

Would further testing of similar samples of Norwegians and Belgians give virtually this same result; or in further testing would the mean difference perchance be reduced to zero, or even reversed in favor of the Belgians?

To answer these questions we have first computed the *SE*'s of the two means and from these the *SE* of the difference between the two means. By formula (39) the *SE*'s of the means are

$$\text{Norwegians:} \quad \sigma_{M_1} = \frac{2.47}{\sqrt{611}} = .0999$$

$$\text{Belgians:} \quad \sigma_{M_2} = \frac{2.42}{\sqrt{129}} = .2130$$

Substituting these *SE*'s in formula (51) we have

$$\sigma_D = \sqrt{(.0999)^2 + (.2130)^2} = .24 \text{ (to two decimals)}$$

The actual difference between the means of Norwegians and Belgians, then, is .19 (12.98 − 12.79) and the *SE* of this difference (σ_D) is .24. In inquiring whether the two groups actually differ in mean performance, we shall set up a null hypothesis, namely, that the

* The "combined scale" included the 8 Alpha tests, the Stanford-Binet, and tests 4, 5, 6, and 7 from Beta. The maximum score was 25. For the data given in this problem, see Brigham, C. C., *A Study of American Intelligence* (Princeton: Princeton University Press, 1923), pp. 120–121.

difference between the population means of Norwegians and Belgians is zero, and that—except for accidental errors—mean differences from sample to sample would *all* be zero. Stated specifically, we ask whether—in view of its *SE*—the mean difference of .19 is really large enough to cast grave doubt upon our null hypothesis.

As a first step in making our test we compute a critical ratio, or *CR*, by dividing the obtained difference by its *SE* $\left(CR = \dfrac{D}{\sigma_D} \right)$* In the present problem, the $CR = .19/.24$ or .79. The distribution of *CR*'s is known to be normal around the population or true difference when *N* is large. Hence, in testing our null hypothesis, we may set up a normal distribution like that shown in Figure 47, in which the mean is set at zero (true difference) and the σ of the distribution of differences is .24 (σ_D). From the critical ratio our obtained difference of .19 is seen to fall at a point $.79\sigma_D$ from the hypothetical mean of zero; and the difference of $-.19$ falls at $-.79\sigma_D$.

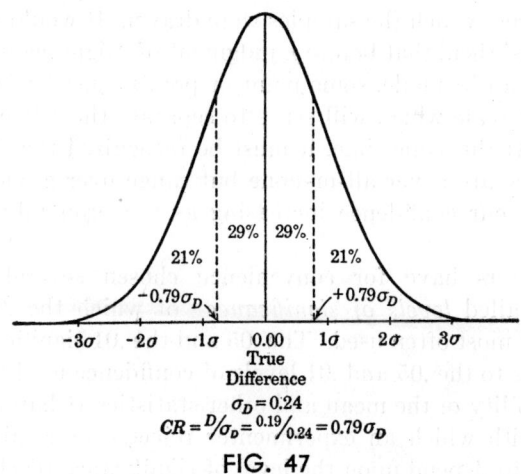

$\sigma_D = 0.24$
$CR = D/\sigma_D = 0.19/0.24 = 0.79\sigma_D$

FIG. 47

Now from Table A we know that $29\% \times 2$ or 58% of the cases in a normal distribution fall between the mean and $\pm .79\sigma_D$; and 42% of the cases fall outside these limits. This means that under the stipulated conditions we can expect differences as large or larger than $\pm .19$ to occur 42 times in 100 comparisons of Norwegians and

* *CR* really equals $\dfrac{(M_1 - M_2) - 0}{\sigma_D}$ or $\dfrac{D - 0}{\sigma_D}$: the difference (*D*) between the two means is measured from zero in terms of σ_D (see Fig. 47).

Belgians. A difference as large as ±.19, therefore, might readily arise as a sampling fluctuation from zero and is clearly not significant. Accordingly, we retain the null hypothesis and conclude with confidence that, on the evidence, there is no real difference between Norwegians and Belgians on the "combined scale." When the null hypothesis is retained (as here) the result may be stated also as follows: there is good reason to believe that these two groups were drawn from the same population with respect to tested intelligence and differ only by sampling errors.

(2) LEVELS OF SIGNIFICANCE

The answer to the question of when a difference is to be taken as *statistically significant* depends upon the probability of the given difference arising "by chance" (p. 87); and it depends also upon the purposes of the experiment (p. 186). Usually a difference will be marked "significant" when the gap between the two sample means points to or signifies a true difference between the parameters in the population from which the samples were drawn. It would seem to be fairly obvious, then, that before a judgment of "significant" or "nonsignificant" can be made, some point or points must be found along a probability scale which will serve to separate these two judgment categories. At the same time, it must be recognized that judgments of significance are never all-or-none but range over a wide scale of probabilities, our confidence increasing as the probability of error decreases.

Experimenters have for convenience chosen several arbitrary standards—called *levels of significance*—of which the .05 and .01 levels are the most often used. The .05 and the .01 significance levels are analogous to the .05 and .01 levels of confidence used in estimating the reliability of the mean and other statistics (Chapter 8). The confidence with which an experimenter rejects—or retains—a null hypothesis will depend upon the level of significance reached. From Table D we know that $\pm 1.96\sigma$ mark off points in the normal distribution to the left and right of which lie 5% of the cases (2½% at each end). When a CR is 1.96 or more, therefore, we reject a null hypothesis at the .05 level of significance—on the grounds that not more than once in 20 trials would a difference occur as large or larger than that obtained, if the true difference were zero. The CR of .79 in the problem of Norwegians and Belgians (p. 214) falls short of 1.96 (does not reach the .05 level of significance) and accordingly the null hypothesis is retained.

The .01 level of significance is more exacting than is the .05 level. From Table D we know that $\pm 2.58\sigma$ mark off points to the left and right of which lies 1% of the cases in a normal distribution. If the CR is 2.58 or more, therefore, we reject the null hypothesis at the .01 level of significance, on the grounds that not more than once in 100 trials would a difference of this size occur if the true difference were zero. The significance of a difference may also be evaluated by establishing confidence-intervals for the true difference—as was done for the TM on page 187. Thus the limits specified by $D \pm 1.96\sigma_D$ define the .95 confidence-interval for the true D; and $D \pm 2.58\sigma_D$ define the .99 confidence-interval for the true D. By way of illustration, we may again take the problem of comparing the intelligence of the Norwegians and Belgians on page 214 where the $D = .19$ and the $\sigma_D = .24$. The .99 confidence-interval for the true D is $.19 \pm 2.58 \times .24$, or from $-.43$ to $.81$. This relatively wide range and the fact that it runs from minus to plus through zero strengthens our confidence in the inference that the true D could well be zero. In fact, acceptance of the null hypothesis *always* means that zero lies within the confidence-interval for the true difference.

(3) TWO-TAILED AND ONE-TAILED TESTS OF SIGNIFICANCE

Under the null hypothesis, differences between obtained means (i.e., $M_1 - M_2$) may be either plus or minus and as often in one direction as in the other from the true difference of zero, so that in determining probabilities we take *both* tails of the sampling distribution (Fig. 47). This *two-tailed* test, as it is sometimes called, is the most *general* test of significance. It should always be used when, in accordance with the null hypothesis, our two groups have conceivably been drawn from the same population with respect to the trait being measured [see Example (1) above].

In many experiments our primary concern is with the *direction* of the difference rather than with its existence in absolute terms.* This situation arises when negative differences, if found, are of no importance practically; or when a difference if it exists at all must of necessity be positive. Suppose, for example, that we wish to determine the increase in vocabulary resulting from additional weekly reading assignments, or want to evaluate the gain in numerical computation brought about by an extra hour of drill per day. It is unlikely that additional reading will lead to an actual loss in vocabulary. More-

* Jones, Lyle V., "Tests of Hypotheses: One-sided vs. Two-sided Alternatives," *Psychol. Bull.*, 1952, 49, 43–46.

over, if drill decreases arithmetic skill it would be the same as though it had no effect—in either event we would drop the drill. Only an increase as a result of drill, therefore, is of any practical interest.

In cases like these the *one-tailed* test of significance is appropriate. We may illustrate with Example (2).

> *Example (2)* We know from experience that intensive coaching increases reading skill. Therefore, if a class has been coached, our hypothesis is that it will gain in reading comprehension—failure to gain or a loss in score is of no interest. At the end of a school year, Class A, which had received special coaching, averaged 5 points higher on a reading test than Class B, which had received no coaching. The standard error of this difference was 3. Is the gain significant?

To evaluate the 5 points gained, i.e., determine its significance, we must use the one-tailed and not the two-tailed test. The critical ratio is 5/3 or 1.67, and from Table D we find that 10% of the cases in a normal distribution lie to the left and right of 1.65, so that 5% ($P/2$) lie to the right of 1.65. Our critical ratio of 1.67 just exceeds 1.65 and is, therefore, significant at the .05 level. We reject the null hypothesis, therefore, since only once in 20 trials would a gain as large or larger than 5 occur by chance. When a critical ratio is 2.33 ($P = .02$ and $P/2 = .01$) we mark a positive difference significant at the .01 level. It may be noted that in using the one-tailed test the experimenter sets up the hypothesis he wishes to test *before* he takes his data. This means that the experiment is designed at the outset to test the hypothesis; an hypothesis cannot be proposed to fit the data after they are in. If in Example (2) we had been interested simply in whether Class A and Class B were significantly different in reading score, the two-tailed test would have been appropriate. As we have seen, the two-tailed test gives us the probability of a mean positive difference of 5 points (A ahead of B), together with the probability of a mean negative difference (loss) of 5 points (B ahead of A). This is true since under the null hypothesis fluctuations of sampling alone will tend to show A-samples better than B-samples, and B better than A, about equally often. A difference in favor of either A or B, therefore, is possible and equally acceptable.

The one-tailed test should be used when we wish to determine the probability of a score occurring beyond a stated value. An illustration is given in Example (3) below.

Example (3) In certain studies of deception among school children the scores achieved on tests given under conditions in which cheating was possible were compared with scores achieved by comparable groups under strictly supervised conditions. In a certain test given under "honest" conditions the mean is 62 and the σ is 10. Several children who took the test under non-supervised conditions turned in scores of 87 and above. Is it probable that these children cheated?

The mean of 62 is 24.5 score units from 86.5, the lower limit of score 87. Dividing 24.5 by 10 we find that scores of 87 and above lie at the point 2.45σ above the mean of 62. On the assumption of normality of distribution, there is less than one chance in 100 that a score of 87 or more will appear in the "honest" distribution. While scores of 87 and above might, of course, be "honest," examinees who make such scores under non-supervised conditions are certainly open to suspicion of having cheated. The one-tailed test is appropriate here as we are concerned only with the positive end of the distribution—the probability of scores of 87 and above.

(4) ERRORS IN MAKING INFERENCES

In testing hypotheses two types of wrong inference can be made and must be reckoned with by the experimenter.* What are called Type I errors are present when the hypothesis is *true* but our test of significance leads us to believe it to be *false*; Type II errors arise when the hypothesis is *false,* but our test of significance leads us to believe it to be *true.* Stated in different terms, we make an error of Type I if we *reject* the null hypothesis when it is true—claim significance when none exists; and we commit an error of Type II if we *accept* the null hypothesis when it is false—mark a finding not-significant when a real difference is present.

Various precautions must be taken to avoid both sorts of erroneous inference. A low significance level (P greater than .05, say) increases the possibility of Type I errors; and a high significance level (.05 to .01) renders such erroneous inferences less likely. How this works out can perhaps be shown best by a simple example. Suppose that a quarter known to us to be a good coin is suspected by an experimenter of a bias in favor of heads.† When our experimenter tosses

---
* Treloar, Alan E., *Elements of Statistical Reasoning* (New York: Wiley and Sons, 1939), Chap. 10, pp. 149–151.
McNemar, Q., *Psychological Statistics* (New York: Wiley and Sons, 1949), pp. 69–71.
† If a coin is "leaded" or weighted on the "tails" side, the "heads" side, being lighter, will tend to appear more often than tails.

this coin 10 times, it turns up 8 heads and 2 tails. The theoretical expectation for a good coin is, of course, 5 heads and 5 tails; and the specific question for the experimenter to decide is whether the occurrence of 8 heads represents a "heads" bias—a significant deviation from the expected 5 heads. The distribution of heads and tails obtained when a single coin is tossed 10 times is given by expansion of the binomial $(p+q)^{10}$, where $p =$ probability of a head and $q =$ probability of a tail (non-head). The mean of $(p+p)^n$ is np and the SD is $\sqrt{npq}$; hence in our example the mean is 5 and the SD is $\sqrt{10 \cdot 1/2 \cdot 1/2}$ or 1.58. A "score" of 8 extends over the interval 7.5–8.5, so that to determine the probability of 8 or *more*, the CR we wish is $\dfrac{7.5 - 5}{1.58}$ or 1.58. (See Fig. 48.) (A problem similar to this

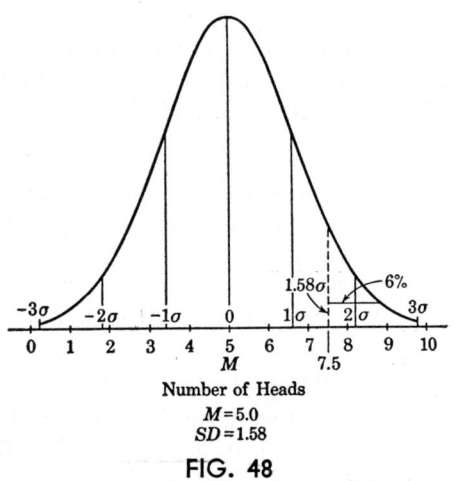

FIG. 48

will be found on p. 252). From Table A we know that 8 or *more* heads, that is, a CR of 1.58, may be expected on the null hypothesis approximately 6 times in 100 trials.* If our experimenter is willing to accept $P = .06$ as significant (i.e., set his standards low), he will *reject* the null hypothesis—although it is true. That is, he will report the coin to be biased in favor of heads, although it is in fact a good coin.

If our experimenter had set his significance level higher (say .01 or even .05) he would have avoided this erroneous inference. Further-

---

* This is a one-tailed test (p. 217) because our experimenter's hypothesis was that the coin is biased in favor of heads.

more, had he increased the number of tosses of the coin from 10 to 100 or even 500, he might have avoided his wrong inference, as heads and tails in a good coin will *tend* to occur equally often. Increasing the experimental data gives the null hypothesis a chance to assert itself (if true) and guards against freak results. We should not be willing to reject a null hypothesis too quickly, as in so doing we must assert the existence of a real difference—often a heavy responsibility.

In direct contradiction to what happens in the case of Type I errors, the possibility of drawing erroneous inferences of Type II (acceptance of the null hypothesis when false) is *increased* when we set very high levels of significance. This can be shown by reference to the coin example above—with a change in conditions. Suppose that a quarter which is known to us to be biased in favor of heads is also suspected by an experimenter of bias in favor of heads. This coin is tossed 10 times and shows, as did the coin before, 8 heads and 2 tails. From the data above, on page 220, we know that in a good coin 8 or more heads can be expected by chance 6 in 100 times—that $P = .06$. Hence, if our experimenter sets .01 as his level of significance (or even .05) he will accept the null hypothesis and mark his result "not significant" although the coin is now actually biased.

How can we guard against both of these types of erroneous inference? Perhaps the wisest course is first to demand more evidence, that is, give the data a chance to refute (or fail to refute) the null hypothesis. Additional data, further repetition of the experiment, and better control will often make possible a definite conclusion. If a coin is biased toward returning heads, this bias will continue to cause more heads than tails to appear in further tosses. For example, if the ratio of 8 heads to 2 tails in the 10 tosses described in the last paragraph holds consistently, we shall get 80 heads and 20 tails in 100 throws. The critical ratio for 100 tosses will be 5.9 * (as compared with 1.58 for 10 tosses), and the probability is far less than .01 that 80 heads is a random fluctuation from the expected 50 heads. Our experimenter would correctly mark this result very significant— i.e., significant beyond the .01 level.

* When $n = 100$, $p = .50$, $q = .50$:
$$M = np = 50$$
$$\sigma = \sqrt{npq} = \sqrt{100 \times 1/2 \times 1/2} = 5$$
$$CR = \frac{79.5 - 50}{5} = 5.9$$

Setting a high level of significance will tend, then, to prevent Type I errors but will encourage the appearance of Type II errors. Hence it appears that an experimenter must decide which kind of wrong inference he would rather avoid, as apparently he can prevent one type of error only at the risk of making the other more likely. In the long run, errors of Type I (rejecting a null hypothesis when true, by marking a non-significant difference significant) are perhaps more likely to prove serious in a research program in psychology than are errors of Type II. If an experimenter claims a significant finding erroneously, for instance, the fact that it is a *positive* result is likely to terminate the research, so that the error persists. When a high level of significance is demanded (.01, say) we may feel assured that significance will be claimed incorrectly not more than once in 100 trials.

Errors of Type II (accepting the null hypothesis when false, i.e., when a real difference exists) must be watched for carefully when the experimental factor or factors are potentially dangerous. Thus, if one is studying the psychological effects of a drug suspected of inducing rather drastic emotional and temperamental changes, an error of Type II might well prove to be disastrous. Fortunately, the fact that a negative finding is inconclusive and often unsatisfactory may lead to further experimental work, and thus obviate somewhat the harm done by Type II errors. Especially is this true when the problem is important enough further to challenge the investigator.

For many years it was customary for investigators in experimental psychology to demand critical ratios of 3.00 or more before marking a difference significant. This extremely high standard almost certainly caused the null hypothesis to be accepted more often than it should have been—a Type II error on the side of conservatism. As a general rule it is probably wise to demand a significance level of at least .01 in most experimental research, i.e., to risk Type II errors by preventing those of Type I. But the .05 level is often satisfactory, especially in preliminary work.

(5) RELIABILITY OF THE DIFFERENCE BETWEEN MEANS IN SMALL INDEPENDENT SAMPLES

When the N's of two independent groups are small (less than 30, say) the SE of the difference between means should depend upon SD's calculated by the formula $SD = \sqrt{\dfrac{\Sigma x^2}{(N-1)}}$, and the degrees of freedom in the two groups must be considered. Table D may then be used conveniently to test the significance of t,* which is the appropriate critical ratio to be used with small samples. An example will illustrate the procedures.

Example (4) An interest test is administered to 6 boys in a Vocational class and to 10 boys in a Latin class. Is there a significant difference in mean score between the two groups?

Scores are as follows:

Vocational Class $N_1 = 6$				Latin Class $N_2 = 10$		
Scores (X_1)	x_1	x_1^2		Scores (X_2)	x_2	x_2^2
28	−2	4		20	−4	16
35	5	25		16	−8	64
32	2	4		25	1	1
24	−6	36		34	10	100
26	−4	16		20	−4	16
35	5	25		28	4	16
6 | 180		110		31	7	49
				24	0	0
$M_1 = 30$				27	3	9
				15	−9	81
				10 | 240		352

$N_1 - 1 = 5$
$N_2 - 1 = 9$
$ \overline{14}$

$M_2 = 24$

$$SD \text{ (or } s) = \sqrt{\frac{110 + 352}{14}} = 5.74 \qquad \text{by (52)}$$

$$SD_D = 5.74\sqrt{\frac{6 + 10}{60}} = 5.74 \times .5163 = 2.96 \qquad \text{by (53)}$$

$$t = \frac{(30 - 24) - 0}{2.96} = 2.03$$

For 14 df, the .05 level (Table D) is 2.14; and the .01 level is 2.98.

The mean of the interest scores made by the 6 boys in the Vocational class is 30, and the mean of the interest scores made by the 10 boys in the Latin class is 24. The mean difference of 6 is to be tested for significance. When two examples are small, as here, we get a better estimate of the "true" SD (σ in the population) by pool-

---

* t is a critical ratio in which a more exact estimate of the σ_D is used. The sampling distribution of t is not normal when N is small (less than 50, say). t is a CR; but all CR's are not t's (see p. 215).

ing the sums of squares of the deviations taken around the means of the two groups and computing a single SD.* The justification for pooling is that under the null hypothesis no real mean difference exists as between the two samples, which are assumed to have been drawn from the same parent population. We have, therefore, only *one* σ (that of the common population) to estimate. Furthermore, by increasing N we get a more stable SD based upon *all* of our cases. The formula for computing this "pooled" SD and the formula for the SE of the difference are as follows:

$$SD = \sqrt{\frac{\Sigma(X_1 - M_1)^2 + \Sigma(X_2 - M_2)^2}{(N_1 - 1) + (N_2 - 1)}} \qquad (52)$$

(SD *when two small independent samples are pooled*)

$$SE_D = SD\sqrt{\frac{N_1 + N_2}{N_1 N_2}} \qquad (53)$$

(SE *of the difference between means in small independent samples*)

In formula (52), $\Sigma(X_1 - M_1)^2 = \Sigma x_1^2$ is the sum of the squared deviations around the mean of Group 1; and $\Sigma(X_2 - M_2)^2 = \Sigma x_2^2$ is the sum of the squared deviations around the mean of Group 2. These sums of squares are combined to give a single SD. In Example (4) the sum of squares in the Vocational class around the mean of 30 is 110; and in the Latin class the sum of squares around the mean of 24 is 352. The df are $(N_1 - 1) = 5$, and $(N_2 - 1) = 9$.† By formula (53), therefore, the $SD = \sqrt{\dfrac{110 + 352}{14}}$ or 5.74. This SD serves as a measure of variability for *each* of the two groups. Thus the $SE_{M_1} = \dfrac{5.74}{\sqrt{6}}$ and the $SE_{M_2} = \dfrac{5.74}{\sqrt{10}}$ [by formula (39), p. 182]. Combining these two SE's by formula (51) we find that $SE_D = \sqrt{\dfrac{(5.74)^2}{6} + \dfrac{(5.74)^2}{10}} = 5.74\sqrt{\dfrac{16}{60}}$ or 2.96. Formula (53) combines the two SE_M's enabling us to calculate SE_D in one operation.

$t = \dfrac{6}{2.96}$ or 2.03; and the df in the two groups (namely, 5 and 9) are combined to give 14 df for use in inferring the significance of the

---

* The SD so computed is subject to a slight negative bias, which is negligible when $N > 20$, say. See Holtzman, W. H., "The Unbiased Estimate of the Population Variance and Standard Deviation," *Amer. Jour. Psychol.*, 1950, 63, 615–617.

† 1 df is "used up" in computing each mean (p. 193).

mean difference. Entering Table D with 14 df, we get the entries 2.14 at the .05 and 2.98 at the .01 levels. Since our t does not reach the .05 level, the obtained mean difference of 6 must be marked "non-significant."

A second example will illustrate further the use of levels of significance when samples are small.

Example (5) On an arithmetic reasoning test 31 ten-year-old boys and 42 ten-year-old girls made the following scores:

	Mean	SD	N
Boys:	40.39	8.69	31
Girls:	35.81	8.33	42

Is the mean difference of 4.58 in favor of the boys significant?

By formula (52) we find

$$SD* = \sqrt{\frac{(8.69)^2 \times 30 + (8.33)^2 \times 41}{71}} \text{ or } 8.48.$$

And by formula (53),

$$SE_D = 8.48\sqrt{\frac{31+42}{31 \times 42}} = 2.01.$$

t is 4.58/2.01 or 2.28 and the degrees of freedom for use in testing the significance of the mean difference are $30 + 41$ or 71. Entering Table D with 71 df we find t-entries of 2.00 at the .05 and of 2.65 at the .01 levels. The obtained t of 2.28 is significant at the .05 but not at the .01 level. Only once in 20 comparisons of boys and girls on this test would we expect to find a difference as large or larger than 4.58 under our null hypothesis. We may be reasonably confident, therefore, that boys do better than girls on this test.

3. The reliability of the difference between two correlated means

(1) THE SINGLE GROUP METHOD

The last section dealt with the problem of determining whether the difference between two means is significant when these means represent the performance of independent groups—boys and girls, Norwegians and Belgians, and the like. A closely related problem is concerned with the significance of the difference between correlated means obtained from the same test administered to the same group

* $SD^2 = \dfrac{\Sigma x^2}{(N-1)}$; hence $\Sigma x^2 = SD^2 \times (N-1)$.

upon two occasions. This experimental design is called the "single group" method. Suppose that we have administered a test to a group of children and two weeks later have repeated the test. We wish to measure the effect of practice or of special training upon the second set of scores; or to estimate the effects of some activity interpolated between test and retest. In order to determine the significance of the difference between the means obtained in the initial and final testing, we must use the formula

$$SE_D = \sqrt{\sigma^2_{M_1} + \sigma^2_{M_2} - 2r_{12}\sigma_{M_1}\sigma_{M_2}} \qquad (54)$$

(SE *of the difference between correlated means*)

in which σ_{M_1} and σ_{M_2} are the SE's of the initial and final test means, and r_{12} is the coefficient of correlation between scores made on initial and final tests.* An illustration will bring out the difference between formula (51) and formula (54).

Example (6) At the beginning of the school year, the mean score of a group of 64 sixth-grade children upon an educational achievement test in reading was 45.00 with a σ of 6.00. At the end of the school year, the mean score on an equivalent form of the same test was 50.00 with a σ of 5.00. The correlation between scores made on the initial and final testing was .60. Has the class made significant progress in reading during the year?

We may tabulate our data as follows:

	Initial Test	Final Test
No. of children:	64	64
Mean score:	45.00 (M_1)	50.00 (M_2)
Standard Deviations:	6.00 (σ_1)	5.00 (σ_2)
Standard errors of means:	.75 (σ_{M_1})	.63 (σ_{M_2})
Difference between means:	5.00	
Correlation between initial and final tests:	.60	

Substituting in formula (54) we get

$$SE_D = \sqrt{(.75)^2 + (.63)^2 - 2 \times .60 \times .75 \times .63} = .63$$

The t-ratio is 5.00/.63 or 7.9. Since there are 64 children there are 64 pairs of scores and 64 differences,† so that the df becomes 64 − 1 or

---

* The correlation between the means of successive samples drawn from a given population equals the correlation between test scores, the means of which are being compared.

† 1 df is lost since SE_D is computed around the mean of the distribution of differences (p. 193).

RELIABILITY OF DIFFERENCE BETWEEN MEANS AND OTHER MEASURES • 227

63. From Table D the t for 63 df is 2.66 at the .01 level. Our t of 7.9 is far greater than 2.66 and hence is very significant. It seems clear, therefore, that this class made substantial progress in reading over the school year.

When groups are small, a procedure called the "difference-method" is often to be preferred to that given above. The following example will serve as an illustration:

Example (7) Twelve subjects are given 5 successive trials upon a digit-symbol test of which only the scores for trials 1 and 5 are shown. Is the gain from initial to final trial significant?

Trial 1	Trial 5	Difference (5 − 1)	x	x^2
50	62	12	4	16
42	40	− 2	−10	100
51	61	10	2	4
26	35	9	1	1
35	30	− 5	−13	169
42	52	10	2	4
60	68	8	0	0
41	51	10	2	4
70	84	14	6	36
55	63	8	0	0
62	72	10	2	4
38	50	12	4	16
572	668	12|96 8		354

$Mean_D = 8.0$

$$SD_D = \sqrt{\frac{354}{11}} = 5.67$$

$$SE_{M_D} = \frac{5.67}{\sqrt{12}} = 1.64$$

$$t = \frac{8 - 0}{1.64} = 4.88$$

From the column of differences between pairs of scores, the mean difference is found to be 8, and the SD around this mean (SD_D) by the formula $SD = \sqrt{\frac{\Sigma x^2}{(N-1)}}$ is 5.67. On our null hypothesis the true difference between the means of Trials 5 and 1 is 0, so that we must test our obtained mean gain of 8 against this hypothetical zero gain.

The SE of the mean difference $\left(SE_{M_D} = \dfrac{SD}{\sqrt{N}}\right)$ is 1.64 and $t\left(\dfrac{D-0}{SE_{M_D}}\right)$ is 4.88. Entering Table D with 11 (12 − 1) degrees of freedom, we find t-entries of 2.20 and 3.11 at the .05 and at the .01 levels. Our t of 4.88 is far above the .01 level and the mean difference of 8 is obviously very significant.

If our hypothesis initially had been that practice *increases* test score, we would have used the one-tailed test. The probability of a positive difference (gain) of 8 or more on the null hypothesis is quite remote. In the one-tailed test, for 11 df the .05 level is read from the .10 column ($P/2 = .05$) to be 1.80 and the .01 level from the .02 column ($P/2 = .01$) is 2.72. Our t of 4.88 is much larger than the .01 level of 2.72 and there is little doubt but that the gain from Trial 1 to Trial 5 is significant.

The result found in Example (7) may be checked by the single group method. By use of formula (27), p. 145, the r between Trials 1 and 5 is found to be .944. Substituting for r_{12} (viz., .944), for σ_{M_1} (3.65) and for σ_{M_2} (4.55) in formula (54) we get a σ_D of 1.63 which checks SE_{M_D} within the error of computation. The "difference-method" is quicker and easier to apply than is the longer method of calculating SE's for each mean and the SE of the difference, and is to be preferred unless the correlation between initial and final scores is wanted.

(2) THE METHOD OF EQUIVALENT GROUPS: MATCHING BY PAIRS

Formula (54) is applicable in those experiments which make use of *equivalent groups* as well as in those using a single group. In the method of equivalent groups the matching is done initially by *pairs* so that each person in the first group has a match in the second group. This procedure enables us to set off the effects of one or more experimentally varied conditions (experimental factors) against the absence of these same variables (control). The following problem is typical of many in which the equivalent group technique is useful.

Example (8) Two groups, X and Y, of seventh-grade children are paired child for child for age and score on Form A of the Otis Group Intelligence Scale. Three weeks later, both groups are given Form B of the same test. Before the second test, Group X, the experimental group, is praised for its performance on the first test and urged to try to better its score. Group Y, the control group, is given the second test without comment. Will the incentive (praise) cause the final scores of Group X and Group Y to differ significantly?

RELIABILITY OF DIFFERENCE BETWEEN MEANS AND OTHER MEASURES • 229

The relevant data may be tabulated as follows:

	Experimental Group X	Control Group Y
No. of children in each group:	72	72
Mean scores on Form A, initial test:	80.42	80.51
SD on Form A, initial test:	23.61	23.46
Mean scores on Form B, final test:	88.63 (M_1)	83.24 (M_2)
SD on Form B, final test:	24.36 (σ_1)	21.62 (σ_2)
Gain, $M_1 - M_2$:		5.39
Standard errors of means, final tests:	2.89	2.57

Correlation between final scores (experimental and control groups) = .65

The means and σ's of the control and experimental groups in Form A (initial test) are almost identical showing the original pairing of scores to have been quite satisfactory. The correlation between the final scores on Form B of the Otis Test is calculated from the paired scores of children who were matched originally in terms of initial score.*

The difference between the means on the final test is 5.39 (88.63 − 83.24). The SE of this difference, σ_D, is found from formula (54) to be

$$\sigma_D = \sqrt{(2.89)^2 + (2.57)^2 - 2 \times .65 \times 2.89 \times 2.57} = 2.30$$

The t-ratio is 5.39/2.30 or 2.34; and since there are 72 pairs, there are (72 − 1) or 71 degrees of freedom. Entering Table D with 71 df we find the t's at .05 and .01 to be 2.00 and 2.65, respectively. The given difference is significant at the .05 but not at the .01 level; and we may feel reasonably certain that the experimental and control groups differ in their final mean scores on Form B of the Otis Test.

It is worth noting that had no account been taken of the correlation between final scores on Form B [if formula (51) had been used instead of (54)], σ_D would have been 3.87 instead of 2.30. t would then have been 1.39 instead of 2.34 and would have fallen considerably below the .05 level of 2.00. In other words, a significant finding would have been marked "not significant." Evidently, it is important that we take account of the correlation between final scores—especially if it is high.

When $r = .00$, formula (54) reduces to (51) since group means are then independent or uncorrelated. Also, when r is positive, the σ_D from formula (54) is smaller than the σ_D from (51) and the larger

---

* Note that the correlation between final scores in the equivalent groups method is analogous to the correlation between initial and final scores in the single group method. In equivalent groups one group is the experimental and the other the control. In the single group, the initial scores furnish the control.

the plus r the greater the reduction in σ_D by use of (54). For a given difference between means, the smaller the σ_D the larger the t and the more significant the obtained difference. The relative efficiency obtained by using a single group or equivalent groups as compared with independent groups can be determined by the *size* of the r between final scores, or between initial and final scores. The correlation coefficient, therefore, gives a measure of the advantage to be gained by matching.

If r is negative, formula (54) gives a larger σ_D than that given by formula (51). In this case, the failure to take account of the correlation will lead to a smaller σ_D and a t larger and apparently more significant than it should be.

One further point may be mentioned. If the difference between the means of two groups is significant by formula (51) it will, of course, be even more significant by formula (54) if r is positive. Formula (51) may be used in a preliminary test, therefore, if we can be sure that the correlation is positive. The correlation between initial and final score is usually positive, though rarely as high as that found in Example (8).

(3) GROUPS MATCHED FOR MEAN AND SD

When it is impracticable or impossible to set up groups in which subjects have been matched person for person, investigators often resort to the matching of groups in terms of mean and σ. The matching variable is usually different from the variable under study but is, in general, related to it and sometimes highly. No attempt is made to pair off individuals and the two groups are not necessarily of the same size, although a large difference in N is not advisable.

In comparing final score means of matched groups the procedure is somewhat different from that used with equivalent groups.* Suppose that X is the variable under study, and Y is the function or variable in terms of which our two groups have been equated as to mean and SD. Then if r_{xy} is the correlation between X and Y *in the population* from which our samples have been drawn, the SE of the difference between means in X is

$$SE_{D_{M_1 - M_2}} = \sigma_D = \sqrt{\left(\sigma^2_{M_{x_1}} + \sigma^2_{M_{x_2}}\right)\left(1 - r^2_{xy}\right)} \qquad (55)$$

(SE *of the difference between the* X *means of groups matched for mean and for* SD *in* Y)

*Wilks, S. S., "The Standard Error of the Means of 'Matched' Samples," *Jour. Educ. Psychol.*, 1931, 22, 205–208.

An example will illustrate the procedure.

Example (9) The achievement of two groups of first-year high-school boys, the one from an academic, the other from a technical high school, is compared upon a Mechanical Ability Test. The two groups are matched for mean and *SD* upon a general intelligence test so that the experiment becomes one of comparing the mechanical ability scores of two groups of boys of "equal" general intelligence enrolled in different curricula. Data are as follows:

	Academic	Technical
No. of boys in each group:	125	137
Means on Intelligence Test (Y):	102.50	102.80
σ's on Intelligence Test (Y):	33.65	31.62
Means on Mechanical Ability Test (X):	51.42	54.38
σ's on Mechanical Ability Test (X):	6.24	7.14

Correlation between the General Intelligence Test and the Mechanical Ability Test for first-year high-school boys is .30.

$$M_{x_1} - M_{x_2} = 54.38 - 51.42 = 2.96$$

By (55) $\sigma_D = \sqrt{\left(\dfrac{(6.24)^2}{125} + \dfrac{(7.14)^2}{137}\right)(1 - .30^2)}$

$= .79$

$t = \dfrac{2.96}{.79} = 3.75$

The difference between the mean scores in the Mechanical Ability Test of the academic and technical high-school boys is 2.96 and the σ_D is .79. The t is 2.96/.79 or 3.75; and the degrees of freedom to be used in testing this t are $(125 - 1) + (137 - 1) - 1$, or 259.* We must subtract the one additional df to allow for the fact that our groups were matched in variable Y. The general rule (p. 193) is that 1 df is subtracted for *each* restriction imposed upon the observations, i.e., for each matching variable.

Entering Table D with 259 df, we find that our t of 3.75 is larger than the entry of 2.59 at the .01 level. The obtained difference in X (mechanical ability), therefore, though small, is highly significant, and boys in the technical high school are reliably better on the Mechanical Ability Test than are boys of "equal" general intelligence in the academic high school.

The correlation term must be introduced into formula (55) because when two groups have been matched in some test or tests their variability is restricted in *all* functions correlated with the matching variable. Height and weight, for example, are highly correlated in 9-year-old boys. Therefore, if a group of 9-year-old boys of the same

* When $df = 259$, little is to be gained by using t instead of CR.

or nearly the same height is selected, the variability in weight of these children will be substantially reduced as compared with 9-year-old boys in general. When groups are matched for several variables, e.g., age, intelligence, socioeconomic status, and the like, and compared with respect to some correlated variable, the correlation coefficient in formula (55) becomes a multiple coefficient of correlation (p. 395). When $r_{xy} = .00$, (55) reduces to (51)—our groups are independent and unrestricted by the matching variable.

Groups matched for mean and σ and equivalent groups in which individuals are paired as to score have been widely used in a variety of psychological and educational studies. Illustrations are found in experiments designed to evaluate the relative merits of two methods of teaching, the effects of drugs, e.g., tobacco or caffeine, upon efficiency, transfer effects of special training, and the like. Other techniques useful in assessing the role of experimental factors are described in Chapter 10.

4. The reliability of the difference between uncorrelated medians

The reliability of the difference between two medians obtained from independent samples may be found from the formula

$$\sigma_{D_{Mdn}} \text{ or } \sigma_{Mdn_1 - Mdn_2} = \sqrt{\sigma^2_{Mdn_1} + \sigma^2_{Mdn_2}} \quad (56)$$

(SE *of the difference between two uncorrelated medians*)

When medians are correlated, the value of r_{12} cannot be determined accurately and the reliability of the median cannot be readily computed. When samples are not independent, therefore, it is better procedure to use means instead of medians.

II. The Significance of the Difference between σ's

1. The reliability of the difference between two standard deviations

(1) SE OF A DIFFERENCE WHEN σ'S ARE UNCORRELATED

In many studies in psychology and education, differences in variability which appear among groups are a matter of considerable importance. The student of race, sex, and experimentally induced differences is oftentimes more interested in knowing whether his groups differ significantly in SD than in knowing whether they differ in mean achievement. And the educational psychologist who is investigating a new way of teaching arithmetic may want to know whether the new method has led to changes in variability greater than those brought about by the old method.

When samples are independent, i.e., when different groups are studied, or when tests given to the same group are uncorrelated, the reliability of a difference between two σ's may be found thus:

$$\sigma_{D_\sigma} \text{ or } \sigma_{\sigma_1 - \sigma_2} = \sqrt{\sigma^2_{\sigma_1} + \sigma^2_{\sigma_2}} \qquad (57)$$

(SE *of the difference between uncorrelated σ's when* N's *are large*)

where σ_{σ_1} is the SE of the first σ and σ_{σ_2} is the SE of the second σ (p. 195).

By way of illustration, we may apply this formula to the data of the Norwegians and Belgians on page 214. The σ of the Norwegians' scores on the combined scale was 2.47; of the Belgians' scores on the same test, 2.42. Is this very small difference in variability significant? Calling the σ of the Norwegians' scores σ_1 and the σ of the Belgians' scores σ_2, we have

$$\sigma_{\sigma_1} = \frac{.71 \times 2.47}{\sqrt{611}} = .071 \qquad \text{by (43)}$$

$$\sigma_{\sigma_2} = \frac{.71 \times 2.42}{\sqrt{129}} = .151 \qquad \text{`` ``}$$

$$\sigma_{D_\sigma} = \sqrt{(.071)^2 + (.151)^2} = .167 \text{ or } .17 \text{ (to two decimals)}$$

The obtained difference in the σ's is .05 (2.47 − 2.42), and CR is .05/.17 or .30. On the null hypothesis ($\sigma_1 - \sigma_2 = 0$), this CR (Table D, last line), is far short of 1.96, the .05 level. As we suspected, the obtained difference is clearly not significant; and there is no reason to suspect that the two groups are not about equally variable.

Formula (57) is adequate for testing the significance of the difference between two uncorrelated SD's when N's are large (greater than 50, say). But formula (57) is not accurate when N's are small, as the SD's computed from small samples drawn at random from the same normal population will exhibit a skewed distribution around the population σ. (See Figure 47 for normal sampling distribution of means.) Instead of testing the difference between two SD's obtained from small independent samples, therefore, by formula (57) we divide the larger of the two variances (SD^2) by the smaller and test the significance of this ratio, called F,* by the one-tailed test. We then double the probability (P) so found, in order to test the general (null) hypothesis, namely, that the two variances do not differ.

We may illustrate the method of using the F-ratio with Example (4), page 223, in which $N_1 = 6$ and $N_2 = 10$, and the sums of squares around the two means are $\Sigma x_1^2 = 110$ and $\Sigma x_2^2 = 352$, respectively. The first variance (viz, SD_1^2) is 110/5 or 22; and the second variance (SD_2^2) is 352/9 or 39.1. The F-ratio found by dividing the larger by the smaller variance is, then, 39.1/22 or 1.78; and entering Table F with $n_1 = 9$ (df of larger variance) and $n_2 = 5$ (df of smaller variance), we get the two entries 4.78 and 10.15. As given in the table, the first of these is the F-ratio significant at the .05 level, and the second is the F-ratio significant at the .01 level. However, since we have used the one-tailed test (have divided only the larger variance by the smaller), these two F-ratios, viz., 4.78 and 10.15, really represent the .10 and the .02 levels of confidence (see p. 217). Our F of 1.78 falls far below the smaller of these values (namely, 4.78) and hence is not significant at the .10 level, much less at the .05 or .01 levels. There is no evidence, therefore, that the two groups really differ with respect to variability.

(2) SE OF A DIFFERENCE WHEN σ'S ARE CORRELATED

When we compare the σ's of the same group upon two occasions or the σ's of equivalent groups on a final test, we must take into account possible correlation between the σ's in the two groups being compared. The formula for testing the significance of an obtained difference in variability when SD's are correlated is

$$\sigma_{D_\sigma} = \sqrt{\sigma^2_{\sigma_1} + \sigma^2_{\sigma_2} - 2r^2_{12}\sigma_{\sigma_1}\sigma_{\sigma_2}} \qquad (58)$$

(SE *of the difference between correlated* σ's *when* N's *are large*)

where σ_{σ_1} and σ_{σ_2} are the SE's of the two SD's and r^2_{12} is the square of the coefficient of correlation between scores in initial and final tests or between final scores of equivalent groups.†

Formula (58) may be applied to the problems on page 226 by

* See pages 278–281 for explanation of the F-ratio; and page 429 for the table of F.

† The correlation between the SD's of samples drawn from a given population equals the square of the coefficient of correlation between the test scores, the SD's of which are being compared.

RELIABILITY OF DIFFERENCE BETWEEN MEANS AND OTHER MEASURES • 235

way of illustration. In the first problem, the SD of 64 sixth-grade children was 6.0 on the initial and 5.0 on the final test. Is there a significant drop in variability in reading after a year's schooling? Putting $\sigma_1 = 6.0$ and $\sigma_2 = 5.0$, we have

$$\sigma_{\sigma_1} = \frac{.71 \times 6.0}{\sqrt{64}} = .53 \qquad \text{by (43)}$$

$$\sigma_{\sigma_2} = \frac{.71 \times 5.0}{\sqrt{64}} = .44$$

The coefficient of correlation between initial and final scores is .60, so that $r^2{}_{12} = .36$. Substituting for r^2 and the σ_σ's in formula (58) we have

$$\sigma_{D_\sigma} = \sqrt{(.53)^2 + (.44)^2 - 2 \times .36 \times .53 \times .44} = .55$$

The difference between the two σ's is 1.0 and the SE of this difference is .55. Therefore, on the null hypothesis of equal σ's, $t = \dfrac{(6-5) - 0}{.55}$ or 1.80. Entering Table D with 63 df, we find t at the .05 level to be 2.00. The obtained t does not quite reach this point, and there is no reason to suspect a true difference in variability between initial and final reading scores.

In the equivalent groups problem on page 228, the SD of the experimental group on the final test was 24.36 and the SD of the control group on the final test was 21.62. The difference between these SD's is 2.74 and the number of children in each group is 72. Did the incentive (praise) produce significantly greater variability in the experimental group as compared with the control? Putting $\sigma_1 = 24.36$, and $\sigma_2 = 21.62$, we have

$$\sigma_{\sigma_1} = \frac{.71 \times 24.36}{\sqrt{72}} = 2.04 \qquad \text{by (43)}$$

$$\sigma_{\sigma_2} = \frac{.71 \times 21.62}{\sqrt{72}} = 1.81$$

The r between final test scores in the experimental and control groups is .65 and $r^2{}_{12}$, therefore, is .42. Substituting for r^2 and the two SE's in formula (58) we have

$$\sigma_{D_\sigma} = \sqrt{(2.04)^2 + (1.81)^2 - 2 \times .42 \times 2.04 \times 1.81}$$
$$= 2.08$$

Dividing 2.74 by 2.08, our t is 1.32; and for 71 degrees of freedom this t falls well below the .05 level of 2.00. There is no evidence, therefore, that the incentive increased variability of response to the test.

III. The Significance of the Difference between Percentages and Correlation Coefficients

1. The reliability of the difference between two percents

(1) SE OF THE DIFFERENCE WHEN PERCENTS ARE UNCORRELATED

On page 196, the formula for the SE of a percentage was given as $SE_{\%} = \sqrt{\dfrac{PQ}{N}}$ where $P =$ percent occurrence of the observed behavior, $Q = (1 - P)$, and N is the size of the sample. One of the most useful applications of the SE formula is in determining the significance of the difference between two percents. In much experimental work, especially in social and abnormal psychology, we are able to get the percent occurrence of a given behavior in two or more independent samples. We then want to know whether the incidence of this behavior is reliably different in the two groups. The following problem which repeats part of Example (1), page 196, will provide an illustration.

Example (1) In a study of cheating * among elementary-school children, 144 or 41.4% of 348 children from homes of good socioeconomic status were found to have cheated on various tests. In the same study, 133 or 50.2% of 265 children from homes of poor socioeconomic status also cheated on the same tests. Is there a true difference in the incidence of cheating in these two groups?

Let us set up the hypothesis that no true difference exists as between the percentages cheating in the two groups and that, with respect to cheating, both samples have been randomly drawn from the same population. A useful procedure in testing this null hypothesis is to consider P_1 (41.4%) and P_2 (50.2%) as being independent determinations of the common population parameter, P; and to estimate P by pooling P_1 and P_2 (see p. 224). A pooled estimate of P is obtained from the equation:

$$P = \frac{N_1 P_1 + N_2 P_2}{N_1 + N_2}$$

Q being, of course, $(1 - P)$.

* Data from Hartshorne, H., and May, M. A., *Studies in Deceit* (New York: Macmillan, 1928), Book II, p. 161.

RELIABILITY OF DIFFERENCE BETWEEN MEANS AND OTHER MEASURES • 237

The estimated percentages, P and Q, may now be put in formula (59) to give the SE of the difference between P_1 and P_2.

$$\sigma_{D_\%} = \sigma_{P_1 - P_2} = \sqrt{\sigma^2_{P_1} + \sigma^2_{P_2}} \qquad (59)$$

$$= \sqrt{PQ\left[\frac{1}{N_1} + \frac{1}{N_2}\right]}$$

(SE *of the difference between two uncorrelated percentages*)

In the present example, $P = \dfrac{348 \times 41.4 + 265 \times 50.2}{348 + 265}$ or 45.2%

and $Q = (1 - P)$ or 54.8%. Substituting these two values in (59) we get

$$\sigma_{P_1 - P_2} = \sqrt{45.2 \times 54.8 \left[\frac{1}{348} + \frac{1}{265}\right]} = 4.06\%$$

The difference between the two percents P_1 and P_2 is 8.8% $(50.2 - 41.4)$; and dividing by 4.06 $\left(CR = \dfrac{(P_1 - P_2) - 0}{\sigma_{P_1 - P_2}}\right)$ we get a CR of 2.17. Entering Table D, last line (there are 611 df), we find that our CR exceeds 1.96 (.05 level) but does not reach 2.58 (.01 level). We can be reasonably confident, therefore, that our two groups do not come from a common population and that the occurrence of cheating in the two groups is reliably different.

(2) SE OF THE DIFFERENCE WHEN PERCENTS ARE CORRELATED

Responses recorded in percentages may be, and usually are, correlated when individuals have been paired or matched in some attribute; or when the same group gives answers (e.g., "Yes"—"No") to the same questions or items. To illustrate with an example:

Example (2) A large group of veterans (250 *) answered as follows the two questions:
1. Do you have a great many bad headaches? Yes 150 No 100
2. Are you troubled with fears of being crushed in a crowd? Yes 125 No 125

		#1		
		No	Yes	
#2	Yes	25	100	125
	No	75	50	125
		100	150	250

		# 1		
		No	Yes	
#2	Yes	(b) 10%	(a) 40%	50%
	No	(d) 30%	(c) 20%	50%
		40%	60%	100%

* The data have been simplified for illustrative purposes.

The data in the 2×2 table on the left show the number who answered "Yes" to both questions, "No" to both questions, "Yes" to one and "No" to the other. In the second diagram (on the right) frequencies are expressed as percents of 250. The letters a, b, c, and d are to designate the four cells (p. 363). We find that a total of 60% answered "Yes" to Question 1, and that a total of 50% answered "Yes" to Question 2. Is this difference between the questions significant?

The general formula for the significance of the difference between two correlated percents is

$$\sigma_{P_1 - P_2} = \sqrt{\sigma^2_{P_1} + \sigma^2_{P_2} - 2r_{P_1 P_2}\sigma_{P_1}\sigma_{P_2}} \qquad (60)$$

(SE *of difference between two correlated percents*)

in which r between the two percents is given by the phi-coefficient (p. 367), a ratio equivalent to the correlation coefficient in 2×2 tables.

If P_1 and P_2 have been averaged in order to provide an estimate of P, the population parameter, formula (60) becomes

$$\sigma_{P_1 - P_2} = \sqrt{2\sigma^2_P (1 - r_{P_1 P_2})} \qquad (61)$$

(SE *of the difference between two correlated percents when* P *is estimated from* P_1 *and* P_2)

In example (2), $P_1 = 60\%$ and $P_2 = 50\%$, so that $P = 55\%$ and $Q = 45\%$. Substituting in (61) we have that

$$\sigma_{P_1 - P_2} = \sqrt{\frac{2 \times .55 \times .45}{250}(1 - .408)} *$$

$$= .0342$$

The obtained difference of .10 (.60 − .50) divided by .034 gives a CR of 2.94. From Table D, last line, we find that this critical ratio exceeds 2.58, the .01 level. We abandon the null hypothesis, therefore, and conclude that our groups differed significantly in their answers to the two questions.

A simpler formula than (61) which avoids the calculation of the correlation coefficient may be used when P has been estimated from P_1 and P_2 under the null hypothesis. This formula † is

---

* The phi-coefficient of .408 was found from formula (93), page 367.
† McNemar, Q., "Note on the Sampling Error of the Difference between Correlated Proportions or Percentages," *Psychometrika*, 1947, 12, 153–157.

RELIABILITY OF DIFFERENCE BETWEEN MEANS AND OTHER MEASURES · 239

$$\sigma_{D_\%} = \sqrt{\frac{(b+c)}{N}} \qquad (62)$$

(SE *of the difference between two correlated percentages*)

In example (2) we read from the second diagram that $c = 20\%$ and $b = 10\%$, N being 250. Substituting in (62) we have

$$\sigma_{D_\%} = \sqrt{\frac{.10 + .20}{250}} = .034$$

which checks the result obtained from (61).

2. The reliability of the difference between two r's

A useful and mathematically exact method of determining the SE of the difference between two r's requires that we first convert the r's into Fisher's z-function. The significance of the difference between two z's is then determined. The formula for the SE of the difference between two z's is

$$\sigma_{D_z} = \sigma_{z_1 - z_2} = \sqrt{\frac{1}{N_1 - 3} + \frac{1}{N_2 - 3}} \qquad (63)$$

(SE *of the difference between two z coefficients*)

where $\sigma_z = \dfrac{1}{\sqrt{N-3}}$ *

The following example will illustrate the procedure.

Example (3) The r between intelligence and achievement in the freshman class of College A is .40, for $N = 400$. And the r between intelligence and achievement in the freshman class of College B is .50 for $N = 600$. Is the relationship between intelligence and achievement higher in College B than in College A?

From Table C we read that r's of .40 and .50 correspond to z's of .42 and .55, respectively. If we put $N_1 = 400$ and $N_2 = 600$, we have on substituting in (63)

$$\sigma_{z_1 - z_2} = \sqrt{\frac{1}{(400 - 3)} + \frac{1}{(600 - 3)}}$$
$$= .065$$

*The two correlated variables take away 2 degrees of freedom; and the transformation into z adds another restriction. Hence we subtract 3 from each N (see p. 193).

Dividing .13 (.55 − .42) by .065, we obtain a CR of 2.00. This CR exceeds slightly the value 1.96 and hence is significant at the .05 level. Based on the evidence we have, the $r = .50$ in College B is reliably higher than the $r = .40$ in College A.

Use of the z transformation for r is especially useful when r's are very high, as the sampling distributions of such r's are known to be skewed—often badly so. To illustrate, suppose that r between two achievement tests is .87 in Grade 6 ($N_1 = 50$) and that the r between the same tests is .72 in Grade 7 ($N_2 = 65$). Is there a significant difference between these two r's?

From Table C we find that r's of .87 and .72 yield z's of 1.33 and .91, respectively; and subtsituting N_1 and N_2 in formula (63) we have

$$\sigma_{z_1 - z_2} = \sqrt{\frac{1}{47} + \frac{1}{62}}$$
$$= .193$$

Dividing .42 (1.33 − .91) by .193 we get a CR of 2.18, well above the .05 level of 1.96 but below the .01 level of 2.58. We may discard the null hypothesis, therefore, and mark the difference between our r's significant at the .05 level.

Measurement of the significance of the difference between two r's obtained from the same sample presents certain complications, as r's from the same group are presumably correlated. Formulas for computing the correlation between two correlated r's are not entirely satisfactory and there is no method of determining the correlation between two z's directly. Fortunately, we may feel sure that *if* the r's are positively correlated in our group, and the CR as determined by the SE from (63) is significant, that the CR would be even more significant if the correlation between the r's were known.

The z-transformation can be usefully employed when r's which differ widely in size are to be averaged or combined (p. 198).

IV. The Significance of Deviations from Normality

Distributions which show deviations from the normal form are said to exhibit skewness or kurtosis or both. Skewed distributions are asymmetric or off-center—shifted to the right or left (Figs. 23 and 24, p. 98); while distributions showing kurtosis are more flat-

RELIABILITY OF DIFFERENCE BETWEEN MEANS AND OTHER MEASURES • 241

tened or peaked than the normal (Fig. 25, p. 100). In many studies the investigator wants to know whether his distributions are too atypical or deviant to be treated as normal, or whether their departures from normality are relatively mild and non-significant. Exact tests of the significance of various degrees of skewness or kurtosis will be found in more advanced text books.* The approximate tests of significance given in this section are accurate enough for many purposes and are relatively easy to apply.

1. The reliability of the percentile measure of skewness

On page 99, the following formula was given for estimating the skewness of a frequency distribution in terms of its median and certain percentiles:

$$Sk = \frac{(P_{90} - P_{10})}{2} - P_{50} \tag{20}$$

According to this formula, the skewness of the 50 Army Alpha scores in Table 1, page 5, is -2.50. The problem, then, is to determine whether this degree of skewness represents a significant departure from zero, the skewness of the normal curve. The SE of the measure of skewness given above is

$$\sigma_{Sk} = \frac{.5185\ D}{\sqrt{N}} \tag{64}$$

[SE *of the measure of skewness given in formula* (20)]

in which $D = (P_{90} - P_{10})$.

In the frequency distribution of the 50 Army Alpha scores, $P_{90} = 187$, $P_{10} = 152$, and $D = 35$. From formula (64), therefore,

$$\sigma_{Sk} = \frac{.5185 \times 35}{\sqrt{50}} = 2.57$$

The deviation of our measure of skewness from 0 skewness is -2.50, and dividing -2.50 by 2.57 ($CR = x/\sigma_{Sk}$) we get a CR of $-.97$. Note that the minus sign of 2.50 indicates simply the direction of skewness. Our Sk, therefore, deviates $-.97\ \sigma_{Sk}$ from 0, the measure of skewness in the normal curve. From Table D we find that $-.97$ falls well within the ± 1.96 limits, which determine the .05 level of

* Johnson, Palmer O., *Statistical Methods in Research* (New York: Prentice-Hall, Inc., 1949), Chap. 7.

significance. Hence it is clear that -2.50 represents no real deviation of this frequency distribution from normality.

The skewness of the distribution of 200 cancellation scores (p. 99) is .03 by formula (20). Since $P_{90} = 128.5$, $P_{10} = 110.4$, and $D = 18.1$, the SE of Sk is

$$\sigma_{Sk} = \frac{.5185 \times 18.1}{\sqrt{200}} = .66$$

Dividing .03 by .66, we get .046; and from Table D we find that this CR is far short of 1.96, the .05 level of significance. In fact, this distribution is almost perfectly symmetrical as is shown in Figure 5, page 18.

2. The reliability of the percentile measure of kurtosis

The formula below for measuring kurtosis in terms of Q and certain percentiles in the distribution was given on page 100:

$$Ku = \frac{Q}{(P_{90} - P_{10})} \tag{21}$$

The kurtosis of the frequency distribution of 50 Army Alpha scores (p. 00) by formula (21) is .237; and this Ku deviates $-.026$ from .263, the Ku of the normal distribution (p. 100). The negative direction of the deviation indicates that the distribution tends toward leptokurtosis.

To estimate the significance of our Ku of $-.026$ from the Ku of the normal curve, we may calculate the SE of Ku by the following formula:

$$\sigma_{Ku} = \frac{.28}{\sqrt{N}} \tag{65}$$

[SE *of the measure of* Ku *given by formula* (21)]

in which N is, of course, the size of the sample.

For the 50 Army Alpha scores (p. 5), $\sigma_{Ku} = \frac{.28}{\sqrt{50}}$ or .039, and the CR (Ku/σ_{Ku}) is $-.026/.039$ or $-.67$. This CR is less than 1.96, the .05 significance level, and there is no evidence—so far as our test is concerned—that this distribution is really more peaked than the normal.

The kurtosis of the 200 cancellation scores (p. 13) is .223 by formula (21). This Ku deviates $-.040$ from $.263$, the Ku of the normal curve. Again the direction of the deviation is toward leptokurtosis. The SE of our Ku of $.223$ is $.020$ by formula (65); and Ku/σ_{Ku} is $-.040/.020$ or -2.00. Deviation from normal kurtosis is slightly greater than 1.96, the .05 significance level, but less than 2.58, the .01 significance level. The narrow dispersion of this distribution ($Q = 4.04$) and the fairly large N leads to a heavy concentration of cases in the middle range; and these factors could well account for the strong tendency of this distribution to be more peaked than the normal. Leptokurtosis is not apparent in the curve itself (Fig. 5, p. 18).

PROBLEMS

1. The difference between two means is 3.60 and $\sigma_D = 3$. Both samples are larger than 100.
   (a) Is the obtained difference significant at the .05 level?
   (b) What percent is the obtained difference of the difference necessary for significance at the .01 level?
   (c) Find the limits of the .99 confidence-interval for the true difference.

2. A personality inventory is administered in a private school to 8 boys whose conduct records are exemplary, and to 5 boys whose records are very poor. Data are given below.

   Group 1:   110   112   95   105   111   97   112   102
   "   2:   115   112   109   112   117

   Is the difference between group means significant at the .05 level? at the .01 level?

3. In which of the following experimental problems would it be more important to avoid Type I errors of inference than Type II errors in determining the significance of a difference?
   (a) Sex differences in reading rate and comprehension in the fifth grade.
   (b) Effects of a new drug upon reaction time—especially when the drugs are potent and probably dangerous.
   (c) Comparison of two methods of learning a new skill.
   (d) Acceptance of a program which involves much time and money and rejection of a less expensive program.
   (e) Comparative efficiency of a speed-up and a normal rate of work in a factory.

4. In the first trial of a practice period, 25 twelve-year-olds have a mean score of 80.00 and a SD of 8.00 upon a digit-symbol learning test. On the

tenth trial, the mean is 84.00 and the SD is 10.00. The r between scores on the first and tenth trials is .40. Our hypothesis is that practice leads to gain.

(a) Is the *gain* in score significant at the .05 level? at the .01 level? (p. 217)

(b) What gain would be significant at the .01 level, other conditions remaining the same?

5. Two groups of high-school pupils are matched for initial ability in a biology test. Group 1 is taught by the lecture method, and Group 2 by the lecture-demonstration method. Data are as follows:

	Group 1 (control)	Group 2 (experimental)
N	60	60
Mean initial score on the biology test	42.30	42.50
σ of initial scores on the biology test	5.36	5.38
Mean final score on the biology test	54.54	56.74
σ of final scores on the biology test	6.34	7.25
r (between final scores on the biology test) =	.50	

(a) Is the difference between the final scores made by Groups 1 and 2 upon the biology test significant at the .05 level? at the .01 level?

(b) Determine the limits of the .95 confidence-interval for the true difference.

(c) Is the difference in the variability of the final scores made by Groups 1 and 2 significant at the .05 level?

6. Two groups of high-school students are matched for M and σ upon a group intelligence test. There are fifty-eight subjects in Group A and seventy-two in Group B. The records of these two groups upon a battery of "learning" tests are as follows:

	Group A	Group B
M	48.52	53.61
σ	10.60	15.35
N	58	72

The correlation of the group intelligence test and the learning battery in the entire group from which A and B were drawn is .50. Is the difference between Groups A and B significant at the .05 level? at the .01 level?

7. Calculate measures of skewness and kurtosis for the first two distributions in Chapter 2, problem 1, page 40. Compute standard errors of Sk and Ku by the formulas given on pages 241 and 242. Determine whether either of these distributions departs significantly from the normal form.

8. In a school of 500 pupils, 52.3% are girls; and in a second school of 300 pupils, 47.7% are girls. Is there a significant difference between the percentages of girls enrolled in the two schools?

9. Given the following data for an item in Stanford-Binet: of 100 nine-year-olds, 72% pass; of 100 ten-year-olds, 78% pass. Is the item more difficult for nine-year-olds than for ten-year-olds?

10. (a) To the question "Would you like to be an aviator?" 145 fifteen-year-old boys in a high-school class of 205 answered "Yes" and 60 answered "No." To the question "Would you like to be an engineer?" 125 said "Yes" and 80 answered "No." The data in the table below show the number who answered "Yes" to both questions, "No" to both questions, "Yes" to one and "No" to the other. Is desire to be an aviator significantly stronger in this group than desire to be an engineer?

	Ques. 1		
	No	Yes	
Ques. 2 Yes	25	100	125
No	35	45	80
	60	145	205

(b) In a group of 64 seventh-grade children, 32 answered Item 23 correctly and 36 answered Item 26 correctly. From the table below, determine whether the difference in the percentage of correct answers is significant.

	Item 23		
	−	+	
Item 26 +	10	26	36
−	22	6	28
	32	32	64

11. In random samples of 100 cases each from four groups, A, B, C, and D, the following results were obtained:

	A	B	C	D
Mean	101.00	104.00	93.00	86.00
σ	10.00	11.00	9.60	8.50

What are the chances that, in general, the mean of

(a) the B's is higher than the mean of the A's.
(b) the A's is higher than the mean of the C's.
(c) the C's is higher than the mean of the D's.

What are the chances that
(a) any B will be better than the mean A.
(b) any B will be better than the mean C.
(c) any B will be better than the mean D.

12. (a) The correlation between height and weight in a sample of 200 ten-year-old boys is .70; and the correlation between height and weight in a sample of 250 ten-year-old girls is .62. Is this difference significant?

(b) In a sample of 150 high-school freshmen the correlation of two educational achievement tests is .65. If from past years the correlation has averaged .60, is the present group atypical? (Does .65 differ significantly from .60?)

ANSWERS

1. (a) No. $CR = 1.20$ (b) 46.5%   (c) -4.14 and 7.74
2. $t = 2.3$; for 11 df, significant at .05, not at .01 level
3. a, c and d
4. (a) Significant at .05, not at .01 level. Since $t = 2.00$ there is approximately 1 chance in 50 that a *plus* difference (gain) of 4 would occur under the null hypothesis.
   (b) 4.66
5. (a) $t = 2.49$; difference in M's significant at .05 but not at .01 level.
   (b) .43 to 3.97
   (c) No. $t = 1.18$
6. Significant at .05 level ($t = 2.57$) and almost significant at .01 level.
7. Distribution Sk/σ_{Sk} Ku/σ_{Ku}
   1      $-.23$ .55   Deviation from normality not significant
   2   .51 $-.38$ "   "   "   "   "
8. No. $CR = 1.24$
9. No. $CR = 1.00$
10. (a) Significant at .05, not at .01 level ($CR = 2.43$)
    (b) Not significant (CR approximately 1.00)
11. (a) 98 in 100
    (b) more than 99 in 100
    (c) more than 99 in 100

    (a) 61 in 100
    (b) 84 in 100
    (c) 95 in 100
12. (a) No. $CR = 1.47$ (b) No. $CR = 1.09$

10

TESTING EXPERIMENTAL HYPOTHESES

The hypothesis proposed in a psychological experiment may take the form of a general theory or a specific inquiry. A specific hypothesis is ordinarily to be preferred to a general proposal, as the more definite and exact the query the greater the likelihood of a conclusive answer. In the preceding chapter, the significance of an obtained difference was tested against a null hypothesis. In the present chapter, we shall consider further the nature of hypotheses and shall present certain useful procedures and methods for answering the questions raised by an experiment.

I. The Null Hypothesis

1. Advantages of the null hypothesis

In Chapter 9 the difference between two statistics was tested against a null hypothesis, namely, that the true difference is zero. The null hypothesis is not confined to zero differences nor to the differences between statistics. Others forms of this hypothesis assert that the results found in an experiment do not differ significantly from results to be expected on a probability basis or stipulated in terms of some theory. A null hypothesis, as we have said on page 213, is ordinarily more useful than other hypotheses because it is exact. Hypotheses other than the null can, to be sure, be stated exactly: we may, for example, assert that a group which has received special training will be 5 points on the average ahead of an untrained (control) group. But it is difficult to set up such precise expectations in most experiments. And for this reason it is usually advisable to test against a null hypothesis, rather than some other, if this can be done.

It is sometimes not fully understood that the rejection of a null hypothesis does not immediately force acceptance of a contrary view * (see p. 215). The extrasensory perception (ESP) experiments † offer a good illustration of what is meant by this statement. In a typical ESP experiment, a pack of 25 cards is used. There are 5 different symbols on these cards, each symbol appearing on 5 cards. In guessing through the pack of 25, the probability of chance success with each card is 1/5. And the number of correct "calls" in a pack of 25 should be 5. If a subject calls the cards correctly much in excess of chance expectation (i.e., in excess of 5) the null (chance) hypothesis is rejected. But rejection of the chance hypothesis does not force acceptance of ESP as the cause of the extra-chance result. Before this claim can be made, one must demonstrate in follow-up experiments that extra-chance results are obtained when *all* likely causes, such as runs of cards, visual and other cues, poor shuffling and recording, and the like have been eliminated. If under rigid controls calls in excess of chance are consistently obtained, we may reject the null (chance) hypothesis and accept ESP. But the acceptance of a positive hypothesis—it should be noted—is the end result of a series of careful experiments. And moreover, it is a logical and not primarily a statistical conclusion.

2. Testing experimentally observed results against the direct determination of probable outcomes

The null hypothesis is often useful when we wish to compare observed results with those to be expected by "chance." Several examples will illustrate the methods to be employed.

Example (1) Two tones, differing slightly in pitch, are to be compared in an experiment. The tones are presented in succession, the subject being instructed to report the second as higher or lower than the first. Presentation is in random order. In ten trials a subject is right in his judgment seven times. Is this result significant, i.e., better than chance?

Since the subject is either right or wrong in his judgment, and since judgments are separate and independent, we may test our result

---

* Morgan, J. J. B., "Credence Given to One Hypothesis Because of the Overthrow of Its Rivals," *Amer. Jour. Psychol.*, 1945, 58, 54–64.

† Rhine, J. B., *et al.*, *Extra-sensory Perception after Sixty Years* (New York: Henry Holt and Co., 1940).

against the binomial expansion (p. 90). Ten judgments may be taken as analogous to ten coins; a right judgment corresponds to a head, say, a wrong judgment to a tail. The odds are even that any given judgment will be right; hence in ten trials (since $p = 1/2$) our subject should in general be right five times by chance alone. The question, then, is whether seven "rights" are significantly greater than the expected five. From page 90 we find that upon expanding $(p + q)^{10}$ the probability of 10 right judgments is 1/1024; of 9 right and one wrong, 10/1024; of 8 right and 2 wrong, 45/1024; and of 7 right and 3 wrong, 120/1024. Adding these fractions we get 176/1024, or .172 as the probability of 7 or *more* right judgments by chance alone. The probability of *just* 7 rights is 120/1024, or approximately .12. Neither of these results is significant at the .05 level of confidence (p. 186) and accordingly the null hypothesis must be retained. On the evidence there is no reason to believe that our subject's judgments are really better than chance expectation.

Note that to get 10 right is highly significant (the probability is approximately .001); to get 9 *or* 10 right is also significant (the probability is 1/1024 + 10/1024, or approximately .01). To get 8 or *more* right is almost significant at the .05 level (the probability is .055); but any number right less than 8 fails to reach our standard. The situation described in Example (1) occurs in a number of experiments—whenever, for example, objects, weights, lights, test items, or other stimuli are to be compared, the odds being 50:50 that a given judgment is correct.

> *Example (2)* Ten photos, 5 of feeble-minded and 5 of normal children (of the same age and sex), are presented to a subject who claims he can identify the feeble-minded from their photographs. The subject is instructed to designate which five photographs are those of feeble-minded children. How many photos must our subject identify correctly before the null hypothesis is disproved?

Since there are 5 feeble-minded and 5 normal photos, the subject has a 50:50 chance of success with each photo and the method of Example (1) could be used. A better test,* however, is to determine the probability that a particular set of 5 photos (namely, the *right* five) will be selected from all possible sets of 5 which may be drawn from the 10 given photos. To find how many combinations of 5 photos can be drawn from a set of 10, we may use conveniently the formula for the combination of 10 things taken 5 at a time. This

---

* Fisher, R. A., *The Design of Experiments* (London: Oliver and Boyd, 1935), Chapter 2, pp. 26–29 especially.

formula * is written $C^{10}_5 = \dfrac{10\,!}{5\,!\,5\,!} = 252$. The symbol C^{10}_5 is read "the combinations of ten things taken five at a time"; 10 ! (read "10 factorial") is 10·9·8·7·6·5·4·3·2·1; and 5 ! is 5·4·3·2·1.

It is possible, therefore, to draw 252 combinations of 5 from a set of 10, and accordingly there is one chance in 252 that a judge will select the 5 correct photos out of all possible sets of 5. If he does select the right 5, this result is obviously significant (the probability is approximately .004) and the null hypothesis must be rejected. Suppose that our judge's set of 5 photos contains 4 feeble-minded and one normal picture; or 3 feeble-minded and 2 normal pictures. Is either of these results significant? The probability of 4 right selections and one wrong selection by chance is $\dfrac{C^5_4 \times C^5_1}{C^{10}_5}$, i.e., the product of the number of ways 4 rights can be selected from the 5 feeble-minded pictures times the number of ways one wrong can be selected from the 5 normal pictures divided by the total number of combinations of 5. Calculation shows this result to be 25/252 or 1/10 (approximately) and hence *not* significant at the .05 level. The probability of getting 3 right and 2 wrong is given by $\dfrac{C^5_3 \times C^5_2}{C^{10}_5}$; namely, the product of the number of ways 3 pictures can be selected from 5 (the 5 feeble-minded pictures) times the number of ways 2 pictures can be selected from the 5 normal pictures divided by the total number of combinations of 5. This result is 100/252 or slightly greater than 1/3, and is clearly not significant.

Our subject disproves the null hypothesis, then, *only* when *all* 5 feeble-minded pictures are correctly chosen. The probabilities of various combinations of right and wrong choices are given below—they should be verified by the student:

Probability of all	5R =	1/252
" "	4R =	25/252
" "	3R =	100/252
" "	2R =	100/252
" "	1R =	25/252
" "	0R =	1/252

It may be noted that by increasing the number of pictures of feeble-minded and normal from 10 to 20, say, the *sensitiveness* of

---

* The general formula for the combinations of n things taken r at a time is $C^n_r = \dfrac{n\,!}{r\,!\,(n-r)\,!}$

the experiment can be considerably enhanced. With 20 pictures it is not necessary to get all 10 feeble-minded photos right in order to achieve a significant result. In fact, 8 right is nearly significant at the .01 level as shown below.

$$C^{20}{}_{10} = \frac{20\,!}{10\,!\ 10\,!} = 184{,}756$$

Combinations	Frequency	Prob. ratio (freq. ÷ 184,756)
10R 0W	1	.000005
9R 1W	100	.0005
8R 2W	2025	.011
7R 3W	14400	.078
6R 4W	44100	.238
5R 5W	63504	.343
4R 6W	44100	.238
3R 7W	14400	.078
2R 8W	2025	.011
1R 9W	100	.0005
0R 10W	1	.000005
	184,756	

3. Testing experimentally observed results against probabilities calculated from the normal curve

When the number of observations or the number of trials is large, direct calculation of expectations by expanding the binomial $(p+q)^n$ becomes highly laborious. Since $(p+q)^n$ yields a distribution (p. 91) which is essentially normal when n is large, in many experiments the normal curve may be usefully employed to provide expected results under the null hypothesis. An example will make the method clear.

> *Example (3)* In answering a test of 100 true-false items, a subject gets 60 right. Is it likely that the subject merely guessed?

As there are only two possible answers to each item, one of which is right and the other wrong, the probability of a correct answer to any item is 1/2, and our subject should by chance answer 1/2 of 100 or 50 items correctly. Letting p equal the probability of a right answer, and q the probability of a wrong answer, we could, by expanding the binomial $(p+q)^{100}$, calculate the probability of various combinations of rights and wrongs on the null hypothesis. When the exponent of the binomial (here, number of items) is as large as 100, however, the resulting distribution is very close to the normal probability curve (p. 87) and may be so treated with little error.

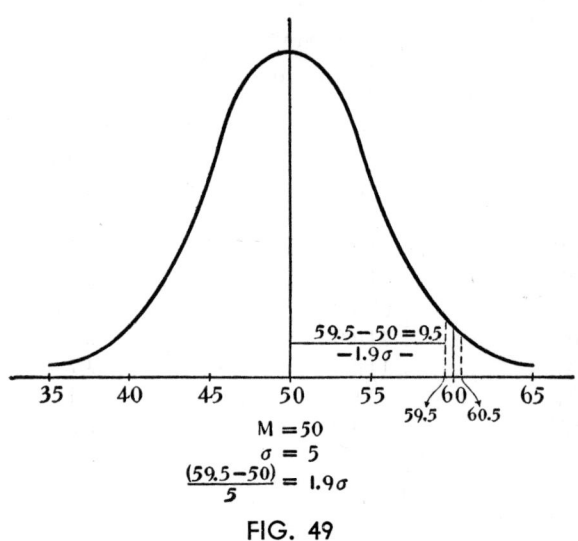

FIG. 49

Figure 49 illustrates the solution of this problem. The mean of the curve is set at 50. The SD of the probability distribution found by expanding $(p+q)^n$ is $\sigma = \sqrt{npq}$; hence for $(p+q)^{100}$, $\sigma = \sqrt{100 \times 1/2 \times 1/2}$ or 5. A score of 60 covers the interval on the baseline from 59.5 up to 60.5. The lower limit of 60 is 1.9σ removed from the mean $\left(\dfrac{59.5 - 50}{5} = 1.9\sigma\right)$; and from Table A we find that 2.87% of the area of a normal curve lies *above* 1.9σ.* There are only three chances in 100 that a score of 60 (or more) would be made if the null hypothesis were true. A score of 60, therefore, is significant at the .05 level. We may reject the null hypothesis with some confidence and conclude that our subject could not have been simply guessing.

Note that the problem above could have been solved equally well in terms of percentages. We should expect our subject to get 50% of the items right by guessing. The SD of this percentage is $\sqrt{\dfrac{50\% \times 50\%}{100}}$ or 5%. A score of 60% (lower limit 59.5%) is 9.5%

* Note that only one end of the normal curve is used. See page 217.

1.9σ distant from the middle of the curve. We interpret this result in exactly the same way as that above.

Example (4) A multiple-choice test of 60 items provides four possible responses to each item. How many items should a subject answer correctly before we may feel sure that he knows something about the test material?

Since there are four responses to each item, only one of which is correct, the probability of a right answer by guessing is 1/4, of a wrong answer 3/4. The final score to be expected if a subject knows nothing whatever about the test and simply guesses is $1/4 \times 60$ or 15. Our task, therefore, is to determine how much better than 15 a subject must score in order to demonstrate real knowledge of the material.

This problem can be solved by the methods of Example (1). By expanding the binomial $(p+q)^n$, for instance, in which $p = 1/4$, $q = 3/4$, and $n = 60$, we can determine the probability of the occurrence of any score from 0 to 60. The direct determination of probabilities from the binomial expansion is straightforward and exact but the calculation is tedious. Fortunately, therefore, a satisfactory approximation to the answer we want can be obtained by using the normal distribution to determine probabilities, as in Example (3). The mean of our "chance" distribution is 1/4 of 60 or 15; and the $\sigma = \sqrt{npq} = \sqrt{60 \times 1/4 \times 3/4}$ or 3.35. From Table A we know that 5% of the frequency in a normal distribution lie above 1.65σ. Multiplying our obtained σ (3.35) by 1.65, we get 5.53; and this value when added to 15 gives us 20.5 as the point above which lie 5% of the "chance" distribution of scores. A score of 21 (20.5 to 21.5), therefore, may be regarded as significant, and if a subject achieves such a score we can be reasonably sure that he is not merely guessing.

For a higher level of assurance, we may take that score which would occur by chance only once in 100 trials. From Table A, 1% of the frequency in the normal curve lies above 2.33σ. This point is 7.81 (3.35×2.33) above 15 or at 22.8. A score of 23, therefore, or a higher score is *very* significant; only once in 100 trials would a subject achieve such a score by guessing.

Use of the normal probability curve in the solution of problems like this always involves a degree of approximation. When p differs considerably from 1/2 and n is small, the distribution resulting from the expansion of $(p+q)^n$ is skewed and is not therefore accurately described by the normal curve. Under these circumstances one must resort to the direct determination of probabilities as in Example (1). When n is large, however, and p not far from 1/2, the normal distribution can be safely used, as will be shown by the chi-square tests on page 261.

II. The χ^2 (Chi-square) Test and the Null Hypothesis

The chi-square test represents a useful method of comparing experimentally obtained results with those to be expected theoretically on some hypothesis.* The formula for chi-square (χ^2) is stated as follows:

$$\chi^2 = \Sigma \left[\frac{(f_o - f_e)^2}{f_e} \right] \tag{66}$$

(*chi-square formula for testing agreement between observed and expected results*)

in which

f_o = frequency of occurrence of observed or experimentally determined facts;

f_e = expected frequency of occurrence on some hypothesis.

The differences between observed and expected frequencies are squared and divided by the expected number in each case, and the sum of these quotients is χ^2. The more closely the observed results approximate to the expected, the smaller the chi-square and the closer the agreement between observed data and the hypothesis being tested. Contrariwise, the larger the chi-square the greater the probability of a real divergence of experimentally observed from expected results. To evaluate chi-square, we enter Table E with the computed value of chi-square and the appropriate number of degrees of freedom. The number of $df = (r - 1)(c - 1)$ in which r is the number of rows and c the number of columns in which the data are tabulated. From Table E we read P, the probability that the obtained χ^2 is significant. Several illustrations of the chi-square test will be given in the sections following.

*Lewis, D., *Quantitative Methods in Psychology* (Ann Arbor: Edwards Bros., 1948), Chap. 8.

I. Testing the divergence of observed results from those expected on the hypothesis of equal probability (null hypothesis)

Example (1) Forty-eight subjects are asked to express their attitude toward the proposition "Should the United States Join a Security Organization of Nations?" by marking F (favorable) I (indifferent) or U (unfavorable). Of the members in the group, 24 marked F, 12 I, and 12 U. Do these results indicate a significant trend of opinion?

The observed data (f_o) are given in the first row of Table 26. In the second row is the distribution of answers to be expected on the null hypothesis (f_e), if each answer is selected equally often. Below the table are entered the differences $(f_o - f_e)$. Each of these differences is squared and divided by its f_e $(64/16 + 16/16 + 16/16)$ to give $\chi^2 = 6$.

TABLE 26

	Answers			
	Favorable	Indifferent	Unfavorable	
Observed (f_o)	24	12	12	48
Expected (f_e)	16	16	16	48
$(f_o - f_e)$	8	4	4	
$(f_o - f_e)^2$	64	16	16	
$(f_o - f_e)^2 / f_e$	4	1	1	

$$\chi^2 = \Sigma \left[\frac{(f_o - f_e)^2}{f_e} \right] = 6 \quad df = 2 \quad P = .05 \text{ (Table E)}$$

The degrees of freedom in the table may be calculated from the formula $df = (r - 1)(c - 1)$ to be $(3 - 1)(2 - 1)$ or 2. Or, the degrees of freedom may be found directly in the following way: Since we know the row totals to be 48, when two entries are made in a row the third is immediately fixed, is not "free." When the first two entries in row 1 are 24 and 12, for example, the third entry must be 12 to make up 48. Since we also know the sums of the columns, only *one* entry in a column is free, the second being fixed as soon as the first is tabulated. There are, then, *two* degrees of freedom for rows and *one* degree of freedom for columns, and $2 \times 1 = 2$ degrees of freedom for the table.

256 • STATISTICS IN PSYCHOLOGY AND EDUCATION

Entering Table E we find in row $df = 2$, a χ^2 of almost 6 (actually, 5.991) in the column headed .05. A P of .05 means that should we repeat this experiment, only once in 20 trials would a χ^2 of 6 (or more) occur if the null hypothesis were true. Our result may be marked "significant at the .05 level," therefore, on the grounds that divergence of observed from expected results is too unlikely of occurrence to be accounted for *solely* by sampling fluctuations. We reject the "equal answer" hypothesis and conclude that our group really favors the proposition. In general, we may safely discard a null hypothesis whenever P is .05 or less.

Example (2) The items in an attitude scale are answered by underlining one of the following phrases: Strongly approve, approve, indifferent, disapprove, strongly disapprove. The distribution of answers to an item marked by 100 subjects is shown in Table 27. Do these answers diverge significantly from the distribution to be expected if there are no preferences in the group?

TABLE 27

	Strongly Approve	Approve	Indifferent	Disapprove	Strongly Disapprove	
Observed (f_o)	23	18	24	17	18	100
Expected (f_e)	20	20	20	20	20	100
($f_o - f_e$)	3	2	4	3	2	
($f_o - f_e$)^2	9	4	16	9	4	
$\frac{(f_o - f_e)^2}{f_e}$	.45	.20	.80	.45	.20	

$\chi^2 = 2.10$ $df = 4$ P lies between .70 and .80

On the null hypothesis of "equal probability" 20 subjects may be expected to select each of the 5 possible answers. Squaring the $(f_o - f_e)$, dividing by the expected result (f_e), and summing, we obtain a χ^2 of 2.10. $df = (5-1)(2-1)$ or 4. From Table E, reading across from row $df = 4$, we locate a χ^2 of 2.195 in column .70. This χ^2 is nearest to our calculated value of 2.10, which lies between the entries in columns .70 and .80. It is sufficiently accurate to describe P as lying between .70 and .80 without interpolation. Since this much divergence from the null hypothesis, namely, 2.10, can be expected to occur upon repetition of the experiment in approximately 75% of the trials, χ^2 is clearly *not* significant and we must retain the null hypothesis. There is no conclusive evidence of either a strongly favorable or unfavorable attitude toward this item.

2. Testing the divergence of observed results from those expected on the hypothesis of a normal distribution

Our hypothesis may assert that the frequencies of an event which we have observed really follow the normal distribution instead of being equally probable. An example illustrates how this hypothesis may be tested by chi-square.

Example (3) Forty-two salesmen have been classified into 3 groups—very good, satisfactory, and poor—by a consensus of sales managers. Does this distribution of ratings differ significantly from that to be expected if selling ability is normally distributed?

TABLE 28

	Good	Satisfactory	Poor	
Observed (f_o)	16	20	6	42
Expected (f_e)	6.7	28.6	6.7	42
($f_o - f_e$)	9.3	8.6	.7	
($f_o - f_e$)²	86.49	73.96	.49	
$\dfrac{(f_o - f_e)^2}{f_e}$	12.90	2.59	.07	

$\chi^2 = 15.56 \quad df = 2 \quad P$ is less than .01

The entries in row 1 give the number of men classified in each of the 3 categories. In row 2, the entries show how many of the 42 salesmen may be expected to fall in each category on the hypothesis of a normal distribution. These last entries were found by dividing the baseline of a normal curve (taken to extend over 6σ) into 3 equal segments of 2σ each. From Table A, the proportion of the normal distribution to be found in each of these segments is as follows:

		Proportion
Between	$+3.00\sigma$ and $+1.00\sigma$	.16
"	$+1.00\sigma$ and -1.00σ	.68
"	-1.00σ and -3.00σ	.16
		1.00

258 • STATISTICS IN PSYCHOLOGY AND EDUCATION

These proportions of 42 have been calculated and are entered in Table 28. The χ^2 in the table is 15.56 and $df = (3-1)(2-1)$ or 2. From Table E it is clear that this χ^2 lies beyond the limits of the table, hence P is listed simply as less than .01. The discrepancy between observed and expected values is so great that the hypothesis of a normal distribution of selling ability must be rejected. Too many men have been described as good, and too few as satisfactory, to make for agreement with our hypothesis.

3. The chi-square test when table entries are small

When the entries in a table are fairly large, χ^2 gives an estimate of divergence from hypothesis which is close to that obtained by other measures of probability. But χ^2 is not stable when computed from a table in which *any* experimental frequency is less than 5. Moreover, when the table is 2×2 fold (when $df = 1$), χ^2 is subject to considerable error unless a correction for continuity (called Yates' correction) is made. Reasons for making this correction and its effect upon χ^2 can best be seen by working through the examples following.

Example (4) In Example (1), page 248, an observer gave seven correct judgments in ten trials. The probability of a right judgment was 1/2 in each instance, so that the expected number of correct judgments was five. Test our subject's deviation from the null hypothesis by computing chi-square and compare the P with that found by direct calculation.

TABLE 29

	Right	Wrong	
Observed (f_o)	7	3	10
Expected (f_e)	5	5	10
($f_o - f_e$)	2	2	
Correction (− .5)	1.5	1.5	
($f_o - f_e$)²	2.25	2.25	
$\frac{(f_o - f_e)^2}{f_e}$	.45	.45	

$\chi^2 = .90$
$df = 1$
$P = .356$ (by interpolation in Table E)
$\tfrac{1}{2}P = .178$

Calculations in Table 29 follow those of previous tables except for the correction which consists in *subtracting* .5 from each $(f_o - f_e)$ difference. In applying the χ^2-test we assume that adjacent frequencies are connected by a continuous and smooth curve (like the normal curve) and are not discrete numbers. In 2×2 fold tables, especially when entries are small, the χ^2 curve is not continuous. Hence, the deviation of 7 from 5 must be written as 1.5 (6.5 − 5) instead of 2 (7 − 5), as 6.5 is the lower limit of 7 in a continuous series. In like manner the deviation of 3 from 5 must be taken from the upper limit of 3, namely, 3.5 (see Fig. 49). Still another change in procedure must be made in order to have the probability obtained from χ^2 agree with the direct determination of probability. P in the χ^2 table gives the probability of 7 or more right answers *and* of 3 or less right answers, i.e., takes account of both ends of the probability curve (see p. 217). We must take 1/2 of P, therefore, if we want only the probability of 7 or more right answers. Note that the $P/2$ of .178 is very close to the P of .172 got by the direct method on page 249. If we repeated our test we should expect a score of 7 or better about 17 times in 100 trials. It is clear, therefore, that the obtained score is not significant and does not refute the null hypothesis.

It should be noted that had we omitted the correction for continuity, chi-square would have been 1.60 and $P/2$ (by interpolation in Table E), .095. Failure to use the correction causes the probability of a given result to be greatly *underestimated* and the chances of its being called significant considerably increased.

When the expected entries in a 2×2 fold table are the same (as in Tables 29, 30) the formula for chi-square may be written in a somewhat shorter form as follows:

$$\chi^2 = \frac{2(f_o - f_e)^2}{f_e} \qquad (67)$$

(*short formula for χ^2 in 2 × 2 fold tables when expected frequencies are equal*)

Applying formula (67) to Table 29 we get a chi-square of $\frac{2(1.5)^2}{5} = .90$.

Example (5) In Example (3), page 251, a subject achieved a score of 60 right on a test of 100 true-false items. From the chi-square test, determine whether this subject was merely guessing. Compare your result with that found on page 252 when the normal curve hypothesis was employed.

TABLE 30

	Right	Wrong	
Observed (f_o)	60	40	100
Expected (f_e)	50	50	100
($f_o - f_e$)	10	10	
Correction ($-.5$)	9.5	9.5	
($f_o - f_e$)^2	90.25	90.25	
$\frac{(f_o - f_e)^2}{f_e}$	1.81	1.81	
$\chi^2 = 3.62$		$P = .059$	
$df = 1$		$\tfrac{1}{2}P = .0295$ or .03	

Although the cell entries in Table 30 are large, use of the correction for continuity will be found to yield a result in somewhat closer agreement with that found on page 252 than can be obtained without the correction. As shown in Figure 49, page 252, the probability of a deviation of 60 or more from 50 is that part of the curve lying above 59.5. In Table E, the P of .059 gives us the probability of scores of 60 or more *and* of 40 or less. Hence we must take 1/2 of P (i.e., .0295) to give us the probability of a score of 60 or more. Agreement between the probability given by the χ^2-test and by direct calculation is very close. Note that when χ^2 is calculated without the correction, we get a $P/2$ of .024, a slight underestimation. In general, the correction for continuity has little effect when table entries are large, 50 or more, say. But failure to use the correction even when numbers are large may lead to some underestimation of the probability; hence it is generally wise to use it.

Example (6) In Example (4), page 253, given a multiple-choice test of 60 items (four possible answers to each item) we were required to find what score a subject must achieve in order to demonstrate knowledge of the test material. By use of the normal probability distribution, it was shown that a score of 21 is reasonably significant and a score of 23 highly significant. Can these results be verified by the chi-square test?

In Table 31 an obtained score of 21 is tested against an expected score of 15. In the first line of the table the observed values (f_o) are 21 right and 39 wrong; in the second line, the expected or "guess" values are 15 right and 45 wrong. Making the correction for continuity we obtain a χ^2 of 2.69, a P of .10 and 1/2 P of .05. Only once

TABLE 31

		R	W	
	f_o	21	39	60
	f_e	15	45	60
$(f_o - f_e)$		6	6	
Correction $(-.5)$		5.5	5.5	
$(f_o - f_e)^2$		30.25	30.25	
$\dfrac{(f_o - f_e)^2}{f_e}$		2.02	.67	

$\chi^2 = 2.69 \qquad\qquad P = .10$
$df = 1 \qquad\qquad\quad \tfrac{1}{2}P = .05$

in 20 trials would we expect a score of 21 or higher to occur if the subject were merely guessing and had no knowledge of the test material. This result checks that obtained on page 253.

In Table 32 a score of 23 is tested against the expected score of 15. Making the correction for continuity, we obtain a χ^2 of 5.00 which yields a P of .0275 and $1/2\,P$ of .0138. Again this result closely checks the answer obtained on page 253 by use of the normal probability curve.

TABLE 32

		R	W	
	f_o	23	37	60
	f_e	15	45	60
$(f_o - f_e)$		8	8	
Correction $(-.5)$		7.5	7.5	
$(f_o - f_e)^2$		56.25	56.25	
$\dfrac{(f_o - f_e)^2}{f_e}$		3.75	1.25	

$\chi^2 = 5.00 \qquad\qquad P = .0275$
$df = 1 \qquad\qquad\quad \tfrac{1}{2}P = .0138 \text{ or } .01$

4. The chi-square test when table entries are in percentages

The chi-square test should not be used with percentage entries unless a correction for size of sample is made. This follows from the fact that in dealing with probability the significance of an event depends upon its *actual* frequency and is not shown by its percentage occurrence. For a penny to fall heads eight times in ten tosses is not as significant as for the penny to fall heads eighty times in 100 tosses, although the percentage occurrence is the same in both cases. If we write the entries in Table 29 as percentages, we have

	R	W	
f_o	70%	30%	100%
f_e	50%	50%	100%
$(f_o - f_e)$	20%	20%	
Correction* (-5%)	15%	15%	
$(f_o - f_e)^2$	225%	225%	

$$\chi^2\% = \frac{2(225)}{50} = 9$$

$$\chi^2 = 9 \times \frac{10}{100} = .90 \text{ (Table 29)}$$

by (67)

It is clear that in order to bring χ^2 to its proper value in terms of original numbers we must multiply the "percent" χ^2 by 10/100 to give .90. A χ^2 calculated from percentages must always be multiplied by $N/100$ ($N =$ number of observations) in order to adjust it to the actual frequencies in the given sample.

5. The chi-square test of independence in contingency tables

We have seen that χ^2 may be employed to test the agreement between observed results and those expected on some hypothesis. A further useful application of χ^2 can be made when we wish to investigate the relationship between traits or attributes which can be classified into two or more categories. The same persons, for example, may be classified as to hair color (light, brown, black, red) and as to eye color (blue, gray, brown), and the correspondence in these attributes noted. Or fathers and sons may be classified with respect to interests or temperament or achievement and the relationship of the attributes in the two groups studied.

Table 33 is a contingency table, i.e., a double entry or two-way table in which the possession by a group of varying degrees of two characteristics is represented. In the tabulation in Table 33, 413 persons have been classified as to "eyedness" and "handedness."

---

* From Table 29 it is clear that the correction of $-.5$ becomes $-.5/10$ or $-.05$; this is -5% when entries in the table are expressed as percents.

Eyedness, or eye dominance, is described as left-eyed, ambiocular, or right-eyed; handedness as left-handed, ambidextrous, or right-handed. Reading down the first column we find that of 118 left-eyed persons, 34 are left-handed, 27 ambidextrous and 57 right-handed. Across the first row we find 124 left-handed persons, of whom 34 are left-eyed, 62 ambiocular and 28 right-eyed. The other columns and rows are interpreted in the same way.

TABLE 33 Comparison of eyedness and handedness in 413 persons *

	Left-Eyed	Ambiocular	Right-Eyed	Totals
Left-handed	(35.4) 34	(58.5) 62	(30.0) 28	124
Ambidextrous	(21.4) 27	(35.4) 28	(18.2) 20	75
Right-handed	(61.1) 57	(101.0) 105	(51.8) 52	214
Totals	118	195	100	413

I. Calculation of independence values (f_e):

$$\frac{118 \times 124}{413} = 35.4 \qquad \frac{195 \times 124}{413} = 58.5 \qquad \frac{100 \times 124}{413} = 30.0$$

$$\frac{118 \times 75}{413} = 21.4 \qquad \frac{195 \times 75}{413} = 35.4 \qquad \frac{100 \times 75}{413} = 18.2$$

$$\frac{118 \times 214}{413} = 61.1 \qquad \frac{195 \times 214}{413} = 101.0 \qquad \frac{100 \times 214}{413} = 51.8$$

II. Calculation of χ^2:

$(-1.4)^2 \div 35.4 = .055 \qquad (3.5)^2 \div 58.5 = .209 \qquad (-2.0)^2 \div 30 = .133$

$(5.6)^2 \div 21.4 = 1.465 \qquad (-7.4)^2 \div 35.4 = 1.547 \qquad (1.8)^2 \div 18.2 = .178$

$(-4.1)^2 \div 61.1 = .275 \qquad (4.0)^2 \div 101.0 = .158 \qquad (.20)^2 \div 51.8 = .001$

$\chi^2 = 4.02 \qquad df = 4 \qquad P$ lies between .30 and .50

The hypothesis to be tested is the null hypothesis, namely, that handedness and eyedness are essentially unrelated or independent. In order to compute χ^2 we must first calculate an "independence value" for each cell in the contingency table. Independence values are represented by figures in parentheses within the different cells; they give the number of people whom we should expect to find possessing the designated eyedness and handedness combinations in the absence of any real association. The method of calculating independence values is shown in Table 33. To illustrate with the first entry, there are 118 left-eyed and 124 left-handed persons. If there

* From Woo, T. L., *Biometrika*, 1936, 20A, pp. 79–118.

264 • STATISTICS IN PSYCHOLOGY AND EDUCATION

were no association between left-eyedness and left-handedness we should expect to find, by chance, $\frac{118 \times 124}{413}$ or 35.4 individuals in our group who are left-eyed *and* left-handed. The reason for this may readily be seen. We know that 118/413 of the entire group is left-eyed. This proportion of left-eyed individuals should hold for any sub-group, if there is *no* dependence of eyedness on handedness. Hence, 118/413 or 28.5% of the 124 left-handed individuals, i.e., 35.4, should also be left-eyed. Independence values for all cells are shown in Table 33.

When the expected or independence values have been computed, we find the difference between the observed and expected values for each cell, square each difference and divide in each instance by the independence value. The sum of these quotients by formula (66) gives χ^2. In the present problem $\chi^2 = 4.02$ and $df = (3-1)(3-1)$ or 4. From Table E we find that P lies between .30 and .50 and hence χ^2 is not significant. The observed results are close to those to be expected on the hypothesis of independence and there is no evidence of any real association between eyedness and handedness within our group.

When the contingency table is 2×2 fold, χ^2 may be calculated without first computing the four expected frequencies—the four independence values. Example (7) illustrates the method.

Example (7) All of the sixth-grade children in a public-school system are given a standard achievement test in arithmetic. A sample of 40 boys, drawn at random from the sixth-grade population, showed 23 at or above the national norm in the test and 17 below the national norm. A random sample of 50 sixth-grade girls showed 22 at or above the national norm and 28 below. Are the boys really better than the girls in arithemetic? Data are arranged in a fourfold table as follows.

	below norm	at or above norm	
Boys	(A) 17	(B) 23	(A + B) 40
Girls	(C) 28	(D) 22	(C + D) 50
	(A + C) 45	(B + D) 45	N 90

In a fourfold table, chi-square is given by the following formula.*

$$\chi^2 = \frac{N(AD-BC)^2}{(A+B)(C+D)(A+C)(B+D)} \qquad (68)$$

(*Chi-square in a fourfold contingency table*)

Substituting for A, B, C, D, in the formula, we have

$$\chi^2 = \frac{90(374-644)^2}{40 \times 50 \times 45 \times 45} = 1.62$$

and for $df = 1$, P is almost .20. χ^2 is not significant and there is no evidence that the table entries really vary from expectation, i.e., that there is a true sex difference in arithmetic.

6. The additive property of χ^2

When several χ^2's have been computed from independent experiments (i.e., from tables based upon different samples), these may be summed to give a new chi-square with $df =$ the sum of the separate df's. The fact that chi-squares may be added to provide an over-all test of a hypothesis is important in many experimental studies. In Example (7) above we have seen that the boys did slightly better than the girls on the arithmetic achievement test, but the chi-square of 1.62 is not large enough to indicate a superiority of boys over girls. Suppose that three repetitions of this experiment are carried out, in each instance groups of boys and girls [of about the same size as in Example (7)] being drawn independently and at random from the sixth grade and listed as scoring "at or above" or "below" the national norm. Suppose further that the three chi-squares from these tables are 2.71, 5.39 and .15, in each case the boys being somewhat better than the girls. We can now combine these four results to get an over-all test of the significance of this sex difference in arithmetic. Adding the three χ^2's to the 1.62 in Example (7) we have a total χ^2 of 9.87 with 4 df's. From Table E this χ^2 is significant at the .05 level, and we may be reasonably sure that sixth-grade boys are, on the average, better than sixth-grade girls in arithmetic. It will be noted that our four experiments taken in aggregate yield a significant result, although only one of the χ^2's (5.39) is itself significant. Combining the data from several experiments will often

* See page 367 for relation of χ^2 to phi-coefficient.

yield a definitive result when the separate experiments taken alone provide only indications or suggestions of a true difference.

PROBLEMS

1. Two sharp clicking sounds are presented in succession, the second being always more intense or less intense than the first. Presentation is in random order. In eight trials an observer is right six times. Is this result significant?
   (a) Calculate P directly (p. 249).
   (b) Check P found in (a) by χ^2-test (p. 258). Compare P's found with and without correction for continuity.

2. A multiple-choice test of fifty items provides five responses to each item. How many items must a subject answer correctly
   (a) to reach the .05 confidence level?
   (b) to reach the .01 confidence level?

3. A multiple-choice test of thirty items provides three responses for each item. How many items must a subject answer correctly before the chances are only one in fifty that he is merely guessing?

4. A pack of fifty-two playing cards contains four suits (diamonds, clubs, spades, and hearts). A subject "guesses" through the pack of cards, naming only suits, and is right eighteen times.
   (a) Is this result better than "chance"? (Hint: In using the probability curve compute area to 17.5, lower limit of 18.0, rather than to 18.0.)
   (b) Check your answer by the χ^2-test (p. 257).

5. Twelve samples of handwriting, six from normal and six from insane adults, are presented to a graphologist who claims he can identify the writing of the insane. How many "insane" specimens must he recognize correctly in order to prove his contention?

6. The following judgments were classified into six categories taken to represent a continuum of opinion:

Categories

	I	II	III	IV	V	VI	Total
Judgments:	48	61	82	91	57	45	384

   (a) Test given distribution versus "equal probability" hypothesis.
   (b) Test given distribution versus normal distribution hypothesis.

7. In 120 throws of a single die, the following distribution of faces was obtained:

	Faces						
	1	2	3	4	5	6	Total
Observed frequencies:	30	25	18	10	22	15	120

Do these results constitute a refutation of the "equal probability" (null) hypothesis?

8. The following table represents the number of boys and the number of girls who chose each of the five possible answers to an item in an attitude scale.

	Approve Strongly	Approve	Indifferent	Disapprove	Strongly Disapprove	Total
Boys	25	30	10	25	10	100
Girls	10	15	5	15	15	60

Do these data indicate a significant sex difference in attitude toward this question? [Note: Test the "independence (null) hypothesis."]

9. The table below shows the number of normals and abnormals who chose each of the three possible answers to an item on a neurotic questionnaire.

	Yes	No	?	Total
Normals	14	66	10	90
Abnormals	27	66	7	100
	41	132	17	190

Does this item differentiate between the two groups? Test the independence hypothesis.

10. From the table below, determine whether Item 27 differentiates between two groups of high and low general ability.

Numbers of Two Groups Differing in General Ability Who Pass Item 27 in a Test

	Passed	Failed	Total
High Ability	31	19	50
Low Ability	24	26	50
	55	45	100

11. Five χ^2's computed from fourfold tables in independent replications of an experiment are .50, 4.10, 1.20, 2.79 and 5.41. Does the aggregate of these tests yield a significant χ^2?

ANSWERS

1. (a) $P = .145$; not significant
   (b) $P = .145$ when corrected; $.085$ uncorrected
2. (a) 15
   (b) 17
3. 15
4. Probability of 18 or better is .08; not significant
5. 5 or 6 (Probability of 5 or 6 $= 37/924 = .04$)
6. (a) $\chi^2 = 27$; P less than .01 and hypothesis of "equal probability" must be discarded.
   (b) $\chi^2 = 356$; P is less than .01, and the deviation from the normal hypothesis is significant.
7. Yes. $\chi^2 = 12.90$, $df = 5$, and P is between .02 and .05.
8. No. $\chi^2 = 7.03$, $df = 4$, and P is between .20 and .10
9. No. $\chi^2 = 4.14$, $df = 2$, and P is between .20 and .10
10. No. $\chi^2 = 1.98$, $df = 1$, and P lies between .20 and .10
11. Yes. $\chi^2 = 14.00$, $df = 5$, and P lies between .02 and .01.

11

ANALYSIS OF VARIANCE IN DETERMINING THE SIGNIFICANCE OF DIFFERENCES BETWEEN MEANS

The methods described under analysis of variance include (1) a variety of procedures called experimental designs, as well as (2) certain statistical techniques devised for use with these procedures. The statistics used in analysis of variance are not new (as they are sometimes thought to be) but are, in fact, adaptations of formulas and methods described earlier in this book. The experimental designs, on the other hand, are in several instances new at least to psychology. These systematic approaches often provide more efficient and exact tests of experimental hypotheses than do the conventional methods ordinarily employed.

This chapter will be concerned with the application of analysis of variance to the important and often-encountered problem of determining the significance of the difference between means. This topic has been treated by classical methods in Chapter 9, and the present chapter will give the student an opportunity to contrast the relative efficiency of the two approaches and to gain, as well, some notion of the advantages and disadvantages of each. Treatment of other and more complex experimental designs through analysis of variance is beyond the scope of this book. After this introductory chapter, however, the interested student should be able to follow the more comprehensive treatments of analysis of variance in the references listed below.*

* Edwards, A. L., *Experimental Design in Psychological Research* (New York: Rinehart and Co., 1950).
McNemar, Q., *Psychological Statistics* (New York: John Wiley and Sons, 1949).

The plan of this chapter is to give, first, an elementary account of the principles of variance analysis. The problem of determining the significance of the difference between two means will then be considered: (1) when the means are *independent*, i.e., when the sets of measures from which the M's are derived are uncorrelated, and (2) when M's are not independent because of correlation among the different sets of measures or scores.

I. How Variance Is Analyzed

1. When pairs of scores are added to yield a composite score

While the variability within a set of scores is ordinarily given by the standard deviation or σ, variability may also be expressed by the "variance" or σ^2. A very considerable advantage of variances over SD's is the fact that variances are often additive and the sums of squares upon which variances are based always are. A simple example will illustrate this. Suppose that we add the two *independent* (uncorrelated) scores X and Y made by Subject A on tests X and Y to give the composite score Z (i.e., $Z = X + Y$). Now if we add the X and Y scores for each person in our group, *after* expressing each score as a deviation from its own mean, we will have for any subject that

$$z = x + y$$

in which $z = Z - M_z$, $x = X - M_x$, and $y = Y - M_y$.

Squaring both sides of this equation, and summing for all subjects in the group, we find in general that

$$\Sigma z^2 = \Sigma x^2 + \Sigma y^2$$

The cross product term $2\Sigma xy$ * drops out as x and y are independent

* The formula is $r = \dfrac{\Sigma xy}{N\sigma_x\sigma_y}$ (p. 139). If $r = 0$, Σxy must also be zero.

Lindquist, E. F., *Statistical Analysis in Educational Research* (Boston: Houghton Mifflin Co., 1940).

Snedecor, G. W., *Statistical Methods* (4th ed.; Ames, Iowa: Iowa State College Press, 1946).

Goulden, C. H., *Methods of Statistical Analysis* (New York: John Wiley and Sons, 1939).

Fisher, R. A., *Statistical Methods for Research Workers* (8th ed.; London: Oliver and Boyd. 1941).

Fisher, R. A., *The Design of Experiments* (London: Oliver and Boyd, 1935). (The Fisher references will be difficult for the beginner.)

(uncorrelated) by hypothesis. Hence we find that the sum of the squares in x plus the sum of the squares in y equals the sum of the squares in z. Dividing by N, we have

$$\frac{\Sigma z^2}{N} = \frac{\Sigma x^2}{N} + \frac{\Sigma y^2}{N}$$

or

$$\sigma^2_z = \sigma^2_x + \sigma^2_y$$

Also

$$\sigma_z = \sqrt{\sigma^2_x + \sigma^2_y}$$

The equation in terms of variances is more convenient and more useful than is the equation in terms of SD's. Thus if we divide each variance by σ^2_z we have

$$1 = \frac{\sigma^2_x}{\sigma^2_z} + \frac{\sigma^2_y}{\sigma^2_z}$$

which tells us what *proportion* of the variance of the composite Z is attributable to the variance of X and what proportion is attributable to the variance of Y. This division of total variability into its independent components cannot be readily done with SD's.

2. When two sets of scores are combined into a single distribution

The breakdown of total variability into its contributing parts may be approached in another way. When two sets of scores, A and B, are thrown together or combined into a single distribution (see p. 57), the sum of the squares of *all* of the scores taken from the M_T of the single total distribution is related to the component distributions A and B as follows:

$$\Sigma x^2_T = \Sigma x^2_A + \Sigma x^2_B + N_A d^2_A + N_B d^2_B$$

where $\Sigma x^2_T =$ SS * of deviations in total distribution T from M_T

$\Sigma x^2_A =$ SS of deviations in total distribution A from M_A

$\Sigma x^2_B =$ SS of deviations in total distribution B from M_B

N_A and N_B are the numbers of scores in distributions A and B, respectively, d_A and d_B are the deviations of the means of A and B from the mean of T, i.e., $(M_A - M_T)^2 = d^2_A$, $(M_B - M_T)^2 = d^2_B$.

The equation given above in terms of Σx^2_T is important in the present connection because it shows that the sum of the squares of

* SS = sum of squares.

deviations around the mean of a single distribution made up of two component distributions can be broken down into two parts: (1) the SS around the M's of the two sets of scores, viz., M_A and M_B, and (2) the sum of squares (times the appropriate N's) of the deviations of M_A and M_B from M_T. An illustration will make the application of this result to variance analysis clearer.

Table 34 shows three sets of scores, 5 for group A, 10 for group B, and 15 for group T which is made up of A and B. The sums of scores, the means and SS around the M's have been calculated for each group. It may be noted that $M_T = \dfrac{18 \times 5 + 21 \times 10}{15} = 20$; and that, in general, $M_T = \dfrac{M_A \times N_A + M_B \times N_B}{N_A + N_B}$ (p. 31).

TABLE 34 *A and B are two distributions and T is a combination of the two*

Distribution A	Distribution B	Distribution T (A+B)
25	17	25
15	20	15
18	26	18
22	18	22
10	20	10
	25	17
	19	20
	26	26
	18	18
	21	20
		25
		19
		26
		18
		21
Sum 90	210	300
M 18	21	20
Σx^2 138	106	274

Substituting the data from Table 34 in the sums equation above we find that

$$274 = 138 + 106 + 5(18 - 20)^2 + 10(21 - 20)^2$$

or

$$274 = 138 + 106 + 20 + 10$$

Of the total SS (274), 244 (138 + 106) is contributed by the variability within the two distributions A and B, and 30 (20 + 10) is contributed by the variability between the means of the two distributions. This breakdown of total SS into the SS's *within* component distributions and *between* the M's of the combining distributions is fundamental to analysis of variance. The method whereby SS's can be expressed as variances will be shown later.

II. The Significance of the Difference between Means Derived from Independent or Uncorrelated Measures or Scores

1. When there are more than two means to be compared

The value of analysis of variance in testing experimental hypotheses is most strikingly demonstrated in those problems in which the significance of the differences among several means is desired. An example will illustrate the procedures and will provide a basis for the discussion of certain theoretical points.

Example (1) Assume that we wish to study the effects of eight different experimental conditions, designated A, B, C, D, E, F, G, H, upon performance on a sensory-motor task. From a total of 48 subjects, 6 are assigned at random to each of 8 groups and the same test is administered to all. Do the mean scores achieved under the 8 experimental conditions differ significantly?

Records for the 8 groups are shown in parallel columns in Table 35. Individual scores are listed under the 8 headings which designate the conditions under which the test was given. Since "conditions" furnishes the category for the assignment of subjects, in the terminology of analysis of variance there is said to be *one* criterion of classification. The first step in our analysis is a breakdown of the total variance (σ^2) of the 48 scores into *two* parts: (1) the variance attributable to the different conditions, or the variance among the 8 means, and (2) the variance arising from individual differences within the 8 groups. The next step is to determine whether the group means differ significantly *inter se* in view of the variability within the separate groups (individual differences). A detailed account of the calculations required (see Table 35) is set forth in the steps on pages 275–279.

274 • STATISTICS IN PSYCHOLOGY AND EDUCATION

TABLE 35 A hypothetical experiment in which 48 subjects are assigned at random to 8 groups of 6 subjects each. These groups are tested under 8 different experimental conditions, designated respectively A, B, C, D, E, F, G and H.

	\multicolumn{8}{c}{Conditions}

	A	B	C	D	E	F	G	H	
	64	73	77	78	63	75	78	55	
	72	61	83	91	65	93	46	66	
	68	90	97	97	44	78	41	49	
	77	80	69	82	77	71	50	64	
	56	97	79	85	65	63	69	70	
	95	67	87	77	76	76	82	68	
Sums	432	468	492	510	390	456	366	372	Grand Sum: 3486
M's	72	78	82	85	65	76	61	62	General Mean = 72.63

A. Calculation of Sums of Squares

Step 1 Correction term $(C) = \dfrac{(3486)^2}{48} = 253{,}171$

Step 2 Total Sum of Squares

$$= (64^2 + 72^2 + \ldots + 70^2 + 68^2) - C$$
$$= 262{,}364 - 253{,}171 = 9193$$

Step 3 Sum of Squares among Means of A, B, C, D, E, F, G and H

$$= \frac{(432)^2 + (468)^2 + (492)^2 + (510)^2 + (390)^2 + (456)^2 + (366)^2 + (372)^2}{6} - C$$

$$= \frac{1540188}{6} - 253{,}171 = 3527$$

Step 4 Sum of Squares *within* Conditions A, B, C, D, E, F, G and H

$$= \text{Total SS} - \text{Among Means SS}$$
$$= 9193 - 3527 = 5666$$

B. Summary: Analysis of Variance

Source of Variation	df	Sums of Squares	Mean Square (Variance)	SD
Among the means of Conditions	7	3527	503.9	
Within Conditions	40	5666	141.6	11.9
Total	47	9193		

$$F = \frac{503.9}{141.6} = 3.56$$

From Table F for
$n_1 = 7$ and $n_2 = 40$

F at $.05 = 2.25$
F at $.01 = 3.12$

C. Tests of Differences by Use of t

For $df = 40$, $t_{.05} = 2.02$ (Table D)
$t_{.01} = 2.71$

$SE_D = 11.9 \sqrt{\frac{1}{6} + \frac{1}{6}}$
$= 11.9 \times .577$
$= 6.87$

$D_{.05} = 2.02 \times 6.87 = 13.9$
$D_{.01} = 2.71 \times 6.87 = 18.6$

Largest difference is between D and G = 24
Smallest difference is between G and H = 1

Distribution of mean differences	f
22–24	2
19–21	3
16–18	3
13–15	4
10–12	4
7–9	3
4–6	5
1–3	4
	28

Approximately 5 differences significant at .01 level

Approximately 10 differences significant at .05 level

Step I

Correction term (C). When the SD is calculated from original measures or raw scores,* the formula $SD^2 = \frac{\Sigma x^2}{N} - C^2$ becomes $SD^2 = \frac{\Sigma X^2}{N} - M^2$. The correction ($C$) equals M directly in this form of the equation, since $C = AM - M$ and the AM (assumed mean)

* See page 54. In analysis of variance calculations it is usually more convenient to work with original measures or raw scores.

here is zero. Replacing σ^2 by $\dfrac{\Sigma x^2}{N}$ we have that $\dfrac{\Sigma x^2}{N} = \dfrac{\Sigma X^2}{N} - M^2$. Now if the correction term M^2 is written $\dfrac{(\Sigma X)^2}{N^2}$ we may multiply this equation through by N to find that $\Sigma x^2 = \Sigma X^2 - \dfrac{(\Sigma X)^2}{N}$. In Table 35 the correction term $\dfrac{(\Sigma X)^2}{N}$ is 253,171. This correction is applied to the sum of squares, ΣX^2.

Step 2

Total sum of squares around the general mean. Since $\Sigma x^2 = \Sigma X^2 - \dfrac{(\Sigma X)^2}{N}$, we need only square and sum the original scores and subtract the correction term to find SS_T (sum of squares around the general mean of all 48 scores). In Table 35, squaring each score and summing we get a total of 262,364; and subtracting the correction, the final SS_T is 9193. This SS_T may also be computed by taking deviations around the general mean directly. The general mean is 72.63. Subtracting 72.63 from each of the 48 scores, squaring these x's and summing we get 9193, checking the calculations from raw scores. The formula for sum of squares around the general mean is

$$SS_T = \Sigma X^2 - \frac{(\Sigma X^2)}{N} \qquad (69)$$

(SS_T *around general mean using raw scores*)

Step 3

Sum of squares among the means obtained under the 8 conditions. To find the sum of squares attributable to condition-differences ($SS_{M's}$), we must first square the *sum* of each column (i.e., each condition), add these sums and divide the total by 6, the number of scores in each group or column. Subtracting the correction found in Step 1, we then get the final $SS_{M's}$ to be 3527. This $SS_{M's}$ is simply the SS of the separate group M's around the one general mean, multiplied by the number of scores in each column. We may carry out these calculations as a check on the result above. Thus for the present example:

ANALYSIS OF VARIANCE • 277

$$SS_{M's} = 6[(72 - 72.63)^2 + (78 - 72.63)^2 + (82 - 72.63)^2$$
$$+ (85 - 72.63)^2 + (65 - 72.63)^2 + (76 - 72.63)^2$$
$$+ (61 - 72.63)^2 + (62 - 72.63)^2] = 3527$$

When, as here, we are working with raw scores, the method of calculation repeats Step 2, except that we divide the square of *each* column total by 6, the number of scores in each column, before subtracting C. The general formula is

$$\text{SS (among means)} = \frac{(\Sigma X_1)^2}{n_1} + \frac{(\Sigma X_2)^2}{n_2} + \cdots + \frac{(\Sigma X_n)^2}{n_n} - C \quad (70)$$

(SS *among means when calculation is with raw scores*)

When the number of scores in the groups differ, the squares of the column sums will be divided by different n's before the correction is subtracted. (See page 282 for illustration.)

Step 4

Sum of squares within conditions (individual differences). The SS within columns or groups (SS_w) always equals the SS_T minus the $SS_{M's}$. Subtracting 3527 from 9193, we have 5666. This SS_w may also be calculated directly from the data (see p. 296).

Step 5

Calculation of the variances from each SS and analysis of the total variance into its components is shown in the B part of Table 35. Each SS becomes a variance when divided by the degrees of freedom (df) allotted to it (p. 193). There are 48 scores in all in Table 35, and hence there are ($N - 1$) or 47 df in all. These 47 df are allocated in the following way. The df for "among the means of conditions" are ($8 - 1$) or 7, less by one than the number of conditions. The df *within* groups or within conditions are ($47 - 7$) or 40. This last df may also be found directly: since there are ($6 - 1$) or 5 df for each condition ($N = 6$ in each group), 5×8 (number of conditions) gives 40 df for within groups. The variance among M's of groups is $3527/7$ or 503.9; and the variance within groups is $5666/40$ or 141.6.

If N = number of scores in all and k = number of categories or groups, we have for the general case that

df for total SS $\quad\quad\quad\quad = (N-1)$

df for within groups SS $\quad = (N-k)$

df for among means of groups SS = $(k-1)$

Also: $\quad (N-1) = (N-k) + (k-1)$

Step 6

In the present problem the null hypothesis asserts that the 8 sets of scores are in reality random samples drawn from the same normally distributed population, and that the means of conditions A, B, C, D, E, F, G and H will differ *only* through fluctuations of sampling. To test this hypothesis we divide the "among means" variance by the "within groups" variance and compare the resulting *variance ratio*, called F, with the F-values in Table F (see p. 429). The F in our problem is 3.56 and the df are 7 for the numerator (n_1) and 40 for the denominator (n_2). Entering Table F, we read from column 7 (n_1) and row 40 (n_2) that an F of 2.25 is significant at the .05 level and an F of 3.12 is significant at the .01 level. Only the .05 and .01 points are given in the table. These entries mean that, for the given df's, variance ratios or F's of 2.25 and 3.12 can be expected once in 20 and once in 100 trials, respectively, when the null hypothesis is true. Since our F is larger than the .01 level, it would occur less than once in 100 trials by chance. We reject the null hypothesis, therefore, and conclude that the means of our 8 groups do in fact differ.

F furnishes a comprehensive or over-all test of the significance of the differences among means. A significant F, does not tell us *which* means differ significantly, but that at least one is reliably different from some others. If F is not significant there is no reason for further testing, as none of the mean differences will be significant (see p. 281). But if F is significant, we may proceed to test the separate differences by the t-test (p. 427) as shown in Table 35 C.

Step 7

The best estimate which we can make of the uncontrolled variability arising from individual differences is given by the SD of 11.9

computed from the "within groups" variance given in Table 35 B. This SD is based upon *all* of our data and is a measure of subject variability *after* the systematic effects arising from differences in column means have been allowed for. In testing mean differences by the t-test, therefore (Table 35 C), the SD of 11.9 is used throughout instead of the SD's calculated from the separate columns, A, B, C, D, E, F, G and H. The standard error of *any* mean (SE_M) is $\dfrac{SD_w}{\sqrt{N}}$ or $11.9/\sqrt{6} = 4.86$. And the SE of the difference (D) between *any* two means is $SE_D = \sqrt{4.86^2 + 4.86^2}$ or 6.87. A general formula for calculating SE_D directly is

$$SE_D = SD_w \sqrt{\frac{1}{n_1} + \frac{1}{n_2}} \qquad (71)$$

(*standard error of the difference between any two means in analysis of variance*)

where SD_w is the within-groups SD, and n_1 and n_2 are the sizes of the samples or groups being compared.

The means of the 8 groups in Table 35 range from 61 to 85, and the mean differences from 24 to 1. To determine the significance of the difference between *any* two selected means we must compute a t-ratio by dividing the given mean difference by its SE_D. The resulting t is then compared with the t in Table D for 40 df, viz., the number of df upon which our SD_w is based. A more summary approach than this is to compute that difference among means which for 40 df will be significant at the .05 or the .01 level and check our differences against these standards. This is done in Table 35 C. We know from Table D that for 40 df, a t of 2.02 is significant at the .05 level; and a t of 2.71 is significant at the .01 level. Since $t =$ mean difference/SE_D, we may substitute 2.02 for t in this equation and 6.87 for SE_D to find that a difference of 13.9 is significant at the .05 level. Using the same procedure, we substitute 2.71 for t in the equation to find that a difference of 18.6 is significant at the .01 level.

Eight means will yield $\dfrac{(8 \times 7)}{2}$ or 28 differences. From the distribution of these 28 differences (Table 35 C) it is clear that approximately 5 differences are significant at the .01 level (i.e., are 18.6 or more); and approximately 10 at the .05 level (i.e., are 13.9 or more). The largest difference is 24 and the smallest is 1.

Discussion *

A few additional comments may clarify the calculations in Table 35.

(1) First, it must be remembered that we are testing the null hypothesis—the hypothesis that there are *no* true differences among our 8 condition-means. Stated differently, we are testing the hypothesis that our 8 groups are in reality random samples drawn from the same normally distributed population. The F-test refutes the null hypothesis by demonstrating differences among our means which cannot be explained by chance: i.e., differences larger than those which would occur by sampling accidents once in 100 trials if the null hypothesis were true.

(2) The 47 df (48 − 1) in the table are broken down into 7 df which are allotted to the 8 condition-means and 40 df which are allotted to individual differences (variations within groups or columns). Variances are calculated by dividing each SS by its own df.

(3) In problems like that of Table 35 (where there is only one criterion of classification), all 3 variances (total, among means and within groups) are in effect *estimates* of the variance in the population of scores from which our 8 samples are drawn. Only two of these variances are *independent*: the variance among condition-means and the variance within groups, since V_T is composed of these two. These two independent estimates of population variance are used in computing the variance ratio and making the F-test. When samples are strictly random these two variances are equal and F is 1.00. Moreover, when F is 1.00, the variance among group means is no greater than the variance within groups; or, put differently, group-means differ no more than do the individuals within the groups. The extent to which F is greater than 1.00 becomes, then, a measure of the significance of the differences among group means. The larger the F the greater the probability that group mean differences are greater than individual variation—sometimes called "experimental error."

(4) According to the traditional method of treating a problem like that of Table 35, 8 SD's would first be computed, one around each of the 8 column means. From these SD's, SE's of the means and SE's of the differences between pairs of means would be calculated. A t-test would then be made of the differences between any two given means and the significance of this difference determined from Table D.

Analysis of variance is an improvement over this procedure in sev-

---

* See Garrett, H. E., and Zubin, J., "The Analysis of Variance in Psychological Research," *Psychol. Bull.*, 1943, 40, 233–267.

ANALYSIS OF VARIANCE • 281

eral respects. In Table 35 we first compute an F-ratio which tells us whether *any* mean differences are significant. If F is significant, we may then compute a single SE_D. This SE_D is derived from the SD_w calculated from the 8 groups after systematic mean-differences have been removed. Moreover, this within-groups SD—based as it is upon all 48 scores and with 40 df—furnishes a better (i.e., more reliable) measure of uncontrolled (or experimental) variation in the table than could be obtained from SD's based upon only 8 scores and 7 df. Pooling of sums to obtain the within-groups SD is permissible, since the deviations in each group have been taken from their own mean.

(5) If the F-test refutes the null hypothesis we may use the t-test to evaluate mean-differences. If the F-test does not refute the null hypothesis there is no justification for further testing, as differences between pairs of means will not differ significantly unless there are a number of them—in which case one or two might by chance equal or approach significance.*

2. When there are only two means to be compared

In order to provide a further comparison of analysis of variance with the methods of Chapter 9, example (4), page 223, is solved in Table 36. This second example will show that when only two means are to be compared, the F-test reduces to the t-test.

TABLE 36 Solution of Example (4), page 223, through methods of analysis of variance

Scores:	
Class 1 ($N_1 = 6$)	Class 2 ($N_2 = 10$)
28	20
35	16
32	25
24	34
26	20
35	28
6⌡180	31
$M_1 = 30$	24
	27
	15
	10⌡240
	$M_2 = 24$

* In 100 strictly random differences, 5 will be significant at the .05 level; that is, 2½% will exceed 1.96σ at each end of the curve of differences (p. 188). Hence in 28 differences (Table 35 C) 1 or 2 might be significant at the .05 level (28 × .05 = 1.40) if differences are randomly distributed around zero.

TABLE 36—(Continued)

A. Sums of Squares
1. Correction: $(420)^2/16 = 11025$
2. $SS_T = 28^2 + 35^2 + \cdots + 15^2 - C$
   $= 11622 - 11025 = 597$
3. $SS_{M's} = \dfrac{(180)^2}{6} + \dfrac{(240)^2}{10} - C$
   $= 11160 - 11025 = 135$
4. $SS_w = 597 - 135 = 462$

B. Analysis of Variance

Source	df	SS	MS(V)
Between means	1	135	135
Within classes	14	462	33
Total	15	597	

$F = \dfrac{135}{33} = 4.09$

$t = \sqrt{F} = 2.02$

From Table F
F at .05 level $= 4.60$
F at .01 level $= 8.86$

Step 1

The sum of all of the 16 scores is $180 + 240$ or 420; and the correction (C) is, accordingly, $(420)^2/16$ or 11025. See page 275.

Step 2

When each score has been squared and the correction subtracted from the total, the SS around the general mean is 597 by formula (69), page 276.

Step 3

The sum of squares between means (135) is found by squaring the sum of each column, dividing the first by 6 (n_1) and the second by 10 (n_2) and subtracting C.

Step 4

The SS within groups is the difference between the SS_T and $SS_{\text{between } M\text{'s}}$. Thus $SS_w = 597 - 135 = 462$.

ANALYSIS OF VARIANCE • 283

Step 5

The analysis of variance is shown in Table 36 B. SS_T is divided into SS between means of groups and SS within groups. Since there are 16 scores in all, there are $(N-1)$ or 15 df for "total." The $SS_{M's}$ is allotted $(k-1)$ or 1 df $(k=2)$. The remaining 14 df are assigned to within groups and may be found either by subtracting 1 from 15 or by adding the 5 df in Class 1 to the 9 df in Class 2. Mean squares or variances are obtained by dividing each SS by its appropriate df.

Step 6

The variance ratio or F is 135/33 or 4.09. The df for between means is 1 (n_1) and the df for within groups is 14 (n_2). Entering Table F with these n's we read in column 1 and row 14 that the .05 level is 4.60 and the .01 level is 8.86. Our F of 4.09 does not quite reach the .05 level so that our mean difference of 6 points must be regarded as not significant. The difference between the two means $(30-24)$ is not large enough, therefore, to be convincing; or, stated more mathematically, a difference of 6 can be expected to occur too frequently to render the null hypothesis untenable.

When there are only two means to be compared as here, $F = t^2$ or $t = \sqrt{F}$ and the two tests (F and t) give exactly the same result. In Table 36 B, for instance, $F = \sqrt{4.09}$ or 2.02 which is the t previously found in example (4) on page 223. From Table D we have found (p. 224) that for 14 df the .05 level of significance for this t is 2.14. Our t of 2.02 does not quite reach this level and hence (like F) is not significant. If we interpolate between the .05 point of 2.14 and the .10 point of 1.76 in Table D, our t of 2.02 is found to fall approximately at .07. In 100 repetitions of this experiment, therefore, we can expect a mean difference of 6 or more to occur about 7 times—too frequently to be significant.

3. Example (5), page 225, solved by analysis of variance

In problems requiring the comparison of two group means either F or t may be employed. From the standpoint of calculation, F is perhaps somewhat easier to apply. In example (5), page 225, it is easier to calculate t because raw scores are not given. But F may be calculated if desired in the following way. The general mean for the two groups is $(40.39 \times 31 + 35.81 \times 42)$ divided by 73, or 37.75: it is the weighted mean obtained from the two group means. The SS between the means of the groups of boys and girls is $31(40.39 - 37.75)^2 + 42(35.81 - 37.75)^2$ or 374.13; namely, the deviation of each group mean from the general mean weighted in each case by the N of the group.

To get the SS within groups we simply square each SD and multiply by $(N - 1)$, remembering that $SD^2 = \dfrac{\Sigma x^2}{(N-1)}$ (p. 189). In example (5) we find that $(8.69)^2 \times 30 = 2265.48$; and $(8.33)^2 \times 41 = 2844.95$. The sum of these two is 5110.43, the SS within groups. The complete analysis of variance and F test are shown in Table 37; $F = 5.20$ and $t = \sqrt{F}$ or 2.28, checking the result given on page 225. Our F of 5.20 exceeds the .05 level of 3.98 but does not reach the .01 level of 7.01. As before, F and t give identical results.

TABLE 37 Solution of example (5), page 225, by analysis of variance

A. Sums of Squares and General Mean

1. General mean = $\dfrac{(40.39 \times 31 + 35.81 \times 42)}{73} = 37.75$
2. SS between means:
   $31(40.39 - 37.75)^2 + 42(35.81 - 37.75)^2 = 374.13$
3. SS within groups:
   $30(8.69)^2 + 41(8.33)^2 = 5110.43$

B. Analysis of Variance

Source of Variation	df	Sums of Squares	Mean Square (Variance)
Between means	1	374.13	374.1
Within groups	71	5110.43	71.9

$F = 374.1/71.9 = 5.20$
$t = \sqrt{F} = \sqrt{5.20} = 2.28$

From Table F
$df = 1/71$
F at .05 = 3.98
F at .01 = 7.01

III. The Significance of the Difference between Means Obtained from Correlated Groups

1. When the same group is measured more than once (single group method)

Means are correlated when the two sets of scores achieved by the group from which the means were derived are correlated. When a test is given and then repeated, analysis of variance may be used to determine whether the mean change is significant. The ex-

TABLE 38   Solution of example (7), page 227, by analysis of variance

A. Sums of Squares
1. Correction $= (1240)^2/24 = \dfrac{1537600}{24} = 64066.67$
2. Total Sum of Squares $= 68952 - 64066.67 = 4885.33$
3. Between trials sum of squares:
$$\frac{(572)^2 + (668)^2}{12} - 64066.67 = 384.00$$
4. Among subjects' sum of squares:
$68391 - 64066.67 = 4324.33$
5. Interaction sum of squares $= 4885.33 - (384.00 + 4324.33)$
$= 177$

B. Analysis of Variance

Source of Variation	df	Sums of Squares	Mean Square (Variance)	SD
Between trials	1	384.00	384.00	
Among subjects	11	4324.33	393.12	
Interaction	11	177.00	16.09	4.01
Total	23	4885.33		

$F_{\text{trials}} = \dfrac{384}{16.09} = 23.86$

$F_{\text{subjects}} = \dfrac{393.12}{16.09} = 24.43$

$t = \sqrt{23.86} = 4.88$

From Table F

	Trials	Subjects
	$df = 1/11$	$df = 11/11$
F at .05 =	4.84	2.82
F at .01 =	9.65	4.46

286 • STATISTICS IN PSYCHOLOGY AND EDUCATION

perimental design here is essentially the same as that of the Single Group Method of Chapter 9, page 225. Hence example (7), page 227, is used in Table 38 to illustrate the methods of analysis of variance and to provide a comparison with the difference-method of page 227.

The procedures for the analysis of variance in example (7) differ in at least two ways from the methods of Section II. First, since there is the possibility of correlation between the scores achieved by the 12 subjects on the first and fifth trials, the two sets of scores should not at the outset be treated as independent (random) samples. Secondly, classification is now in terms of *two* criteria: (a) trials and (b) subjects. Because of these two criteria, the total SS must be broken down into three parts: (a) SS attributable to trials; (b) SS attributable to subjects; and (c) a residual SS usually called "interaction." Steps in the calculation of these three variances, shown in Table 38 A, may be summarized as follows.

Step 1

Correction (C). As in Section II, $C = \dfrac{(\Sigma X)^2}{N}$. In example (7) C is $(1240)^2/24$ or 64066.67.

Step 2

Total SS around general mean. Again the calculation repeats the procedure of Section II.

$$SS_T = (50^2 + 42^2 + \ldots + 72^2 + 50^2) - 64066.67$$
$$= 68952 - 64066.67 = 4885.33$$

Step 3

SS between the means of trials. There are two trials of 12 scores each. Therefore,

$$SS_{\text{trials}} = \frac{(572)^2 + (668)^2}{12} - 64066.67$$
$$= 64450.67 - 64066.67 = 384.0$$

Step 4

SS among the means of subjects. A second "between means" SS is required to take care of the second criterion of classification. There are 12 subjects and each has two trials. Hence,

$$SS_{subjects} = \frac{112^2 + 82^2 + \ldots + 134^2 + 88^2}{2} - 64066.67$$

$$= 68391.00 - 64066.67 = 4324.33$$

Step 5

Interaction SS. The residual variation or interaction is whatever is left when the systematic effects of trial differences and subject differences have been removed from the total SS. Interaction measures the tendency for subject performance to vary along with trials: it measures the factors attributable *neither* to subjects *nor* trials acting alone, but rather to both acting together. Interaction is obtained most simply * by subtracting trials SS plus subjects SS from total SS. Thus

$$\text{Interaction SS} = SS_T - (SS_{subjects} + SS_{trials})$$

$$= 4885.33 - (384 + 4324.33)$$

$$= 177$$

Step 6

As before, SS's become variances when divided by their appropriate df. Since there are 24 trials in all we have $(24-1)$ or 23 df for the total SS. Two trials receive 1 df, and 12 subjects, 11. The remaining 11 df are assigned to interaction. The rule is that the df for interaction is the product of the df for the two interacting variables, here 1×11. In general if $N =$ total number of scores, $r =$ rows and $k =$ columns, we have

df for total SS $= (N-1)$

df for column SS (trials) $= (k-1)$

df for row SS (subjects) $= (r-1)$

df for interaction SS $= (k-1)(r-1)$

The three measures of variance appear in Table 38. Note that we may now calculate two F's, one for trial differences and one for subject differences. In both cases the interaction variance is placed in the denominator of the variance ratio, since it is our best estimate of residual variance (or experimental error) after the systematic influences of trials and subjects have been removed. The F for trials is

* Interaction may be calculated directly from the data.

23.86 and is much larger than the 9.65 we find in Table F for the .01 point when $n_1 = 1$ and $n_2 = 11$. This means that the null hypothesis with respect to trials is untenable and must be abandoned. The evidence is strong that real improvement took place from trial 1 to trial 5.

Ordinarily in most two-criteria experiments we are concerned primarily with one criterion, as here. It is possible, however (and sometimes desirable), to test the second criterion—viz., differences among subjects. The F for subjects is 24.43 and again is far larger than the .01 point of 4.46 in Table F for $n_1 = 11$ and $n_2 = 11$. It is obvious that some subjects were consistently better than others without regard to trial.

Since there are two trials, we have two trial means. Hence, if we compute a t from the F for trials, it should be equal to that found by the difference-method. The F of 23.86 yields a t of $\sqrt{23.86}$ or 4.88 which checks the t of 4.88 on page 227.

Computations needed for the difference-method of example (7), page 227, are somewhat shorter than are those for analysis of variance, and the difference-method would probably be preferred if one wished to determine only the significance of the difference between the two trial means. If, however, the significance of the differences in the second criterion (differences among subject means) is wanted, analysis of variance is more useful. Moreover, through a further analysis of variance we can determine whether individual differences (differences among subjects) are significantly greater than practice differences (differences between trials). Thus if we divide the V_{subjects} by the V_{trials}, the resulting F is 393.12/384 or 1.02. For an $n_1 = 11$ and $n_2 = 1$, the .05 point is 243. Hence, in the present experiment, at least, we may feel quite sure that individual differences were no greater than practice differences. Since the reverse is usually true, the implication to be drawn is that practice in the present experiment must have been quite drastic: a conclusion borne out by the F-test for trials.

2. When in evaluating the differences between two or more groups on a test we wish to allow for initial differences among the groups on the same or different measures

In many experimental situations, especially in the fields of memory and learning, we wish to compare groups that are initially unlike, either in the variable under study or some presumably related variable. In Chapter 9, two methods were given for equating groups

ANALYSIS OF VARIANCE • 289

initially—having them "start from scratch." In the first method, experimental and control groups were made equivalent initially by person-to-person matching; and in the second method, groups were matched initially for mean and σ in one or more related variables. Neither of these methods is entirely satisfactory and neither is always easy to apply. Equivalent groups often necessitate a sharp reduction in size of N (and also in variability) when the matching of scores is difficult to accomplish. Furthermore, in matched groups it is often difficult to get the correlation between the matching variable and the experimental variable in the population from which our samples were drawn (p. 231).

Analysis of covariance represents an extension of analysis of variance to allow for the correlation between initial and final scores. Covariance analysis is especially useful to experimental psychologists when for various reasons it is impossible or quite difficult to equate control and experimental groups at the start: a situation which often obtains in actual experiments. Through covariance one is able to effect adjustments in final or terminal scores which will allow for differences in some initial variable. (For many other uses of covariance the reader should consult the references on page 268.)

Table 39 presents a numerically simple illustration of the application of analysis of covariance. The data in Example (1) are artificial

Example (1) Suppose that fifteen children have been given one trial *(X)* of a test. Five are then assigned at random to each of three groups, A, B and C. After two weeks, say, group A is praised lavishly, group B scolded severely and the test repeated *(Y)*. At the same time, a second trial *(Y)* is also given to group C, the control group, without comment.

TABLE 39   To illustrate covariance analysis

Original Data [Example (1)]

	Group A (praised)			Group B (scolded)			Group C (control)		
	X_1	Y_1	X_1Y_1	X_2	Y_2	X_2Y_2	X_3	Y_3	X_3Y_3
	15	30	450	25	28	700	5	10	50
	10	20	200	10	12	120	10	15	150
	20	25	500	15	20	300	20	20	400
	5	15	75	15	10	150	5	10	50
	10	20	200	10	10	100	10	10	100
Sums	60	110	1425	75	80	1370	50	65	750
M's	12	22		15	16		10	13	

For all 3 groups: $\Sigma X = 185$ $\Sigma Y = 255$
$\Sigma X^2 = 2775$ $\Sigma Y^2 = 5003$ $\Sigma XY = 3545$

and are purposely meager so that the procedure will not be swamped by the numerical calculations.

Step 1. Correction terms:

$$C_x = (185)^2/15 = 2282$$
$$C_y = (255)^2/15 = 4335$$
$$C_{xy} = \frac{185 \times 255}{15} = 3145$$

Step 2. Total SS

$$\text{For } x = 2775 - 2282 = 493$$
$$y = 5003 - 4335 = 668$$
$$xy = 3545 - 3145 = 400$$

Step 3. Among Group Means SS

$$\text{For } x = \frac{60^2 + 75^2 + 50^2}{5} - 2282 = 63$$
$$y = \frac{110^2 + 80^2 + 65^2}{5} - 4335 = 210$$
$$xy = \frac{60 \times 110 + 75 \times 80 + 50 \times 65}{5} - 3145 = 25$$

Step 4. Within Groups SS

$$\text{For } x = 493 - 63 = 430$$
$$y = 668 - 210 = 458$$
$$xy = 400 - 25 = 375$$

Step 5. Analysis of Variance of X and Y scores, taken separately

Source of Variation	df	SS_x	SS_y	$MS_x (V_x)$	$MS_y (V_y)$
Among Means	2	63	210	31.5	105
Within Groups	12	430	458	35.8	38.2
Total	14	493	668		

$$F_x = \frac{31.5}{35.8} = .88$$

$$F_y = \frac{105}{38.2} = 2.75$$

From Table F
df 2/12
F at .05 level = 3.88
F at .01 level = 6.93

ANALYSIS OF VARIANCE • 291

Neither F is significant. Mean differences on final trial approach significance.
$F_x = .88$ shows that the experimenter was quite successful in getting random samples in Groups A, B, C.

Step 6. Computation of Adjusted SS for Y: i.e., $SS_{y.x}$

$$\text{Total SS} = 668 - \frac{(400)^2}{493} = 343$$

$$\text{Within SS} = 458 - \frac{(375)^2}{430} = 131$$

$$\text{Among } M\text{'s SS} = 343 - 131 = 212$$

Analysis of Covariance

Source of Variation	df	SS_x	SS_y	SS_{xy}	$SS_{y.x}$	$MS_{y.x}(V_{y.x})$	$SD_{y.x}$
Among Means	2	63	210	25	212	106	
Within Groups	11 *	430	458	375	131	12	3.46
Total	13	493	668	400	343		

$$F_{y.x} = \frac{106}{12} = 8.83$$

From Table F
df 2/11
F at .05 level $= 3.98$
F at .01 level $= 7.20$

Step 7. Correlation and Regression

$$r_{\text{total}} = \frac{400}{\sqrt{493 \times 668}} = .70 \qquad b_{\text{total}} = \frac{400}{493} = .81$$

$$r_{\text{among means}} = \frac{25}{\sqrt{63 \times 210}} = .22 \qquad b_{\text{among means}} = \frac{25}{63} = .40$$

$$r_{\text{within}} = \frac{375}{\sqrt{430 \times 458}} = .84 \qquad b_{\text{within}} = \frac{375}{430} = .87$$

Step 8. Calculation of Adjusted Y-Means

Groups	N	M_X	M_Y	$M_{Y.X}$ (adjusted)
A	5	12	22	22.3
B	5	15	16	13.7
C	5	10	13	15.0
General Means		12.3	17	17.0

* 1 df lost, see page 294.

$$M_{Y.X} = M_Y - b(M_X - GM_X)$$

For Group A: $M_Y - bx = 22 - .87(12 - 12.3) = 22.3$

B: $M_Y - bx = 16 - .87(15 - 12.3) = 13.7$

C: $M_Y - bx = 13 - .87(10 - 12.3) = 15.0$

Step 9. Significance of differences among adjusted Y-Means

$$SD_{y.x} = \sqrt{12} = 3.46$$

$$SE_{M_{y.x}} = \frac{3.46}{\sqrt{5}} = 1.55$$

SE_D between any two adjusted means = $SD_{y.x}\sqrt{\dfrac{1}{n_1} + \dfrac{1}{n_2}}$

$$= 3.46\sqrt{\frac{1}{5} + \frac{1}{5}} = 3.46 \times .63 = 2.18 \tag{71}$$

For $df = 11$, $t_{.05} = 2.20$; $t_{.01} = 3.11$ (Table D)

Significant difference at .05 level = $2.20 \times 2.18 = 4.80$

Significant difference at .01 level = $3.11 \times 2.18 = 6.78$

A differs significantly from both B and C at .01 level.

B and C are not significantly different.

We thus have three groups—two experimental and one control—with initial scores (X) and final scores (Y). The problem is to determine whether the groups differ in the final trial (Y) as a result of the incentives. The method permits us to determine whether initial differences in (X) are important and to allow for them if they are.

Table 39 gives the necessary computations. The following steps outline the procedure.

Step 1

Correction term (C). There are three correction terms to be applied to SS's, one for X, one for Y and one for the cross products in X and Y. Calculation of C_x and C_y follows the method of page 275. The formula for C_{xy} is $\dfrac{\Sigma X \times \Sigma Y}{N}$ or in our problem $\dfrac{185 \times 225}{15}$.

Step 2

SS for totals. Again we have three SS's for totals: SS_x, SS_y and

SS_{xy}, of which only SS_{xy} is new. The formula for SS_{xy} is

$$SS_{xy} = \Sigma XY - C_{xy} \tag{72}$$

(*sum of squares for* xy *in analysis of covariance*)

The SS_{xy} is found by multiplying pairs of X and Y scores, summing over the range and subtracting C_{xy}: thus $(15 \times 30 + 10 \times 20 + \ldots + 10 \times 10) - 3145 = 400$.

Step 3

SS among means of the three groups. Calculations shown in Table 39 follow the method of page 289 for X and Y. The "among means" term for xy is the sum of the corresponding X and Y column totals (e.g., $60 \times 110 + 75 \times 80 + 50 \times 65$) divided by 5 and minus C_{xy}.

Step 4

SS within groups. For x, y, and xy these SS's are found by subtracting the "among means" SS's from the SS_T.

Step 5

A preliminary analysis of variance of the X and Y trials, taken separately, has been made in Table 39. The F test applied to the initial (X) scores $(F_x = .88)$ falls far short of significance at the .05 level, from which it is clear that the X-means do not differ significantly and that the random assignment of subjects to the three groups was quite successful. The F-test applied to the final (Y) scores $(F_y = 2.75)$ approaches closer to significance, but is still considerably below 3.88, the .05 level. From this preliminary analysis of variance of the Y-means *alone* we must conclude that neither praise nor scolding is more effective in raising scores than is mere repetition of the test.

Step 6

The computations carried out in this step are for the purpose of correcting the final (Y) scores for differences in initial (X) scores. The symbol $SS_{y.x}$ means that the SS_y have been "adjusted" for any variability in Y contributed by X, or that the variability in X is held constant. The general formula (see p. 297) is

$$SS_{y.x} = SS_y - \frac{(SS_{xy})^2}{SS_x} \tag{73}$$

(SS in y when variability contributed by x has been removed or held constant)

For SS_T we have that $SS_{y.x} = 668 - \frac{(400)^2}{493}$ or 343; for SS_{within} that $SS_{y.x} = 458 - \frac{(375)^2}{430} = 131$. The SS for among means is the adjusted SS_T minus adjusted SS_{within}. This last $SS_{y.x}$ cannot readily be calculated directly.*

From the various adjusted sums of squares the variances ($MS_{y.x}$) can now be computed by dividing each SS by its appropriate df. Owing to the restriction imposed by the use of formula (73) (reduction of variability in X) 1 df is lost and the analysis of covariance (Table 39) shows only 11 df for within groups instead of 12, and only 13 instead of 14 for total.

The value of analysis of covariance becomes apparent in Table 39 when the F-test is applied to the adjusted *among* and *within* variances. $F_{y.x} = 106/12$ or 8.83, and is highly significant—far beyond the .01 level (.01 = 7.20). This $F_{y.x}$ should now be compared with the F_y of 2.75 (p. 290) obtained *before* correcting for variability in initial (X) scores. It is clear from $F_{y.x}$ that the three final means—which depend upon the three incentives—differ significantly *after* they have been adjusted for initial differences in X. To find which of the three possible differences is significant or whether all are significant we must apply the t-test (in Step 9).

Step 7

An additional step is useful, however, before we proceed to the t-test for adjusted means. From the SS's in x, y and xy it is possible to compute several coefficients of correlation. These are helpful in the interpretation of the result obtained in Step 6. The general formula used is $r = \frac{\Sigma xy}{\sqrt{\Sigma x^2 \cdot \Sigma y^2}}$ (p. 139); it may be applied to the appropriate SS's for total, among means and within groups.

* See McNemar, Q., *op. cit.*, p. 324.

ANALYSIS OF VARIANCE • 295

The within groups correlation of .84 is a better measure of the relationship between initial (X) and final (Y) scores than is the total correlation of .70, as systematic differences in means have been eliminated from the within r. It is this high correlation between X and Y which accounts for the marked significance among Y-means when the variability in X is held constant. High correlation within groups *reduces* the denominator of the variance ratio, $F_{y.x}$, while low correlation between X and Y means (namely, .22) does not proportionally affect the numerator. Thus we note that the within groups variance of 38.2 is reduced through analysis of covariance to 12, while the among means variance is virtually unchanged (from 105 to 106). When correlation among scores is *high* and correlation among means *low* (as here), analysis of covariance will often lead to a significant F when analysis of variance fails to reveal significant differences among the Y-means. These two r's may be used, therefore, in a preliminary way to decide whether analysis of covariance is worth while.

Regression coefficients for total, among means and within groups have been calculated by use of the formula $b = \dfrac{\Sigma xy}{\sqrt{x^2}}$ (p. 297). The b_{within} is the most nearly unbiased estimate of the regression of X on Y, since any systematic influence due to differences among means has been removed. Therefore, b_{within} is used in the computation of the adjusted Y-means in Step 8.

Step 8

Y-means can be adjusted directly for differences in the X-means by use of the formula $M_{X.Y} = M_Y - b(M_X - Gen.M_X)$ * in which the regression coefficient, b, is the b_{within} of .87. M_Y is the original or uncorrected Y-mean of a group; M_X is the corresponding X-mean of a group and $Gen.M_X$ is the mean of *all* X scores. It will be noted that the B and C means receive more correction than the A mean which is only slightly changed.

$F_{y.x}$ tells us, it must be remembered (p. 294), that at least *one* of our adjusted Y-means differs significantly from one other mean. To determine which mean differences are significant we must first compute the adjusted Y-means and then test these differences by the t-test.

* See p. 292. $y - bx =$ adjusted value of y, or $M_Y - bx = M_{Y.x}$. Substitute $x = (M_X - Gen.M_X)$ to give $M_{Y.x} = M_Y - b(M_X - Gen.M_X)$.

Step 9

The Variance$_{y.x}$ is 12 (Table 39) as compared with the Variance$_y$ of 38.2 and the $SD_{y.x}$ is $\sqrt{12}$ or 3.46. From formula (71) we find that the standard error of the difference between any two means is 2.18. For 11 df, t is 2.20 at the .05 and 3.11 at the .01 level. Substituting for $t_{.05}$ and SE_D in the equation $t = D/SE_D$, we obtain significant differences at the .05 level and .01 level of 4.80 and 6.78, respectively. It is clear by reference to Step 8 that the adjusted A mean is significantly higher than the B and C means (at the .01 level) but that B and C do not differ significantly. We may conclude, therefore, that when initial differences are allowed for, praise makes for significant changes in final score, but that scolding has no greater effect than mere repetition of the test. Neither of these last two factors makes for significant changes in test score.

Appendix to Chapter 10

(a) Calculation SS_w [Example (1), p. 274]

Columns

A: $[64^2 + 72^2 + \ldots + 95^2] - \dfrac{(432)^2}{6} = 890$

B: $[73^2 + \ldots\ldots + 67^2] - \dfrac{(468)^2}{6} = 944$

C: $[77^2 + \ldots\ldots + 87^2] - \dfrac{(492)^2}{6} = 454$

D: $[78^2 + \ldots\ldots + 77^2] - \dfrac{(510)^2}{6} = 302$

E: $[63^2 + \ldots\ldots + 76^2] - \dfrac{(390)^2}{6} = 710$

F: $[75^2 + \ldots\ldots + 76^2] - \dfrac{(456)^2}{6} = 488$

G: $[78^2 + \ldots\ldots + 82^2] - \dfrac{(366)^2}{6} = 1540$

H: $[55^2 + \ldots\ldots + 68^2] - \dfrac{(372)^2}{6} = 338$

$\overline{5666}$

(b) Derivation of the formula

$$\mathrm{SS}_{y.x} = \mathrm{SS}_y - \frac{(\mathrm{SS}_{xy})^2}{\mathrm{SS}_x}$$

Let X = dependent variable
Y = independent variable
r_{xy} = correlation between X and Y

Then $\sigma^2_{y.x} = \sigma^2_y(1 - r^2_{xy}) = \sigma^2_y - \sigma^2_y r^2_{xy}$ p. 162

$$r^2_{xy} = \frac{(\Sigma xy)^2}{\Sigma x^2 \cdot \Sigma y^2}$$ p. 139

Substituting, $\sigma^2_{y.x} = \sigma^2_y - \dfrac{(\Sigma xy)^2}{N\Sigma x^2}$

In terms of SS: $\mathrm{SS}_{y.x} = \mathrm{SS}_y - \dfrac{(\mathrm{SS}_{xy})^2}{\mathrm{SS}_x}$

(c) Derivation of formula

$$b = \frac{\Sigma xy}{\sqrt{\Sigma x^2}}$$

$$b = r\frac{\sigma_y}{\sigma_x}$$ p. 155

$$r = \frac{\Sigma xy}{N\sigma_x\sigma_y}$$

Substituting $b = \dfrac{\Sigma xy}{N\sigma^2_x} = \dfrac{\Sigma xy}{\dfrac{N\Sigma x^2}{N}}$

$$= \frac{\Sigma xy}{\Sigma x^2}$$

PROBLEMS

1. In a learning experiment, 10 subjects are assigned at random to each of six groups. Each group performs the same task but under slightly different experimental conditions. Do the groups differ in mean performance?

	1	2	3	4	5	6	
	41	40	36	14	41	55	
	40	36	33	38	35	36	
	39	40	29	51	52	41	
	41	34	30	41	41	36	
	39	34	45	36	34	48	
	41	39	39	36	10	36	
	36	36	33	36	44	42	
	35	34	32	32	26	42	
	35	41	34	38	54	34	
	37	37	34	36	30	40	Grand sum
Sums	384	371	345	358	367	410	2235

2. Solve problem (2), page 243, by the methods of analysis of variance.

3. Twenty subjects are paired on the basis of their initial scores on a test. Ten (one member of each pair) are then assigned to an experimental and 10 to a control group. The experimental group is given special practice and both groups are retested. Data for final scores are as follows:

	Pairs of Subjects										
	1	2	3	4	5	6	7	8	9	10	Total
Control group	25	46	93	45	15	64	47	56	73	66	530
Experimental group	36	57	89	67	19	78	46	59	69	70	590

(a) Do the groups differ significantly in mean performance?
(b) Do subject-pairs differ significantly?
(c) Check the result in (a) by taking the difference between pairs of scores, and testing the mean difference (by t-test) against null hypothesis.

4. In the following table * the entries represent blood cholesterol readings taken from 18 patients in April and in May.

(a) Is the rise from April to May significant?
(b) Are there significant individual differences, regardless of month?

* Fertig, John W., "The Use of Interaction in the Removal of Correlated Variation." *Biometric Bull.*, 1936, 1, 1–14.

(c) From the column of differences, compute M_D and SD_D. Using the t-test, measure the significance of M_D against the null hypothesis. Compare with the result in (a).

Individual	April	May	Difference	Sum
1	158.0	190.5	32.5	348.5
2	158.5	177.0	18.5	335.5
3	137.5	172.0	34.5	309.5
4	145.5	152.5	7.0	298.0
5	130.5	147.0	16.5	277.5
6	141.0	127.0	−14.0	268.0
7	150.5	149.5	− 1.0	300.0
8	142.5	152.5	10.0	295.0
9	148.0	147.0	− 1.0	295.0
10	137.5	130.5	− 7.0	268.0
11	137.0	133.0	− 4.0	270.0
12	160.0	145.5	−14.5	305.5
13	145.0	124.5	−20.5	269.5
14	149.5	156.0	6.5	305.5
15	145.0	143.5	− 1.5	288.5
16	132.5	146.0	13.5	278.5
17	139.0	148.0	9.0	287.0
18	151.0	161.0	10.0	312.0
Sum	2608.5	2703.0	94.5	5311.5
SS	379288.25	410872.0	4311.25	1576009.25

5. In an experiment by Mowrer,* previously unrotated pigeons were tested for clockwise postrotational nystagmus. The rate of rotation was one revolution in 1½ sec. An average initial score for each pigeon based upon 2 tests is indicated by the symbol X. The 24 pigeons were then divided into 4 groups of 6 each. Each group was then subjected to 10 daily periods of rotation under one of the experimental conditions indicated below. The rotation speed was the same as during the initial test and the rotation periods lasted 30 sec., with a 30-sec. rest interval between each period. Groups 1, 2 and 3 were practiced in a clockwise direction only. For Group 4 the environment was rotated in a counterclockwise direction. At the end of 24 days of practice, each group was tested again under the same conditions as on the initial test. These records are called Y.

* From Edwards, A. L., *Experimental Design in Psychological Research* (New York: Rinehart, 1950), p. 357.

300 • STATISTICS IN PSYCHOLOGY AND EDUCATION

Group 1 Rotation of body only. Vision excluded		Group 2 Rotation of body only. Vision permitted		Group 3 Rotation of body and environ- ment		Group 4 Rotation of environment only	
Initial X	Final Y	Initial X	Final Y	Initial X	Final Y	Initial X	Final Y
23.8	7.9	28.5	25.1	27.5	20.1	22.9	19.9
23.8	7.1	18.5	20.7	28.1	17.7	25.2	28.2
22.6	7.7	20.3	20.3	35.7	16.8	20.8	18.1
22.8	11.2	26.6	18.9	13.5	13.5	27.7	30.5
22.0	6.4	21.2	25.4	25.9	21.0	19.1	19.3
19.6	10.0	24.0	30.0	27.9	29.3	32.2	35.1
134.6	50.3	139.1	140.4	158.6	118.4	147.9	151.1

(a) Test the significance of the differences among X-means. (Compute the among groups and within groups variance and use F-test.)
(b) Do same as in (a) for the Y-scores.
(c) By analysis of covariance test the differences among the adjusted means in Y. How much is the variance among Y-means reduced when X is held constant?
(d) Compute the adjusted Y-means, $M_{Y.X}$ by the method of p. 292.
(e) From the t-test find that difference among adjusted Y-means which is significant at the .05 level; at the .01 level.

ANSWERS

1. No. $F = \dfrac{50.8}{54.7}$ or .93, and differences among means may be attributed entirely to sampling fluctuations.
2. $F = 5.16$ and $t = 2.3$ ($\sqrt{F}$)
3. (a) No. $F = \dfrac{180}{35.3} = 5.10$
   (b) Yes. $F = \dfrac{911.8}{35.3} = 25.83$
   (c) $t = \dfrac{6}{2.66} = 2.26$ $t^2 = F = 5.10$
4. (a) No. $F = \dfrac{248.0}{112.22} = 2.21$. $df = 1/17$ and $F_{.05} = 4.45$ (Table F)
   (b) Yes, just barely. $F = \dfrac{255.12}{112.22} = 2.27$ $df = 17/17$ and $F_{.05} = 2.28$
   (c) $M_D = 5.25$; $SE_D = 3.53$. $t = \dfrac{5.25}{3.53} = 1.49$; $F = t^2 = 2.22$. $df = 17$
5. (a) Difference among X-means not significant. $F_x = \dfrac{18.7}{23.1} = .81$

(b) Y-means differ significantly. $F_y = \dfrac{341.4}{24.9} = 13.7$. For df of 3/20, $F_{.01} = 4.94$.

(c) $F_{y.x} = \dfrac{303.4}{19.8} = 15.3$. Variance among Y-means is reduced 11%— from 341.4 to 303.4.

(d) 9.3, 23.9, 18.6 and 24.9

(e) 5.31; 7.26

12

THE SCALING OF MENTAL TESTS AND OTHER PSYCHOLOGICAL DATA

Various devices, many of them based upon the normal probability curve, have been used in the scaling of psychological and educational data. As used in mental measurement, a *scale* may be thought of as a continuum or continuity along which items, tasks, problems and the like have been located in terms of difficulty or some other attribute. The units of a scale are arbitrary and depend upon the method employed by the investigator. Ideally, scale units should be equal, have the same meaning, and remain stable throughout the scale. Several scaling procedures will be described in this chapter.

I. The Scaling of Test Items

1. Scaling individual test items in terms of difficulty (σ-scaling)

We sometimes wish to construct a test which shall contain problems or tasks graded in difficulty from very easy to very hard by known steps or intervals. If we know what proportion of a large group is able to solve each problem, it is comparatively easy to arrange our items in a percentage order of difficulty. Such an arrangement constitutes a scale, to be sure, but a crude one, as percentage differences are not satisfactory indices of differences in difficulty (p. 314).

If we are justified in assuming normality in the trait being measured, the *variability* (i.e., σ) of the group will give us a better scaling unit than will percentage passing (p. 315). Test items may be "set" or spaced in terms of σ-difficulty at definite points along a difficulty

SCALING OF MENTAL TESTS AND OTHER PSYCHOLOGICAL DATA · 303

continuum; their positions with respect to each other as well as with respect to some reference point or "zero" is then known in terms of a stable unit. To illustrate σ-scaling, suppose that we wish to construct a scale for measuring "reasoning ability" (e.g., by means of syllogisms) in 12-year-olds; or a scale for measuring mechanical ingenuity in high-school juniors; or a scale for determining degree of suggestibility in college freshmen. The steps in constructing such a device may be outlined briefly as follows:

(1) Compile a large number of problems or other test items. These items should vary in difficulty from very easy to very hard and all sample the behavior to be tested.
(2) Administer the items to a large group drawn randomly from those for whom the final test is intended.
(3) Compute the percentage of the group which can solve each problem. Discard duplicate items and those too easy or too hard or unsatisfactory for other reasons.* Arrange the problems retained in an order of percentage difficulty. An item done correctly by 90% of the group is obviously less difficult than one solved by 75%; while the second problem is less difficult than one solved by only 50%. The larger the per cent passing, the lower the item in a scale of difficulty.
(4) By means of Table A convert the per cent solving each problem into a σ-distance above or below the mean. For example: an item done correctly by 40% of the group is 10% or .25σ above the mean. A problem solved by 78% is 28% (78% − 50%) or .77σ below the mean. We may tabulate the results for 5 items, taken at random, as follows (see Fig. 50):

Problems	A	B	C	D	E
Per cent solving:	93	78	55	40	14
Distance from the mean in percentage terms:	−43	−28	− 5	10	36
Distance from the mean in σ-terms:	−1.48	−.77	−.13	.25	1.08

Problem A is solved by 93% of the group, i.e., by the upper 50% (the right half of the normal curve) plus the 43% to the *left* of the mean. This puts Problem A at a point −1.48σ from the mean. In the same way, the percentage distance of each prob-

* Adkins, D. C., et al., *Construction and Analysis of Achievement Tests* (Washington, D. C.: U. S. Government Printing Office, 1947), Chap. II.

lem from the mean (measured in the plus or minus direction) can be found by subtracting the per cent passing from 50%. From these percentages, the σ-distance of the problem above or below the mean is read from Table A.

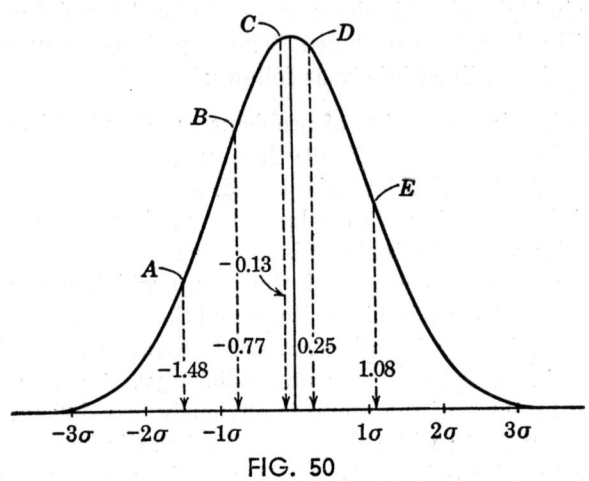

FIG. 50

(5) When the σ-distance of each item has been established, calculate the σ-distance of each item from the zero point of ability in the trait. A zero point may be located as follows: Suppose that 5% of the entire group fail to solve a single problem. This would put the level of zero ability 45% of the distribution below the mean, or at a distance of -1.65σ from the mean.* The σ-value of each item in the scale may then be computed from this zero. To illustrate with the 5 problems above:

Problems	A	B	C	D	E
σ-distance from mean:	−1.48	−.77	− .13	.25	1.08
σ-distance from arbitrary zero, −1.65	.17	.88	1.52	1.90	2.73

The simplest way to find σ-distances from a given zero is to subtract the zero point algebraically from the σ-distance of each item from the mean. Problem A, for example, is $-1.48 - (-1.65)$ or

---

* This is, of course, an arbitrary, not a true zero. It will serve, however, as a reference point (level of minimum ability) from which to measure performance. The point -3.00σ is often taken as a convenient reference point.

SCALING OF MENTAL TESTS AND OTHER PSYCHOLOGICAL DATA • 305

.17σ from the arbitrary zero; and Problem E is 1.08 − (−1.65) or 2.73σ from our zero.

(6) When the distance of each item from the given zero has been determined, the difficulty value of each item with respect to the other items and with respect to zero is known and the scaling is finished. The next steps depend upon the purpose of the investigator. He may select items separated by fixed σ-distances (.5σ, say) to cover a wide range of talent. Or he may limit the range of talent from −2.50σ to 2.50σ, say, and not attempt to establish equal difficulty steps. Norms are derived from the final scale for age, grade, occupational or other groups.

2. Scaling total scores on a test

In the last section we saw how individual test items can be scaled in σ-units by assuming normality in the trait being measured. We shall now describe two methods of scaling score totals or aggregates of items—procedures generally followed in constructing aptitude and achievement tests.

(1) σ-SCORES AND STANDARD SCORES

Let us suppose that the mean of a test is 122 and the σ is 24. Then if John earns a score of 146 on this test, his deviation from the mean is 146 − 122 or 24. Dividing John's deviation of 24 by the σ of the test, we give him a σ-score of 24/24 or 1.00. If William's score is 110 on this test, his deviation from the mean is 110 − 122 or −12; and his score in σ-units is −.5. Deviations from the mean expressed in σ-terms are called σ-scores, z-scores, and reduced scores. Of these designations, σ-score is certainly the most descriptive, but the other terms are often used. We have already used the concept of a σ-score in the problems in Chapter 5, p. 104.

The mean of a set of σ-scores is always 0 (the reference point) and the σ is always unity or 1.00. As approximately half of the scores in a distribution will lie below and half above the mean, about half of our σ-scores will be negative and half positive. In addition, σ-scores are often small decimal fractions and hence somewhat awkward to deal with in computation. For these reasons, σ-scores are usually converted into a new distribution with M and σ so selected as to make all scores positive and relatively easy to handle. Such scores are called standard scores. Raw test scores of the Army General Classification Test, for example, are expressed as standard scores in a distribution of $M = 100$ and $\sigma = 20$; sub-tests of the Wechsler-Bellevue are converted into standard scores in a distribution of $M = 10$ and $\sigma = 3$; and the tests of the Graduate Record Examination into standard scores in a distribution of $M = 500$ and $\sigma = 100$.

The shift from raw to standard score requires a linear transformation.* This transmutation does not change the *shape* of the distribution in any way; if the original distribution was skewed (or normal), the standard score distribution will be skewed or normal in exactly the same fashion. The formula for conversion of raw to standard score is as follows:

Let X = a score in the original distribution
X' = a standard score in the new distribution
M and M' = means of the raw score and standard score distributions
σ and σ' = SD's of raw and standard scores

Then $\dfrac{X' - M'}{\sigma'} = \dfrac{X - M}{\sigma}$

or $X' = \dfrac{\sigma'}{\sigma}(X - M) + M'$ \hfill (74)

(*formula for converting raw scores to standard scores*)

An illustration will show how the formula works.

Example (1) Given a distribution with Mean = 86 and $\sigma = 15$. Tom's score is 91 and Mary's 83. Express these raw scores as standard scores in a distribution with a mean of 500 and σ of 100.

By formula (74)

$$X' = \frac{100}{15}(X - 86) + 500$$

Substituting Tom's score of 91 for X we have

$$X' = 6.67(91 - 86) + 500$$
$$= 533$$

Substituting Mary's score of 83 for X,

$$X' = 6.67(83 - 86) + 500$$
$$= 480$$

* When the equation connecting two variables, y and x, is that of a straight line, changing x's into y's involves a linear transformation. (Formula (74) is the equation of a straight line, analogous to the general equation of a straight line, $y = mx + b$.

SCALING OF MENTAL TESTS AND OTHER PSYCHOLOGICAL DATA • 307

In a distribution with a mean of 10 and a σ of 3, Tom's standard score would be 11 and Mary's 9.4; in a distribution with a mean of 100 and a σ of 20, Tom's standard score would be 107 and Mary's 96. Other scaling distributions may, of course, be employed.

Scores made by the same individual upon several tests cannot usually be compared directly owing to differences in test units. Thus a score of 162 on a group intelligence test and a score of 126 on an educational achievement examination cannot be compared meaningfully. If scores like these are expressed as standard scores, however, they can be compared *provided* the distributions of raw scores are of the same form. Fortunately, most distributions of scores are so nearly bell-shaped (p. 113) that no great error is made in treating them as normal. When we can assume normality, a score of 1.00σ on a mechanical aptitude test and a score of 1.00σ on a test of mechanical interests represent the same relative degree of achievement: both are exceeded by approximately 16% of those taking the two tests (Table A). A problem will illustrate further this important aspect of standard scores.

Example (2) Given a reading test with a mean of 81 and σ of 12; and an arithmetic test with a mean of 33 and a σ of 8. Sue's score is 72 in reading and 27 in arithmetic. Assuming the distributions of reading and arithmetic scores to be of the same form (approximately normal), convert Sue's scores into a standard score distribution with Mean = 100 and σ = 20 and compare them.

In the reading test Sue's score is 9 below the mean of 81. Hence, her score is at $-.75\sigma(-9/12)$ and her new score is $85(100 - .75 \times 20)$. In arithmetic Sue's score is 6 points below the mean; again her score is at $-.75\sigma$ and her new score $85(100 - .75 \times 20)$. Sue's two standard scores are comparable, and are also equivalent (represent same degree of achievement), if our assumption of normality of distributions is tenable.

(2) NORMALIZING THE FREQUENCY DISTRIBUTION; THE T-SCALE

Instead of into standard scores, the raw scores of a frequency distribution may be converted into a system of "normalized" standard scores by transforming them into equivalent points in a normal distribution. Equivalent scores (p. 306) are measures which indicate the same level of talent. Suppose that, in a certain test, 20% of the group achieve scores better than 73. Now from Table A we find that 20% of the area of the normal probability curve lies above .84σ (30% falls between the mean and .84σ). Hence score 73 is equivalent to .84σ in the normal distribution, as both reflect the same degree of achievement.

Normalized standard scores are generally called T-scores. T-scaling was devised by McCall * and first used by him in the construction of a series of reading tests designed for use in the elementary grades. The original T-scale was based upon the reading scores achieved by 500 12-year-olds; and the scores earned by other age groups on the same reading test were expressed in terms of 12-year-old performance. Since this first use of the method, T-scaling has been employed with various groups and with different tests so that it no longer has reference specifically to 12-year-olds nor to reading tests.

T-scores are normalized standard scores converted into a distribution with a mean of 50 and σ of 10. In the σ-scaling of individual items, the mean, as we know, is at zero and σ is 1.00. The point of reference, therefore, is zero and the unit of measurement is 1. If the point of reference is moved from the mean of the normal curve to a point 5 σ below the mean, this new reference point becomes zero in the scale and the mean is 5. As shown in Figure 51, the σ-divisions above the mean (1σ, 2σ, 3σ, 4σ, 5σ) become 6, 7, 8, 9 and 10; and the σ-divisions below the mean ($-1σ, -2σ, -3σ, -4σ, -5σ$) are 4, 3, 2, 1 and 0. The σ of the distribution remains, of course, equal to 1.00.

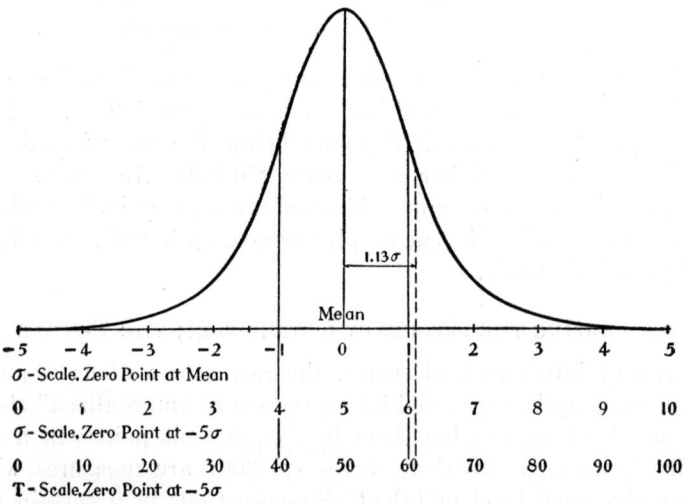

FIG. 51 To illustrate σ-scaling and T-scaling in a normal distribution

* McCall, William A., *Measurement* (New York: Macmillan, 1939), Chap. 22.

SCALING OF MENTAL TESTS AND OTHER PSYCHOLOGICAL DATA

Only slight changes are needed in order to convert this σ-scale into a T-scale. The T-scale begins at -5σ and ends at $+5\sigma$. But σ is multiplied by 10 so that the mean is 50 and the other divisions are 0, 10, 20, 30, 40, 50, 60, 70, 80, 90 and 100. The relationship of the T-scale to the ordinary σ-scale is shown in Figure 51. Note that the T-scale ranges from 0 to 100; that its unit, i.e., T, is 1 and that the mean is 50. T, of course, equals .1 of σ which is equal to 10. The reference point on the T-scale is set at -5σ in order to have the scale cover exactly 100 units. This is convenient but it puts the extremes of the scale far beyond the ability ranges of most groups. In actual practice, T-scores range from about 15 to 85, i.e., from -3.5σ to 3.5σ.

The procedure to be followed in T-scaling a set of scores can best be shown by an example. We shall outline the process in a series of steps, illustrating each step by reference to the data of Table 40.

TABLE 40 To illustrate the calculation of T-scores

(1) Test Score	(2) f	(3) Cum. f	(4) Cum. Freq. below Score + ½ on Given Score	(5) Col. (4) in %'s	(6) T-Scores
10	1	62	61.5	99.2	74
9	4	61	59	95.2	67
8	6	57	54	87.1	61
7	10	51	46	74.2	56
6	8	41	37	59.7	52
5	13	33	26.5	42.7	48
4	18	20	11	17.7	41
3	2	2	1	1.6	29
	$N = 62$				

(1) Compile a large and representative group of test items which vary in difficulty from easy to hard. Administer these items to a sample of subjects (children or adults) for whom the final scale is intended.

(2) Compute the per cent passing each item. Arrange the items in an order of difficulty in terms of these percentages.

(3) Administer the test to a representative sample and tabulate the distribution of total scores. Total scores may now be scaled as shown in Table 40 for 62 subjects. In column (1) the test scores are entered; and in column (2) are listed the frequencies—number of subjects achieving each score. Two subjects had scores of 3, 18 had scores of 4, 13 scores of 5, and so on. In column (3) scores have been cumulated (p. 63) from the low to the high

end of the frequency distribution. Column (4) shows the number of subjects who fall *below* each score plus one-half of those who earn the given score. The entries in this column may readily be computed from columns (2) and (3). There are no scores below 3 and 2 scores on 3, so that the number below 3 plus one-half on 3 equals 1. There are 2 scores below 4 [see column (3)] and 18 on 4 [column (2)]; hence the number of scores below 4 plus one-half on 4 is $2 + 9$ or 11. There are 20 scores below 5 ($2 + 18$) and 13 scores on 5 [column (2)] so that the number below 5 plus one-half on 5 is $20 + 6.5$ or 26.5. The reason why one-half of the frequency *on* a given score must be added to the frequency falling *below* that score is that each score is an interval—not a point on the scale. The score of 4, for example, covers the interval 3.5–4.5, midpoint 4.0. If the 18 frequencies on score 4 are thought of as distributed evenly over the interval, 9 will lie *below* and 9 *above* 4.0, the midpoint. Hence, if we add 9 to the 2 scores below 4 (i.e., below 3.5) we obtain 11 as the number of scores below 4.0, the midpoint of the interval 3.5–4.5. Each sum in column (4) is taken up to the midpoint of a score-interval.

(4) In column (5) the entries in column (4) are expressed as per cents of N (here 62). Thus, 99.2% of the scores lie below 10.0 midpoint of the interval 9.5–10.5; 95.2% of the scores lie below 9.0, midpoint of 8.5–9.5, etc.

(5) Turn the per cents in column (5) into T-scores by means of Table G. T-scores in Table G corresponding to percentages nearest to those wanted are taken without interpolation, as fractional T-scores are a needless refinement. Thus for 1.6% we take 1.79 (T-score $= 29$); for 17.7% we take 18.41% (T-score $= 41$), and so on.

In Table G, percentages lying to the *left* of (i.e., below) succeeding σ-points expressed as T-scores have been tabulated, rather than per cents between the mean and given σ-points as in Table A. In Table G, we are enabled, therefore, to read T-scores directly; but the student will note that T-scores can also be read from Table A. To illustrate with score 8 in Table 40, which has a percentage-below-plus one-half-reaching of 87.1, note that a score failed by 87.1% lies 37.1% (87.1% $-$ 50.0%) to the *right* of the mean. From Table A, we read that 37.1% of the distribution lies between the mean and 1.13σ. Since the σ of the T-scale is 10, 1.13σ becomes 11 in T-units;

SCALING OF MENTAL TESTS AND OTHER PSYCHOLOGICAL DATA • 311

and adding 11 to 50, the mean, we get 61 as the required T-score (see Fig. 51).

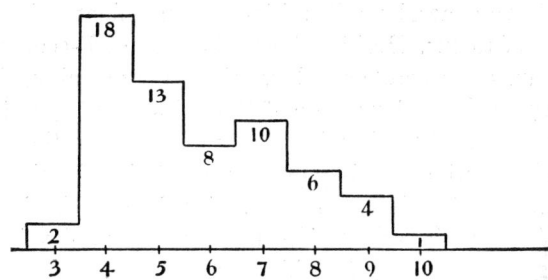

FIG. 52 Histogram of the sixty-two scores in Table 40

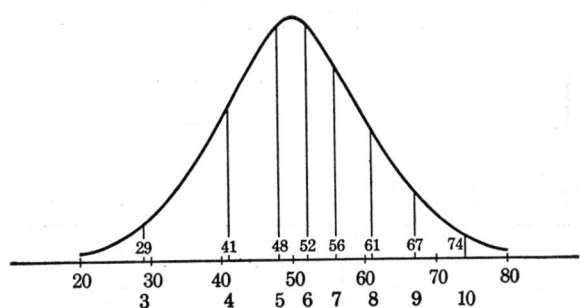

FIG. 53 Normalized distribution of the scores in Table 40 and Figure 52. Original scores and T-score equivalents are shown on baseline

Figure 52 shows a histogram plotted from the distribution of 62 scores in Table 40. Note that the scores of 3, 4, 5, etc., are spaced at equal intervals along the baseline, i.e., along the scale of scores. When these raw scores are transformed into normalized standard scores—into T-scores—they occupy the positions in the normal curve shown in Figure 53. The unequal scale distances between the scores in Figure 53 show clearly that, when normality is forced upon a trait, the original scores do not represent equal difficulty steps. In other words, normalizing a distribution of test scores alters the original test units (stretching them out or compressing them) and the more skewed the raw score distribution, the greater is the change in unit.

T-scores have general applicability, a convenient unit, and cover a wide range of talent. Besides these advantages, T-scores from different tests are comparable and have the same meaning, since reference is always to a standard scale of 100 units based upon the normal probability curve. T-scaling forces normality upon the scores of a frequency distribution and is unwarranted if the distribution of the trait in the *population* is not normal. For the distributions of most mental abilities in the population, however, normality is a reasonable—and is often the only feasible—assumption.

(3) A COMPARISON OF T-SCORES AND STANDARD SCORES

T-scores are sometimes confused with standard scores, but the assumptions underlying the two sorts of measures are quite different. Table 41 repeats the data of Table 40, and shows the T-score equiva-

TABLE 41 Comparison of T-scores and standard scores

		(Data from Table 40)	
Test Score	f	T-Scores	Standard Scores $M = 50, \sigma = 10$
10	1	74	75
9	4	67	69
8	6	61	63
7	10	56	57
6	8	52	52
5	13	48	46
4	18	41	40
3	2	28	34

$N = 62$

For test scores:
$M = 5.73$
$\sigma = 1.72$

Equation for converting test scores into standard scores (see p. 306)

$$\frac{X - 5.73}{1.72} = \frac{X' - 50}{10}$$

$$X' = \frac{10X}{1.72} - \frac{57.3}{1.72} + 50$$

$$X' = 5.82X - 33.3 + 50$$

$$X' = 5.82X + 16.7$$

lents to the given raw scores. Standard scores with a mean of 50 and σ of 10 are listed in column (4) for comparison with the T-scores. These standard scores were calculated by means of formula (74) on page 306. The mean of the raw scores is 5.73 and the σ is 1.72; and the mean of the "new" standard score distribution is, of course, 50, with σ of 10. Substituting these values in formula (74) we have

$$X' = 5.82X + 16.7$$

as our transformation equation. Putting 3, 4, 5, etc., for X in this equation we find X''s of 34, 40, 46, etc. These X' scores will be found to correspond fairly closely to the T-scores. This is often the case, and the more nearly normal the distribution of raw scores the closer the correspondence. The two kinds of scores are not interchangeable, however. With respect to original scores, T-scores represent equivalent scores in a normal distribution. Standard scores, on the other hand, always have the same form of distribution as raw scores, and are simply original scores expressed in σ-units. Standard scores represent the kind of conversion we make when we change inches to centimeters or kilograms to pounds; that is, the transformation is linear. Standard scores correspond exactly to T-scores when the distribution of raw scores is strictly normal.

(4) PERCENTILE SCALING

A child who earns a certain score on a test can be assigned a percentile rank (PR) * of 27, 42 or 77, say, depending upon his position in the score distribution. Percentile rank locates a child on a scale of 100, and tells us immediately what proportion of the group has achieved scores *lower* than he. Moreover, when a child has taken several tests, a comparison of his PR's provides measures of relative achievement, which may be combined into a final total score. As a method of scaling test scores, PR's have the practical advantage of being readily calculated and easily understood. But the percentile scale also possesses marked disadvantages which limit its usefulness.

Percentile scales assume that the difference between a rank of 10 and a rank of 20 is the same as the difference between a rank of 40 and a rank of 50, namely, that percentile differences are equal throughout the scale. This assumption of equal percentile units holds strictly only when the distribution of scores is rectangular in shape; it does not hold when the distribution is bell-shaped, or approximately normal. Figure 54 shows graphically why this is true. In the diagram we have a rectangular distribution and a normal curve of the *same area* plotted over it. When the rectangle is divided into 5 equal segments, the areas of the small rectangles are all the same

* For method of computing PR's, see p. 68.

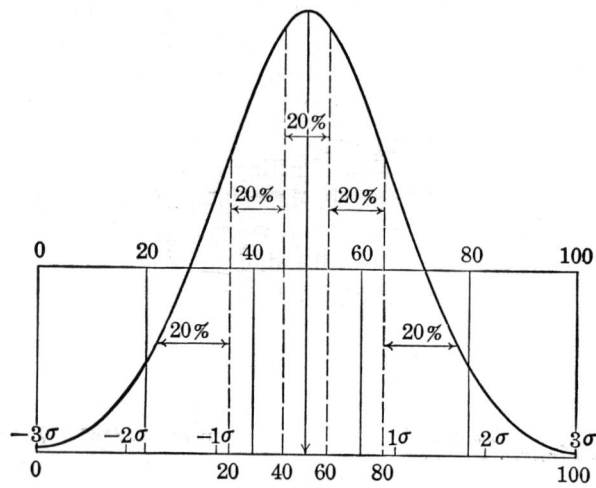

FIG. 54 To illustrate the position of the same five percentiles in rectangular and normal distributions

(20%) and the distances from 0 to 20, 20 to 40, 40 to 60, 60 to 80, and 80 to 100 are all equal. These percentiles, P_{20}, P_{40}, etc., have been marked off along the top of the rectangle.

Now let us compare the distances along the baseline of the normal curve when these are determined by successive 20% slices of area. These baseline intervals can be found in the following way. From Table A we read that the 30% of area to the left of the mean extends to $-.84\sigma$. The first 20% of a normal distribution, therefore, falls between -3.00σ and $-.84\sigma$: covers a distance of 2.16σ along the baseline. The second 20% (P_{20} to P_{40}) lies between $-.84\sigma$ and $-.25\sigma$ (since $-.25\sigma$ is at a distance of 10% from the mean); and covers a distance of $.59\sigma$ along the baseline. The third 20% (P_{40} to P_{60}) lies between $-.25\sigma$ and $.25\sigma$: straddles the mean and covers $.50\sigma$ on the baseline. The fourth and fifth 20%'s occupy the same relative positions in the upper half of the curve as the second and first 20%'s occupy in the lower half of the curve. To summarize:

First 20% of area covers a distance of 2.16σ
Second 20% of area covers a distance of $.59\sigma$
Third 20% of area covers a distance of $.50\sigma$
Fourth 20% of area covers a distance of $.59\sigma$
Fifth 20% of area covers a distance of 2.16σ

SCALING OF MENTAL TESTS AND OTHER PSYCHOLOGICAL DATA • 315

It is clear (1) that intervals along the baseline from the extreme left end (0 to P_{20}, P_{20} to P_{40}, etc.) to the extreme right end of the normal curve are not equal when determined by successive 20% slices of area; and (2) that inequalities are relatively greater at the two ends of the distribution, so that the two end fifths are 4 times as long as the middle one.

Distributions of raw scores are rarely if ever rectangular in form. Hence equal per cents of N (area) cannot be taken to represent equal increments of achievement and the percentile scale does not progress by equal steps. Between Q_1 and Q_3, however, equal per cents of area are more nearly equally spaced along the baseline (see Fig. 54), so that the PR's of a child in two or more tests may be safely combined or averaged if they fall within these limits. But high and low PR's (above 75 and below 25) should be combined, if at all, with full knowledge of their limitations.

TABLE 42 Percentile distributions for nine-year-olds on three tests

Tests	Method of Combining the Percentile Ranks of a Single Individual										S's Score	S's Perc. Rank
	Percentiles											
	0	10	20	30	40	50	60	70	80	90	100	
Picture Completion..	62	240	297	325	372	407	440	450	499	577	646	445	65
Substitution	219	190	173	158	152	141	133	126	121	109	80	126	70
Seguin Form-Board..	34	24	21	20	18	18	17	16	15	13	17	60
Median Percentile Rank...												65

Table 42 gives an illustration of the value of percentile scaling when tests scored in different units are to be compared and combined. Percentile distributions for 9-year-olds are shown for three tests from the Pintner-Paterson Scale of Performance Tests.* The subject, a 9-year-old boy, made a score of 445 on the Completion Test which gave him a PR of 65 (midway between 60 and 70). On the Substitution Test, a score of 126 gave him a PR of 70; and on the Seguin Form Board a score of 17 gave him a PR of 60. The scores in the last two tests are in time units (seconds) so that the lowest scores numerically represent the highest performance. The median of this boy's PR's is 65, indicating that he stands somewhat above the average of 9-year-olds. Since none of these PR's is extremely high or low, they may be combined with little error.

* Pintner, R., and Paterson, D. G., *A Scale of Performance Tests* (New York: D. Appleton & Co., 1925), pp. 189, 197.

II. The Scaling of Judgments

1. Converting judgments into normal curve units (product scales)

We have seen in the last section how test scores may be scaled on the principle that the σ-value determined from the percentage passing a given item is an acceptable index of difficulty. It often happens, however, that the ability or trait in which we are interested is of such a nature that achievement cannot be expressed by a test score. This necessitates the construction of what are called *product scales*. In such scales excellence of performance is evaluated by comparing an individual's production with various "standard productions" the values of which have been determined beforehand by a consensus of expert judgment. Handwriting, compositions, and drawings are well-known examples of product scales. The excellence of a person's penmanship, for example, can be determined by comparing a sample of his writing with various specimens of handwriting, the quality of which has been measured against some criterion.

Product scales are constructed on the principle that "equally often noticed differences" in quality are equal. If composition A, for example, is rated better than composition B by 75% of a group of competent judges, and composition X is rated better than composition Y by 75% of the same judges, then the difference between A and B is taken to the be same as the difference between X and Y (because equally often observed).

The assumption that "equally often noticed differences are equal" has been criticized [*] and is most doubtful when applied to the scaling of items at the extremes of the qualitative range. The variability of judgments upon extremely good or extremely poor specimens will ordinarily be less than the range of judgments made upon intermediate specimens. In most product scales the accurate measurement of these extreme specimens is, perhaps, not so important as is the accurate scaling of those items which constitute the main body of the scale. For this reason, the assumption that equally often noticed differences are equal will give scales which are just as valuable practically as those resulting from the use of more refined techniques.

[*] Thurstone. L. L., "Equally Often Noticed Differences," *Journal of Educational Psychology*, 1927, 18, 289–293.
Thurstone, L. L., "Psychophysical Analysis," *American Journal of Psychology*, 1927, 38, 368–389.

SCALING OF MENTAL TESTS AND OTHER PSYCHOLOGICAL DATA • 317

Steps in constructing a product scale may be set down as follows:

(1) Collect a large number of samples of the product to be scaled (e.g., handwriting, drawings, jokes, pictures). These specimens should range by gradual stages from very poor to excellent.

(2) Persuade a number of competent persons to act as judges of the comparative excellence of the specimens. Instruct these judges to compare every specimen with every other specimen, so that a consensus may be obtained on each. The order of merit method, the paired comparisons method, or some variation of these, should ordinarily be employed here, as these experimental techniques provide a systematic attack upon the problem of ranking samples for excellence.*

(3) Reduce the number of times each specimen is ranked above each other specimen to percentage terms, and express these percents as σ-distances between each pair of specimens. To illustrate, if drawing A is judged better than drawing B by 65% of the group, $A - B = 39\sigma$; if B is judged better than C by 77%, $B - C = .74\sigma$. These σ-differences are read from Table A and are found in the following way: If a sample is judged better than another by just 50%, there is no observable difference between the two and their σ-difference is zero. But if A is judged better than B by 65%, the difference between A and B (in excess of chance) is 15%, which from Table A corresponds to a σ-difference of .39. In exactly the same way the difference between B and C (in excess of chance) is 27%, which corresponds to a σ-difference of .74. Figure 55 shows graphically how percentage differences can be converted into σ-differences. The distributions of judgments upon A, B, and C are assumed to be normal and are taken to be equal in range and variability. The mean value of A (its scale value) is .39σ above the mean value of B, the mean value of which is, in turn, .74σ above the mean value of C.

(4) Determine a difference for each pair of specimens, and express each item finally selected for the scale as so many σ-units from the arbitrary zero. The procedure may be illustrated by two items, numbers eight and nine, taken from the Hillegas Composition Scale.† Hillegas had each of 202 judges arrange a number of English compositions in order of merit. An artificial

---

* Woodworth, R. S., *Experimental Psychology* (New York: Henry Holt & Co., 1938), pp. 372–378.
† Hillegas, Milo B., *A Scale for the Measurement of Quality in English Composition by Young People*, Teachers College Record, 1912, 13, 4, 5–55.

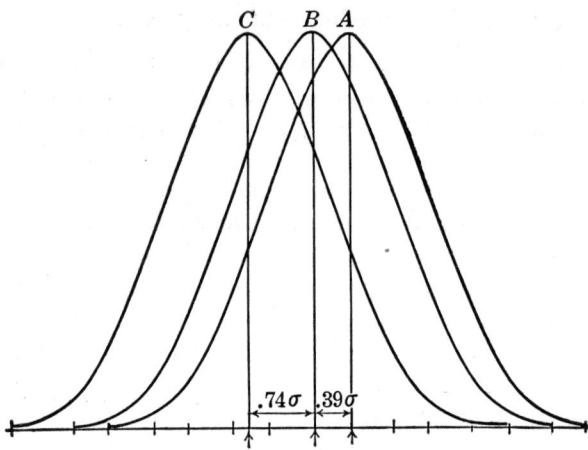

FIG. 55 To illustrate σ-scale differences between specimens A, B, and C. The distributions of judgments on the three specimens are taken to be normal, and equal in range and variability

composition was selected as being of just zero merit, and assigned the value of 0 on the scale. Of the 202 judges, 136 or 67.33% ranked specimen 9 as better than specimen 8. From Table A, we find that a percentage difference of 17.33 (67.33 − 50) indicates a PE difference of .65, and this value expresses the amount by which 9 is better than 8. The value of specimen 8 had already been found to be 7.72PE * above the zero point on the scale. Hence, specimen 9 is 7.72 + .65 or 8.37PE above the zero composition. The values of the nine compositions on the Hillegas Scale as measured in PE units from the zero composition are 1.83, 2.60, 3.69, 4.74, 5.85, 6.75, 7.72, 8.37, and 9.37. Note that the steps on the scale are fairly regular and are about 1PE apart.

2. Transforming qualitative data into numerical scores

It is possible to express many kinds of qualitative data in quantitative terms, if we can assume that measures of the trait or ability which we have sampled are normally distributed in the population. Several techniques based upon the normal curve will be considered in this section.

---

* The PE was the unit used by Hillegas. $PE = .6745σ$, p. 97.

(1) THE SCALING OF ANSWERS TO A QUESTIONNAIRE

Answers to the queries or statements in most questionnaires admit of several possible replies, such as Yes, No, ?; or Most, Many, Some, Few, No; or there are four or five answers one of which is to be checked. It is often desirable to "weight" these different alternatives in accordance with the degree of divergence from the "typical answer" which they indicate. First we assume that the attitude or personality trait expressed in answering a given proposition is normally distributed. From the percentage who accept each alternative answer to a question or statement, we may then find a σ-equivalent, which will express the value or weight to be given that answer. Likert's * Internationalism Scale furnishes an example of this scaling technique. This questionnaire contains 24 statements upon each of which the subject is requested to give an opinion. Approval or

TABLE 43   Data for statement No. 16 of the Internationalism Scale

Answers	Strongly Approve	Approve	Undecided	Disapprove	Strongly Disapprove
Percent checking	13	43	21	13	10
Equivalent σ-values	-1.63	$-.43$	.43	.99	1.76
Standard-scores	34	46	54	60	68

disapproval of any statement is indicated by checking one of five possibilities "strongly approve," "approve," "undecided," "disapprove," and "strongly disapprove." The method of scaling as applied to statement No. 16 on the Internationalism Scale is shown in Table 43 above. This statement reads as follows:

16. All men who have the opportunity should enlist in the Citizens' Military Training Camps.
   Strongly approve   Approve   Undecided   Disapprove
   Strongly disapprove

The percentage selecting each of the possible answers is shown in the table. Below the percent entries are the σ-equivalents assigned to each alternative on the assumption that opinion on the question is normally distributed—that few will wholeheartedly agree or disagree, and many take intermediate views. The σ-values in Table 43

---

* Likert, R., *A Technique for the Measurement of Attitudes*, Archives of Psychology, 1932, No. 140.

have been obtained from Table H (p. 435) in the following way: Reading down the first column headed 0, we find that beginning at the upper extreme of the normal distribution, the highest 10% has an average σ-distance from the mean of 1.76. Said differently, the mean of the 10% of cases at the upper extreme of the normal curve is at a distance of 1.76σ from the mean of the whole distribution. Hence, the answer "strongly disapprove" is given a σ-equivalent of 1.76 (see Fig. 56).

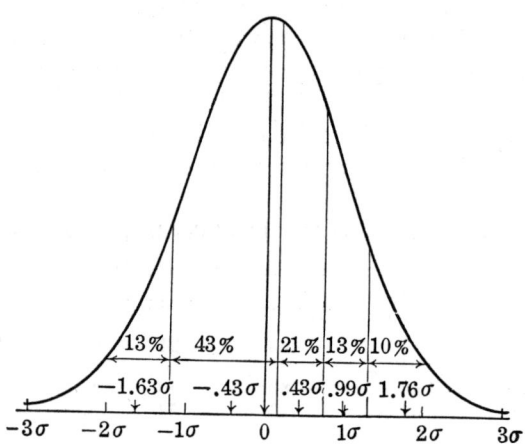

FIG. 56 To illustrate the scaling of the five possible answers to statement 16 on Likert's Internationalism Scale

To find the σ-value for the answer "disapprove," we select the column headed .10 and running down the column take the entry opposite 13, namely, .99. This means that when 10% of the distribution reading from the upper extreme have been accounted for, the average distance from the mean of the next 13% is .99σ. Reference to Figure 56 will make this clearer. Now from the column headed 23 (13% + 10% "used up" or accounted for), we find entry .43 opposite 21. This means that when the 23% at the upper end of the distribution have been cut off, the mean σ-distance from the general mean of the next 21% is .43σ, which becomes the weight of the preference "undecided." The weight of the fourth answer "approve" must be found by a slightly different process. Since a total of 44% from the upper end of the distribution have now been accounted for, 6% of the 43% who marked "approve" will lie to the *right* of the mean, and 37% to the *left* of the mean, as shown in Figure 56. From the column headed 44 in Table H, we take .08 (entry opposite 6%) which is the average distance from the general mean of the 6% lying just above the mean. Then from the column headed 13 (50% − 37%) we take entry .51 (now −.51) opposite 37%, as the mean distance from the general mean of the 37% just below the mean. The algebraic sum $\frac{-.51 \times .37 + .08 \times .06}{.43} = -.43$, which is the weight assigned to the preference "approve." The 13% left, those marking "strongly approve," occupy the 13% at the extreme (low end) of the curve. Returning to the column headed 0, we find that the mean distance from the general mean of the 13% at the extreme of the distribution is −1.63σ.

In order to avoid negative values, each σ-weight in Table 43 can be expressed as a σ-distance from −3.00σ (or −5.00σ). If referred to −3.00σ, the weights become in order 1.37, 2.57, 3.43, 3.99, and 4.76. Dropping decimals, and taking the first two digits, we could also assign weights of 14, 26, 34, 40, and 48. Again each σ-value in Table 43 may be expressed as a standard score in a distribution the mean of which is 50 and the σ 10. The category "strongly approve" is −16(−1.63 × 10) from the mean of 50, or at 34. Category "approve" is −4(−.43 × 10) from 50 or at 46. The other three categories have standard scores of 54, 60, and 68.

When all 24 statements on the Internationalism Scale have been scaled as shown above, a person's "score" (his attitude toward internationalism in general) is found by adding up the weights assigned to the various preferences which he has selected. An individual whose opinions are extreme, e.g., who tends strongly to disapprove many statements, will receive a proportionally larger total score when the choices are σ-scaled than he would receive if the five possibilities were assigned arbitrary weights of 1, 2, 3, 4, and 5. It has been shown, however, that σ-scaling yields results which, *for the test as a whole,* are little if any more reliable or more discriminatory than the results obtained when the five answers are scored simply 1, 2, 3, 4, and 5. This virtual equality of scaling and rule-of-thumb method is a rather familiar finding in mental measurement. In the present instance, it probably arises from the fact that the greater differentiation which the σ-scaling technique provides for *single* items is lost in the process of adding or averaging the score weights from many items. A real advantage of σ-scaling is that the units of the scale are equal and may be compared from item to item or from scale to scale. Also, σ-scaling gives a more accurate picture of the extent to which extreme or biased opinions on a given question are divergent from the typical opinion than does the arbitrary weighting method.

(2) THE SCALING OF RATINGS

In many psychological problems individuals are rated or ranked for their possession of characteristics or attributes not readily measured in terms of performance. Honesty, interest in one's work, tactfulness, originality, are illustrations of such traits. Suppose that two teachers A and B have rated a group of forty pupils for "social responsibility" on a 5-point scale. A rating of 1 means that the trait is possessed in marked degree, a rating of 5 that it is almost if not entirely absent, and ratings of 2, 3, and 4 indicate intermediate degrees. Assume that the percentage of children assigned each rating is as follows:

Social Responsibility

Rating	A	B
1	10%	20%
2	15%	40%
3	50%	20%
4	20%	10%
5	5%	10%

It is obvious that B rates more leniently than A, so that a rating of 1 by B may not represent the same degree of "social responsibility" as a rating of 1 by A. Can we assign "weights" or numerical scores so as to make the ratings of the two teachers comparable? The answer is "yes," provided we can assume that the distribution of the trait "social responsibility" is normal, and that one teacher is as competent a judge as the other. From Table H, we may read σ-equivalents to the percents given each rating by A and B as follows:

Rating	A	B
1	1.76	1.40
2	.95	.27
3	.00	− .53
4	−1.07	−1.04
5	−2.10	−1.76

These σ-values are read from Table H in exactly the same way as were the σ-equivalents in the previous problem (p. 431). If we assume −3.00σ as an arbitrary reference point, the σ-values for the ratings of A and B all become positive:

SCALING OF MENTAL TESTS AND OTHER PSYCHOLOGICAL DATA

Rating	A	B
1	4.76	4.40
2	3.95	3.27
3	3.00	2.47
4	1.93	1.96
5	.90	1.24

Dropping decimals, and taking only the first two digits, A's and B's ratings become:

Rating	A	B
1	48	44
2	40	33
3	30	25
4	19	20
5	9	12

or, expressed as standard scores in a distribution with a mean of 50 and a σ of 10,

Rating	A	B
1	68	64
2	60	53
3	50	45
4	39	40
5	29	32

The ratings of A and B may be combined by adding or by averaging them.

Table H will prove valuable in enabling one to transmute many kinds of qualitative data into quantitative terms or scores. Almost any attribute upon which relative judgments can be obtained may be assigned scores in a normal distribution in terms of the σ of the judgments.

(3) CHANGING ORDERS OF MERIT INTO NUMERICAL SCORES

It is often desirable to transmute orders of merit into units of amount or "scores." This may be done by means of tables, if we are justified in assuming normality for the trait. To illustrate, suppose that 15 salesmen have been ranked in order of merit for selling efficiency, the most efficient salesman being ranked 1, the least efficient being ranked 15. If we are justified in assuming that "selling efficiency" follows the normal probability curve in the general population we can, with the aid of Table 44 (p. 324), assign to each man a "selling score" on a scale of 10 or of 100 points. Such a score will define ability as a salesman better than will a rank of 2, 5, or 14. The problem may be stated specifically as follows:

Example (1) Given 15 salesmen, ranked in order of merit by their sales manager, (*a*) transmute these rankings into scores on a scale of 10 points; (*b*) a scale of 100 points.

First, by means of the formula

$$\text{Percent position} = \frac{100(R - .5)}{N} \qquad (75)$$

(*formula for converting ranks into percents of the normal curve*)

in which R is the rank of the individual in the series * and N is the number of individuals ranked, determine the "percent position" of each man. Then from these percent positions read the man's score on a scale of 10 or 100 points from Table 44. Salesman A, who ranks No. 1, has a percent position of $\frac{100(1 - .5)}{15}$ or 3.33, and his score from Table 44 is 9 or 85 (finer interpolation unnecessary). Salesman B, who ranks No. 2, has a percent position of $\frac{100(2 - .5)}{15}$ or 10, and his score, accordingly, is 8 or 75. The scores of the other salesmen, found in exactly the same way, are given in Table 45.

TABLE 44 The transmutation of orders of merit into units of amount or "scores" †

Example: If $N = 25$, and $R = 3$, Percent Position is $\frac{100(3 - .5)}{25}$ or 10 (formula (75) and from the table, the equivalent rank is 75, on a scale of 100 points.

Percent	Score	Percent	Score	Percent	Score
.09	99	22.32	65	83.31	31
.20	98	23.88	64	84.56	30
.32	97	25.48	63	85.75	29
.45	96	27.15	62	86.89	28
.61	95	28.86	61	87.96	27
.78	94	30.61	60	88.97	26
.97	93	32.42	59	89.94	25
1.18	92	34.25	58	90.83	24
1.42	91	36.15	57	91.67	23
1.68	90	38.06	56	92.45	22
1.96	89	40.01	55	93.19	21
2.28	88	41.97	54	93.86	20
2.63	87	43.97	53	94.49	19
3.01	86	45.97	52	95.08	18
3.43	85	47.98	51	95.62	17
3.89	84	50.00	50	96.11	16
4.38	83	52.02	49	96.57	15

* A rank is an interval on a scale; .5 is subtracted from each R because its midpoint best represents an interval. E.g., $R = 5$ is the 5th interval, namely 4–5, and 4.5 (or 5 − .5) is the midpoint.

† From Hull, C. L., "The Computation of Pearson's *r* from Ranked Data," *Journal of Applied Psychology*, 1922, 6, pp. 385–390.

SCALING OF MENTAL TESTS AND OTHER PSYCHOLOGICAL DATA • 325

TABLE 44—(Continued)

Percent	Score	Percent	Score	Percent	Score
4.92	82	54.03	48	96.99	14
5.51	81	56.03	47	97.37	13
6.14	80	58.03	46	97.72	12
6.81	79	59.99	45	98.04	11
7.55	78	61.94	44	98.32	10
8.33	77	63.85	43	98.58	9
9.17	76	65.75	42	98.82	8
10.06	75	67.48	41	99.03	7
11.03	74	69.39	40	99.22	6
12.04	73	71.14	39	99.39	5
13.11	72	72.85	38	99.55	4
14.25	71	74.52	37	99.68	3
15.44	70	76.12	36	99.80	2
16.69	69	77.68	35	99.91	1
18.01	68	79.17	34	100.00	0
19.39	67	80.61	33		
20.93	66	81.99	32		

It has been frequently pointed out that the assumption of normality in a trait implies that differences at extremes of the trait are relatively much greater than differences around the mean. This is clearly brought out in Table 45; for, while all differences in the order of merit series equal 1, the differences between the transmuted scores vary considerably. The largest differences are found at the ends of the series, the smallest in the middle. For example, the difference in score between A and B or between N and O (on a scale of 100) is three times the difference between G and H. Clearly, it is three times as hard for a salesman to improve sufficiently to move from second to first place as it is to move from eighth to seventh place.

TABLE 45 The order of merit ranks of 15 salesmen converted into normal curve "scores"

Salesmen	Order of Merit Ranks	Percent Position (Table 44)	Scores Scale (10)	Scale (100)	PR's
A	1	3.33	9	85	97
B	2	10.00	8	75	90
C	3	16.67	7	69	83
D	4	23.33	6	64	77
E	5	30.00	6	60	70
F	6	36.67	6	57	63
G	7	43.33	5	53	57
H	8	50.00	5	50	50
I	9	56.67	5	47	43
J	10	63.33	4	43	37
K	11	70.00	4	40	30
L	12	76.67	4	36	23
M	13	83.33	3	31	17
N	14	90.00	2	25	10
O	15	96.67	1	15	3

The percentile ranks (PR's) of our 15 salesmen in example (1) have been entered in Table 45 for comparison with the normal curve scores. These PR's were calculated by means of the following formula, which converts orders of merit into percentile ranks.

$$PR = 100 - \frac{(100R - 50)}{N} \qquad (76)$$

(*percentile ranks for individuals arranged in order of merit*)

The R in the formula is the rank position of the individual, counting No. 1 as the highest rank. Thus, the salesman who ranks No. 1 in 15 has a PR of $100 - \frac{(100 \times 1 - 50)}{15} = 96.66$ or 97; the salesman who ranks 5th has a PR of $100 - \frac{(100 \times 5 - 50)}{15} = 70$. Note that the steps between adjacent PR's are all equal. Orders of merit as well as PR's assume the distribution of ability to be rectangular so that equal slices of area correspond directly to equal distances along the baseline.

If there are 100 subjects in our group, each occupies one division of the percentile scale. Hence the rank of the poorest subject is .5 (midpoint of the interval 0–1) and the rank of the best subject is 99.5 (midpoint of interval 99–100). The person who ranks 50th in the group has a PR of $100 - \frac{(100 \times 50 - 50)}{100}$ or 50.5, midpoint of interval 50–51. Since a subject's PR is always the midpoint of an interval on a scale which runs from 0 to 100, it follows that no one can have a PR of 0 or 100. These two points constitute the boundaries or limits of the percentile scale.

Another use to which Table 44 may be put is in the combination of incomplete order of merit rankings. To illustrate:

Example (2) Six persons, A, B, C, D, E, and F, are to be ranked for honesty by three judges. Judge 1 knows all six well enough to rank them; Judge 2 knows only three well enough to rank them; and Judge 3 knows four well enough to rank them. Can we obtain a fair composite order of merit ranking for all six persons by combining these three sets of rankings, two of which are incomplete?

We may tabulate our data as follows:

	Persons					
	A	B	C	D	E	F
Judge 1's ranking	1	2	3	4	5	6
Judge 2's ranking		2		1		3
Judge 3's ranking	2		1		3	4

SCALING OF MENTAL TESTS AND OTHER PSYCHOLOGICAL DATA • 327

It seems fair that A should get more credit for ranking first in a list of six than D for ranking first in a list of three, or C for ranking first in a list of four. In the order of merit ratings, all three individuals are given the same rank. But when we assign scores to each person, in accordance with his position in the list, by means of formula 75 and Table 25, A gets 77 for his first place, D gets 69 for his, and C gets 73 for his. See table below:

	\multicolumn{6}{c}{Persons}
	A	B	C	D	E	F
Judge 1's ranking	1	2	3	4	5	6
score	77	63	54	46	37	23
Judge 2's ranking		2		1		3
score		50		69		31
Judge 3's ranking	2		1		3	4
score	56		73		44	27
Sum of scores	133	113	127	115	81	81
Mean	67	57	64	58	41	27
Order of Merit	1	4	2	3	5	6

All of the ratings have been transmuted as shown in example (1) above. Separate scores may be combined and averaged to give the final order of merit shown in the table.

By means of formula (75) and Table 44 it is possible to convert any set of ranks into "scores," if we may assume a normal distribution in the trait for which the ranking is made. The method is useful in the case of those attributes which are not easily measured by ordinary methods, but for which individuals may be arranged in order of merit, as, for example, athletic ability, personality, beauty, and the like. It is also valuable in correlation problems when the only available criterion * of a given ability or aptitude is a set of ranks. Transmuted scores may be combined or averaged like other test scores.

A word of explanation may be added with regard to Table 44. This table represents a normal frequency distribution which has been cut off at $\pm 2.50\sigma$. The baseline of the curve is 5σ, divided into 100 parts, each $.05\sigma$ long. The first $.05\sigma$ from the upper limit of the curve takes in .09 of 1% of the distribution and is scored 99 on a scale of 100. The next $.05\sigma$ ($.10\sigma$ from the upper end of the curve) takes in .20 of 1% of the entire distribution and is scored 98. In each case, the percent position gives the fractional part of the normal distribution which lies to the right of (above) the given "score" on baseline.

PROBLEMS

1. Five problems are passed by 15%, 34%, 50%, 62%, and 80%, respectively, of a large unselected group. If the zero point of ability in this

* For definition of a criterion, see Chapter 13. p. 345.

test is taken to be at -3σ, what is the σ-value of each problem as measured from this point?

2. (a) The fifth grade norms for a reading examination are $Mean = 60$ and $SD = 10$; for an arithmetic examination, $Mean = 26$ and $SD = 4$. Tom scores 55 on the reading and 24 on the arithmetic test. Compare his σ-scores. In which test is he better?

(b) Compare his standard scores in a distribution with M of 100 and SD of 20.

3. (a) Locate the deciles in a normal distribution in the following way. Beginning at -3σ, count off successive 10%'s of area up to $+3\sigma$. Tabulate the σ-values of the points which mark off the limits of each division. For example, the limits of the first 10% from -3σ are -3.00σ and -1.28σ (see Table A). Label these points in order from -3σ as .10, .20, etc. Now compare the distances in terms of σ between successive ten percent points. Explain why these distances are unequal.

(b) Divide the baseline of the normal probability curve (take as 6σ) into ten equal parts, and erect a perpendicular at each point of division. Compute the percentage of total area comprised by each division. Are these percents of area equal? If not, explain why. Compare these percents with those found in (a).

4. Fifty workers are rated on a 7-point scale for efficiency on the job. The following data represent the distributions of ratings (in which 1 is best and 7 worst) for two judges. Judge X is obviously very lenient and Judge Z is very strict. To make these two sets of judgments comparable, use the following three procedures:

(a) Percentile scaling: divide each distribution into 5 parts by finding successive 20%'s of N. Let A = first 20%, B the next 20%, and so on to E, the fifth 20%.

(b) Standard scores: Find the M and SD for each distribution and convert each rating into a common distribution with M of 50 and SD of 10.

(c) T-scores: Find T-scores corresponding to ratings of 1, 2, 3 . . . 7. Now compare Judge X's rating of 3 with Judge Z's rating of 3 by the three methods.

Judge X Rating	f	Judge Z Rating	f
1	5	1	2
2	10	2	4
3	20	3	4
4	5	4	5
5	4	5	20
6	4	6	10
7	2	7	5
	$N = 50$		$N = 50$

SCALING OF MENTAL TESTS AND OTHER PSYCHOLOGICAL DATA • 329

5. In a large group of competent judges, 77% rank composition A as better than composition B; 65% rank B as better than C. If C is known to have a σ-value of 3.50 as measured from the "zero composition," i.e., the composition of just zero merit, what are the σ-values of B and A as measured from this zero point?

6. Twenty-five men on a football squad are ranked by the coach in order of merit from 1 to 25 for all-around playing ability. On the assumption that general playing ability is normally distributed, transmute these ranks into "scores" on a scale of 100 points. Compare these scores with the PR's of the ranks.

7. (a) In accordance with their scores upon a learning test, 20 children are ranked in order of merit. Calculate the percentile rank of each child.
   (b) If 60 children are ranked in order of merit, what is the percentile rank of the first, tenth, fortieth, and sixtieth?

8. On an Occupational Interest Blank, each occupation is followed by five symbols, L! L ? D D!, which denote different degrees of "liking" and "disliking." The answers to one item are distributed as follows:

L!	L	?	D	D!
8%	20%	38%	24%	10%

   (a) By means of Table H convert these percents into σ-units.
   (b) Express each σ-value as a distance from "zero," taken at -3σ, and multiply by 10 throughout.
   (c) Express each σ-value as a standard score in a distribution of mean 50, σ 10.

9. Letter grades are assigned three classes by their teachers in English, history, and mathematics, as follows:

Mark	English	History	Mathematics
A	25	11	6
B	21	24	15
C	32	20	25
D	6	8	20
F	1	2	8
	85	65	74

   (a) Express each distribution of grades in percents, and by means of Table H transform these percents into σ-values.
   (b) Change these σ-values into 2-digit numbers and into standard scores following the method on page 305.
   (c) Find average grades [from (b)] for the following students:

Student	English	History	Mathematics
S.H.	A	B	C
F.M.	C	B	A
D.B.	B	D	F

10. Calculate T-scores in the following problem:

Scores	f	Percent below given score Plus One-half Reaching	T-score
91	2	99.5	76
90	4	98.0	71
89	6		
88	20		
87	24		
86	28		
85	40		
84	36		
83	24		
82	12		
81	4		
	200		

11. Calculate T-scores for the midpoints of the class-intervals in the following distribution:

Scores	f	Percent below given interval Plus One-half reaching Midpoint	T-score
40–44	8	94.6	66
35–39	12		
30–34	20		
25–29	15		
20–24	15		
15–19	5		
	75		

ANSWERS

1. In order: 4.04; 3.41; 3.00; 2.69; 2.16.
2. (a) In neither, same score in both
   (b) Reading 90, Arithmetic 90
3. (a)

	.00	.10	.20	.30	.40	.50	.60	.70	.80	.90	1.00
	−3.00	−1.28	−.84	−.52	−.25	0	.25	.52	.84	1.28	3.00
Diffs:		1.72	.44	.32	.27	.25	.25	.27	.32	.44	1.72

   (b) Percents of area in order: .68; 2.77; 7.92; 15.92; 22.57; 22.57; 15.92; 7.92; 2.77; .68.
4. (a) C vs. A;   (b) 52 vs. 61;   (c) 50 vs. 60
5. B, 3.89; A, 4.63

6.
Rank:	1	2	3	4	5	6	7	8	9	10	11	12	13
Score:	89	80	75	71	68	65	63	60	58	56	54	52	50
PR's:	98	94	90	86	82	78	74	70	66	62	58	54	50
Rank:	14	15	16	17	18	19	20	21	22	23	24	25	
Score:	48	46	44	42	40	37	35	32	29	25	20	11	
PR's:	46	42	38	34	30	26	22	18	14	10	6	2	

8.
	L!	L	?	D	D!
(a)	−1.86	−.94	−.08	.80	1.76
(b)	11	21	29	38	48
(c)	31	41	49	58	68

9.
		F	D	C	B	A
(a)	English	−2.70	−1.74	−.65	.22	1.18
	History	−2.28	−1.38	−.53	.39	1.49
	Math.	−1.71	− .71	.13	.94	1.86

(b)
	English −3.00σ Stan. Score		History −3.00σ Stan. Score		Mathematics −3.00σ Stan. Score	
A	42	62	45	65	49	69
B	32	52	34	54	39	59
C	24	44	25	45	31	51
D	13	33	16	36	23	43
F	3	23	7	27	13	33

(c) S. H., 36 or 56; F. M., 36 or 56; D. B., 20 or 40

10. T-scores:
76, 71, 67, 62, 58, 54, 49, 44, 39, 34, 27

11. T-scores
66, 59, 53, 47, 40, 32

13

THE RELIABILITY AND VALIDITY OF TEST SCORES

I. The Reliability of Test Scores

The reliability of a test, as of any measuring instrument, depends upon the *consistency* with which it gauges the abilities of those to whom it has been applied. When a test is reliable, scores made by the members of a group—upon retest with the same test or with alternate forms of the same test—will differ very little or not at all from their original values. A reliable test, therefore, is relatively free of chance errors of measurement, and scores earned on it are stable and trustworthy. If a subject scores 84, say, on a reliable test, we feel confident that this score is close to his true achievement. Scores made on an unreliable test, on the other hand, are subject to large errors of measurement and are neither stable nor trustworthy. When a test is unreliable, subsequent testings will reveal many discrepancies between scores achieved by the same persons on different occasions.

1. Methods of determining test reliability

There are three procedures in common use for determining the reliability (sometimes called the self-correlation) of a test. These are (1) the test-retest (repetition) method; (2) the alternate or parallel forms method; and (3) the split-half method. In addition to these three, a fourth method—the method of "rational equivalence"—is also being widely used. All of these procedures furnish "estimates" of the reliability of test scores; sometimes one method and sometimes another will give the best estimate.

(1) TEST-RETEST (REPETITION) METHOD

Repetition of a test is the simplest method of determining reliability: the test is given and then repeated on the same group and the correlation is calculated between the first and second sets of scores. While the test-retest method is sometimes the only feasible procedure, it is open to various objections. If the test is repeated immediately, many subjects will recall their first answers and spend their time on new material, thus increasing their scores. Besides the memory effect, practice and the confidence induced by familiarity with the material will almost certainly affect scores when one takes a test for the second time. Transfer effects are likely to be different from person to person. If the net effect of transfer is to make for closer agreement between scores achieved on the first and second giving of a test than would otherwise be the case, the reliability coefficient will be too high. When a sufficient time interval has elapsed between the first and second administrations of the test to offset (in part, at least) memory, practice, and other effects, the reliability coefficient will be a closer estimate of the actual consistency of test scores. If the interval between tests is long, however (say, six months or so), and the subjects are children, growth or maturity changes will affect the retest.

The test-retest method will estimate less accurately the reliability of tests which contain novel features and which are highly susceptible to practice than it will the reliability of tests involving routine operations little affected by practice. Because of the difficulty in controlling the conditions which influence scores on different administrations of a test, the test-retest method is used less generally than are the other two methods.

(2) ALTERNATE OR PARALLEL FORMS METHOD

When alternate or parallel forms of a test have been constructed, the correlation between Form A, say, and Form B is taken as a measure of the self-correlation of the test. This method is employed by the authors of most standard psychological and educational tests, for which alternate forms are usually available.

The alternate forms method is satisfactory if sufficient time has intervened between the administration of the two forms to weaken or eliminate memory and practice effects. When Form B of a test follows Form A very closely, scores on the second test will usually be increased through practice and familiarity. When such increases are approximately constant (say, three to five points for each score) the reliability coefficient of the test will not be affected, since paired A and B scores maintain their same relative positions in the two distributions. When the mean increase due to practice has been determined, a constant amount can be subtracted from Form B scores to make them comparable to Form A scores.* In drawing up alternate forms of a test, one should be careful to match test materials for content, difficulty, and form; but one must be careful not to make the test forms too much alike. If alternate forms are practically identical, the reliability coefficient of the test will be too high; while if parallel forms are not sufficiently "duplicate" the reliability coefficient will be too low.

(3) THE SPLIT-HALF METHOD

In the split-half method the test is broken into two equivalent parts and the correlation of these half tests is computed. From the half-test reliability, the self-correlation of the whole test is estimated by the Spearman-Brown formula described on page 339.

The split-half method is employed when it is not feasible to construct an alternate form of the test nor wise to repeat the test. This situation occurs with many performance tests, as well as with tests and questionnaires dealing with personality traits, attitudes, and the like. A performance test (e.g., picture completion, puzzle solving, form board) is often a very different task when repeated, as the child is familiar with procedure and content. Likewise, many personality tests cannot be given in alternate form nor repeated because of radical changes in the subject's attitude and interests when taking such tests for the second time.

The split-half method is often regarded as the best of the methods for determining test reliability. Perhaps its main advantage is that all of the data for determining test reliability are obtained upon *one* occasion; hence variations introduced by differences between the two testing situations are eliminated. A disadvantage of the split-half method is that chance errors may affect the scores on both halves of the test in the same way, thus tending to make the reliability coefficient too high. The longer the test, the less the probability that the effects of temporary and variable disturbances will be cumula-

* In the Otis Self-Administering Test of Mental Abilities, Higher Examination, for instance, the author suggests that when Form B, which is slightly more difficult than Form A, is given first, 4 points be added to each score. This is to make scores equivalent to the norms for Form B when this test is given after Form A, as it usually is. See *Manual of Directions,* Otis S-A Test (Yonkers: World Book Co., 1928), p. 2.

tive and in one direction, and the more accurate the estimate of reliability.

Objection has been raised to the split-half method on the ground that a test can be divided into two parts in a variety of ways so that the reliability coefficient is not a unique value. This criticism is strictly true only when items are of equal difficulty. When items are placed in order of merit from least to most difficult, the split into odds and evens gives a unique determination of the reliability coefficient.

(4) THE METHOD OF "RATIONAL EQUIVALENCE"

The method of rational equivalence * represents an attempt to get an estimate of the reliability of a test, free from the objections raised against the methods outlined above. Two forms of a test are defined as "equivalent" when corresponding items a, A, b, B, etc., are interchangeable; and when the inter-item correlations are the same for both forms. The method of rational equivalence stresses the intercorrelations of the items in the test and the correlations of the items with the test as a whole. Four formulas for determining test reliability have been derived, of which the one given below is perhaps the most useful:

$$r_{11} = \frac{n}{(n-1)} \times \frac{\sigma^2_t - \Sigma pq}{\sigma^2_t} \qquad (77)$$

(*reliability coefficient of a test in terms of the difficulty and the intercorrelations of test items*)

in which:

r_{11} = reliability coefficient of the whole test;
n = number of items in the test;
σ_t = the *SD* of the test scores;
p = the proportion of the group answering a test item correctly;
q = $(1-p)$ = the proportion of the group answering a test item incorrectly.

To apply formula (77) the following steps are necessary:

Step I

Compute the *SD* of the test scores for the whole group, namely, σ_t.

* Kuder, G. F., and Richardson, M. W., "The Theory of Estimation of Test Reliability," *Psychometrika*, 1937, 2, 151–160.
Richardson, M. W., and Kuder, G. F., "The Calculation of Test Reliability Coefficients Based upon the Method of Rational Equivalence," *Journal of Educational Psychology*, 1939, 30, 681–687.

Step 2

Find the proportions passing *each* item (p) and the proportions failing *each* item (q).

Step 3

Multiply p and q for each item and sum for all items. This gives Σpq.

Step 4

Substitute the calculated values in formula (77).

To illustrate, suppose that a test of sixty items has been administered to a group of eighty-five subjects; $\sigma_t = 8.50$ and $\Sigma pq = 12.43$. Applying (77) we have

$$r_{11} = \frac{60}{59} \times \frac{72.25 - 12.43}{72.25} = .842$$

which is the realibility coefficient of the test.

A simple approximation to formula (77) has been devised.* This formula is useful to teachers and others who want to determine quickly the reliability of short objective classroom examinations or other tests. It reads:

$$r_{11} = \frac{n\sigma^2_t - M(n - M)}{\sigma^2_t(n - 1)} \qquad (78)$$

[*approximation to formula* (77)]

in which

r_{11} = reliability of the whole test;
n = number of items in the test;
σ_t = SD of the test scores;
M = the mean of the test scores.

Formula (78) is a labor saver since only the mean, SD and number of items in the test need be known in order to get an estimate of reliability. The correlation need not be computed between alternate forms or between halves of the test. Suppose that an objective test of forty multiple-choice items has been administered to a small class

---

* Froelich, G. J., "A Simple Index of Test Reliability," *Journal of Educational Psychology,* 1941, 32, 381–385.

of students. An item answered correctly is scored 1, an item answered incorrectly is scored 0. The mean test score is 25.70 and $\sigma_t = 6.00$. What is the reliability coefficient of the test? Substituting in (78), we have

$$r_{11} = \frac{40 \times 36.00 - 25.70(40 - 25.70)}{36.00 \times 39}$$
$$= .76$$

The assumption is made in formula (78) that all test items have the same degree of difficulty, i.e., that the same *proportion* of subjects (but not necessarily the same *persons*) pass each item. In a power test items are never of equal difficulty. Formula (78) will give a satisfactory approximation to the test's reliability, however, even when the test items cover a wide range of difficulty. Formula (78) always underestimates to a slight degree the reliability of a test as found by the split-half technique and the Spearman-Brown formula, and the more widely items vary in difficulty the greater the underestimation. This formula provides a minimum estimate of reliability—we may feel sure that the test is at least as reliable as we have found it to be by (78).

Formulas (77) and (78) are not strictly comparable to the three methods for determining the reliability of test scores given above. In a sense, these formulas provide an estimate of the internal consistency of the test rather than an estimate of the dependability of test scores. The method of rational equivalence is superior to the split-half technique in certain theoretical aspects, but differences in reliability as found by the two methods are never very large (of the order .02, etc.). Formula (78) is often to be preferred to the split-half method because of the time and calculation it saves rather than for other reasons.

2. Factors influencing the reliability of test scores: chance and constant errors

Many factors affect the reliability of a test besides fluctuations in interest and attention, shifts in emotional attitude, and the differential effects of memory and practice. To these "psychological" factors must be added environmental disturbances such as distractions, noises, interruptions, errors in scoring, and the like. All of these variable influences (environmental and psychological) are subsumed under the head "chance errors." Errors, to be truly "chance," must influence a score in such a way as to cause it to vary above—as often as below—its "true" value. The reliability coefficient is a quantitative estimate of the importance of chance or variable influences upon test scores.

Constant errors, as distinguished from chance errors, work in only one direction. Constant errors may raise or lower all of the scores on a retest or on the alternate forms of the test, but will not affect the reliability coefficient. If every person taking Form B of a test is scored 5 points too high, for example, the self-correlation of the test will not be affected (i.e., the correlation between Forms A and B) but all of the scores on the second form will be in error by 5 points.

How high should the self-correlation of a test be in order for the reliability of the test to be considered satisfactory? This is an important question, and its answer depends upon the nature of the test, the size and variability of the group tested, and the purpose for which the test was given. To distinguish reliably between the means of two relatively small groups of narrow range of ability (for example, a fifth grade and a sixth grade) a reliability coefficient need be no higher than .50 or .60. If the test is to be used to differentiate among the individuals in the group, however, its reliability should be .90 or more. Most of the authors of intelligence tests and educational achievement examinations report correlations of .90 or more between alternate forms of their tests. Since the self-correlation of a test is directly affected by the variability within the group, in reporting a test's reliability coefficient the standard deviation of the group should always be given.

3. The effect upon reliability of lengthening or repeating a test

(1) THE RELIABILITY COEFFICIENT FROM MANY APPLICATIONS OR REPETITIONS OF A GIVEN TEST

The mean of five determinations of height will, in general, be more reliable than a single determination (p. 183), and the mean of ten determinations will (in general) be more reliable than the mean of five. On the same principle, increasing the length of the test, or averaging the results obtained from several applications of the test, or from alternate forms, will tend to increase reliability. If the self-correlation of a test is not satisfactory what will be the effect of doubling or tripling the test's length? To answer this question experimentally would require considerable time and labor. Fortunately, a good measure of the effect of lengthening or repeating a test may be obtained from the Spearman-Brown "prophecy formula":

$$r_{nn} = \frac{nr_{1I}}{1 + (n-1)r_{1I}} \tag{79}$$

(*Spearman-Brown formula for estimating the correlation between* n *forms of a test, and* n *other similar forms*)

in which

r_{nn} = the correlation between n forms of a test and n alternate forms (or the mean of n forms against the mean of n other forms);
r_{1I} = the reliability coefficient.

The subscripts ("1I") show that the correlation is between two forms of the *same* test.

To illustrate the use of formula (79) suppose that in a group of 100 adults the self-correlation of a test is .70. What will be the effect upon test reliability of tripling the length of the test? Substituting $r_{1I} = .70$ and $n = 3$ in formula (79) and solving for r_{nn}, we have

$$r_{nn} = \frac{3 \times .70}{1 + 2 \times .70} = \frac{2.10}{2.40} = .88$$

Tripling the test's length, therefore, increases its reliability coefficient from .70 to .88. Instead of tripling the length of the test we could give *three* parallel forms of the test and average the three scores made by each person. The reliability of these mean scores (each based upon three measures) will be the same, as far as purely statistical factors are concerned, as the reliability got by tripling the length of the test.

The prophecy formula may also be used to find how many times a test should be repeated in order for test scores to reach a given standard of reliability. Suppose that the self-correlation of a test is .80. How much will the test have to be lengthened or how many times repeated, in order to insure a reliability coefficient of .95? Substituting $r_{1I} = .80$ and $r_{nn} = .95$ in the formula, and solving for n, we have

$$.95 = \frac{.80n}{1 + .80n - .80} = \frac{.80n}{.20 + .80n}$$

and

$$n = 4.75 \text{ or } 5 \text{ in whole numbers}$$

The test must be five times its present length, therefore, or *five* alternate forms must be given and averaged, before the self-correlation of the test will reach .95.

Predictions of test reliability by the Spearman-Brown formula are valid only when the items or questions added to the test cover the same ground, are of equal range of difficulty, and are comparable in other respects to the items of the original test. When these conditions are satisfied, there would appear to be no reason, as far as the mathematical process is concerned, why we could not boost the self-correlation of a test to any desired figure, simply by continuing to increase its length or by continuing to repeat it. But it is highly improbable that the reliability coefficient of a test could be so increased indefinitely. In the first place, it is impracticable if not impossible to increase a test's length, say, ten or fifteen times. Furthermore, beyond a certain point, boredom, fatigue, loss of incentive, and the like inevitably affect our results and lead to "diminishing returns." When the material added to the test is strictly comparable to the original test items, and when motivation remains substantially constant, the experimental evidence * indicates that a test may be increased to six or seven times its original length, and the Spearman-Brown formula will still give a close estimate of empirically determined results. But after the first four or five lengthenings the prophecy formula may "over-predict"—give higher estimated reliabilities than those obtained by actual calculation. This is not an especially serious drawback, however, as a test which needs so much lengthening in order to yield reliable results should be radically changed in form or content, or better still, perhaps, discarded in favor of another test.

The Spearman-Brown formula may be applied to ratings, judgments, and other estimates as well as to test items. When measuring the reliability of a personality rating scale, for instance, by correlating the ratings made by two equally competent judges, we may employ the prophecy formula to estimate the increased reliability which might be expected if there were four, six or more judges.†

(2) THE RELIABILITY COEFFICIENT FROM ONE APPLICATION OF A TEST

When a test has no alternate form and cannot well be repeated, we may calculate the reliability of *half* of the test and then proceed to

---

* Holzinger, K. J., and Clayton, B., "Further Experiments in the Application of Spearman's Prophecy Formula," *Journal of Educational Psychology*, 1925, 16, 289–299.

Ruch, G. M., Ackerson, Luton, and Jackson, J. D., "An Empirical Study of the Spearman-Brown Formula as Applied to Educational Test Material," *Journal of Educational Psychology*, 1926, 17, 309–313.

† Remmers, H. H., Shock, N. W., and Kelly, E. L., "An Empirical Study of the Validity of the Spearman-Brown Formula as Applied to the Purdue Rating Scale," *Journal of Educational Psychology*, 1927, 18, 187–195.

estimate the reliability of the *whole* test by the Spearman-Brown formula. This method is called the "split-half technique" (p. 334). The procedure is to make up two sets of scores by combining, say, alternate exercises or items in the test. The first set of scores represents, for example, performance on the odd-numbered items, 1, 3, 5, 7, etc.; and the second set of scores performance on the even-numbered items, 2, 4, 6, 8, etc. Other ways of making the two halves of the test as comparable as possible in content, difficulty, and susceptibility to practice may be employed, but the method described is the one most commonly used. From the self-correlation of the half test, the reliability coefficient of the whole test may be estimated from the formula

$$r_{II} = \frac{2r_{\frac{1}{2}II}}{1 + r_{\frac{1}{2}II}} \qquad (80)$$

(*Spearman-Brown formula for estimating reliability from two comparable halves of a test*)

in which

r_{II} = the reliability coefficient of the whole test;

$r_{\frac{1}{2}II}$ = the reliability coefficient of one-half of the test, found experimentally.

When the reliability coefficient of one-half of a test ($r_{\frac{1}{2}II}$) is .60 it follows from formula (80) that the reliability of the whole test (r_{II}) is .75.

4. The index of reliability

An individual's "true score" on a test (p. 185) is defined as the mean of a very large number of determinations made of the given person on the same test or parallel forms of the test administered under approximately identical conditions. The correlation between a series of obtained scores and their corresponding theoretically "true" scores may be found by the formula

$$r_{1\infty} = \sqrt{r_{II}} \qquad (81)$$

(*correlation between obtained scores on a given test and true scores in the function measured by the test*)

in which

r_{II} = the reliability coefficient of the given test;

$r_{1\infty}$ = the correlation between obtained and true scores.

The symbol "∞" (infinity) designates "true scores," that is, scores obtained from an "infinite" number of administrations of the test to the same group.

The coefficient $r_{1\infty}$ is called the *index of reliability*; it measures the trustworthiness of test scores by showing how well obtained scores agree with their theoretically true counterparts. The index of reliability gives the maximum correlation which the given test is capable of yielding. This follows from the fact that "the highest possible correlation which can be obtained (except as chance might occasionally lead to higher spurious correlation) between a test and a second measure is with that which truly represents what the test actually measures, that is, the correlation between the test and the true scores of individuals in just such tests." *

To illustrate the application of the index of reliability, suppose that for a given test the self-correlation is .64. Then $r_{1\infty} = \sqrt{.64}$ or .80; and .80 is the highest correlation of which this test is capable, since it represents the relationship between obtained test scores and true test scores in the same function. If the self-correlation of a test is only .25, so that $r_{1\infty} = \sqrt{.25}$ or .50, it is obviously a waste of time to continue using this test without lengthening or otherwise improving it. A test whose index of reliability is only .50 is an extremely poor estimate of the function which it is trying to measure.

5. The standard error of an obtained score

The effects of variable or chance errors in producing divergencies of obtained scores from their true counterparts may be estimated by the formula

$$\sigma_{1\infty} = \sigma_1 \sqrt{1 - r_{1I}} \qquad (82)$$

(*standard error of an obtained score*)

in which

$\sigma_{1\infty}$ = the standard error of an obtained score (sometimes called the "standard error of measurement");
σ_1 = the standard deviation of the test scores;
r_{1I} = the reliability coefficient of the test.

The subscript "$_{1\infty}$" indicates this standard deviation to be a measure of the error made in taking an obtained score (i.e., 1) as an estimate

* Kelley, T. L., "The Reliability of Test Scores," *Journal of Educational Research*, 1921, 3, 327.

of the true score (i.e., ∞). To illustrate the use of $\sigma_{1\infty}$ suppose that in a group of 300 college freshmen the reliability coefficient of an aptitude test in mathematics is .92 and the *SD* of this distribution is 15.00. From formula (82) we have

$$\sigma_{1\infty} = 15\sqrt{1 - .92} = 4.2 \text{ or } 4 \text{ in whole numbers}$$

and the odds are 2:1 that the obtained score made by *any* individual in the group does not differ from his true score by more than ± 4 points. If subject *AB* has a score of 85, we may feel confident (the chances are .95) that his score "actually" lies between 77 and 93 ($\pm 1.96 \times 4.2$).* Generalizing for the entire group, we should expect about two-thirds of the 300 scores to be in error by 4 points or less; the other one-third (or 100) to be in error by more than 4 points.

The reader should note carefully the difference between $\sigma_{(est)}$ (see p. 162) and $\sigma_{1\infty}$. The first formula enables us to say with what degree of assurance we can predict an individual's score on *one* test when we know his score on a *second* (and usually a different) test. The actual prediction of the most probable score is made, of course, by way of the regression equation connecting the two variables (p. 159). The *SE* of an obtained score, $\sigma_{1\infty}$, is also an estimate formula; it tells us how adequately an obtained score represents the true score. Although the true score is unknown, we can, nevertheless, tell from $\sigma_{1\infty}$ how much our obtained score probably misses the true value. The *SE* of an obtained score is the best method of expressing the reliability of a test, since it takes account of the *self-correlation* of the test as well as of the *variability* within the group.

Formula (82) provides a general estimate of the *SE* of any score over the entire range of the test. When the range is wide, the agreement of scores on two forms of the test may differ considerably at successive parts of the scale. To refine our estimate of the reliability of our test scores, we may compute $\sigma_{1\infty}$ for different levels of achievement. This has been done for the new Stanford-Binet; the $\sigma_{1\infty}$ for I.Q.'s 130 and above, for example, is 5.24, for I.Q.'s 90–109, 4.51, for I.Q.'s 70 and below, 2.21, etc. The method is described in the references given below.†

---

*See page 187.
† Terman, L. M., and Merrill, M. A., *Measuring Intelligence* (Boston: Houghton Mifflin Co., 1937), p. 46.
McNemar, Quinn, "The Expected Average Difference between Individuals Paired at Random," *Journal of Genetic Psychology*, 1933, 43, 438–439.

6. The dependence of the reliability coefficient upon the range and variability of the group

The reliability coefficient of a test administered to a group of small range (a single grade, say), cannot be compared directly with the reliability coefficient of the same test administered to a group of greater range, e.g., to the children in several grades. The self-correlation of a test (like any correlation coefficient) is affected by the variability of the group; and the larger and more heterogeneous the group, the greater test variability tends to be. If we know the self-correlation of a test in a narrow range we can estimate the self-correlation of the same test in an increased range (ordinarily a larger group) by the formula

$$\frac{\sigma_s}{\sigma_l} = \frac{\sqrt{1 - r_{ll}}}{\sqrt{1 - r_{ss}}} \qquad (83)$$

(relation between σ's and reliability coefficients obtained in different ranges when the test is equally effective throughout both ranges)

in which

σ_s and σ_l = the σ's of the test scores in the small and large ranges, respectively;

r_{ss} and r_{ll} = the reliability coefficients in the small and large ranges.

To illustrate the use of formula (83) suppose that for a single fifth grade, $r_{ss} = .50$, and $\sigma_s = 5.00$; and that for a larger group made up of children from grades three to seven, $\sigma_l = 15.00$. Assuming our test to be as effective in the wide range as in the narrow, what is the reliability coefficient of the test in the wide range? If we substitute for σ_s, σ_l and r_{ss} in formula (83) $r_{ll} = .94$. This means that a reliability coefficient of .50 in the narrow range indicates as high a degree of test consistency as a reliability coefficient of .94 in a group in which the range is three times as wide.

II. The Validity of Test Scores

The validity of a test, or of any measuring instrument, depends upon the *fidelity* with which it measures whatever it purports to measure. A homemade yardstick is valid when measurements made by it are proved to be accurate by standard measuring rods. And in the same way a test is valid when the capacity which it gauges corresponds to the same capacity as otherwise objectively measured and defined. The difference between validity and reliability can be made clear, perhaps, by an illustration. Suppose a clock is set forward twenty minutes. If the clock is a good timepiece, the time it "tells" will be reliable (i.e., consistent), but it will not be valid as judged by "standard time." The reliability of the measurements made by scales, thermometers, yardsticks, chronoscopes, clocks, etc., is determined by making repeated measurements of the same facts; and validity is determined by comparing the measures returned by the given instrument with highly precise (if arbitrary) standard measures. The reliability of mental measures is found in the same way. But since precise and independent standards (criteria) are rarely found in mental measurement, the validity of a test can never be estimated as precisely as can the validity of a thermometer or a rheostat.

1. The determination of validity through correlation with a criterion

The validity of a test is determined directly, whenever possible, by finding the correlation between the test and some independent criterion. A criterion is an objective measure in terms of which the value of the test is estimated or judged. The criteria for evaluating a general intelligence examination, for example, may be school marks, ratings for aptitude in learning, or some other test believed to be valid, such as Stanford-Binet. A trade test may be validated against demonstrated ability to carry on the required operations as shown in actual performance.* A high correlation between a test and a criterion is evidence of validity provided the test and the criterion are both reliable. But before accepting criterion correlations, we must know the reliability of the test and if possible the reliability of the criterion.

When a criterion is not immediately available, indirect methods may be utilized for estimating the validity of a test. We may, for example, compute the average correlation which each test in a battery shows with all of the other tests, and estimate the validity (i.e., the representativeness) of each test by the size of its correlations. Again, following essentially the same method, we may combine the

* Stead, W. H., and Shartle, C. L., *Occupational Counseling Techniques*, op. cit., Chapters 5 and 8 especially.

scores on a number of tests designed to measure the same function (memory, say), and consider as most valid that test which correlates highest with the average of them all. Anastasi,* for example, found that of eight tests of immediate memory, the paired-associates test (geometric form paired against numbers) had the largest average correlation (i.e., .49), with the other tests of the battery. This test, then, is the most valid measure of the function tapped in common by all of the tests.

2. The correction for attenuation

The correlation between a test and its criterion will be reduced if either the test scores or the criterion scores or both are unreliable. In order to estimate the correlation between true scores in two variables, we need to make a correction which will take account of the unreliability in both sets of measures. Such a correction is given by the formula

$$r_{\infty\infty} = \frac{r_{12}}{\sqrt{r_{1I} \times r_{2II}}} \qquad (84)$$

(*correlation between true measures in Tests 1 and 2*)

in which

$r_{\infty\infty}$ = correlation between true scores in Tests 1 and 2;
r_{12} = correlation between obtained scores in Tests 1 and 2;
r_{1I} = reliability coefficient of Test 1;
r_{2II} = reliability coefficient of Test 2.

Formula (84) is the well-known correction for attenuation formula. It provides a correction for the effects of those chance or accidental errors in the two tests which lower the reliability coefficients of both tests and thus affect the correlation between them. To illustrate the application of formula (84), let the obtained correlation between two tests A and B be .60, the reliability coefficient of Test A be .80 (r_{1I}) and the reliability coefficient of Test B be .90 (r_{2II}). What is the correlation between Tests A and B freed of chance errors? Substituting the given values in formula (84), we have

$$r_{\infty\infty} = \frac{.60}{\sqrt{.80 \times .90}} = .71$$

as the estimated correlation between true scores in A and B. Our

* Anastasi, A., "A Group Factor in Immediate Memory," *Archives of Psychology*, 1930, 120, p. 41.

corrected coefficient of correlation represents the relationship which we should expect to obtain if our two sets of test scores were perfect measurements.

It is clear from formula (84) that correcting for chance errors will always raise the correlation between two tests—unless the reliability coefficients are both 1.00. Chance errors, therefore, always lower or attenuate an obtained correlation coefficient. The expression $\sqrt{r_{1I} \times r_{2II}}$ sets an upper limit to the correlation which we can obtain between two tests as they stand. In the example above, $\sqrt{.80 \times .90}$ = .85; hence, Tests A and B cannot correlate higher than .85, as otherwise their corrected r would be greater than 1.00.

Let us assume the correlation between first-year college grades and a general intelligence test to be .46; the reliability of the intelligence test to be .82; and the reliability of college grades to be .70. The maximum correlation which we could hope to obtain between these two measures is $\dfrac{.46}{\sqrt{.70 \times .82}}$ or .60. Knowing that the correlation between grades and general intelligence, corrected for errors of measurement, has a probable maximum value of .60 gives us a better notion of the "intrinsic" relationship between the two variables. At the same time, the investigator should remember that the $r_{\infty\infty}$ of .60 is a theoretical, not an obtained, value; that it gives an estimate of the relationship to be expected when the tests are more effective than they actually were in the present instance. If many sources of error are present so that considerable correction is necessary, it would be better experimental technique to improve the tests and the experimental conditions than to correct the obtained r.

The investigator must be careful how he applies formula (84) to correlations which have been averaged, as in such cases the reliability coefficients may be lower than the correlations between the two tests. When this happens $r_{\infty\infty}$ is greater than 1.00. Such a result is logically and psychologically meaningless. If a corrected r is 1.00, or is only slightly greater than 1.00, however, it may be taken as indicating complete agreement between the two variables within the error of computation.

3. The estimation of the true σ of a test

Chance or variable errors have a marked effect upon the standard deviation of a test, as well as upon the r between tests. The relation of the σ calculated from obtained scores on a test to the σ of true scores on the same test is given by the formula

$$\sigma_\infty = \sigma_1\sqrt{r_{11}} \qquad (85)$$

(*relation between true and obtained σ's for a set of test scores*)

in which

σ_∞ = the σ of the true test scores;
σ_1 = the σ of the obtained test scores;
r_{11} = the reliability coefficient of the test.

Suppose an educational achievement test of seventy-five items has been administered to a group of fifty children. The obtained standard deviation, σ_1, is 10, and the reliability coefficient of the test (r_{11}) is .50. What is σ_∞, the σ of the true scores from which variable or accidental errors have been eliminated? Substituting $\sigma_1 = 10$, and $r_{11} = .50$ in formula (85)

$$\sigma_\infty = 10\sqrt{.50}$$
$$= 7.1$$

and the "true σ" of the test is about **7** points.

It is clear from (85) that σ_∞ will *always* be smaller than σ_1, except in the improbable case in which $r_{11} = 1.00$. The effect of chance errors of measurement, then, is always to increase the spread (σ_1) of obtained test scores or of criterion scores.

4. Validation of a test battery *

A criterion of job efficiency, say, or of success in salesmanship may be forecast by a battery consisting of four, five, or more tests. The validity of such a battery is determined by the multiple correlation coefficient, R, between the battery and the criterion. The weights to be attached to scores on the sub-tests of the battery are given directly by the regression coefficients (p. 393).

If the regression weights are small fractions (as they often are) whole numbers may be substituted for them with little if any loss in accuracy. For example, suppose that the regression equation joining the criterion and the tests in a battery reads as follows:

$$C(\text{criterion}) = 4.32X_1 + 3.12X_2 - .65X_3 + 8.35X_4 + K(\text{constant})$$

Dropping fractions and taking the nearest whole numbers, we have

---

* Gulliksen, H., *Theory of Mental Tests* (New York: John Wiley and Sons, 1950), Chapter 20 especially.

$$C = 4X_1 + 3X_2 - 1X_3 + 8X_4 + K$$

Scores in Test 1 should be multiplied by 4, scores in Test 2 by 3, scores in Test 3 by -1, and scores in Test 4 by 8, in order to provide the best forecast of C, the criterion. The fact that Test 3 has a negative weight does not mean that this test has no value in forecasting C, but simply that the best estimate of C is obtained by giving scores in Test 3 a negative value.

III. Item Analysis

In Section II above, we considered the validity of final test scores. The validity of a test score also depends directly upon the care with which the *items* in the test have been chosen. While the subject of item analysis properly belongs in a book on test construction, the main features of the process may be outlined here. Item analysis may be divided into three main topics: (1) item selection, (2) item difficulty, and (3) item validity.

1. Item selection

The initial choice of test items depends upon the judgment of competent persons as to the suitability of the material for the purposes of the test. Certain types of items, for instance, have proved to be generally useful in intelligence examinations. Problems in mental arithmetic, for example, vocabulary, analogies and number series completion, are often encountered; also, items requiring generalization, interpretation and the ability to see relations. The validity of most standard tests of educational achievement depends upon the consensus of teachers and other competent judges as to the adequacy of the items included. Courses of study, requirements for different grades, curricula from different sections of the country are carefully culled over by the test makers to determine what material in history, English, geography, etc., should be included in an educational achievement battery designed, say, for the seventh grade. In its final form the educational achievement test represents items carefully selected from all available sources of information.

Items used in personal data sheets, interest inventories, attitude scales and the like, also represent a consensus of experts as to the most diagnostic items in the areas sampled.

2. Item difficulty

The difficulty of an item is determined by the proportion of some standard group able to solve the item correctly. The scaling of separate test items has been described in Chapter 12, page 301. When normality of distribution can be assumed for the ability being measured, single items or groups of items (scores) may be scaled, i.e., given difficulty values along a scale in terms of σ. It has been customary to select items for a test which vary in difficulty from easy to hard. The average person in the standardization group will then pass about one-half (50%) of the items in the test. It can be shown, however, that the sharpest discrimination as between good and poor subjects is provided by items which are passed by 50% of the members of a group. A test made up of items all of which are passed by approximately 50% (but by different persons, of course) would theoretically be the most discriminating test. But it would be difficult to construct such an examination and it is probable that a test made up of items covering a wider range of difficulty is psychologically a better measuring device. In standardizing a test care much be taken that few, if any, subjects achieve perfect or zero scores, as in neither case is the person measured by the test.

3. Item validity

An often-used method of validating a test item is to determine whether the item discriminates between subjects differing sharply in the function being measured. This "criterion of internal consistency" admits into the final test or questionnaire only those items which have been found to separate high-scoring and low-scoring members of the group. In an internally consistent test, items "hang together" in the sense that they work in the same direction and measure the same common trait.* In one study,† eighty-six items were selected out of 222 on the basis of their ability to discriminate among the lower, middle, and upper thirds of the group. These eighty-six "good" items did a better job (higher reliability and validity) than a test two and a half times as long.

The validity of a single test item may also be determined by find-

* Ferguson, G. A., "The Factorial Interpretation of Test Difficulty," *Psychometrika*, 1941, 6, 323–329.
† Anderson, J. E., "The Effect of Item Analysis upon the Discriminative Power of an Examination," *Journal of Applied Psychology*, 1935, 19, 237–244.

ing its correlation with total scores in the test of which it is a part, or by finding its correlation with scores in some independent criterion. The bi-serial method (p. 356) is the standard procedure for determining item validity through correlation. Application of bi-serial r to each item in a test requires considerable computation, however. For this reason various short-cut methods for selecting good items by formula and by graphical methods have been devised. References given below should be consulted.*

PROBLEMS

1. The reliability coefficient of a test is .60.
   (a) How much must this test be lengthened in order to raise the self-correlation to .90?
   (b) What effect will doubling the test's length have upon its reliability coefficient? tripling the test's length?
2. A test of fifty items has a reliability coefficient of .78. What is the reliability coefficient
   (a) of a test having 100 items comparable to the items in the given test?
   (b) of a test having 125 comparable items?
3. A given test has a reliability coefficient of .80 and a σ of 20.
   (a) What is the maximum correlation which this test is capable of yielding as it stands?
   (b) What is the standard error of a score obtained on this test?
   (c) What is the estimated reliability coefficient of this test in a group in which the σ is 15?
4. A test of 100 items is given to a group of 225 subjects with the following results: $M = 62.50$; $\sigma = 9.62$.
   (a) What is the reliability coefficient of the test by formula (78)?
   (b) What is the estimated true σ of this test?
   (c) What is the standard error of a score on this test?

---

*Long, John A., and Sandiford, Peter, *The Validation of Test Items*, Bulletin 3, 1935, University of Toronto, Department of Educational Research.
Flanagan, J. C., "General Considerations in the Selection of Test Items," *Journal of Educational Psychology*, 1939, 30, 674–680.
Guilford, J. P., "The Phi-coefficient and Chi-square as Indices of Item Validity," *Psychometrika*, 1941, 6, 11–19.
Richardson, M. W., and Adkins, D. C., "A Rapid Method of Selecting Test Items," *Journal of Educational Psychology*, 1928, 29, 547–552.
Hawkes, H. E., Lindquist, E. R., and Mann, C. R., *Achievement Examinations* (Boston: Houghton Mifflin Co., 1936), Chapters 2 and 3, especially.
Gulliksen, H., *Theory of Mental Tests*, op. cit., Chapter 21.
Davis, F. B., *Item-Analysis Data: their computation, interpretation, and use in test construction*, Cambridge, Mass.: Harvard Educ. Papers, #2, 1946.

5. Show (a) that when the reliability coefficient is zero, the standard error of an obtained score equals the standard deviation of the test; and (b) that when the reliability coefficient is 1.00, the standard error of an obtained score equals zero.

6. A mathematics test has a reliability coefficient of .82, and a mechanical ability test has a reliability coefficient of .76. The r between the two tests is .52.
   (a) What would the correlation be if *both* tests were perfect measures?
   (b) What is the maximum correlation possible with the mathematics test as it stands?
   (c) What is the maximum correlation possible with the mechanical ability test as it stands?

7. An intelligence examination shows a correlation of .50 with first-year scholarship. The reliability coefficient of the test is .85, and of school grades (i.e., the criterion) is .65. What is the highest validity coefficient which we can hope to get with this test (i.e., corrected correlation between test and grades)?

8. A test of seventy-five items has a σ_t of 12.35. The $\Sigma pq = 16.46$. What is the reliability coefficient by formula (77)?

ANSWERS

1. (a) six times
   (b) $r_{11} = .75$ (doubling length); $r_{11} = .82$ (tripling length)
2. (a) .88
   (b) .90
3. (a) .89
   (b) 8.9
   (c) .64
4. (a) .75
   (b) 8.34
   (c) 4.81
6. (a) .66
   (b) .91
   (c) .87
7.   .68
8.   .90

14

FURTHER METHODS OF CORRELATION

In Chapter 6 we described the linear, or product-moment correlation method, and in Chapter 7 showed how, by means of r and the regression equations, one can "predict" or "forecast" values of one variable from a knowledge of the other. Test scores, as we have seen, represent a series of determinations of a continuous variable taken along a numerical scale. The correlation coefficient is valuable to psychology and education as a measure of the relationship between test scores and other measures of performance. But many situations arise in which the investigator does not have scores and must work with data in which differences in a given attribute can be expressed only by ranks (e.g., in orders of merit); or by classifying an individual into one of several descriptive categories. This is especially true in vocational and applied psychology and in the field of personality and character measurement. Again, there are problems in which the relationship among the measurements made is *non-linear,* and cannot be described by the product-moment r. In all of these cases other methods of determining correlation must be employed; and the purpose of this chapter is to develop some of the more useful of these techniques.

I. Computing Correlation from Ranks

Differences among individuals in many traits can often be expressed by *ranking* the subjects in one-two-three order when such differences cannot be measured directly. For example, persons may be ranked in order of merit for honesty, athletic ability, salesmanship, or social adjustment when it is impossible to *measure* these complex behaviors. In like manner, various products or specimens, such as advertisements, color combinations, handwriting, compositions, jokes, and pictures, which are admittedly hard to measure, may be put in order of merit for esthetic quality, beauty, humor, or some other characteristic. In computing the correlation between two series of ranks, special methods which take account of relative position have been devised. These methods may also be applied to *scores* which have been arranged in order of merit. When we have only a few scores (less than 25, say), it is often advisable to rank these scores in order of merit and compute the correlation by the rank-difference method instead of by the longer and more laborious product-moment method. Coefficients of correlation calculated from a few cases are not very reliable at best, and their chief value lies in suggesting the possible existence of relationship—as in a preliminary survey. In such situations the rank-difference method will give as adequate a result as that obtained by a more refined technique, and is much easier to apply.

1. Calculation of ϱ (rho) from rank-differences

The rank-difference method is illustrated in Table 46. The problem is to find the relationship between the length of service and the selling-efficiency of twelve salesmen. The names of the men (A, B, C, etc.) are listed in column (1) of the table, and in column (2), opposite the name of each man, is given the number of years he has been in the service of the company. In column (3), the men are ranked in order of merit in accordance with their length of service. For example, G, who has been longest with the company, is ranked 1; C, whose length of service is next longest, is ranked 2; and so on down the list. Note that both A and J have the same period of service, and that each is ranked 7.5. Instead of ranking the first man 7 and the second man 8, or both 7 or both 8, we compromise by ranking both 7.5 and F, who follows, 9.*

In column (4) the men have been ranked by the sales manager in order of merit for efficiency as salesmen: C, the most efficient man, is ranked 1; and B, the least efficient, is ranked 12. In column (5) the difference (designated D) between each man's efficiency rank and his years-of-service rank is entered, and in the last column each of these D's has been squared. Since each D is squared in column (6), no account need be taken of $+$ and $-$ signs in column (5). The correla-

---

* If three men receive the same rank, e.g., 7, 8, 9, each is ranked 8 and next man in order is ranked 10. If four men receive the same rank, e.g., 7, 8, 9, and 10, each is ranked 8.5 and the next in order 11.

FURTHER METHODS OF CORRELATION • 355

TABLE 46 To illustrate the rank-difference method of measuring correlation

(1) Salesmen	(2) Years of Service	(3) Order of Merit (Service)	(4) Order of Merit (Efficiency)	(5) Difference between Ranks (D)	(6) Difference Squared (D^2)
A	5	7.5	6	1.5	2.25
B	2	11.5	12	.5	.25
C	10	2	1	1.0	1.00
D	8	4	9	5.0	25.00
E	6	6	8	2.0	4.00
F	4	9	5	4.0	16.00
G	12	1	2	1.0	1.00
H	2	11.5	10	1.5	2.25
I	7	5	3	2.0	4.00
J	5	7.5	7	.5	.25
K	9	3	4	1.0	1.00
L	3	10	11	1.0	1.00
$N = 12$					58.00

$$\rho = 1 - \frac{6\Sigma D^2}{N(N^2-1)} = 1 - \frac{6 \times 58}{12(143)} = .80 \qquad (86)$$

tion between the two orders of merit may be computed by substituting for ΣD^2 and N in the formula

$$\varrho = 1 - \frac{6\Sigma D^2}{N(N^2-1)} \qquad (86)$$

(*rank correlation coefficient*, ϱ)

in which D represents the difference in rank of an individual in the two series; ΣD^2 is the sum of the squares of all such differences; and N is the number of cases. Substituting 58 for the ΣD^2 and 12 for N in formula (86), we obtain a ϱ of .80. The symbol ϱ (read as *rho*) is the rank order coefficient of correlation. ϱ may be transmuted into a product-moment r by means of tables, but the difference between ϱ and its equivalent r is so small that with little loss of accuracy ϱ may be taken as approximately equal to r.

2. The significance of ϱ (rho)

Since ϱ is at best only an approximate measure of the relationship indicated by r, it is hardly worth while computing its SE. Perhaps the best way of estimating the reliability of ϱ if it is wanted is to test the obtained value of ϱ against the null hypothesis by means of Table 25, p. 200. Thus for the problem in Table 46 we find for $(N - 2)$ or 10 df that an r must be .71 to be significant at the .01 level. Our computed ρ of .80 is considerably larger than .71 and hence is statistically significant though based upon only 12 ranks.

3. Summary on rank-difference correlation

The product-moment method deals with the size of the score as well as its position in the series. Rank-differences, on the other hand, take account only of the positions of the items in the series, making no allowance for the size of the gaps between adjacent scores. Individuals, for example, who score 90, 89, and 70 on a given test are ranked 1, 2, 3 in order of merit, although the difference between 90 and 89 is 1, and the difference between 89 and 70 is 19. Considerable accuracy may be lost in translating scores over into ranks, as gaps will appear in the rankings when a number of scores, all of the same size, receive the same rating. The rank-difference coefficient is rarely used with test scores when N is larger than 30 and is often an exploratory and preliminary device.

II. Measuring Correlation from Data Grouped into Categories

1. Bi-serial correlation

In many problems it becomes important to calculate the correlation between traits or attributes, when the members of the group can be measured (i.e., given scores) in the one variable, but can only be classified into *two* categories in the second or "dichotomous" variable. (The term dichotomous means "cut into two parts.") We may, for instance, wish to know the correlation between MA and "social adjustment" in a group of nursery-school children, when our subjects have been given scores in the first trait, but are simply classified as "socially adjusted" or "not socially adjusted" in the second trait. Other examples of dichotomous classification with reference to some attribute are athletic-nonathletic, radical-conservative, socially minded-mechanically minded, literate-illiterate, above eighth grade in school-below eighth grade, and the like. The correlation between a set of scores and two-category classifications like those listed cannot readily be found by the ordinary product-moment r or by the rank-difference formula. We can, however, compute a *bi-serial* coefficient of correlation if we may assume that the trait in which we have made a two-way split would be continuous and normally distributed if more information were available.

Many test and question items are scored to give two responses: for example, problems marked *Passed* or *Failed*, statements *True* or *False*, personality inventory items *Yes* or *No*, interest items *Like* or *Dislike*, and so on. When a two-category split cannot be regarded as representing a normal distribution but is in fact two separate groupings, the *point bi-serial r* provides a useful measure of relation.

(1) CALCULATION OF BI-SERIAL r

The calculation of bi-serial r is illustrated in Table 47. The problem is to find the correlation between total scores on a test and the answers to a single item in the test (Item 72); or put differently, to find whether those who make high scores on the test tend to answer Item 72 "Yes" more often than "No." The first column of Table 47 gives the class-intervals of the score distribution. Column two gives

TABLE 47 To illustrate the calculation of the bi-serial r between total scores on a test and the answers to a single item on the test

Scores on Test	Responses to Item 72 "Yes"	"No"	f
80–84	3		3
75–79	4	2	6
70–74	6	2	8
65–69	5	5	10
60–64	10	9	19
55–59	10	5	15
50–54	15	5	20
45–49	4	3	7
40–44	3	2	5
35–39		4	4
30–34		2	2
25–29		1	1
	60 (p)	40 (q)	100

$M = 58.05$; mean of all scores ($N = 100$)

$\sigma = 11.63$; σ of all scores ($N = 100$)

$M_p = 60.08$; mean of "Yes" responses ($N = 60$)

$M_q = 55.00$; mean of "No" responses ($N = 40$)

$p = .60$; proportion answering "Yes" to Item 72

$q = .40$; proportion answering "No" to Item 72

$z = .386$; height of ordinate separating 60% from 40% in a normal distribution (Table 48)

$$r_{\text{bis}} = \frac{M_p - M_q}{\sigma} \cdot \frac{pq}{z} \quad (87)$$

$$= \frac{60.08 - 55.00}{11.63} \times \frac{(.60)(.40)}{.386}$$

$$= .27$$

$$\sigma_{r_{\text{bis}}} = \frac{\left(\frac{\sqrt{pq}}{z} - r^2_{\text{bis}}\right)}{\sqrt{N}} \quad (88)$$

$$= \frac{\left(\frac{\sqrt{.24}}{.386} - (.27)^2\right)}{\sqrt{100}}$$

$$= .12$$

the distribution of scores made by the sixty subjects who answered "Yes" to Item 72, and column three the distribution of scores made by the forty subjects who answered "No." The sum of all of the frequencies on the score-intervals gives the total distribution of 100 cases (column four). The steps in calculating bi-serial r from here on are as follows:

Step 1

Calculate M_p, the mean of the scores made by the sixty subjects who answered "Yes" to Item 72. Also calculate M_q, the mean of the scores made by the forty subjects who answered "No" to Item 72. In our problem, $M_p = 60.08$, and $M_q = 55.00$.

Step 2

Calculate the σ of the whole distribution—the distribution of the 100 scores. This σ, which equals 11.63, gives the spread of the test scores in the entire group.

Step 3

Sixty percent of the group (p) answered "Yes" to Item 72, and 40% (q) answered "No" (p always equals $1 - q$). Assuming a normal distribution of opinion on this item (varying from complete agreement on through indifference to complete disagreement) upon which a dichotomous division has been forced, we place the dividing line between the "Yes" and "No" groups at a distance of 10% from the middle of the curve, as shown in the figure below.

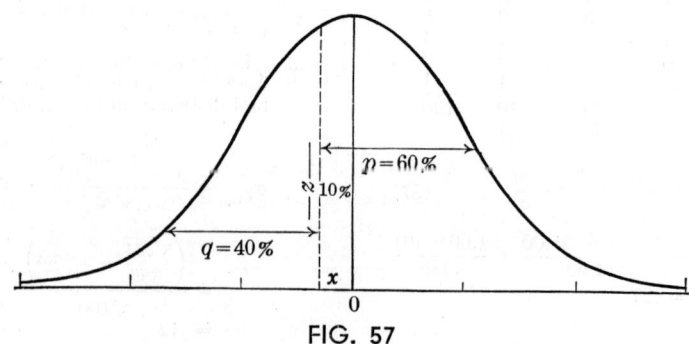

FIG. 57

FURTHER METHODS OF CORRELATION • 359

From Table 48, the height of the ordinate (i.e., z) which is 10% from the mean of a normal distribution is .386.

Step 4

Having computed M_p, M_q, σ, p, q, and z, we find r_{bis} from the formula

$$r_{\text{bis}} = \frac{M_p - M_q}{\sigma} \times \frac{pq}{z} \tag{87}$$

(*bi-serial coefficient of correlation or bi-serial* r)

in which, as illustrated by the problem above, and shown in Table 47

M_p = mean of the group in the first category (usually the group showing superior or more desirable characteristics)
M_q = mean of the group in the second category
σ = standard deviation of the entire group
p = proportion of the whole group in category one
q = proportion of the whole group in category two ($p = 1 - q$)
z = height of the ordinate in the normal curve dividing p from q

In Table 47, r_{bis} is .27, indicating a tendency, though not a strong one, for "Yes" answers to Item 72 to accompany high total scores.

(2) THE SE OF BI-SERIAL r

Provided neither p nor q is very small (e.g., smaller than .05), an approximate formula for the standard error of bi-serial r is

$$\sigma_{r_{\text{bis}}} = \frac{\left(\frac{\sqrt{pq}}{z} - r^2_{\text{bis}}\right)}{\sqrt{N}} \tag{88}$$

(SE *of* r_{bis} *for values of* p *and* q *greater than .05*)

A comparison of formula (88) with the classical SE_r formula for a product-moment r (see p. 197) shows that $SE_{r_{\text{bis}}}$ is somewhat larger than SE_r and becomes increasingly larger as the difference between p and q widens: from $p = .50$, $q = .50$ to $p = .95$, $q = .05$, say. In the problem of Table 47, $r_{\text{bis}} = .27$ and $SE_{r_{\text{bis}}} = .12$. To test the reliability of this r_{bis} in terms of its SE, we must assume that the sampling distribution of r is normal, put the population r at the center of the distribution (Fig. 46, p. 355), and take SE_r to be the SD of the sampling distribution of r's. When we do this, the .95 confidence-interval for the true r_{bis} is from .03 to .51 ($r_{bis} \pm 1.96 \times SE_{r_{bis}}$ or .27 ± .24). This wide range shows that r_{bis} is probably indicative of *some* degree of positive correlation (the lower limit of the confidence-interval is .03), but it is impossible to say accurately just how much.

TABLE 48 Deviates (x/σ) in terms of σ-units and ordinates (z) for given areas measured from the mean of a normal distribution whose total area = 1.00

[x/σ = x]

Area from the Mean	x or (x/σ)	z	Area from the Mean	x or (x/σ)	z
.00	.000	.399	.26	.706	.311
.01	.025	.399	.27	.739	.304
.02	.050	.398	.28	.772	.296
.03	.075	.398	.29	.806	.288
.04	.100	.397	.30	.842	.280
.05	.126	.396	.31	.878	.271
.06	.151	.394	.32	.915	.262
.07	.176	.393	.33	.954	.253
.08	.202	.391	.34	.995	.243
.09	.228	.389	.35	1.036	.233
.10	.253	.386	.36	1.080	.223
.11	.279	.384	.37	1.126	.212
.12	.305	.381	.38	1.175	.200
.13	.332	.378	.39	1.227	.188
.14	.358	.374	.40	1.282	.176
.15	.385	.370	.41	1.341	.162
.16	.412	.366	.42	1.405	.149
.17	.440	.362	.43	1.476	.134
.18	.468	.358	.44	1.555	.119
.19	.496	.353	.45	1.645	.103
.20	.524	.348	.46	1.751	.086
.21	.553	.342	.47	1.881	.068
.22	.583	.337	.48	2.054	.048
.23	.613	.331	.49	2.326	.027
.24	.643	.324	.50	∞	.000
.25	.675	.318			

(3) AN ALTERNATIVE FORMULA FOR BI-SERIAL r

There is another—and slightly different—formula for bi-serial r which is often useful. This is

$$r_{bis} = \frac{M_p - M_T}{\sigma} \times \frac{p}{z} \qquad (89)$$

(*bi-serial coefficient of correlation or bi-serial* r *in terms of* M_T, *the mean of the total group*)

in which

M_p = mean of the group in the first (or p) category

M_T = mean of entire group
σ = standard deviation of entire group
p = proportion of whole group in category one
z = height of ordinate in normal curve dividing p from q

Substituting in formula (89) the values for M_p, M_T, σ, p, and z, shown in Table 47, we have

$$r_{\text{bis}} = \frac{60.08 - 58.05}{11.63} \times \frac{.600}{.386} = .27$$

which checks our previous result.

Formula (89) is especially well suited to those problems in which sub-groups having different characteristics are drawn from a larger group, the larger group mean (M_T) remaining the same.

The bi-serial correlation method has frequently been used in determining item validity,* that is, in finding whether success or failure upon a given item is correlated with total score in the test or with score in some criterion (Table 47). If those who achieve high scores in the criterion get an item right more often than those who make low scores, the item will be positively correlated with the criterion. Such an item is a good measure of the criterion while one which correlates zero or negatively with criterion scores is a poor measure.

(4) THE POINT BI-SERIAL COEFFICIENT

When items are scored 1 if correct and 0 if incorrect, that is, as either-or, the assumption of normality in the distribution of right-wrong responses is unwarranted.† In such cases the *point bi-serial r* rather than bi-serial r should be used. The point bi-serial method assumes that the behavior which has been classified into two categories can be thought of as occurring at two distinct *points* or modes instead of along a graduated scale or continuum. Point bi-serial r has proved to be useful in item analysis. The formula is

$$r_{p_{\text{bis}}} = \frac{M_p - M_q}{\sigma} \cdot \sqrt{pq} \tag{90}$$

(*point bi-serial coefficient of correlation*)

While (87) is often used in item analysis, (90) is somewhat more defensible and is easier to apply. Point bi-serial r's are lower than

---
* Long, J. A., and Sandiford, Peter, *The Validation of Test Items*, Department of Educational Research, University of Toronto, 1935, Bulletin #3, 16–17.
† Richardson, M. W., and Stalnaker, J. L., "A Note on the Use of Bi-serial r in Test Research," *Journal of Genetic Psychology*, 1933, 8, 463–465.

bi-serial r's and are not directly comparable either to r_{bis}'s or to product-moment r's. For example, the validity index of Item 72 (Table 47) by formula (90) is .21 as compared with the r_{bis} of .27.

2. Tetrachoric correlation

We have seen in the last section that when one variable is continuous and is expressed in the form of test scores, and the other is dichotomous or in a twofold classification, bi-serial r provides a measure of relationship between the two. An extension of the problem of finding correlation between categories to which bi-serial r is not applicable presents itself when *both* variables are dichotomous. We then have a 2×2 or fourfold table, from which a modified form of the product-moment coefficient, called *tetrachoric r*, may be calculated. Tetrachoric r is useful when one wishes to find the relationship between two characters or attributes neither of which is directly measurable, but both of which are capable of being separated into two categories. Thus, if we wish to measure the correlation between school attendance and employment, persons might be classified into those who have attended high school and those who have not; and into those who are employed and those who are unemployed. Or, if we wish to discover the correlation between intelligence and social maturity, children might be classified as above average and below average in intelligence, on the one hand, and as socially mature and socially immature on the other. Tetrachoric correlation assumes that the two variables being studied are essentially *continuous*, and would be *normally distributed* if it were possible to classify them more exactly into finer groupings.

(1) CALCULATION OF TETRACHORIC r

Table 49 illustrates a 2×2 fold table, and shows the steps involved in calculating tetrachoric r. The problem is to find whether a larger number of successful than of unsuccessful salesmen tend to be "socially well adjusted." The data are artificial. The X-variable (along the top of the diagram) is divided into two categories "successful" and "unsuccessful"; and the Y-variable (along the left of the diagram) is divided into two categories "socially well adjusted" and "socially poorly adjusted." The sums of the rows show that sixty salesmen $(a + b)$ out of the sample of 100 are classed as well adjusted socially, and that forty salesmen $(c + d)$ are classed as

FURTHER METHODS OF CORRELATION

TABLE 49 To illustrate the calculation of tetrachoric r (r_t)

(The data are hypothetical)

	X-variable		Totals
	100 Salesmen		
	Unsuccessful	Successful	
Y-variable — Socially Well Adjusted	25 (b)	35 (a)	60 $p = 60\%$
Socially Poorly Adjusted	30 (d)	10 (c)	40 $q = 40\%$
Totals	55 $q' = 55\%$	45 $p' = 45\%$	100

For $p = .60$, $q = .40$, $\alpha = .10$ For $p' = .45$, $q' = .55$, $\alpha = .05$
$x = -.253$ ⎡Table 48⎤ $x' = .126$ ⎡Table 48⎤
$z = .386$ ⎣Fig. 58⎦ $z' = .396$ ⎣Fig. 58⎦

$$\frac{ad - bc}{N^2 zz'} = r + \frac{xx'r^2}{2} \qquad (91)$$

$$\frac{1050 - 250}{100^2(.386)(.396)} = r + \frac{(-.253)(.126)r^2}{2}$$

$$.523 = r - .016r^2$$

or
$$.016r^2 - r + .523 = 0*$$

$$r = \frac{+1 \pm \sqrt{1 - 4(.016)(.523)}}{2 \times .016} = \frac{+1 \pm \sqrt{1 - .033472}}{.032}$$

$$= \frac{+1 \pm .9831}{.032}$$

$= .53$ (taking numerator as $+1 - .9831$)
$= +62$ (taking numerator as $+1 + .9831$)

* The general form of a quadratic equation is $ax^2 + bx + c = 0$. The two values of x (i.e., the roots of the equation) may be computed by the formula
$$x = \frac{-b \pm \sqrt{b^2 - 4ac}}{2a}$$
In the equation $.016r^2 - r + .523 = 0$, $a = .016$; $b = -1.00$; and $c = .523$. Hence,
$$r = \frac{+1 \pm \sqrt{1 - 4(.016)(.523)}}{2 \times .016}$$
$= .53$ or 62 (an impossible value)

poorly adjusted socially.* The proportions in each category (p and q) are 60% and 40%, respectively. The sums of the columns show that fifty-five of the 100 salesmen are classified as unsuccessful, and forty-five as successful; the proportions are 55% (q') and 45% (p'). On the assumption that "social adjustment" is distributed normally, from the proportions $p = .60$, and $q = .40$, we obtain an $x = -.253$, and $z = .386$. These last two values are read from Table 48 as follows: The perpendicular line (i.e., the ordinate, z) separating the *upper* 60% from the *lower* 40% in a normal curve is just 10% from the mean. Hence, entering the first column of Table 48 with $\alpha = .10$, we read $x = -.253$ and $z = .386$. See diagram below.

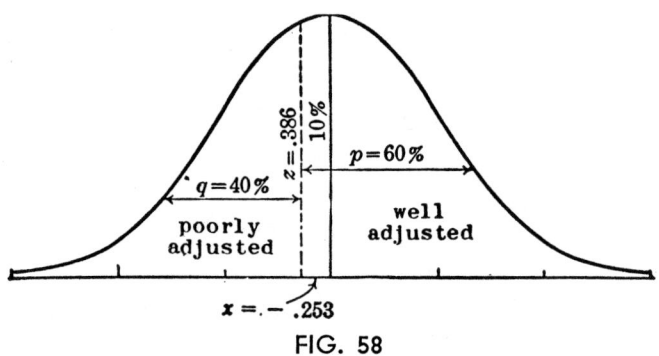

FIG. 58

The x' and z' values corresponding to $p' = .45$ and $q' = .55$ are calculated in the same way. The perpendicular line dividing the upper 45% (the percent successful) from the lower 55% (the percent unsuccessful) is 5% from the mean; and from Table 48, for $\alpha = .05$, $x' = .126$ and $z' = .396$. See diagram on page 365.

An approximate formula for tetrachoric r may be written as follows:

$$\frac{ad - bc}{N^2 zz'} = r_t + \frac{xx' r^2_t}{2} \qquad (91)$$

(*approximate formula for tetrachoric* r)

in which

x and $x' = \sigma$-distances from the means to the points separating the

* To accord with the plan of the ordinary correlation table (p. 128), the categories in Table 49 have been so arranged that concentration of data in the *first* and *third* quadrants (a and d) denotes positive correlation; concentration of data in the *second* and *fourth* (b and c) quadrants negative correlation.

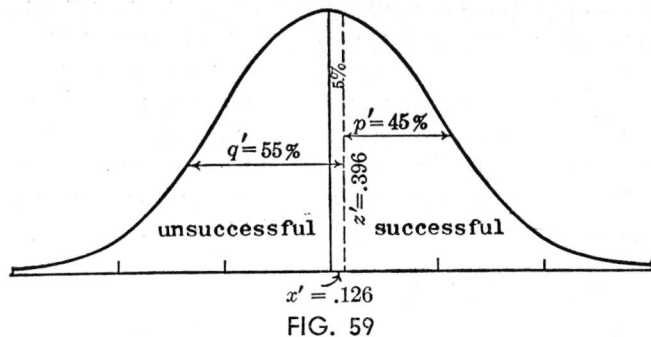

FIG. 59

proportion in the upper category from the proportion in the lower category;
z and z' = the heights of the ordinates *at* the points of division;
a, b, c, d = entries in the four cells, see Table 49;
N = number of cases; i.e., sum of entries in the four cells;
r_t = the tetrachoric coefficient of correlation.

In Table 49, ad is found to equal 1050, and bc to equal 250. Substituting for these quantities, and for x, x', z, z', and N^2 in formula (91), we obtain $r_t = .53$. This coefficient indicates a fairly substantial correlation between success in salesmanship and social adjustment. In order to compute r_t it is necessary that we solve a quadratic equation. The method of carrying through this solution is given in Table 49 and in the footnote at the bottom of the table. Note that only the first of the two solutions for r_t is a possible value, as the second is greater than unity.

The investigator who finds it necessary to calculate many tetrachoric r's may greatly shorten his work by using the computing diagrams devised by Thurstone and his co-workers.* These charts enable one to obtain a solution for r_t by graphic methods as soon as the proportion within each of the four cells of the table is known.

(2) THE SE OF A TETRACHORIC r

The formula for SE_{r_t} is mathematically complex and is too long to be useful practically. Its derivation can be found in books that deal with the mathematics of statistical theory.† If a standard error is

---

* Chesire, L., Saffir, M., and Thurstone, L. L., *Computing Diagrams for the Tetrachoric Correlation Coefficient*, University of Chicago Bookstore, 1933.
† Peters, C. C., and Van Voorhis, W. R., *Statistical Procedures and Their Mathematical Bases* (New York: McGraw-Hill, 1940), pp. 370–375.

wanted, an approximation to SE_{r_t} may be found in the following way. When p is close to .50 and N is large, SE_{r_t} is about 70% higher than the SE of a product-moment r of the same size as r_t and based upon the same N. The SE of a product-moment r of .53 is .07 for $N = 100$. Hence, the SE_{r_t} of an $r_t = .53$ is approximately .12 $(.07 \times 1.70)$. The .95 confidence-interval for the true r_t is .29 to .77 (i.e., $.53 \pm 1.96 \times .12$ or $.53 \pm .24$). The obtained r_t of .53 is, therefore, indicative of a positive r probably as high as .29.

(3) TETRACHORIC r IN TEST EVALUATION

Tetrachoric r is often used as a means of evaluating a test's efficiency in separating two contrasted or "criterion" groups. An example is given in Table 50 (the data are artificial). The problem is to

TABLE 50 To illustrate the use of tetrachoric r in evaluating a given test

$N = 125$

		X-variable		
		College Juniors		
		Non-Science Majors	Science Majors	
Y-variable	Above Test Mean	24% (b)	35% (a)	$p = 59\%$
	Below Test Mean	29% (d)	12% (c)	$q = 41\%$
		$q' = 53\%$	$p' = 47\%$	100%

For $p = .59, q = .41$ For $p' = .47, q' = .53$
$x = -.228$ $x' = .075$
$z = .389$ $z' = .398$

$$\frac{.1015 - .0288}{(.389)(.398)} = r + \frac{(-.228)(.075)r^2}{2} \tag{91}$$

$.470 = r - .009r^2$

or $.009r^2 - r + .470 = 0$

$$r = \frac{+1 \pm \sqrt{1 - 4(.009)(.470)}}{2(.009)}$$

$$= \frac{+1 \pm .9915}{.018}$$

$= .47$, or 111 (an impossible value)

find whether a test of deductive reasoning (here, a syllogism test) will differentiate fifty-nine college juniors majoring in science from sixty-six college juniors majoring in literature or languages (non-science). The X-variable is divided into science majors and non-science majors; the Y-variable into those above and those below the mean of the test, i.e., the mean score established by the entire junior class. The entries in the cells, a, b, c, and d, are expressed in percents, so that N^2 in formula (91) is 1.00. As shown in Table 50, the correlation between majoring in science and high scores on the syllogism test is .47. If one were investigating a number of tests with a view toward determining their relative values as indicators of scientific aptitude, the worth of each test could be measured in accordance with its ability to separate the two criterion groups.*

3. The phi-coefficient (fourfold point coefficient)

In a 2×2 fold table, the ϕ-coefficient provides a measure of correlation which is equivalent to r. Like the point bi-serial r, *phi* measures relationship between items when the classification is truly dichotomous and is concentrated at two separate points or into two distinct classes. Phi is sometimes used also with continuous variables which have been forced into two categories.

The diagrams below show the same fourfold tables; in the first the entries represent frequencies or scores, in the second proportions.

	−	+				−	+	
+	B	A	$A+B$	+		b	a	p
−	D	C	$C+D$	−		d	c	q
	$B+D$	$A+C$				q'	p'	

The formula for phi in terms of frequencies is

$$\phi = \frac{AD - BC}{\sqrt{(A+B)(C+D)(B+D)(A+C)}} \quad (92)$$

(*phi-coefficient of correlation*)

which expressed in proportions becomes

$$\phi = \frac{ad - bc}{\sqrt{pq\,p'q'}} \quad (93)$$

The phi-coefficient must always be used to determine the significance of the difference between correlated percents or proportions. In example (2), page 237, for example, $\phi = \dfrac{.12 - .02}{\sqrt{.50 \times .50 \times .40 \times .60}}$

---

* The phi-coefficient is also useful here.

or .41. In general, ϕ is lower than the corresponding r_t's and is not comparable to them. The phi-coefficient for the data in Table 49, for example, is .33 as against an r_t of .53; in Table 50 it is .31 as against an r_t of .47.*

Phi is related to χ^2 by the equation $\chi^2 = N\phi^2$ or $\phi = \sqrt{\dfrac{\chi^2}{N}}$. The significance of a ϕ may be estimated, therefore, by converting it into a χ^2 and determining the significance of χ^2. ϕ is valuable when we want to know how performance on one item is related to performance on another item (see problem 5, p. 375). Phi has proved to be especially useful in item analysis,† where the values 1 and 0 are usually assigned to answers right and wrong.

4. The contingency coefficient, C

The coefficient of contingency, C, is used to determine relationship when the variables under study have been put into two or more classes or categories. The contingency coefficient can be derived directly from χ^2 (p. 254); but C differs from χ^2 in that it provides a measure of *correlation* ‡ which under certain conditions (p. 371) is comparable to product-moment r. C bears the following relation to χ^2:

$$C = \sqrt{\dfrac{\chi^2}{N + \chi^2}} \qquad (94)$$

(*formula for C, the contingency coefficient in terms of* χ^2)

In Table 33, page 263, the association between eyedness and handedness was found to be expressed by a χ^2 of 4.02, which for 4 df was not significant. By formula (94) the C for Table 33 is $\sqrt{\dfrac{4.02}{413 + 4.02}}$ or .10 (to two decimals). Taken at face value and alone, this C would indicate a negligible relationship between eyedness and handedness. The SE needed to test C is a complex expression laborious to compute; § so that the significance of C is best tested by its equivalent χ^2. In the present problem, the χ^2 of 4.02 is not significant and in consequence our C of .10 is not significant.

---

* Guilford, J. P., and Perry, N. C., "Estimation of other coefficients of correlation from the phi coefficient," *Psychometrika*, 1951, 16, 335–346.

† Guilford, J. P., ed., *Printed Classification Tests, Report No. 5*, Army Air Forces Aviation Psychology Program Research Reports (Washington, D. C.: U. S. Gov't Printing Office, 1947).

‡ χ^2 is a measure of *probability* of association.

§ Kelley, T. L., *Fundamentals of Statistics* (Cambridge, Mass.: Harvard University Press, 1947).

(1) METHOD OF CALCULATING C

Table 51 illustrates the computation of C from a 4×4 fold contingency table. The table gives the classification of 1000 fathers and sons with respect to eye color. The independence values for each cell

TABLE 51 To illustrate the calculation of C, the coefficient of contingency

	Father's Eye Color					II. Calculation of C
Son's Eye Color		Blue	Gray	Hazel	Brown	Totals
	Blue	(120) 194	(88) 70	(60) 41	(66) 30	335
	Gray	(102) 83	(75) 124	(51) 41	(56) 36	284
	Hazel	(49) 25	(36) 34	(25) 55	(27) 23	137
	Brown	(87) 56	(64) 36	(44) 43	(48) 109	244
	Totals	358	264	180	198	1000

II. Calculation of C

$\dfrac{(194)^2}{120} = 313.6$

$\dfrac{(83)^2}{102} = 67.5$

$\dfrac{(25)^2}{49} = 12.8$

$\dfrac{(56)^2}{87} = 36.0$

$\dfrac{(70)^2}{88} = 55.7$

$\dfrac{(124)^2}{75} = 205.0$

$\dfrac{(34)^2}{36} = 32.1$

$\dfrac{(36)^2}{64} = 20.3$

$\dfrac{(41)^2}{60} = 28.0$

$\dfrac{(41)^2}{51} = 33.0$

$\dfrac{(55)^2}{25} = 121.0$

$\dfrac{(43)^2}{44} = 42.0$

$\dfrac{(30)^2}{66} = 13.6$

$\dfrac{(36)^2}{56} = 23.1$

$\dfrac{(23)^2}{27} = 19.6$

$\dfrac{(109)^2}{48} = 247.5$

I. Independence Values

$\dfrac{335 \times 358}{1000} = 120$ $\dfrac{137 \times 358}{1000} = 49$

$\dfrac{335 \times 264}{1000} = 88$ $\dfrac{137 \times 264}{1000} = 36$

$\dfrac{335 \times 180}{1000} = 60$ $\dfrac{137 \times 180}{1000} = 25$

$\dfrac{335 \times 198}{1000} = 66$ $\dfrac{137 \times 198}{1000} = 27$

$\dfrac{284 \times 358}{1000} = 102$ $\dfrac{244 \times 358}{1000} = 87$

$\dfrac{284 \times 264}{1000} = 75$ $\dfrac{244 \times 264}{1000} = 64$

$\dfrac{284 \times 180}{1000} = 51$ $\dfrac{244 \times 180}{1000} = 44$

$\dfrac{284 \times 198}{1000} = 56$ $\dfrac{244 \times 198}{1000} = 48$

$S = 1270.8$
$N = 1000$
$S - N = 270.8$

$$C = \sqrt{\dfrac{S-N}{S}} = \sqrt{\dfrac{270.8}{1270.8}} = .46$$

have been computed as shown in Table 51. From the top row, for example, we know that 335/1000 of *all* sons are described as blue-eyed. This proportion of 358 $\left(\text{i.e., } \dfrac{335 \times 358}{1000}\right)$ gives 120 as the number of fathers who can be expected to have blue-eyed sons "by chance," as contrasted with the 194 fathers who actually did have blue-eyed sons. When the independence values have been found, we square each obtained cell entry, and divide by its own independence value as shown in Table 51. The sum of these quotients gives S; and from S and N, C is calculated by the formula

$$C = \sqrt{\frac{S - N}{S}} \qquad (95)$$

(*formula for* C, *coefficient of contingency, calculated directly*)

In Table 51, C is .46. From (94) the χ^2 corresponding to this C is 268, which for 9 df is highly significant—far beyond the .01 level (Table E).

C possesses certain advantages over ϕ and r_t. In computing C, for example, no assumption of normality in the distributions of the variables classified need be made; in fact any type of distribution, skewed or rectangular, may be utilized. C may be either plus or minus, the sign of the coefficient depending upon an inspection of the contingency table itself. In Table 51 it is clear that pigmentation of eyes in father and son is positively correlated * and that C must be positive.

A disadvantage of C is that it does not remain constant for the same data when the number of classes varies. The C computed from a 2×2 or 3×3 table will ordinarily not be comparable to the C computed for the same data from a 5×5 table, say. Furthermore, the maximum value which C can take depends upon the fineness of the classification used so that C is not directly comparable to bi-serial r or to r_t. It can be shown that

when the number of classes = 2, the maximum C is .707
when the number of classes = 3, the maximum C is .816
when the number of classes = 4, the maximum C is .866
when the number of classes = 5, the maximum C is .894

* We note, for example, that 194 blue-eyed fathers have blue-eyed sons, while only 30 brown-eyed fathers have blue-eyed sons. Moreover, 109 brown-eyed fathers have brown-eyed sons while only 56 blue-eyed fathers have brown-eyed sons. Comparisons of this sort will show that association between pigmentation in the eyes of father and son is positive.

when the number of classes = 6, the maximum C is .913
when the number of classes = 7, the maximum C is .926
when the number of classes = 8, the maximum C is .935
when the number of classes = 9, the maximum C is .943
when the number of classes = 10, the maximum C is .949

In the light of this table, Yule and Kendall * recommend that we "restrict the use of the 'coefficient of contingency' to 5×5 or finer classifications" in order that the maximum value of C may be as near unity as possible. At the same time, we should avoid a too-fine classification or C will be affected by slight or "casual irregularities of no physical significance"; and, in addition, the arithmetic of calculation will be greatly (and needlessly) increased. A correction † for "broad categories" may be applied to C's calculated from 4×4 fold or broader groupings if C is to be compared with r. For 5×5 fold or finer classifications, this correction is so small that for practical purposes it may be disregarded.

The relation of C to r is, under certain conditions, very close. C is substantially equivalent to r (1) when the grouping is relatively fine—5×5 fold or finer; (2) when the sample is large; (3) when the two variables may legitimately be classified into categories; and (4) when we are justified in assuming that the variables under investigation are normally distributed.

III. Curvilinear or Non-Linear Relationship

The relationship between the paired values of two sets of measures, X and Y, may be described in a general way as "linear" or "nonlinear." When the means of the arrays of the successive columns and rows in a correlation table follow straight lines (at least approximately), the regression is said to be linear or straight-line (p. 133). When the drift or trend of the means of the arrays (columns or rows) cannot be well described by a straight line, but can be represented by a *curve* of some kind, the regression is said to be curvilinear or in general non-linear.

Our discussion in Chapter 6 was concerned entirely with linear relationship, the extent or degree of which is measured by the product-moment coefficient of correlation, r. It sometimes happens in

---

* Yule, G. U., and Kendall, M. G., *An Introduction to the Theory of Statistics* (12th ed.; London: C. Griffin, 1940).
† Peters, C. C., and Van Voorhis, W. R., *op. cit.*, pp. 391–393.

mental measurement, however, that the relationship between two variables is definitely non-linear; and when this is true, r is not an adequate measure of the degree of correspondence or correlation. When the regression is non-linear, a curve joining the means of successive arrays (in the columns, say) will fit these mean values more exactly than will a straight line. Hence, should a truly curvilinear relationship be described by a straight line, the scatter or spread of the paired values about the regression line will be greater than the scatter about the better-fitting regression curve. The smaller the spread of the paired scores about the regression line or the regression curve which relates the variables X and Y (or Y and X), the higher the relationship between the two variables. For this reason, an r calculated from a correlation table in which the regression is curvilinear will *always be less* than the true relationship. An example will make this situation clearer. The correlation between the following two short series, as given by the product-moment formula, is $r = .93$ [formula (24), p. 139]. The *true* correlation between the two series,

Variable X	Variable Y
1	.25
2	.50
3	1.00
4	2.00
5	4.00

however, is clearly perfect, since changes in Y are directly related to changes in X. As X increases by 1 (i.e., in arithmetic progression) Y doubles (i.e., increases in geometric progression). The reason why r is less than 1.00 becomes obvious as soon as we plot the paired X and Y values. As shown in Figure 60, the relationship between X and Y is curvilinear, and is exactly described by a curve which passes through the successively plotted points. When linear relationship is forced upon these data, the plotted points do not fall along the straight line, and the product-moment coefficient, r, is less than 1.00. However, the correlation-ratio, or coefficient of non-linear relationship η (read as *eta*) for the given data is 1.00.

True non-linear relationship is encountered in psychophysics and in experiments dealing with fatigue, practice, forgetting, and learning. Whenever an experiment is carried on to the point of diminishing returns, relationship will necessarily be curvilinear. Most mental and educational tests, however, when administered to large samples, exhibit linear or approximately linear relationships. The coefficient

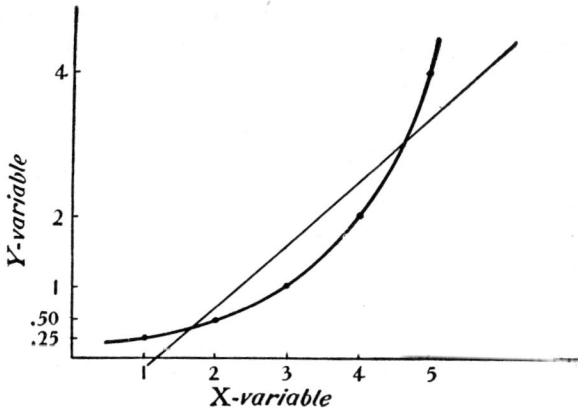

FIG. 60 To illustrate non-linear relationship

of correlation, r, therefore, has been employed in psychology and education to a far greater extent than has η; and for this reason the calculation of η is not given here.* If regression is significantly non-linear, it makes considerable difference whether η or r is the measure of relation. But if the correlation is low and the regression not significantly curvilinear, r will give as adequate a measure of relationship as η.

The coefficient of correlation has the advantage over η in that knowing r we can write down at once the straight-line regression equation connecting X and Y or Y and X. This is not possible with the correlation ratio. In order to estimate one variable from another (say, Y from X) when regression is non-linear, a curve must be fitted to the means of the Y-columns. The equation of this curve then serves as a "regression equation" from which estimates can be made.†

* See references, page 450.
† See Chapter 7.

PROBLEMS

1. Compute the correlation between the following two series of test scores by the rank-difference method and test its significance.

Individual	Intelligence Score	Cancellation Score (A-Test $+$ Number Group Checking Test)
1	185	110
2	203	98
3	188	118
4	195	104
5	176	112
6	174	124
7	158	119
8	197	95
9	176	94
10	138	97
11	126	110
12	160	94
13	151	126
14	185	120
15	185	118

[Note: The cancellation scores are in *seconds*; hence the two smallest scores numerically (i.e., 94) are highest and are ranked 1.5 each.]

2. Check the product-moment correlations obtained in problems 6 and 7, pages 150–151, Chap. 6, by the rank-difference method.

3. The following data give the distributions of scores on the Thorndike Intelligence Examination made by entering college freshmen who presented 12 or more recommended units, and entering freshmen who presented less than 12 recommended units. Compute bi-serial r by formula (87) and test its significance.

Thorndike Scores	12 or more recommended units	Less than 12 recommended units
90–99	6	0
80–89	19	3
70–79	31	5
60–69	58	17
50–59	40	30
40–49	18	14
30–39	9	7
20–29	5	4
	186	80

4. The following data give the distributions of scores on a general educational achievement test made by those who answered 50% or more, and those who answered less than 50% of the items in an arithmetic test correctly. Compute bi-serial r and test its significance.

Achievement Test	Subjects answering 50% or more of the items on arithmetic test correctly	Subjects answering less than 50% of the items on arithmetic test correctly
185–194	7	0
175–184	16	0
165–174	10	6
155–164	35	15
145–154	24	40
135–144	15	26
125–134	10	13
115–124	3	5
105–114	0	5
	120	110

5. Compute tetrachoric r's for the following tables and test for significance.

   (1) Relation of alcoholism and health in 811 fathers and sons. Entries are expressed as proportions.

		Sons		
		Unhealthy	Healthy	Totals
Fathers	Non-Alcoholic	.343	.405	.748
	Alcoholic	.102	.151	.252
	Totals	.445	.556	1.000

   (2) Correspondence of Yes and No answers to two items of a neurotic inventory.

		Question 1		
		No	Yes	Totals
Question 2	Yes	83	187	270
	No	102	93	195
	Totals	185	280	465

6. (a) Compute the ϕ-coefficients for the two tables in example (10), p. 245. Test the significance of ϕ by method on p. 368.

   (b) Compute the $r_{p_{bis}}$ for example (4), above.

   (c) Compute ϕ for the table in 5 (2) above.

7. Calculate the coefficient of contingency, C, for the two tables given below.

(1) Marriage-Adjustment Score of Husbands

		Very Low	Low	High	Very High	Totals
Education of Husbands	Graduate work	4	9	38	54	105
	College	20	31	55	99	205
	High School	23	37	41	51	152
	Grade School	11	10	11	19	51
	Totals	58	87	145	223	513

(2) Kind of Music Preferred

		English	French	German	Italian	Spanish	Totals
Nationality of Subject	English	32	16	75	47	30	200
	French	10	67	42	41	40	200
	German	12	23	107	36	22	200
	Italian	16	20	44	76	44	200
	Spanish	8	53	30	43	66	200
	Totals	78	179	298	243	202	1000

8. Convert the C's in example 7, above, to χ^2's and test for significance.

9. Compute C for example 3, Chapter 6, page 149.

10. (a) In the following table, compute r by the product-moment method.
    (b) Plot the relationship between X and Y as shown in Figure 60, page 373. Is the relation linear?

X	Y
1	1
2	2
3	4
4	8
5	16
6	32

ANSWERS

1. $\rho = .19$; not significant
3. $r_{bis} = .34$ $SE_{r_{bis}} = .07$; significant at .01 level
4. $r_{bis} = .47$ $SE_{r_{bis}} = .07$; significant at .01 level
5. (1) $r_t = -.09$ not significant; $SE_{r_t} = .06$ (approximately)
   (2) $r_t = .33$ $SE_{r_t} = .07$ (approximately). Significant at .01 level.

6. (a) $\phi = .25$ in (a) and $\phi = .50$ (b). Both ϕ's are significant by χ^2 test.
   (b) $r_{p_{\text{bis}}} = .38$ (c) $\phi = .22$
7. (1) $C = .24$ (2) $C = .40$
8. (1) Significant by χ^2 test at .01 level
   (2) Significant by χ^2 test at .01 level
9. $C = .72$
10. (a) $r = .85$ (b) Relationship is non-linear

15

PARTIAL AND MULTIPLE CORRELATION

1. The Meaning of Partial and Multiple Correlation

Partial and multiple correlation represent an important extension of the theory and technique of simple or two-variable correlation to problems which involve three or more variables. In computing the correlation between two sets of scores, it is often desirable to allow for the influence of factors which through their common relationship to the variables being correlated obscure results or make them difficult to interpret. To illustrate, suppose that the correlation between intelligence test scores and chronological age in a large group of children, seven to fourteen years old, is .50; that the correlation between school achievement and age in the same group is .40; and that the correlation between intelligence and school achievement is .70. Since intelligence test scores and school achievement both increase with age (the correlations are .50 and .40) the correlation between these two measures will be raised when age is allowed to vary. The correlation coefficient of .70, therefore, is not only a measure of the role of intelligence in school achievement, but is a measure of the influence of intelligence *plus* the indirect effects of differences in age or maturity upon school achievement.

To discover the relationship between intelligence and school achievement, uninfluenced by maturity, we must rule out or control the factor of age. This could be accomplished *experimentally* by selecting children all of whom are of the same age. But this procedure offers many difficulties, the principal one being that it is well-nigh impossible to find a large sample of children of exactly the same age. It becomes necessary, then, to determine what age range is permissible; and the more closely we limit our group with respect to age, the smaller the number left. In fact, the experimental control of a variable by the method of selection may so limit the size of the group that correlations are of doubtful value.

Because of the difficulties which arise in attempting to control a variable (or variables) experimentally, the method of partial correlation is often employed. By this method the relationship between two variables can be determined when one or more related variables are held constant. Thus, the partial correlation between general intelligence and school achievement, i.e., the correlation with age "partialled out," gives us the correlation between these two variables uninfluenced by the factor of age differences. Such a partial coefficient represents the *net* correlation between general intelligence and school achievement for children of the *same age*; or the net correlation between intelligence and school achievement when age is a constant factor. Expressed in still another way, our partial coefficient tells us what relationship exists between general intelligence test scores and school achievement when differences in maturity no longer affect *either* variable.

A second illustration of partial correlation may be helpful. A teacher finds in her class a correlation of .60 between test scores in history and arithmetic. In looking for an explanation of this correlation (since there is apparently little reason to *expect* a high relationship between these two abilities), she finds that achievement in arithmetic seems to depend in part upon ability to read and understand the problems. Obviously, ability to read well is also an important factor in determining achievement in history. Suppose that our teacher calculates the correlations of history and arithmetic with a *third* test, namely, one of reading comprehension. Knowing these r's, she may determine (by methods given on p. 387) the net or partial correlation between history and arithmetic when differences in reading comprehension have been allowed for. If this partial coefficient is .30, say—considerably smaller than the "whole" coefficient (of .60) between history and arithmetic—the hypothesis that the apparent relationship was due in part to the common dependence of both tests upon reading is verified. When a factor (or factors) is "partialled out" from a given correlation the effect is to eliminate the differences among individuals introduced by the variable thus controlled. The method of eliminating factor variability through partial correlation may be employed whenever the correlation can be computed between the factor or factors to be controlled and the two variables the net correlation of which we are seeking. Since *all* of the data are utilized, partial correlation has a decided advantage over experimental control in many problems.

In addition to its value as a means of controlling conditions by eliminating the effects of "disturbing" or other variables, partial correlation is useful in other ways. It enables us, for example, to build up a regression equation involving three or more variables from which a "criterion" score may be predicted when we know the scores made by a subject on several correlated tests. The accuracy of the regression equation in estimating criterion scores—its reliability as a "prediction" instrument—can be determined by the *coefficient of multiple correlation*. A multiple correlation coefficient gives the correlation between a single test or criterion on the one hand and a *team* of tests on the other. The meaning of the multiple coefficient of correlation will be better understood when the student has worked through an actual problem such as that given in Table 52.

II. An Illustrative Correlation Problem Involving Three Variables

Perhaps the most straightforward approach to an understanding of the meaning of partial and multiple correlation, and of the techniques of calculation involved, is through the solution of a problem. The present section, therefore, will show the application of partial and multiple correlation to a three-variable problem. Following this, the general formulas and further applications of the method will be considered.

The problem in Table 52 is taken from a study [*] of the factors which influence "academic success." In that part of the study from which the present data are drawn, the problem was to discover how accurately one can predict the academic success of freshmen from a knowledge of their general intelligence and of their study habits. Academic success was defined specifically as the number of credit or "honor" points obtained by a student at the end of his first semester in college. The number of honor points earned depended upon the number of A, B, and C grades made by the student in his freshman courses. A grade of A carried three honor points; a grade of B two honor points; a grade of C one honor point; and a grade of D, which

---

[*] May, M. A., "Predicting Academic Success," *Journal of Educational Psychology*, 1923, 14, 429–440.

PARTIAL AND MULTIPLE CORRELATION • 381

TABLE 52 A correlation problem involving three variables
(To illustrate partial and multiple correlation)

Step 1. Primary Data ($N = 450$)

(1) Honor Points   (2) General Intelligence   (3) Average Hours of Study per Week

$M_1 = 18.5$ $M_2 = 100.6$ $M_3 = 24$
$\sigma_1 = 11.2$ $\sigma_2 = 15.8$ $\sigma_3 = 6$
$r_{12} = .60$ $r_{13} = .32$ $r_{23} = -.35$

Step 2. Calculation of Partial Coefficients of Correlation

$$r_{12.3} = \frac{r_{12} - r_{13}r_{23}}{\sqrt{1 - r^2_{13}}\sqrt{1 - r^2_{23}}} = \frac{.60 - .32(-.35)}{.9474 \times .9367} = .80 \quad (96)$$

$$r_{13.2} = \frac{r_{13} - r_{12}r_{23}}{\sqrt{1 - r^2_{12}}\sqrt{1 - r^2_{23}}} = \frac{.32 - .60(-.35)}{.8000 \times .9367} = .71 \quad (96)$$

$$r_{23.1} = \frac{r_{23} - r_{12}r_{13}}{\sqrt{1 - r^2_{12}}\sqrt{1 - r^2_{13}}} = \frac{(-.35) - .60 \times .32}{.8000 \times .9474} = -.72 \quad (96)$$

Step 3. The Regression Equations and Partial Regression Coefficients

$$\bar{x}_1 = b_{12.3}x_2 + b_{13.2}x_3 \quad \text{(Deviation Form)} \quad (98)$$

or $\bar{X}_1 = b_{12.3}X_2 + b_{13.2}X_3 + K$ (Score Form)   (99)

in which $b_{12.3} = r_{12.3} \dfrac{\sigma_{1.23}}{\sigma_{2.13}}$ and $b_{13.2} = r_{13.2} \dfrac{\sigma_{1.23}}{\sigma_{3.12}}$ (102)

Step 4. Calculation of the Partial σ's

(1) $\sigma_{1.23} = \sigma_1\sqrt{1 - r^2_{12}}\sqrt{1 - r^2_{13.2}} = 11.2 \times .8000 \times .7042 = 6.3$ (97)
(2) $\sigma_{2.13} = \sigma_2\sqrt{1 - r^2_{23}}\sqrt{1 - r^2_{12.3}} = 15.8 \times .9367 \times .6000 = 8.9$ (97)
(3) $\sigma_{3.12} = \sigma_3\sqrt{1 - r^2_{23}}\sqrt{1 - r^2_{13.2}} = 6 \times .9367 \times .7042 = 4.0$ (97)

Step 5. Calculation of the Partial Regression Coefficients, and Partial Regression Equation

Substituting for $r_{12.3}, r_{13.2}, \sigma_{1.23}, \sigma_{2.13}, \sigma_{3.12}$, we have

$$b_{12.3} = .80 \times \frac{6.3}{8.9} = .57; \; b_{13.2} = .71 \times \frac{6.3}{4.0} = 1.12$$

Hence the regression equation becomes:

$\bar{x}_1 = .57x_2 + 1.12x_3$ (Deviation Form)

or $\bar{X}_1 = .57X_2 + 1.12X_3 - 66$ (Score Form)

Step 6. Calculation of the Standard Error of Estimate

$$\sigma_{(\text{est. } X_1)} = \sigma_{1.23} = 6.3 \quad (105)$$

Step 7. Calculation of the Coefficient of Multiple Correlation

$$R_{1(23)} = \sqrt{1 - \frac{\sigma^2_{1.23}}{\sigma^2_1}} \quad (107)$$
$$= .83$$

---

was a passing mark, carried no honor point credit. The maximum number of points which a freshman taking the regulation number of courses in one semester could obtain was forty-eight.

General intelligence was measured by a combination of the Miller

Mental Ability Test and the Dartmouth Completion of Definitions Test. The first test contains 120 items and the second 40, so that the maximum score was 160. The scores of the 450 students in this sample ranged from 50 to 150, the distribution being fairly normal. As a measure of interest and application it was decided to take the average number of hours per week spent in study. Information with regard to study habits was obtained by means of a questionnaire given at the beginning and again at the middle of the first semester. Among other items in the questionnaire upon which information was requested were the number of hours spent per week at meals, in sleeping, etc. These and other questions were included in order that the student might think that he was being checked upon the distribution of his total time and not upon his study habits alone. The correlation between the student's estimates of the number of hours spent in study, given on the first and second questionnaires, was .86, indicating a satisfactory degree of reliability.

As stated above, the main object of this study was to find how accurately the number of honor points which a student earns can be predicted from a knowledge of his study habits and his general intelligence. Other factors, of course, such as health, personality, previous preparation, and the like, are undoubtedly of importance in determining the number of honor points received. The two factors selected were chosen because they are important and are also objective and measurable. As the first step in solving our problem, we shall calculate the partial coefficient which shows to what extent honor points are related to general intelligence when the variable factor of study hours per week is held constant. Next the partial coefficient will be calculated which shows to what extent honor points are related to study hours when the variable effect of general intelligence is rendered constant. Apart from the employment of these partial coefficients in the regression equation from which we predict honor points, the information which they yield will prove in itself to be of considerable interest. The solution of the problem is outlined in the following series of steps; the necessary data and calculations will be found in Table 52.

Step I

The mean and σ of each series of measures and the intercorrelations are first calculated. These intercorrelations are product-moment r's computed as shown in Chapter 6. The correlation between (1) honor points and (2) general intelligence, written r_{12}, is .60; the correlation between (1) honor points and (3) the number of hours per week spent on the average in study, written r_{13}, is .32; and the correlation between (2) general intelligence and (3) hours of study per week, written r_{23}, is $-.35$. The low correlation between honor points and study hours is of decided interest; but the most surprising correlation is the $-.35$ between study hours and general intelligence. Evidently the brighter the student, the less he studies.

Step 2

Having found the intercorrelations of our three variables, we may then calculate the net correlation between (1) honor points and (2) general intelligence with the influence of (3) study hours partialled out or held constant. This net or partial coefficient of correlation, written $r_{12.3}$, is found from the following formula:

$$r_{12.3} = \frac{r_{12} - r_{13}r_{23}}{\sqrt{1 - r^2_{13}} \sqrt{1 - r^2_{23}}} \qquad (96), \text{ page } 388$$

Substitution of the values for r_{12}, r_{13}, and r_{23} in the formula gives a partial coefficient, $r_{12.3}$, of .80. This means that if *all* of our 450 students had studied exactly the same number of hours per week, the coefficient of correlation between honor points earned and general intelligence test scores would have been .80 instead of .60. In other words, when all students spend the *same number of hours in study*, there is a closer correspondence between general intelligence test score and honor points earned than there is when the number of study hours varies.

The partial coefficient of correlation between (1) honor points and (3) hours spent in study per week with (2) general intelligence partialled out, or its influence held constant, is found from the formula

$$r_{13.2} = \frac{r_{13} - r_{12}r_{23}}{\sqrt{1 - r^2_{12}} \sqrt{1 - r^2_{23}}} \qquad (96)$$

Substitution of the values for r_{13}, r_{12}, and r_{23} gives a partial coefficient, $r_{13.2}$, of .71, as against an obtained coefficient (r_{13}) of .32. This result means that if our group possessed the same general intelligence [*] there would be a much closer correspondence between the

---

[*] By "same general intelligence" is meant the same *score* on the given general intelligence tests.

number of honor points received and the number of hours spent in study than there is when the members of the group possess varying degrees of intelligence. This is certainly the result to be expected.

The last partial coefficient of correlation $r_{23.1}$ equals $-.72$. This coefficient gives the net correlation between (2) general intelligence and (3) study hours when the influence of (1) honor points is held constant. It is found from the formula

$$r_{23.1} = \frac{r_{23} - r_{12}r_{13}}{\sqrt{1 - r^2_{12}} \sqrt{1 - r^2_{13}}} \qquad (96)$$

Like the two partial r's above, we may interpret $r_{23.1}$ to mean that the correlation between general intelligence and hours spent in study in a group in which every student earns the same number of honor points would be much higher (in the *inverse* direction) than the "raw" correlation between the same two factors in an unselected group. By an unselected group is meant here a group in which the number of honor points received by different students varies. It seems evident that the brighter student not only studies less than the average and dull (since $r_{23} = -.35$) but that the brighter the student, the less he *needs* to study in order to reach a given standard of academic success—earn a given number of honor points.

Step 3

Knowing the partial coefficients of correlation, we may write the multiple regression equation from which the *most probable* number of honor points a student will receive may be estimated when we know his score in the general intelligence test and the number of hours he studies per week. The regression equation for three variables (in *deviation form*) is as follows:

$$\bar{x}_1 = b_{12.3}x_2 + b_{13.2}x_3 \qquad (98), \text{ page } 391$$

In this equation $\bar{x}_1$ stands for honor points and is the *dependent* variable or criterion; x_2 and x_3 stand for general intelligence and study hours, respectively, and are the *independent* variables. Note the resemblance of this equation to the simple regression equation for two variables $\bar{y} = b_{12} \times x$ (p. 155). If $\bar{x}_1$ is put for $\bar{y}$, and x_2 for x in the two-variable equation, we have $\bar{x}_1 = b_{12} \times x_2$.

When written in *score form*, the multiple regression equation for three variables becomes

PARTIAL AND MULTIPLE CORRELATION

$$(X_1 - M_1) = b_{12.3}(X_2 - M_2) + b_{13.2}(X_3 - M_3)$$

or transposing and collecting terms,

$$\overline{X}_1 = b_{12.3}X_2 + b_{13.2}X_3 + K \text{ (a constant)} \quad (99), \text{ page } 391$$

It is clear that before we can use this equation we must find the value of the *partial regression coefficients* $b_{12.3}$ and $b_{13.2}$. These may be found from the formulas

$$b_{12.3} = r_{12.3}\frac{\sigma_{1.23}}{\sigma_{2.13}} \text{ and } b_{13.2} = r_{13.2}\frac{\sigma_{1.23}}{\sigma_{3.12}} \quad (102), \text{ page } 392$$

and, as we already have the values of $r_{12.3}$ and $r_{13.2}$, it is only necessary that we find $\sigma_{1.23}$, $\sigma_{2.13}$, and $\sigma_{3.12}$ (the partial σ's) in order to replace the partial regression coefficients in the equation by numerical values.

Note that the partial coefficient of correlation $r_{23.1}$, although of interest as giving us the relation between general intelligence and hours spent in study for a constant number of honor points earned, is not actually needed in the regression equation $\overline{x}_1 = b_{12.3}x_2 + b_{13.2}x_3$. In order to evaluate the constants $b_{12.3}$ and $b_{13.2}$ in our regression equation, we need *only* $r_{12.3}$ and $r_{13.2}$. In fact, in *any* problem involving three variables, only *two* partial coefficients of correlation need be computed, if we are interested primarily in the prediction of X_1 scores from known values of X_2 and X_3.

Step 4

The partial σ's may be found from the formulas

$$\sigma_{1.23} = \sigma_1\sqrt{1 - r^2_{12}}\sqrt{1 - r^2_{13.2}}$$
$$\sigma_{2.13} = \sigma_{2.31} = \sigma_2\sqrt{1 - r^2_{23}}\sqrt{1 - r^2_{12.3}} \quad (98), \text{ page } 391$$
$$\sigma_{3.12} = \sigma_{3.21} = \sigma_3\sqrt{1 - r^2_{23}}\sqrt{1 - r^2_{13.2}}$$

Substituting the known values of the raw and partial r's in these formulas we find that $\sigma_{1.23} = 6.3$; $\sigma_{2.13} = 8.9$; and $\sigma_{3.12} = 4.0$. (For the calculations see Table 52.)

Step 5

From the partial σ's and the partial r's the numerical values of the partial regression coefficients $b_{12.3}$ and $b_{13.2}$ are found to be .57

and 1.12, respectively. We may now write the multiple regression equation in deviation form as

$$\bar{x}_1 = .57x_2 + 1.12x_3$$

In order to write this multiple regression equation in score form we replace x_1 by $(X_1 - 18.5)$; x_2 by $(X_2 - 100.6)$; and x_3 by $(X_3 - 24)$. The equation then becomes

$$\overline{X}_1 = .57X_2 + 1.12X_3 - 66$$

Given a student's general intelligence test score (X_2) and the number of hours per week he spends in study (X_3), we can estimate from this equation the "most probable" number of honor points he will receive during his first semester in college. Suppose that student J. N. has a general intelligence test score of 120 and that he studies on the average 20 hours per week: how many honor points will he then most probably receive during the first semester? Substituting $X_2 = 120$ and $X_3 = 20$ in the regression equation, we find that

$$\overline{X}_1 = (.57 \times 120) + (1.12 \times 20) - 66 = 25$$

The most probable number of honor points which student J. N. will receive, therefore, using the given measures as the basis of our forecast, is **25**.

Step 6

This forecast, like every other "most probable" number of honor points predicted from the regression equation, has an "error of estimate." The standard error of estimate of any X_1 predicted from the regression equation, $\overline{X}_1 = b_{12.3}X_2 + b_{13.2}X_3 + K$ is written $\sigma_{(\text{est. } x_1)}$, and equals $\sigma_{1.23}$ directly (p. 381).

The standard error of estimate in the present problem is 6.3, and in the illustration given above, the twenty-five honor points estimated for J. N. have a $SE_{(\text{est. } x_1)}$ of about 6 points. This means that the chances are about two in three that our forecast of twenty-five honor points will not miss the actual number of honor points received by J. N. by more than ±6. In general we may say that two-thirds of all predicted honor point values will lie within ±6 points of their actual values.

Step 7

The final step in the solution of our three-variable correlation problem is the computation of the coefficient of multiple correlation. "Multiple r," generally written R, is defined (see p. 380) as the coefficient of correlation between scores *actually made* on the criterion test and scores on the same test *predicted* from the regression equation. For the data of Table 52, R gives the correlation between *earned* honor points (X_1) and honor points *estimated* by means of the two variables, general intelligence (X_2) and hours of study (X_3), when these two are *combined* into a team by means of the regression equation. The formula for R when we are dealing with three variables is

$$R_{1(23)} = \sqrt{1 - \frac{\sigma^2_{1.23}}{\sigma^2_1}} \qquad (106), \text{page } 395$$

In the present problem $R_{1(23)} = .83$. This means that if the most probable number of honor points which each student in our group of 450 will receive is predicted from the regression equation given on page 381, the correlation between these 450 *predicted scores* and the 450 *scores actually received* will be .83. Multiple R tells us to what extent X_1 is determined by the combined action of X_2 and X_3; or, in the present instance, to what extent honor points are related to general intelligence together with number of study hours per week.

The methods described in this section are not practicable when are more than four variables. For multiple correlation problems involving a large number of tests it is advisable to use short-cut to lessen the amount of numerical calculation. An efficient ing method is described in Appendix A ndike's John Wiley correlation to find the net relationship between two variables when the influence of a third is ruled out or held constant. By an extension of the partial correlation method, we may obtain the net correlation between X_1 and X_2 when *two* or *more* variables have been held constant. The partial coefficient of correlation $r_{12.34}$, for example, means by analogy to $r_{12.3}$ that the correlation between X_1 and X_2 has been freed of the influence of *both* X_3 and X_4; and the partial coefficient of correlation $r_{12.34\ldots n}$ means that the correlation between X_1 and X_2 has been freed of the influence of a large number of disturbing factors.

In every partial coefficient of correlation, e.g., $r_{12.34}$, the *primary* subscripts to the *left* of the point (1 and 2) define the two variables whose net correlation we are seeking. The *secondary* subscripts to the *right* of the point (3 and 4) denote the variables ruled out or held constant. The *order* in which the secondary subscripts are written is immaterial, i.e., $r_{12.34} = r_{12.43}$. The order of the primary subscripts is of importance, however, as it tells us which variable is taken to be dependent and which independent. The r_{12} means that X_1 is dependent—is to be predicted from X_2; while r_{21} means that X_2 is dependent—is to be predicted from X_1. The numerical values r_{12} and r_{21} are, of course, the same. The order of a partial r is determined by the *number* of its secondary subscripts. Thus r_{12}, an "entire" or "total" r, is a coefficient of zero order; $r_{12.3}$ is a partial of the *first* order; $r_{12.345}$ is a coefficient of the *third* order.

The general formula for a partial r is

$$r_{12.34\ldots(n-1)} = \frac{r_{12.34\ldots(n-1)} - r_{1n.34\ldots(n-1)} r_{2n.34\ldots(n-1)}}{\sqrt{1 - r^2_{1n.34\ldots(n-1)}} \sqrt{1 - r^2_{2n.34\ldots(n-1)}}}$$

(partial correlation coefficient in terms of the coefficient of lower order—n variables)

From this formula partial r's of any given variable problem, for example, $(n-$
$r_{12.345}$ is written

$$r_{12.345} = \frac{r_{12.34} - r_{15}}{\sqrt{1 - r^2_{15}}}$$

that is, in terms of the partial order partial r's must then be the first order before the calculating partial r's

five-

There are several methods akin to partial correlation which are useful in certain special problems. Two of these, *part correlation* and *semi-partial correlation,* may be mentioned briefly. These procedures differ from partial correlation in that they give the net effect secured by ruling out the influence of one or more variables from only *one* of the two correlated measures, instead of from *both.* For example, one may wish to know the relation (semi-partial) between reaction time and speed of reading when differences in size of vocabulary are held constant with respect to reading only. Part correlation and semi-partial correlation have not been widely used in mental measurement. For a discussion of formulas and for illustrations see references below.*

(2) SIGNIFICANCE OF A PARTIAL r

The significance of a partial r (like that of a zero-order r) may be tested against the null hypothesis. We may use either Table 25, page 200, or Table J, column headed 2 variables. The degrees of freedom for a partial r are $(N - m)$ where $N =$ number of cases and $m =$ number of variables entering into the partial r. Thus if $r_{12.345} = .40$ and $N = 75$, $m = 5$ and $(N - m) = 75 - 5$ or 70. The .05 and .01 significance levels for this r are .23 and .30.

In Table 52, $r_{12.3} = .80$, $N = 450$, $m = 3$, and $(N - m) = 447$. From Table J, column 2, the r entries by interpolation for $N = 447$ are .09 and .12 at the .05 and .01 levels. The probability that the obtained $r_{12.3}$ of .80 arose from fluctuations of sampling is much less than .01; and this is true, also, of $r_{13.2}$ of .71 and $r_{23.1}$ of $-.72$. All three partial r's, in fact, are highly significant.

2. Partial σ's of any order

(1) GENERAL FORMULAS

Just as the correlation between two sets of scores can be determined when the influence of $1, 2, 3 \ldots n$ factors is held constant, so the variability (σ) of a set of scores can be computed when the influence of $1, 2, 3 \ldots n$ variables is ruled out. As an illustration, consider $\sigma_{1.23}$ of Table 52. This partial σ gives the variability of X_1 (honor points) *freed* of the influence upon variability exerted by the

---

* Ezekiel, M., *Methods of Correlation Analysis* (2nd ed.; New York: John Wiley and Sons, 1941), p. 213.
Dunlap, J. W., and Cureton, E. E., "On the Analysis of Causation," *Journal of Educational Psychology,* 1930, 21, 657–680.

two factors X_2 (general intelligence) and X_3 (study hours per week). The general formula for partial σ's of any order is

$$\sigma_{1.234\ldots n} = \sigma_1 \sqrt{1 - r^2_{12}} \sqrt{1 - r^2_{13.2}} \sqrt{1 - r^2_{14.23}} \ldots \sqrt{1 - r^2_{1n.23\ldots(n-1)}} \quad (97)$$

(*partial σ for* n *variables*)

This formula may be used to compute the net σ's in correlation problems which involve any number of variables. In a five-variable problem, for example, $\sigma_{1.2345}$ is written

$$\sigma_{1.2345} = \sigma_1 \sqrt{1 - r^2_{12}} \sqrt{1 - r^2_{13.2}} \sqrt{1 - r^2_{14.23}} \sqrt{1 - r^2_{15.234}}$$

This partial σ is of the *fourth* order since it has four secondary subscripts, and the order of a partial σ, like the order of a partial r, is determined by the number of its secondary subscripts.

By a simple rearrangement of the secondary subscripts, any higher order σ may be written in more than one way. A partial σ of the second order may be written in two ways: for example, $\sigma_{1.23}$ which is given on page 385 as

$$\sigma_{1.23} = \sigma_1 \sqrt{1 - r^2_{12}} \sqrt{1 - r^2_{13.2}}$$

may also be written

$$\sigma_{1.32} = \sigma_1 \sqrt{1 - r^2_{13}} \sqrt{1 - r^2_{12.3}}$$

In like manner $\sigma_{2.13}$ may be written

(1) $\quad\quad\quad \sigma_{2.13} = \sigma_2 \sqrt{1 - r^2_{12}} \sqrt{1 - r^2_{23.1}}$

or

(2) $\quad\quad\quad \sigma_{2.31} = \sigma_2 \sqrt{1 - r^2_{23}} \sqrt{1 - r^2_{12.3}}$

and $\sigma_{3.12}$ may be written

(1) $\quad\quad\quad \sigma_{3.12} = \sigma_3 \sqrt{1 - r^2_{13}} \sqrt{1 - r^2_{23.1}}$

or

(2) $\quad\quad\quad \sigma_{3.21} = \sigma_3 \sqrt{1 - r^2_{23}} \sqrt{1 - r^2_{13.2}}$

These alternate forms of a partial σ are useful as a check upon arithmetic calculations; also they make unnecessary the calculation of unused partial r's. Use of the *second* forms of $\sigma_{2.13}$ and $\sigma_{3.12}$ instead of the *first* (see Table 52 for example), makes it unnecessary to compute $r_{23.1}$ so far as the partial σ's in the regression equation are concerned. Furthermore, if $r_{23.1}$ is not wanted for other purposes, it need not be calculated at all (see p. 381). Two partial r's are all that are required in order to write the regression equation of a three-variable problem.

3. Multiple regression equations and partial regression coefficients

(1) THE MULTIPLE REGRESSION EQUATION FOR ANY NUMBER OF VARIABLES

The regression equation which expresses the relationship between a single dependent or criterion variable, X_1, and any number of independent variables, $X_2, X_3, X_4 \ldots X_n$ may be written in *deviation form* as follows:

$$\bar{x}_1 = b_{12.34\ldots n}x_2 + b_{13.24\ldots n}x_3 + \cdots + b_{1n.23\ldots (n-1)}x_n \qquad (98)$$

(*regression equation, deviation form, for* n *variables*)

and in *score form*

$$\bar{X}_1 = b_{12.34\ldots n}X_2 + b_{13.24\ldots n}X_3 + \cdots + b_{1n.23\ldots (n-1)}X_n + K \qquad (99)$$

(*regression equation, score form, for* n *variables*)

The partial regression coefficient $b_{12.34\ldots n}$, $b_{13.24\ldots n}$, etc., give the *weights* to be attached to the scores of each independent variable when X_1 is to be estimated from all of these in combination. Furthermore, the regression coefficients give the weight which each variable exerts in determining X_1 when the influence of the other variables is excluded. Hence, we can tell from the regression equation just what role each of the several test variables plays in determining the score on Test 1, the test taken as the criterion.

(2) THE MULTIPLE REGRESSION EQUATION FOR THREE VARIABLES (SPECIAL FORM)

When a problem involves only three variables, the regression equation, as we have seen, is written

$$\bar{x}_1 = b_{12.3}x_2 + b_{13.2}x_3 \quad \text{(deviation form)}$$

If the partial r's and the partial σ's are of no special interest, it is possible to express the equation above in a somewhat more convenient form for calculation, as follows:

$$\bar{x}_1 = \frac{\sigma_1(r_{12} - r_{13}r_{23})}{\sigma_2(1 - r^2_{23})} x_2 + \frac{\sigma_1(r_{13} - r_{12}r_{23})}{\sigma_3(1 - r^2_{23})} x_3 \qquad (100)$$

(*regression equation for three variables, special form*)

or in score form

$$\bar{X}_1 = \frac{\sigma_1(r_{12} - r_{13}r_{23})}{\sigma_2(1 - r^2_{23})} X_2 + \frac{\sigma_1(r_{13} - r_{12}r_{23})}{\sigma_3(1 - r^2_{23})} X_3 + K \qquad (101)$$

(*regression equation for three variables, special form*)

As this equation involves *only* zero order r's and zero order σ's, X_1 may be estimated from it without the computation of any partial r's or partial σ's. We may illustrate using the data given in Table 52, page 381. Substituting for $\sigma_1 = 11.2$, $\sigma_2 = 15.8$, $\sigma_3 = 6$, $r_{12} = .60$, $r_{13} = .32$, and $r_{23} = -.35$, we have

$$\bar{x}_1 = \frac{11.2(.60 + .32 \times .35)}{15.8(1 - .35^2)} x_2 + \frac{11.2(.32 + .60 \times .35)}{6(1 - .35^2)} x_3$$

$$\bar{x}_1 = .57x_2 + 1.12x_3$$

which checks the regression equation as calculated in Table 52.

(3) PARTIAL REGRESSION COEFFICIENTS (b's)

Partial regression coefficients may be computed from the formula

$$b_{12.34\ldots n} = r_{12.34\ldots n} \frac{\sigma_{1.234\ldots n}}{\sigma_{2.134\ldots n}} \qquad (102)$$

(*partial regression coefficients in terms of partial coefficients of correlation and standard errors of estimate—n variables*)

When the problem involves three variables, the regression coefficients, $b_{12.3}$ and $b_{13.2}$ are, like $r_{12.3}$ and $r_{13.2}$, of the *first* order. The first regression coefficient, $b_{12.3}$, equals $r_{12.3} \frac{\sigma_{1.23}}{\sigma_{2.13}}$ and the second regression coefficient, $b_{13.2}$, equals $r_{13.2} \frac{\sigma_{1.23}}{\sigma_{3.12}}$.

Partial regression coefficients which involve more than three variables may be calculated from formula (102). In a five-variable problem, for example, the regression coefficients (of the *third* order) are

$$b_{12.345} = r_{12.345} \frac{\sigma_{1.2345}}{\sigma_{2.1345}}$$

$$b_{13.245} = r_{13.245} \frac{\sigma_{1.2345}}{\sigma_{3.1245}} \text{ etc.}$$

In order to find these partial regression coefficients we first compute the third order partial r's and the fourth order partial σ's.

The b's are determined by the σ's of the tests and these in turn depend upon the units in terms of which the test is scored. The b-coefficients give the weights of *scores* in the independent variables, X_2, X_3, etc., but not the contribution of these variables without regard to the scoring system employed. The latter contribution is given by the "beta weights," described in (4) below.

(4) THE BETA (β) COEFFICIENTS

When expressed in terms of σ-scores, partial regression coefficients are usually called beta coefficients. The beta coefficients may be calculated directly from the b's as follows:

$$\beta_{12.34\ldots n} = b_{12.34\ldots n} \frac{\sigma_2}{\sigma_1} \qquad (103)$$

(beta *coefficients calculated from partial regression coefficients*)

The multiple regression equation for n variables may also be written in σ-scores as

$$z_1 = \beta_{12.34\ldots n} z_2 + \beta_{13.24\ldots n} z_3 + \cdots + \beta_{1n.23\ldots(n-1)} z_n \qquad (104)$$

(*multiple regression equation in terms of σ-scores*)

Beta coefficients are often called "beta weights" to distinguish them from the "score weights" (b's) of the ordinary multiple regression equation. When all of our tests have been expressed in σ-scores (all Means $=.00$ and all σ's $=1.00$) differences in test units as well as differences in variability are allowed for. We are then able to determine from the correlations alone the relative weight with which each independent variable "enters in" or contributes to the criterion, independently of the other factors.

To illustrate with the data in Table 52, we find that $\beta_{12.3} = .57 \times \frac{15.8}{11.2}$ or $.81$ and that $\beta_{13.2} = 1.12 \times \frac{6.0}{11.2}$ or $.60$. From (104) above we get

$$\bar{z}_1 = .81 z_2 + .60 z_3$$

This equation should be compared with the multiple regression equation $\bar{x}_1 = .57 x_2 + 1.12 x_3$ in Table 52 which gives the weights to be attached to the *scores* in X_2 and X_3. The weights of $.57$ and 1.12 tell us the amount by which scores in X_2 and X_3 must be multiplied in order to give the "best" prediction of X_1. But these weights do not give us the relative importance of general intelligence and study habits in determining the number of honor points a freshman will receive. This information is given by the beta weights. It is of interest to note that while the actual score weights are as 1:2 (.57 to 1.12), the independent contributions of general intelligence (z_2) and study habits (z_3) are in the ratio of .81 to .60 or as 4:3. When the variabilities (σ's) of our tests are all equal and scoring units are comparable, general intelligence has a proportionately greater influence than study habits in determining academic achievement. This is certainly the result to be expected.

4. The standard error of estimate for multiple regression equations

All X_1 scores estimated from a multiple regression equation have a standard error of estimate which measures the error made in taking scores given by the regression equation instead of *actual* scores (those earned on the criterion test). The standard error of estimate is given directly by $\sigma_{1.234\ldots n}$ as follows

$$\sigma_{(est.\ X_1)} = \sigma_{1.234\ldots n} \qquad (105)$$

(*standard error of estimate for* n *variables*)

Since $\sigma_{1.234\ldots n}$ must be computed in order to evaluate the partial regression coefficients (p. 390), $\sigma_{(est.\ X_1)}$ is always calculated in the course of the problem. In Table 52, the $\sigma_{(est.\ X_1)}$ of a prediction of honor points is 6.3. The chances are about seven in ten or two in three that the "most probable" honor point score forecast for any student will be in error by 6 points or *less*.

It is worth while examining further into the meaning of $\sigma_{(est.\ X_1)}$. This standard error of estimate equals $\sigma_{1.23}$; and the latter indicates the effect upon the variability of Test 1 (honor points) obtained by eliminating (or holding constant) the influence of Tests 2 and 3 (general intelligence and study effort). The *smaller* $\sigma_{1.23}$ is with respect to σ_1, the greater the influence exerted by our two factors upon Test 1's variability. In Table 52 it is clear that in ruling out the variability in Test 1 attributable to Tests 2 and 3, we reduce σ_1 from 11.2 to 6.3 ($\sigma_{1.23}$) or by nearly one-half. This means that students *alike* in general intelligence and in study habits differ much *less* in scholastic achievement than do students in general.

From the multiple regression equation $\overline{X}_1 = .57X_2 + 1.12X_3 - 66$ (see p. 381), X_1 (honor points) can be predicted with a *smaller error of estimate* than from any other *linear* equation. Put differently, the standard error of estimate is a *minimum* when the regression equation is used to estimate X_1 scores.* Hence, the values of X_1 predicted from the multiple regression equation are the "best estimates" of the actual X_1 values which can be made from a linear equation containing the given variables.

5. The coefficient of multiple correlation, R

(1) GENERAL FORMULAS

The correlation between a single dependent or criterion variable X_1 and $(n-1)$ independent variables combined by means of a multiple regression equation is given by the formula

$$R_{1(23\ldots n)} = \sqrt{1 - \frac{\sigma^2_{1.23\ldots n}}{\sigma^2_1}} \qquad (106)$$

(*multiple correlation coefficient in terms of partial σ's — n variables*)

in which

$R_{1(23\ldots n)}$ = the coefficient of multiple correlation
σ_1 = the standard deviation of the criterion (X_1) scores
$\sigma_{1.23\ldots n}$ = the variability left in Test 1 when the variability of Tests 2, 3 ... n is held constant through partial correlation.

When there are only three variables, the multiple coefficient of correlation becomes

$$R_{1(23)} = \sqrt{1 - \frac{\sigma^2_{1.23}}{\sigma^2_1}}$$

when there are five variables

$$R_{1(2345)} = \sqrt{1 - \frac{\sigma^2_{1.2345}}{\sigma^2_1}}$$

If we replace $\sigma_{1.23\ldots n}$ in formula (106) by its value in terms of the entire and partial r's [see formula (97)] we may write the general formula for $R_{1(234\ldots n)}$ as follows:

$$R_{1(234\ldots n)} = \sqrt{1 - [(1 - r^2_{12})(1 - r^2_{13.2}) \ldots (1 - r^2_{1n.23\ldots(n-1)})]} \qquad (107)$$

(*multiple coefficient of correlation in terms of partial coefficients of correlation—n variables*)

* Yule, G. U., and Kendall, M. G., *An Introduction to the Theory of Statistics, op. cit.*, pp. 262–267.

Since a higher order σ may be written in a variety of ways, the number depending upon its order (see p. 389), there are several alternate forms for R. These serve as valuable means of checking the accuracy of our arithmetical calculations. In a three-variable problem, for example, $R_{1(23)}$ may be written as

$$R_{1(23)} = \sqrt{1 - [(1 - r^2_{12})(1 - r^2_{13.2})]}$$

or as

$$R_{1(32)} = \sqrt{1 - [(1 - r^2_{13})(1 - r^2_{12.3})]}$$

The standard error of estimate is a minimum when the multiple regression equation is employed in estimating X_1 scores (p. 395). Hence the multiple coefficient of correlation, R, is the *maximum correlation* obtainable between *actual* X_1 scores and $\overline{X}_1$ scores estimated from a knowledge of the variables X_2, X_3 ... X_n in the regression equation. The truth of this statement is contingent upon linearity of regression in *all* of the correlations. R indicates how accurately a given combination of variables represents the actual values of X_1 (the criterion) when our test scores are combined in accordance with the "best" linear equation.

(2) MULTIPLE R IN TERMS OF β COEFFICIENTS

R^2 may be expressed in terms of the beta coefficients and the zero order r's:

$$R^2_{1(23\ ..\ n)} = \beta_{12.34\ ..\ n} r_{12} + \beta_{13.24\ ..\ n} r_{13} + \cdots + \beta_{1n.23\ ..\ (n-1)} r_{1n} \quad (108)$$

(*multiple* R^2 *in terms of* β *coefficients and zero order* r's)

For three variables (108) becomes

$$R^2_{1(23)} = \beta_{12.3} r_{12} + \beta_{13.2} r_{13}$$

From page 393 we find $\beta_{12.3} = .81$ and $\beta_{13.2} = .60$; and from Table 52 that $r_{12} = .60$ and $r_{13} = .32$. Substituting in (108) above, we get

$$R^2_{1(23)} = .81 \times .60 + .60 \times .32$$
$$= .49 + .19$$
$$R^2_{1(23)} = .68$$
$$R_{1(23)} = .82$$

$R^2_{1(23\ ...\ n)}$ gives the proportion of the variance of the criterion measure (X_1) attributable to the joint action of the variables X_2, $X_3 ... X_n$. As shown above, $R^2_{1(23)} = .68$; and, accordingly, 68% of whatever makes freshmen differ in (1) school achievement can be attributed to differences in (2) general intelligence and (3) study habits. By means of formula (108) the total contribution of .68 can be broken down further into the independent contributions of general intelligence (X_2) and study habits (X_3). Thus from the equation $R^2_{1(23)} = .49 + .19$, we know that 49% is the contribution of general intelligence to the variance of honor points, and 19% is the contribution of study habits. The remaining 32% of the variance of X_1 must be attributed to factors not measured in our problem.

(3) THE SIGNIFICANCE OF R

Multiple R is positive,* always less than 1.00, and always greater than the correlation coefficients $r_{12}, r_{13}, \ldots r_{1n}$. The significance of an R can best be tested, perhaps, against the null hypothesis by means of Table J. This table must be entered with the number of variables (m) in the problem and with ($N - m$) degrees of freedom. To illustrate with Table 52, $R = .83$, $N = 450$, $m = 3$ and ($N - m$) = $450 - 3$ or 447. From the column headed "3" in Table J we read that for 447 degrees of freedom the R's at the .05 and .01 levels (by interpolation) are .116 and .143. Only once in twenty trials would an R of .116 arise by sampling fluctuations on the null hypothesis, and only once in 100 trials would an R of .143 occur. As our R is very much larger than .14, it is highly significant. Table J may be used with problems involving up to nine variables. Suppose that $R_{1(2345)} = .526$ and $N = 40$. From the column headed "5 variables" in Table J, we find that for $40 - 5$ or 35 degrees of freedom, the R's are .482 and .556 at the .05 and .01 levels. The obtained R is significant, therefore, at the .05, but not at the .01, level.

6. Factors determining the selection of tests in a battery

The effectiveness with which the composite score obtained from a battery of tests measures the criterion depends (1) upon the intercorrelations of the tests in the battery as well as (2) upon the correlations of these tests with the criterion—their validity coefficients. This appears clearly in Table 53 in which the criterion correlation of each test is .30, but the intercorrelations of the tests of the battery vary from .00 to .60. When the tests are uncorrelated (all criterion r's being .30), an increase in size of the battery from 1 to 9 tests raises multiple R from .30 to .90. However, when the intercorrela-

---

* Since R is always taken as positive, chance errors are cumulative and may be large if the sample is small and the number of variables large. For the correction of R for chance errors, see formula (109), page 407.

tions of the tests are all .60 and the battery is increased in size from 1 to 9 tests, multiple R goes from .30 to .37. Even when the number of tests in the battery is 20 multiple R is only .38.

TABLE 53 * Effect of intercorrelations on multiple correlation

Multiple R's for different numbers of tests, when criterion correlations (validities) of all tests are .30, and the intercorrelations are the same and vary from .00 to .60. Example: In a battery of 4 tests, all with validities of .30 and intercorrelations of .30, multiple R is .44.

Number of Tests	Size of Intercorrelations			
	.00	.10	.30	.60
1	.30	.30	.30	.30
2	.42	.40	.37	.34
4	.60	.53	.44	.36
9	.90	.67	.48	.37
20	†	.79	.52	.38

A single test can add to the validity of a battery by "taking out" some of the as yet unmeasured part of the criterion. Such a test will show a high r with the criterion but relatively low r's with the other tests in the battery. (See Table 53 and Fig. 61.) Usually it is difficult to find tests, after the first 4 or 5, which fulfill these requirements. In most group tests of general intelligence where the criterion is relatively homogeneous (ability to deal with abstract verbal relations, say) the sub-tests of a battery may exhibit high intercorrelations. This is true to a lesser degree of educational achievement tests and of many tests of aptitudes. When the criterion is a complex made up of a number of variables (job performance, success in salesmanship, or professional competence) it is easier to find tests of acceptable validity which will show low relationships with the other tests of the battery. But even here the maximum multiple R is often reached rather quickly (see p. 407).

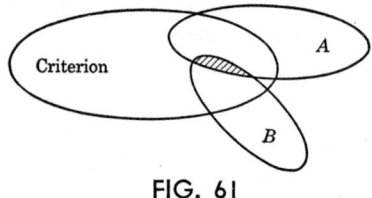

FIG. 61

* From R. L. Thorndike, *Personnel Selection* (New York: John Wiley and Sons, 1949), p. 191.

† It is mathematically impossible for 20 tests all to correlate 0.30 with some measure and still have zero intercorrelations.

A test may also add to the validity of a battery by acting as a "suppressor" variable. Suppose that Test A correlates .50 with a criterion—has good validity—while Test B correlates only .10 with the criterion but .60 with Test A. The $R_{1(23)} = .56$ despite the low validity of Test B. This is because Test B acts as a suppressor—takes out some of Test A's "non-valid" variance, thus raising the criterion correlation of the battery.* (See Fig. 62.) The weights of these two tests in the regression equation connecting the criterion with A and B are .69 and $-.31$. The negative weight of Test B serves to suppress that part of Test A not related to the criterion and thus gives a better (more valid) measure of the criterion than can be obtained with Test A, alone.

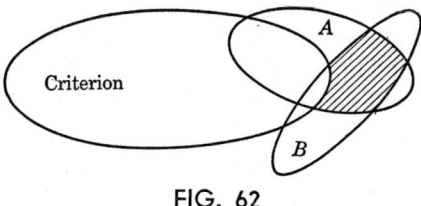

FIG. 62

IV. Spurious Correlation

The correlation between two sets of test scores is said to be *spurious* when it is due in some part, at least, to factors other than those which determine performance in the tests themselves. In general, the cause of spurious correlation lies in a failure to control conditions; and the most usual effect of this lack of control is a "boosting" or inflation of the coefficient. Some of the situations which may lead to spurious correlation will be given in this section.

1. Spurious correlation arising from heterogeneity

We have shown elsewhere (p. 378) how a lack of uniformity in age conditions will lead to correlations which are spuriously high. Failure to take account of heterogeneity introduced by the age factor is a prolific source of error in correlational work. To cite an example, within a group of boys ten to eighteen years old, a substantial cor-

---

* See also Table 52. Here Tests 2 and 3 take out relatively distinct parts of 1 (the criterion)—they are negatively correlated—so that $R_{1(23)}$ (.83) is significantly increased over r_{12} (.60).

relation will appear between strength of grip and memory span, quite apart from any intrinsic relationship, due solely to the fact that both variables increase with age. In stating the correlation between two tests, or the reliability coefficient of a test, one should always be careful to specify the range of ages, grades included, and other data bearing upon physical, mental, and cultural differences, in order to show the degree of heterogeneity in the group. Without this information, the r may be of little value.

Heterogeneity is introduced by other factors than age. If alcoholism, degeneracy, and bad heredity are all positively related, the r between alcoholism and degeneracy will be too high (because of the effect of heredity upon both factors) unless heredity can be "held constant." Again, assume that we have measured two distinctly different groups, 500 college seniors and 500 day laborers, upon a cancellation test and upon a general intelligence test. The mean ability in both tests will be definitely higher in the college group. Now even if the correlation between the two tests is zero within each group taken separately, if the two groups are combined a positive correlation will appear because of the heterogeneity of the group with respect to age, intelligence, and educational background. Such a correlation is, of course, spurious.*

To be a valid measure of relationship, a correlation coefficient must be freed of the extraneous influences which affect the relationship between the variables concerned. This may be accomplished (1) by selecting samples or groups in which age, or whatever the factor to be controlled, is constant; or (2) by using partial correlation when the factor to be controlled can be measured and its correlation with the variables studied can be calculated.

2. Spurious index correlation †

Even when three variables, X_1, X_2, and X_3, are uncorrelated, a correlation between the indices Z_1 and Z_2 (where $Z_1 = X_1/X_3$ and $Z_2 = X_2/X_3$) may appear which is as large as .50. To illustrate, if two individuals observe a series of magnitudes (e.g., Galton bar settings) independently, the absolute errors of observation (X_1 and X_2)

---

* Garrett, H. E., and Anastasi, A., "The Tetrad-Difference Criterion and the Measurement of Mental Traits," *Annals New York Academy of Sciences*, 1932, 33, 233–282.

† Yule, G. U., *An Introduction to the Theory of Statistics, op. cit.*, pp. 215–216.

Thomson, G. H., and Pintner, R., "Spurious Correlation and Relationship between Tests," *Journal of Educational Psychology*, 1924, 15, 433–444.

may be uncorrelated, and still an appreciable correlation appear between the errors made by the two observers, when these are expressed as *percents* of the observed magnitudes (X_3). The spurious element here, of course, is the common factor X_3 in the denominator of the ratios.

One of the commonest examples of a spurious index relationship in psychology is found in the correlation of I.Q.'s or E.Q.'s obtained from intelligence and achievement tests. If the I.Q.'s of 500 children ranging in age from three to fourteen years are calculated from two tests X_1 and X_2, the correlation is between $\frac{\text{M.A.}_1}{\text{C.A.}}$ and $\frac{\text{M.A.}_2}{\text{C.A.}}$. If C.A. were a *constant* (the same for all children) it would have no effect on the correlation and we would simply be correlating M.A.'s. But when C.A. varies from child to child there is usually a correlation between C.A. and M.A. which tends to increase the r between I.Q.'s —sometimes considerably.

3. Spurious correlation between averages

Spurious correlation usually results when the average scores made by a number of different groups on a given test are correlated against the average scores made by the same groups on a second test. An example is furnished by the correlations reported between *mean* intelligence test scores, by states, and such "educational" factors as number of schools, books sold, magazines circulated in the states, etc. Most of these correlations are high—many above .90. If average correlations by states are compared with the correlations between intelligence scores and number of years spent in school within the separate states, these latter r's are usually much lower. Correlations between averages become "inflated" because a large number of factors which ordinarily reduce the correlation within a single group cancel out when averages are taken from group to group. Average intelligence test scores, for instance, increase regularly as we go up the occupational scale from day laborer to the professions; but the correlation between intelligence and status (training, salary, etc.) at a given occupational level is far from perfect.

PROBLEMS

1. The correlation between a general intelligence test and school achievement in a group of children from eight to fourteen years old is .80. The

correlation between the general intelligence test and age in the same group is .70; and the correlation between school achievement and age is .60. What is the correlation between general intelligence and school achievement in children of the same age? Comment upon your result.

2. In a group of 100 college freshmen, the correlation between (1) intelligence and (2) the A-cancellation test is .20. The correlation between (1) intelligence and (3) a battery of controlled association tests in the same group is .70. If the correlation between (2) cancellation and (3) controlled association is .45, what is the "net" correlation between intelligence and cancellation in this group? Between intelligence and controlled association? Interpret your results.

3. Explain why some variables are of such a nature that it is difficult to hold them "constant," and hence to employ them in problems involving partial correlation.

4. Given the following data for fifty-six children:

X_1 = Stanford-Binet I.Q.
X_2 = Memory for Objects
X_3 = Cube Imitation

$M_1 = 101.71$	$M_2 = 10.06$	$M_3 = 3.35$
$\sigma_1 = 13.65$	$\sigma_2 = 3.06$	$\sigma_3 = 2.02$
$r_{12} = .41$	$r_{13} = .50$	$r_{23} = .16$

(a) Work out the regression equation of X_2 and X_3 upon X_1, using the method of Section II.
(b) Compute $R_{1(23)}$ and $\sigma_{(est.\ x_1)}$.
(c) If a child's score is 12 in Test X_2 and 4 in Test X_3, what is his most probable score in X_1 (I.Q.)?

5. Let X_1 be a criterion and X_2 and X_3 be two other tests. Correlations and σ's are as follows:

$r_{12} = .60 \qquad \sigma_1 = 5.00$
$r_{13} = .50 \qquad \sigma_2 = 10.00$
$r_{23} = .20 \qquad \sigma_3 = 8.00$

How much more accurately can X_1 be predicted from X_2 and X_3 than from either alone?

6. Given a team of two tests, each of which correlates .50 with a criterion. If the two tests correlate .20
   (a) How much would the addition of another test which correlates .50 with the criterion and .20 with each of the other tests improve the predictive value of the team?
   (b) How much would the addition of two such tests improve the predictive value of the team?

7. Test A correlates .60 with a criterion and .50 with Test B, which correlates only .10 with the criterion. What is the multiple R of A and B with the criterion? Why is it higher than the correlation of A with the criterion?

8. Two absolutely independent tests B and C completely determine the criterion A. If B correlates .50 with A, what is the correlation of C and A? What is the multiple correlation of A with B and C?

9. Comment upon the following statements:
   (a) It is good practice to correlate E.Q.'s achieved upon two educational achievement tests, no matter how wide the age range.
   (b) The positive correlation between average AGCT scores by states and the average elevation of the states above sea level proves the close relationship of intelligence and geography.
   (c) The correlation between memory test scores and tapping rate in a group of 200 eight-year-old children is .20; and the correlation between memory test scores and tapping rate in a group of 100 college freshmen is .10. When the two groups are combined the correlation between these two tests becomes .40. This shows that we must have large groups in order to get high correlations.

ANSWERS

1. $r = .67$.
2. r (intelligence and cancellation) $= -.19$; r (intelligence and controlled association) $= .70$.
4. (a) $\bar{X}_1 = 1.47 X_2 + 2.98 X_3 + 76.95$
   (b) $R_{1(23)} = .60$; $\sigma_{(\text{est. } x_1)} = 10.93$
   (c) 106.50 or 107
5. From X_2 alone, $\sigma_{(\text{est. } x_1)} = 4.0$
   From X_3 alone, $\sigma_{(\text{est. } x_1)} = 4.3$
   From X_2 and X_3, $\sigma_{(\text{est. } x_1)} = 3.5$
6. (a) R increases from .64 to .73
   (b) R increases from .64 to .79
7. $R_{Cr(AB)} = .65$
8. $r_{AC} = .87$; $R_{A(BC)} = 1.00$

16

MULTIPLE CORRELATION IN TEST SELECTION

I. The Wherry-Doolittle Test Selection Method *

The method of solving multiple correlation problems outlined in Section II and Table 52 of Chapter 15 is adequate enough when there are only three (or not more than four) variables. In problems involving more than four variables, however, the mechanics of calculation become almost prohibitive unless some systematic scheme of solution is adopted (p. 387). The Wherry-Doolittle test selection method, to be presented in this section, provides a method of solving certain types of multiple correlation problems with a minimum of statistical labor. This method selects the tests of the battery analytically and adds them one at a time until a maximum R is obtained. To illustrate, suppose we wish to predict aptitude for a certain technical job in a factory. Criterion ratings for job proficiency have been obtained and eight tests tried out as possible indicators of job aptitude. By use of the Wherry-Doolittle method we can (1) select those tests (e.g., three or four) which yield a maximum R with the criterion and discard the rest; (2) calculate the multiple R after the addition of each test, stopping the process when R no longer increases; (3) compute a multiple regression equation from which the criterion can be predicted with the highest precision of which the given list of tests is capable.

The application of the Wherry-Doolittle test selection method to an actual problem is shown in Example (1) below. Steps in computation are outlined in order and are illustrated by reference to the data of Example (1), so that the student may follow the process in detail.

* Stead, W. H., Shartle, C. L., et al., *Occupational Counseling Techniques*, *op. cit.*, Appendix 5.

MULTIPLE CORRELATION IN TEST SELECTION • 405

I. Solution of a multiple correlation problem by the Wherry-Doolittle Test Selection Method

Example (1) In Table 54 are presented the intercorrelations of ten tests administered in the Minnesota study of Mechanical Ability. The criterion—called the "quality" criterion—was a measure of the excellence of mechanical work done by 100 junior high-school boys. The tests in Table 62 are fairly representative of the wide range of measures used in the Minnesota study. Our immediate problem is to choose from among these variables the most valid battery of tests, i.e., those tests which will predict the criterion most efficiently. Selection of tests is made by the Wherry-Doolittle method.

TABLE 54 Intercorrelations of ten tests and a criterion

(Data from the Minnesota Study of Mechnical Ability *)

List of Tests ($N = 100$)
C = Quality criterion
1 = Packing blocks
2 = Card sorting
3 = Minnesota spatial relations boards, A, B, C, D
4 = Paper form boards, A and B
5 = Stenquist Picture I
6 = Stenquist Picture II
7 = Minnesota assembly boxes, A, B, C
8 = Mechanical operations questionnaire
9 = Interest analysis blank
10 = Otis intelligence test

	1	2	3	4	5	6	7	8	9	10
C	.26	.19	.53	.52	.24	.31	.55	.30	.55	.26
1		.52	.34	.14	.18	.21	.30	.00	.34	.00
2			.23	.14	.10	.24	.13	−.12	.23	.08
3				.63	.42	.39	.56	.22	.55	.23
4					.37	.30	.49	.24	.61	.56
5						.54	.46	.24	.23	.11
6							.40	.19	.13	.21
7								.40	.41	.13
8									.25	.18
9										.38

Steps in the solution of Example (1) may be outlined in order.

Step I

Draw up work sheets like those of Tables 55 and 56. The correlation coefficients between tests and criterion are entered in Table 54.

* Paterson, D. G., Elliott, R. M., et al., *Minnesota Mechanical Ability Tests* (Minneapolis: The University of Minnesota Press, 1930), Appendix 4.

Step 2

Enter these coefficients *with signs reversed* in the V_1 row of Table 55.* The numbers heading the columns refer to the tests.

TABLE 55

	\multicolumn{10}{c}{Tests}
	1	2	3	4	5	6	7	8	9	10
V_1	−.260	−.190	−.530	−.520	−.240	−.310	−.550	−.300	−.550	−.260
V_2	−.095	−.118	−.222	−.250	.013	−.090		−.080	−.324	−.188
V_3	−.010	−.049	−.097	−.091	.029	−.103		−.047		−.061
V_4	.005	−.034		−.057	.004	−.046		−.053		−.056
V_5	−.012	−.039			.012	−.039		−.051		−.018

$$\frac{V_1^2}{Z_1} = \frac{(-.550)^2}{1.000}; \quad \frac{V_2^2}{Z_2} = \frac{(.324)^2}{.832}; \quad \frac{V_3^2}{Z_3} = \frac{(.097)^2}{.563}; \quad \frac{V_4^2}{Z_4} = \frac{(.057)^2}{.489}; \quad \frac{V_5^2}{Z_5} = \frac{(-.051)^2}{.829}$$

$$= .3025 \qquad = .1261 \qquad = .0167 \qquad = .0066 \qquad = .0031$$

Step 3

Enter the numbers 1.000 in each column of the row Z_1 in Table 56.

TABLE 56

	\multicolumn{10}{c}{Tests}
	1	2	3	4	5	6	7	8	9	10
Z_1	1.000	1.000	1.000	1.000	1.000	1.000	1.000	1.000	1.000	1.000
Z_2	.910	.983	.686	.760	.788	.840		.840	.832	.983
Z_3	.853	.945	.563	.559	.786	.839		.831		.854
Z_4	.839	.931		.489	.748	.782		.829		.852
Z_5	.796	.927			.737	.775		.829		.637

$$\frac{1}{.832} = 1.202$$

$$\frac{1}{.563} = 1.776$$

$$\frac{1}{.489} = 2.045$$

Step 4

Select that test having the highest $\frac{V_1^2}{Z_1}$ quotient as the *first* test of the battery. From Tables 55 and 56 we find that Tests 7 and 9 both have correlations of .550 with the criterion, and that these are the

---

* Correlation coefficients are assumed to be accurate to three or to four decimals in subsequent calculations to avoid the loss of precision which results when decimals are rounded to two places. (See p. 20.)

largest r's in the table. Either Test 7 or Test 9 could be selected as the first test of our battery. We have chosen Test 7 because it is the more objective measure of performance.

Step 5

Apply the Wherry shrinkage formula

$$\bar{R}^2 = 1 - K^2\left(\frac{N-1}{N-m}\right) \tag{109}$$

in which $\bar{R}$ is the "shrunken" multiple correlation coefficient, the coefficient from which chance error has been removed.* This corrected R may be calculated in a systematic way as follows:

(1) Prepare a work sheet similar to that shown in Table 57.

TABLE 57

a	b	c	d	e	f	g	
m	$\dfrac{V_m^2}{Z_m}$	K^2	$\dfrac{N-1}{N-m}$	$\bar{K}^2$	$\bar{R}^2$	$\bar{R}$	Test #
0		1.000	$(N-100)$				
1	.3025	.6975	1.000	.6975	.3025	.5500	7
2	.1261	.5714	1.010	.5771	.4229	.6503	9
3	.0167	.5547	1.021	.5663	.4337	.6586	3
4	.0066	.5481	1.031	.5651	.4349	.6595	4
5	.0031	.5450	1.042	.5679	.4321	.6573	8

(2) Enter 1.000 in column c, row 0, under K^2. Enter $N = 100$ in column d.

(3) Enter the quotient $\dfrac{V_1^2}{Z_1}$ in column b, row 1. $\dfrac{V_1^2}{Z_1} = \dfrac{(-.550)^2}{1.000} = .3025$ †

(4) Subtract .3025 from 1.000 to give .6975 as the entry in column c under K^2.

(5) Find the quotient $\dfrac{(N-1)}{(N-m)}$ and record it in column d. $(N-1) = 99$; and since m (number of tests selected) is 1, $(N-m)$ also equals 99 and $\dfrac{(N-1)}{(N-m)} = 1.000$.

---

* Wherry, R. J., "A New Formula for Predicting the Shrinkage of the Coefficient of Multiple Correlation," *Annals of Mathematical Statistics*, 1931, Vol. 2. 440–451.

† Quotient is taken to four decimals (p. 406).

(6) Write the product of columns c and d in column e: $.6975 \times 1.000 = .6975$.
(7) Subtract the column e entry from 1.000 to obtain $\bar{R}^2$ (the shrunken multiple correlation coefficient) in column f. In Table 57 the $\bar{R}^2$ entry, of course, is .3025.
(8) Find the square root of the column f entry and enter the result in column g under $\bar{R}$. Our entry is .5500, the correlation of Test 7 with the criterion. No correction for chance errors is necessary for one test.

Step 6

To aid in the selection of a *second* test to be added to our battery of one, a work sheet similar to that shown in Table 58 should be prepared. Calculations in Table 58 are as follows:

(1) Leave a_1 row blank.
(2) Enter in row b_1 the correlations of Test 7 (*first* selected test) with each of the other tests in Table 54. These r's are .300, .130, .560, etc., and are entered in the columns numbered to correspond to the tests. Enter 1.000 in the column for Test 7. In column $-C$ enter the correlation of Test 7 with the criterion *with sign reversed,* i.e., as $-.550$.
(3) Write the algebraic sum of the b_1 entries in the "Check Sum" column. This sum is 3.730.
(4) Multiply each b_1 entry by the *negative reciprocal* of the b_1 entry for Test 7, the *first* selected test. Enter these products in the c_1 row. Since the negative reciprocal of Test 7's b_1 entry is -1.000, we need simply write the b_1 entries in the c_1 row with signs reversed.

Step 7

Draw a vertical line under Test 7 in Table 55 to show that it has been selected. To select a *second* test proceed as follows:

(1) To each V_1 entry in Table 55, add algebraically the product of the b_1 entry in the criterion $(-C)$ column of Table 58 by the c_1 entry for each of the other tests. Enter results in the V_2 row. The formula for V_2 is $V_2 = V_1 + b_1$ (criterion) $\times c_1$ (each test). To illustrate, from Table 58 and Table 55 we have

For Test 1: $V_2 = -.260 + (-.550) \times (-.300) =$
$-.260 + .165 = -.095$

TABLE 58

	1	2	3	4	5	6	7	8	9	10	−C	Check Sum	Test #
a_1													7
b_1	.300	.130	.560	.490	.460	.400	1.000	.400	.410	.130	−.550	3.730	
c_1	−.300	−.130	−.560	−.490	−.460	−.400	−1.000	−.400	−.410	−.130	.550	−3.730	
a_2	.340	.230	.550	.610	.230	.130	.410	.250	1.000	.380	−.550	3.580	9
b_2	.217	.177	.320	.409	.041	−.034		.086	.832	.327	−.324	2.051	
c_2	−.261	−.213	−.385	−.492	−.049	.041		−.103	−1.000	−.393	.389	−2.465	
a_3	.340	.230	1.000	.630	.420	.390	.560	.220	.550	.230	−.530	4.040	3
b_3	.088	.089	.563	.199	.146	.179		−.037		.031	−.097	1.161	
c_3	−.156	−.158	−1.000	−.353	−.259	−.318		.066		−.055	.172	−2.062	
a_4	.140	.140	.630	1.000	.370	.300	.490	.240	.610	.560	−.520	3.960	4
b_4	−.145	−.042		.489	.073	.058		.015		.324	−.057	.715	
c_4	.297	.086		−1.000	−.149	−.119		−.031		−.663	.117	−1.462	

For Test 4: $V_2 = -.520 + (-.550) \times (-.490) =$
$-.520 + .270 = -.250$

For Test 9: $V_2 = -.550 + (-.550) \times (-.410) =$
$-.550 + .226 = -.324$

(2) To each Z_1 in Table 56 add algebraically the product of the b_1 and c_1 entries for each test got from Table 58. Enter these results in the Z_2 row. The formula is $Z_2 = Z_1 + b_1$ (a given test) $\times c_1$ (same test). To illustrate, from Tables 55 and 58.

For Test 1: $Z_2 = 1.000 + (.300) \times (-.300) = 1.000 - .090$
$= .910$

For Test 4: $Z_2 = 1.000 + (.490) \times (-.490) = 1.000 - .240$
$= .760$

For Test 9: $Z_2 = 1.000 + (.410) \times (-.410) = 1.000 - .168$
$= .832$

Step 8

Now select the test having the largest $\dfrac{V_2^2}{Z_2}$ quotient, as the *second* test for our battery. The quantity $\dfrac{V_2^2}{Z_2}$ is a measure of the amount which the second test contributes to the squared multiple correlation coefficient, $\bar{R}^2$. From Tables 55 and 56 we find that Test 9 has the largest $\dfrac{V_2^2}{Z_2}$ quotient: $\dfrac{(.324)^2}{.832} = .1261$.

Step 9

To calculate the new multiple correlation coefficient when Test 9 is added to Test 7, proceed as follows:

(1) The quantity $.1261 \left(\dfrac{V_2^2}{Z_2}\right)$ is entered in column b, row 2 of Table 57.

(2) Subtract the ratio $\dfrac{V_2^2}{Z_2}$ from the K^2 entry in column c, row 1, and enter the result in column c, row 2; e.g., for the entry in column c, row 2, we have $.6975 - .1261$, or $.5714$.

(3) Find the quotient $\dfrac{(N-1)}{(N-m)}$. Since $N = 100$ and m (number of tests chosen) $= 2$, we have $\dfrac{(N-1)}{(N-m)}$ or $\dfrac{99}{98} = 1.010$, as the column d, row 2 entry.

(4) Record the product of the c and d columns in column e: .5714 × 1.010 = .5771.
(5) Subtract .5771 (column e) from 1.000 to give .4229 as the entry in column f, row 2.
(6) Take the square root of .4229 and enter the result, .6503, in column g. This is the multiple coefficent $\bar{R}$ corrected for chance errors. It is clear that by adding Test 9 to Test 7 we increase $\bar{R}$ from .5500 to .6503, a substantial gain.

Step 10

Since $\bar{R}$ for Tests 7 and 9 is larger than the correlation for Test 7 alone, we proceed to add a *third* test in the hope of further increasing the multiple $\bar{R}$. The procedure is shown in Step 11.

Step 11

Return to Table 58 and

(1) Record in the a_2 row the correlation coefficient of the *second* selected test (i.e., Test 9) with each of the other tests *and* with the criterion. (Read r's from Table 54.) The correlation of Test 9 with the criterion is entered *with sign reversed* (i.e., as $-.550$).
(2) Enter the algebraic sum of the a_2 entries (i.e., 3.580) in the Check Sum column.
(3) Draw a vertical line down through the b_2 and c_2 rows for Test 7, the *first* selected test. This indicates that Test 7 has already been chosen.
(4) Compute the b_2 entry for each test by adding to the a_2 entry the product of the b_1 entry of the given test by the c_1 entry of the *second* selected test (i.e., Test 9). The formula is $b_2 = a_2 + b_1$ (given test) $\times c_1$ (*second* selected test). To illustrate:

For Test 2: $b_2 = .230 + (.130)(-.410) = .230 - .053 = .177$

For Test 6: $b_2 = .130 + (.400)(-.410) = .130 - .164 = -.034$

For Test 10: $b_2 = .380 + (.130)(-.410) = .380 - .053 = .327$

Compute b_2 entries for criterion and Check Sum column in

the same way. For the criterion column we have $-.550 + (-.550)(-.410)$ or $-.324$. For the Check Sum column we have $3.580 + (3.730)(-.410)$ or 2.051.

(5) There are three checks for the b_2 row. (a) The entry for the *second* selected test (Test 9) should equal the Z_2 entry for the same test in Table 56. Note that both entries are .832. (b) The entry in the criterion column should equal the V_2 entry of the second selected test (Test 9) in Table 55; both entries are $-.324$. (c) The entry in the Check Sum column should equal the sum of all of the entries in the b_2 rows. Adding .217, .177, .320, etc., we get 2.051, checking our calculations to the third decimal.

(6) Multiply each b_2 entry by the *negative reciprocal* of the b_2 entry for the *second* selected test (Test 9), and record results in the c_2 row. The negative reciprocal of .832 is -1.202. The c_2 entry for Test 1 is $.217 \times -1.202$ or $-.261$; for Test 2, $-.177 \times -1.202$ or $-.213$; and so on for the other tests. For the criterion column the c_2 entry is $(-.324) \times -1.202$ or $.389$; and for the Check Sum the c_2 entry is 2.051×-1.202 or -2.465.

(7) There are three checks for the c_2 entries. (a) The c_2 row entry of the second selected test (Test 9) should be -1.000. (b) The c_2 entry in the Check Sum column should equal the sum of all c_2 entries. Adding the c_2 entries in Table 58, we find the sum to be -2.465, the Check Sum entry. (c) The product of the b_2 and c_2 entries in the criterion column should equal the quotient $\dfrac{V_2^2}{Z_2}$ in column b, row 2, of Table 57 in absolute value. Note that the product $(-.324 \times .389) = -.1261$, thus checking our entry (disregard signs).

Step 12

Draw a vertical line under Test 9 in Table 55, to indicate that it has been selected as our second test. Then proceed as in Step 7 to compute V_3 and Z_3 in order to select a *third* test. The formula for V_3 is $V_3 = V_2 + b_2$ (criterion) $\times c_2$ (each test). The formula for Z_3 is $Z_3 = Z_2 + b_2$ (a given test) $\times c_2$ (same test). The third selected test is that one which has the largest $\dfrac{V_3^2}{Z_3}$ quotient in Table 55. This is Test 3, for which $V_3 = -.222 + (-.324)(-.385)$ or $-.097$; and $Z_3 = .686 + (.320)(-.385) = .563$. The quotient $\dfrac{V_3{}^2}{Z_3} = .0167$.

Step 13

Entering $.0167 \left(\dfrac{V_3{}^2}{Z_3}\right)$ in column b, row 3, of Table 57, follow the procedure of Step 9 to get $\bar{R} = .6586$. Note that $\dfrac{(N-1)}{(N-m)} = 99/97$ or 1.021; and that the new $\bar{R}$ is larger than the $.6503$ found for the two tests, 7 and 9. We include Test 3 in our battery, therefore, and proceed to calculate a_3, b_3, and c_3 (Table 58), following Step 11, in order to select a *fourth* test.

Step 14

The a_3 entries in Table 58 are the correlations of Test 3 with each of the other tests including the criterion. The criterion correlation is entered in the $-C$ column with a negative sign (i.e., as $-.530$).

(1) The formula for b_3 is $b_3 = a_3 + b_1$ (given test) $\times c_1$ (*third* selected test) $+ b_2$ (given test) $\times c_2$ (*third* selected test). To illustrate,

For Test 1: $b_3 = .340 + (.300)(-.560) + (.217)(-.385)$
$= .088$

For Test 4: $b_3 = .630 + (.490)(-.560) + (.409)(-.385)$
$= .199$

Check the b_3 entries by Step 11 (5). (a) Note that the b_3 entry for the *third* selected test (Test 3) equals the Z_3 entry for Test 3 in Table 56, namely, $.563$. (b) The entry in the criterion column equals the V_3 entry of the *third* selected test (Test 3) in Table 55, i.e., $-.097$. (c) The Check Sum entry (1.161) equals the sum of the entries in the b_3 row.

(2) The formula for c_3 is $b_3 \times$ the *negative reciprocal* of the b_3 entry for the *third* selected test (Test 3). The negative reciprocal of $.563$ is -1.776. To illustrate the calculation for Test 5, $c_3 = .146 \times -1.776 = -.259$. Check the c_3 entries by Step 11 (7). (a) The c_3 row entry of the *third* selected test (Test 3) equals -1.000. (b) The c_3 entry in the Check Sum column, namely, -2.062, equals the sum of the c_3

row. (c) The product of the b_3 and c_3 entries in the criterion column (namely, $-.097 \times .172$) equals the quotient $\left(\dfrac{V_3{}^2}{Z_3}\right)$ (i.e., .0167) in absolute value.

Step 15

Repeat Step 12 to find V_4 and Z_4. The formula for V_4 is $V_4 = V_3 + b_3$ (criterion) $\times c_3$ (each test). Also, the formula for Z_4 is $Z_3 + b_3$ (a given test) $\times c_3$ (same test). For Test 4, $V_4 = -.091 + (-.097)(-.353)$ or $-.057$; and $Z_4 = .559 + (.199)$ $(-.353)$ or .489. The quotient, $\dfrac{V_4{}^2}{Z_4}$, equals $\dfrac{(-.057)^2}{.489}$ or .0066. While none of the V_4 entries is large, Test 4 has the largest $\dfrac{V_4{}^2}{Z_4}$ quotient, and hence is selected as our *fourth* test. Enter .0066 $\left(\dfrac{V_4{}^2}{Z_4}\right)$ in column b, row 4, of Table 57. Follow the procedure of Step 9 to get $\bar{R} = .6595$. Note that $\dfrac{(N-1)}{(N-m)}$ is 99/96 or 1.031; and that the new $\bar{R}$ is but slightly larger than the $\bar{R}$ of .6586 found for the three tests, 7, 9, and 3. When $\bar{R}$ decreases or fails to increase, there is no point in adding new tests to the battery. The increase in $\bar{R}$ is so small as a result of adding Test 4 that it is hardly profitable to enlarge our battery by a fifth test. We shall add a fifth test, however, in order to illustrate a further step in the selection process.

Step 16

To choose a *fifth* test, calculate a_4, b_4, and c_4, following Step 11, and enter the results in Table 58. The a_4 entries are the correlations of the *fourth* selected test (Test 4) with each of the other tests including the criterion (*with sign reversed*).

(1) The formula for b_4 may readily be written by analogy to the formulas for b_3 and b_2 as follows: $b_4 = a_4 + b_1$ (given test) $\times c_1$ (*fourth* selected test) $+ b_2$ (given test) $\times c_2$ (*fourth* selected test) $+ b_3$ (given test) $\times c_3$ (*fourth* selected test). To illustrate

For Test 6: $b_4 = .300 + (.400)(-.490) + (-.034)(-.492)$
$+ (.179)(-.353) = .058$

For Test 10: $b_4 = .560 + (.130)(-.490) + (.337)(-.492)$
$+ (.031)(-.353) = .324$

Check the b_4 entries by Step 11 (5). (a) The b_4 entry for the *fourth* selected test (Test 4) equals the Z_4 entry for Test 4 in Table 56, namely, .489. (b) The entry in the criterion column equals the V_4 entry of the *fourth* selected test (Test 4), i.e., $-.057$. (c) The Check Sum (.715) equals the sum of the entries in the b_4 row.

(2) To find the entries c_4, multiply each b_4 by the *negative reciprocal* of the b_4 entry for the *fourth* selected test (Test 4). The negative reciprocal of .489 is -2.045. To illustrate,

For Test 1: $c_4 = -.145 \times -2.045 = .297$.

Check the c_4 entries by Step 11 (7). (a) The c_4 row entry of the *fourth* selected test (Test 4) equals -1.000. (b) The c_4 entry in the Check Sum column, namely, -1.462, equals the sum of the c_4 row. (c) The product of the b_4 and c_4 entries in the criterion column (namely, $-.057 \times .117$) equals the quotient $\dfrac{V_4^2}{Z_4}$ (i.e., .0066) in absolute value.

Step 17

Repeat Step 12 to find V_5 and Z_5. $V_5 = V_4 + b_4$ (criterion) $\times c_4$ (each test); and $Z_5 = Z_4 + b_4$ (a given test) $\times c_4$ (same test). Test 8 has the largest $\left(\dfrac{V_5^2}{Z_5}\right)$ quotient (i.e., .0031) and this number is entered in column b, row 5, of Table 57. Following Step 9, we get $\bar{R} = .6573$. This multiple correlation coefficient is smaller than the preceding $\bar{R}$. We need go no further, therefore, as we have reached the point of diminishing returns and the addition of a sixth test will not increase the multiple $\bar{R}$. It may be noted that four (really three) tests constitute a battery which has the highest validity of any combination of tests chosen from our list of ten. The multiple $\bar{R}$ between the criterion and all ten tests would be somewhat lower—when corrected for chance error—than the $\bar{R}$ we have found for our battery of four tests. The Wherry-Doolittle method not only selects the most economical battery but saves a large amount of statistical work.

2. Calculation of the multiple regression equation for tests selected by the Wherry-Doolittle Method

Steps involved in setting up a multiple regression equation for the tests selected in Table 58 may be set down as follows:

TABLE 59

	7	9	3	4	− C
C_1	− 1.000	− .410	− .560	− .490	.550
C_2		− 1.000	− .385	− .492	.389
C_3			− 1.000	− .353	.172
C_4				− 1.000	.117

Step 1

Draw up a work sheet like that shown in Table 59. Enter the C entries for the four selected tests (namely, 7, 9, 3, and 4) and for the criterion, following the order in which the tests were selected for the battery. When equated to zero, each row in Table 59 is an equation defining the *beta* weights.

For our four tests, the equations are

$$-1.000\beta_7 - .410\beta_9 - .560\beta_3 - .490\beta_4 + .550 = 0$$
$$-1.000\beta_9 - .385\beta_3 - .492\beta_4 + .389 = 0$$
$$-1.000\beta_3 - .353\beta_4 + .172 = 0$$
$$-1.000\beta_4 + .117 = 0$$

Step 2

Solve the fourth equation to find $\beta_4 = .117$.

Step 3

Substitute for $\beta_4 = .117$ in the third equation to get $\beta_3 = .131$.

Step 4

Substitute for β_3 and β_4 in the second equation to get $\beta_9 = .280$. Finally, substitute for β_3, β_4, and β_9 in the first equation to get $\beta_7 = .305$.

Step 5

The regression equation for predicting the criterion from the four selected tests (7, 9, 3, and 4) may be written in σ-score form by means of formula (104), page 393, as follows:

$$\bar{z}_c = \beta_7 z_7 + \beta_9 z_9 + \beta_3 z_3 + \beta_4 z_4$$

in which $\beta_7 = \beta_{c7.934}$; $\beta_9 = \beta_{c9.734}$; $\beta_3 = \beta_{c3.974}$; $\beta_4 = \beta_{c4.973}$. Substituting for the β's we have

$$\bar{z}_c = .305 z_7 + .280 z_9 + .131 z_3 + .117 z_4.$$

To predict the criterion score of any subject in our group, substitute his scores in Tests 7, 9, 3, and 4 (expressed as σ-scores) in this equation.

Step 6

To write the regression equation in score form the β's must be transformed into b's by means of formula (103), page 393, as follows:

$$b_7 = \frac{\sigma_c}{\sigma_7}\beta_7; \quad b_9 = \frac{\sigma_c}{\sigma_9}\beta_9; \quad b_3 = \frac{\sigma_c}{\sigma_3}\beta_3; \quad b_4 = \frac{\sigma_c}{\sigma_4}\beta_4.$$

The σ's are the SD's of the test scores: σ_7 of Test 7, σ_9 of Test 9, σ_c of the criterion, etc. In general, $b_p = \frac{\sigma_c}{\sigma_p}\beta_p$.

Step 7

The regression equation in score form may now be written

$$\overline{X}_c = b_7 X_7 + b_9 X_9 + b_3 X_3 + b_4 X_4 + K \qquad *\text{ (99) page 391}$$

and the $\sigma_{est.X_c} = \sigma_c \sqrt{1 - \overline{R}^2_{c(7934)}}$ (33) page 162

3. Checking the β weights and multiple R

Step 1

The β weights may be checked by formula (108), page 396 in which R is expressed in terms of beta coefficients. In the present example, we have

$$R^2_{c(7934)} = \beta_7 r_{c7} + \beta_9 r_{c9} + \beta_3 r_{c3} + \beta_4 r_{c4}$$

in which c equals the criterion and the r's are the correlations between the criterion (c) and the Tests, 7, 9, 3, and 4. Substituting for the r's and β's (computed in the last section) we have

$$R^2_{c(7934)} = .305 \times .550 + .280 \times .550 + .131 \times .530 + .117 \times .520$$
$$= .1678 + .1540 + .0694 + .0608 = .4520$$
$$R_{c(7934)} = .6723$$

From $R^2_{c(7934)}$ we know that our battery accounts for 45% of the variance of the criterion. Also (p. 396) our four tests (7, 9, 3, and 4) contribute 17%, 15%, 7%, and 6%, respectively, to the variance of the criterion.

* This equation is not written for our four tests because means and SD's are not given in Table 54.

Step 2

The R^2 of .4520 calculated above should equal $(1 - K^2)$ when K^2 is taken from column c, row 4, in Table 57. From Table 57 we find that $1 - K^2 = 1 - .5481$ or .4519 which checks the R^2 found above —and hence the β weights—very closely.

Step 3

It will be noted that the multiple correlation coefficient of .6723 found above is somewhat larger than the shrunken $\bar{R}$ of .6595 found between the criterion and our battery of four tests in Table 57. The multiple correlation coefficient obtained from a sample always tends —through the operation of chance errors—to be *larger* than the correlation in the population from which the sample was drawn, especially when N is small or the number of test variables large. For this reason, the calculated R must be "adjusted" in order to give us a better estimate of the correlation in the population.* The relationship of the $\bar{R}$, corrected for chance errors, to the R as usually calculated, is given by the following equation:

$$\bar{R}^2 = \frac{(N-1)R^2 - (m-1)}{(N-m)} \tag{110}$$

(*relation of* R *to* R̄ *corrected for chance errors*)

Substituting .4520 for R^2, 99 for $(N-1)$, 96 for $(N-m)$ and 3 for $(m-1)$, we have from (110) that

$$\bar{R}^2 = \frac{99 \times .4520 - 3}{96} = .4349$$

and

$$\bar{R} = .6595 \text{ (see Table 57)}$$

The $\bar{R}$ of .6595 is the corrected multiple correlation between our criterion and test battery, or the multiple correlation coefficient estimated for the population from which our sample was drawn. In the present problem, shrinkage in multiple R is quite small (.6723 − .6595 = .0128) as the sample is fairly large and there are only four tests in the multiple regression equation.

* Ezekiel, M., *Methods of Correlation Analysis, op. cit.*, 323–324.

II. Limitations to the Use of Partial and Multiple Correlation

Certain cautions in the use of partial and multiple correlation may be indicated in concluding this chapter.

(1) In order that partial coefficients of correlation be valid measures of relationship, it is necessary that all zero order coefficients be computed from data in which the regression is linear.

(2) The number of cases in a multiple correlation problem should be large, especially if there are a number of variables; otherwise the coefficients calculated from the data will have little significance. Coefficients which are misleadingly high or low may be obtained when studies which involve many variables are based on relatively few cases. The question of accuracy of computation is also involved. A general rule advocated by many workers is that results should be carried to as many decimals as there are variables in the problem. How strictly this rule is to be followed must depend upon the accuracy of the original measures.

(3) A serious limitation to a clear-cut interpretation of a partial r arises from the fact that most of the tests employed by psychologists probably depend upon a large number of "determiners." When we "partial out" the influence of clear-cut and relatively objective factors such as age, height, school grade, etc., we have a reasonably clear notion of what the "partials" mean. But when we attempt to render variability due to "logical memory" constant by partialling out memory test scores from the correlation between general intelligence test scores and educational achievement, the result is by no means so unequivocal. The abilities determining the scores in general intelligence *and* in school achievement undoubtedly overlap the memory test in other respects than in the "memory" involved. Partialling out a memory test score from the correlation between general intelligence and educational achievement, therefore, will render constant the influence of many factors not strictly "memory," i.e., partial out too much.

To illustrate this point again it would be fallacious to interpret the partial correlation between reading comprehension and arithmetic, say, with the influence of "general intelligence" partialled out, as giving the net relationship between these two variables for a constant degree of intelligence. Both reading and arithmetic enter with heavy, but unknown, weight into most general intelligence tests; hence the partial correlation between these two, for general intelligence constant, cannot be interpreted in a clear-cut and meaningful way.

Partial r's obtained from psychological and educational tests, though often difficult to interpret, may be used in multiple regression equations when the purpose is to determine the relative weight to be assigned the various tests of a battery. But we should be cautious in attempting to give psychological meaning to such residual, i.e., partial, r's. Several writers have discussed this problem, and should be referred to by the investigator who plans to use partial and multiple correlation extensively.*

(4) Perhaps the chief limitation to R, the coefficient of multiple correlation, is the fact that, since it is always positive, variable errors of sampling tend to accumulate and thus make the coefficient too large. A correction to be applied to R, when the sample is small and the number of variables large, has been given on page 407. This correction gives the value which R would most probably take in the population from which our sample was drawn.

PROBLEMS

1. The following data † were assembled for sixteen large cities (of around 500,000 inhabitants) in a study of factors making for variation in crime.

X_c (criterion) = crime rate: number known offenses per 1000 inhabitants

X_1 = percentage of male inhabitants

X_2 = percentage of male native whites of native parentage

X_3 = percentage of foreign-born males

X_4 = number children under five per 1000 married women fifteen to forty-four years old

X_5 = number Negroes per 100 of population

X_6 = number male children of foreign-born parents per 100 of population

X_7 = number males and females ten years and over, in manufacturing, per 100 of population

---

*Burks, B. S., "On the Inadequacy of the Partial and Multiple Correlation Technique," *Journal of Educational Psychology*, 1926, 17, 532–540.

Moore, T. V., "Partial Correlations," *Studies in Psychology and Psychiatry from the Catholic University of America*, 1932, 3, 1–39.

† Ogburn, W. F., "Factors in the Variation of Crime Among Cities," *Journal of the American Statistical Association*, 1935, 30, 12–34.

$M_c = 19.9$ $M_1 = 49.2$ $M_2 = 22.8$ $M_3 = 10.2$ $M_4 = 481.4$ $M_5 = 4.7$
$\sigma_c = 7.9$ $\sigma_1 = 1.3$ $\sigma_2 = 7.2$ $\sigma_3 = 4.6$ $\sigma_4 = 74.4$ $\sigma_5 = 4.0$
$M_6 = 13.1$ $M_7 = 21.7$
$\sigma_6 = 4.2$ $\sigma_7 = 4.3$

Intercorrelations

	1	2	3	4	5	6	7
C	.44	.44	−.34	−.31	.51	−.54	−.20
1		.01	.25	−.19	−.15	.01	.22
2			−.92	−.54	.55	−.93	−.30
3				.44	−.68	.82	.40
4					−.06	.52	.74
5						−.67	−.14
6							.21

(a) By means of the Wherry-Doolittle method select those variables which give a maximum correlation with the criterion.
(b) Work out the regression equation in score form (p. 393) and $\sigma_{(\text{est. } x_c)}$.
(c) Determine the independent contribution of each of the selected factors to crime rate (to R^2).
(d) Compare R and $\bar{R}$. Why is the adjustment fairly large? (see p. 418)

2. (a) What is the probable crime rate (from Problem 1) for a city in which $X_6 = 15.0$, $X_1 = 50\%$, $X_5 = 6.0$ and $X_7 = 20.0$?
(b) For a city in which $X_6 = 13$, $X_1 = 48\%$, $X_5 = 5.0$ and $X_7 = 22.0$?
(c) By how much does the use of multiple R reduce $\sigma_{(\text{est. } x_c)}$?

3. In Problem 4, page 402:
(a) Work out the regression equation using the Wherry-Doolittle method.
(b) How much shrinkage is there when $R_{1(23)}$ is corrected for chance errors (p. 407)?

ANSWERS

1. (a) The $\bar{R}$'s are, for Test 6, .540; for Tests 6 and 1, .674; for Tests 6, 1, and 5, .713; for Tests 6, 1, 5, and 7, .722. $\bar{R}$ drops to .702, when Test 4 is added.
(b) $\bar{X}_c = -.42X_6 + 3.35X_1 + .82X_5 - .40X_7 - 134.59$.
$\sigma_{(\text{est. } x_c)} = 5.47$
(c) $R^2_{c(6157)} = .121 + .242 + .210 + .043$. Tests 6, 1, 5, and 7 contribute 12%, 24%, 21%, and 4%, respectively.
(d) $R = .785$; $\bar{R} = .722$; shrinkage is .063.

2. (a) 23.53
   (b) 16.05
   (c) From 7.9 to 5.5 or 30%
3. (b) $\overline{R}_{1(23)}$ is .59; $R_{1(23)} = .60$

APPENDIX OF TABLES

A. Areas, Normal Probability Curve.
B. Ordinates of the Normal Probability Curve.
C. Pearson r into Equivalent z.
D. Table of t.
E. Chi-square Table
F. F-Table.
G. Calculation of T-Scores
H. Mean σ-distances from the mean, of various percents of a normal distribution.
I. To Infer $\sqrt{1-r^2}$ from r.
J. Significance of Coefficients of Correlation

TABLE A   Fractional parts of the total area (taken as 10,000) under the normal probability curve, corresponding to distances on the baseline between the mean and successive points laid off from the mean in units of standard deviation

Example: between the mean and a point 1.38σ $\left(\dfrac{x}{\sigma} = 1.38\right)$ are found 41.62% of the entire area under the curve.

$\dfrac{x}{\sigma}$	.00	.01	.02	.03	.04	.05	.06	.07	.08	.09
0.0	0000	0040	0080	0120	0160	0199	0239	0279	0319	0359
0.1	0398	0438	0478	0517	0557	0596	0636	0675	0714	0753
0.2	0793	0832	0871	0910	0948	0987	1026	1064	1103	1141
0.3	1179	1217	1255	1293	1331	1368	1406	1443	1480	1517
0.4	1554	1591	1628	1664	1700	1736	1772	1808	1844	1879
0.5	1915	1950	1985	2019	2054	2088	2123	2157	2190	2224
0.6	2257	2291	2324	2357	2389	2422	2454	2486	2517	2549
0.7	2580	2611	2642	2673	2704	2734	2764	2794	2823	2852
0.8	2881	2910	2939	2967	2995	3023	3051	3078	3106	3133
0.9	3159	3186	3212	3238	3264	3290	3315	3340	3365	3389
1.0	3413	3438	3461	3485	3508	3531	3554	3577	3599	3621
1.1	3643	3665	3686	3708	3729	3749	3770	3790	3810	3830
1.2	3849	3869	3888	3907	3925	3944	3962	3980	3997	4015
1.3	4032	4049	4066	4082	4099	4115	4131	4147	4162	4177
1.4	4192	4207	4222	4236	4251	4265	4279	4292	4306	4319
1.5	4332	4345	4357	4370	4383	4394	4406	4418	4429	4441
1.6	4452	4463	4474	4484	4495	4505	4515	4525	4535	4545
1.7	4554	4564	4573	4582	4591	4599	4608	4616	4625	4633
1.8	4641	4649	4656	4664	4671	4678	4686	4693	4699	4706
1.9	4713	4719	4726	4732	4738	4744	4750	4756	4761	4767
2.0	4772	4778	4783	4788	4793	4798	4803	4808	4812	4817
2.1	4821	4826	4830	4834	4838	4842	4846	4850	4854	4857
2.2	4861	4864	4868	4871	4875	4878	4881	4884	4887	4890
2.3	4893	4896	4898	4901	4904	4906	4909	4911	4913	4916
2.4	4918	4920	4922	4925	4927	4929	4931	4932	4934	4936
2.5	4938	4940	4941	4943	4945	4946	4948	4949	4951	4952
2.6	4953	4955	4956	4957	4959	4960	4961	4962	4963	4964
2.7	4965	4966	4967	4968	4969	4970	4971	4972	4973	4974
2.8	4974	4975	4976	4977	4977	4978	4979	4979	4980	4981
2.9	4981	4982	4982	4983	4984	4984	4985	4985	4986	4986
3.0	4986.5	4986.9	4987.4	4987.8	4988.2	4988.6	4988.9	4989.3	4989.7	4990.0
3.1	4990.3	4990.6	4991.0	4991.3	4991.6	4991.8	4992.1	4992.4	4992.6	4992 9
3.2	4993.129									
3.3	4995.166									
3.4	4996.631									
3.5	4997.674									
3.6	4998.409									
3.7	4998.922									
3.8	4999.277									
3.9	4999.519									
4.0	4999.683									
4.5	4999.966									
5.0	4999.997133									

TABLE B Ordinates of the normal probability curve expressed as fractional parts of the mean ordinate, y_o

The height of the ordinate erected at the mean can be computed from $y_o = \dfrac{N}{\sigma\sqrt{2\pi}}$ where $\sqrt{2\pi} = 2.51$ and $\dfrac{1}{\sqrt{2\pi}} = .3989$. The height of any other ordinate, in terms of y_o, can be read from the table when one knows the distance which the ordinate is from the mean. For example: the height of an ordinate a distance of -2.37σ from the mean is $.06029\ y_o$. Decimals have been omitted in the body of the table.

$\dfrac{x}{\sigma}$	0	1	2	3	4	5	6	7	8	9
0.0	100000	99995	99980	99955	99920	99875	99820	99755	99685	99596
0.1	99501	99396	99283	99158	99025	98881	98728	98565	98393	98211
0.2	98020	97819	97609	97390	97161	96923	96676	96420	96156	95882
0.3	95600	95309	95010	94702	94387	94055	93723	93382	93024	92677
0.4	92312	91399	91558	91169	90774	90371	89961	89543	89119	88688
0.5	88250	87805	87353	86896	86432	85962	85488	85006	84519	84060
0.6	83527	83023	82514	82010	81481	80957	80429	79896	79359	78817
0.7	78270	77721	77167	76610	76048	75484	74916	74342	73769	73193
0.8	72615	72033	71448	70861	70272	69681	69087	68493	67896	67298
0.9	66689	66097	65494	64891	64287	63683	63077	62472	61865	61259
1.0	60653	60047	59440	58834	58228	57623	57017	56414	55810	55209
1.1	54607	54007	53409	52812	52214	51620	51027	50437	49848	49260
1.2	48675	48092	47511	46933	46357	45783	45212	44644	44078	43516
1.3	42956	42399	41845	41294	40747	40202	39661	39123	38569	38058
1.4	37531	37007	36487	35971	35459	34950	34445	33944	33447	32954
1.5	32465	31980	31500	31023	30550	30082	29618	29158	28702	28251
1.6	27804	27361	26923	26489	26059	25634	25213	24797	24385	23978
1.7	23575	23176	22782	22392	22008	21627	21251	20879	20511	20148
1.8	19790	19436	19086	18741	18400	18064	17732	17404	17081	16762
1.9	16448	16137	15831	15530	15232	14939	14650	14364	14083	13806
2.0	13534	13265	13000	12740	12483	12230	11981	11737	11496	11259
2.1	11025	10795	10570	10347	10129	09914	09702	09495	09290	09090
2.2	08892	08698	08507	08320	08136	07956	07778	07604	07433	07265
2.3	07100	06939	06780	06624	06471	06321	06174	06029	05888	05750
2.4	05614	05481	05350	05222	05096	04973	04852	04734	04618	04505
2.5	04394	04285	04179	04074	03972	03873	03775	03680	03586	03494
2.6	03405	03317	03232	03148	03066	02986	02908	02831	02757	02684
2.7	02612	02542	02474	02408	02343	02280	02218	02157	02098	02040
2.8	01984	01929	01876	01823	01772	01723	01674	01627	01581	01536
2.9	01492	01449	01408	01367	01328	01288	01252	01215	01179	01145
3.0	01111	00819	00598	00432	00309	00219	00153	00106	00073	00050
4.0	00034	00022	00015	00010	00006	00004	00003	00002	00001	00001
5.0	00000									

TABLE C Conversion of a Pearson r into a corresponding Fisher's z coefficient

r	z	r	z	r	z	r	z	r	z	r	z
.25	.26	.40	.42	.55	.62	.70	.87	.85	1.26	.950	1.83
.26	.27	.41	.44	.56	.63	.71	.89	.86	1.29	.955	1.89
.27	.28	.42	.45	.57	.65	.72	.91	.87	1.33	.960	1.95
.28	.29	.43	.46	.58	.66	.73	.93	.88	1.38	.965	2.01
.29	.30	.44	.47	.59	.68	.74	.95	.89	1.42	.970	2.09
.30	.31	.45	.48	.60	.69	.75	.97	.90	1.47	.975	2.18
.31	.32	.46	.50	.61	.71	.76	1.00	.905	1.50	.980	2.30
.32	.33	.47	.51	.62	.73	.77	1.02	.910	1.53	.985	2.44
.33	.34	.48	.52	.63	.74	.78	1.05	.915	1.56	.990	2.65
.34	.35	.49	.54	.64	.76	.79	1.07	.920	1.59	.995	2.99
.35	.37	.50	.55	.65	.78	.80	1.10	.925	1.62		
.36	.38	.51	.56	.66	.79	.81	1.13	.930	1.66		
.37	.39	.52	.58	.67	.81	.82	1.16	.935	1.70		
.38	.40	.53	.59	.68	.83	.83	1.19	.940	1.74		
.39	.41	.54	.60	.69	.85	.84	1.22	.945	1.78		

TABLE D Table of *t*, for use in determining the reliability of statistics

Example: When the *df* are 35 and $t = 2.03$, the .05 in column 3 means that 5 times in 100 trials a divergence as large as that obtained may be expected in the positive *and* negative directions.

Degrees of Freedom	Probability (P)			
	0.10	0.05	0.02	0.01
1	$t = 6.34$	$t = 12.71$	$t = 31.82$	$t = 63.66$
2	2.92	4.30	6.96	9.92
3	2.35	3.18	4.54	5.84
4	2.13	2.78	3.75	4.60
5	2.02	2.57	3.36	4.03
6	1.94	2.45	3.14	3.71
7	1.90	2.36	3.00	3.50
8	1.86	2.31	2.90	3.36
9	1.83	2.26	2.82	3.25
10	1.81	2.23	2.76	3.17
11	1.80	2.20	2.72	3.11
12	1.78	2.18	2.68	3.06
13	1.77	2.16	2.65	3.01
14	1.76	2.14	2.62	2.98
15	1.75	2.13	2.60	2.95
16	1.75	2.12	2.58	2.92
17	1.74	2.11	2.57	2.90
18	1.73	2.10	2.55	2.88
19	1.73	2.09	2.54	2.86
20	1.72	2.09	2.53	2.84
21	1.72	2.08	2.52	2.83
22	1.72	2.07	2.51	2.82
23	1.71	2.07	2.50	2.81
24	1.71	2.06	2.49	2.80
25	1.71	2.06	2.48	2.79
26	1.71	2.06	2.48	2.78
27	1.70	2.05	2.47	2.77
28	1.70	2.05	2.47	2.76
29	1.70	2.04	2.46	2.76
30	1.70	2.04	2.46	2.75
35	1.69	2.03	2.44	2.72
40	1.68	2.02	2.42	2.71
45	1.68	2.02	2.41	2.69
50	1.68	2.01	2.40	2.68
60	1.67	2.00	2.39	2.66
70	1.67	2.00	2.38	2.65
80	1.66	1.99	2.38	2.64
90	1.66	1.99	2.37	2.63
100	1.66	1.98	2.36	2.63
125	1.66	1.98	2.36	2.62
150	1.66	1.98	2.35	2.61
200	1.65	1.97	2.35	2.60
300	1.65	1.97	2.34	2.59
400	1.65	1.97	2.34	2.59
500	1.65	1.96	2.33	2.59
1000	1.65	1.96	2.33	2.58
∞	1.65	1.96	2.33	2.58

TABLE E χ^2 Table. P gives the probability of exceeding the tabulated value of χ^2 for the specified number of degrees of freedom (df). The values of χ^2 are printed in the body of the table

Adapted from R. A. Fisher's *Statistical Method for Research Workers*, Oliver & Boyd, by permission of publishers.

df	0.95	0.90	0.80	0.70	0.50	0.30	0.20	0.10	0.05	0.02	0.01
1	0.00393	0.0158	0.0642	0.148	0.455	1.074	1.642	2.706	3.841	5.412	6.635
2	0.103	0.211	0.446	0.713	1.386	2.408	3.219	4.605	5.991	7.824	9.210
3	0.352	0.584	1.005	1.424	2.366	3.665	4.642	6.251	7.815	9.837	11.345
4	0.711	1.064	1.649	2.195	3.357	4.878	5.989	7.779	9.488	11.668	13.277
5	1.145	1.610	2.343	3.000	4.351	6.064	7.289	9.236	11.070	13.388	15.086
6	1.635	2.204	3.070	3.828	5.348	7.231	8.558	10.645	12.592	15.033	16.812
7	2.167	2.833	3.822	4.671	6.346	8.383	9.803	12.017	14.067	16.622	18.475
8	2.733	3.490	4.594	5.527	7.344	9.524	11.030	13.362	15.507	18.168	20.090
9	3.325	4.168	5.380	6.393	8.343	10.656	12.242	14.684	16.919	19.679	21.666
10	3.940	4.865	6.179	7.267	9.342	11.781	13.442	15.987	18.307	21.161	23.209
11	4.575	5.578	6.989	8.148	10.341	12.899	14.631	17.275	19.675	22.618	24.725
12	5.226	6.304	7.807	9.034	11.340	14.011	15.812	18.549	21.026	24.054	26.217
13	5.892	7.042	8.634	9.926	12.340	15.119	16.985	19.812	22.362	25.472	27.688
14	6.571	7.790	9.467	10.821	13.339	16.222	18.151	21.064	23.685	26.873	29.141
15	7.261	8.547	10.307	11.721	14.339	17.322	19.311	22.307	24.996	28.259	30.578
16	7.962	9.312	11.152	12.624	15.338	18.418	20.465	23.542	26.296	29.633	32.000
17	8.672	10.085	12.002	13.531	16.338	19.511	21.615	24.769	27.587	30.995	33.409
18	9.390	10.865	12.857	14.440	17.338	20.601	22.760	25.989	28.869	32.346	34.805
19	10.117	11.651	13.716	15.352	18.338	21.689	23.900	27.204	30.144	33.687	36.191
20	10.851	12.443	14.578	16.266	19.337	22.775	25.038	28.412	31.410	35.020	37.566
21	11.591	13.240	15.445	17.182	20.337	23.858	26.171	29.615	32.671	36.343	38.932
22	12.338	14.041	16.314	18.101	21.337	24.939	27.301	30.813	33.924	37.659	40.289
23	13.091	14.848	17.187	19.021	22.337	26.018	28.429	32.007	35.172	38.968	41.638
24	13.848	15.659	18.062	19.943	23.337	27.096	29.553	33.196	36.415	40.270	42.980
25	14.611	16.473	18.940	20.867	24.337	28.172	30.675	34.382	37.652	41.566	44.314
26	15.379	17.292	19.820	21.792	25.336	29.246	31.795	35.563	38.885	42.856	45.642
27	16.151	18.114	20.703	22.719	26.336	30.319	32.912	36.741	40.113	44.140	46.963
28	16.928	18.939	21.588	23.647	27.336	31.391	34.027	37.916	41.337	45.419	48.278
29	17.708	19.768	22.475	24.577	28.336	32.461	35.139	39.087	42.557	46.693	49.588
30	18.493	20.599	23.364	25.508	29.336	33.530	36.250	40.256	43.773	47.962	50.892

APPENDIX OF TABLES • 429

TABLE F   F-ratios for .05 (roman) and .01 (boldface) levels of significance

Degrees of freedom for greater mean square

Degrees of freedom for smaller mean square	1	2	3	4	5	6	8	12	24	∞
1	161.45 **4052.10**	199.50 **4999.03**	215.72 **5403.49**	224.57 **5625.14**	230.17 **5764.08**	233.97 **5859.39**	238.89 **5981.34**	243.91 **6105.83**	249.04 **6234.16**	254.32 **6366.48**
2	18.51 **98.49**	19.00 **99.01**	19.16 **99.17**	19.25 **99.25**	19.30 **99.30**	19.33 **99.33**	19.37 **99.36**	19.41 **99.42**	19.45 **99.46**	19.50 **99.50**
3	10.13 **34.12**	9.55 **30.81**	9.28 **29.46**	9.12 **28.71**	9.01 **28.24**	8.94 **27.91**	8.84 **27.49**	8.74 **27.05**	8.64 **26.60**	8.53 **26.12**
4	7.71 **21.20**	6.94 **18.00**	6.59 **16.69**	6.39 **15.98**	6.26 **15.52**	6.16 **15.21**	6.04 **14.80**	5.91 **14.37**	5.77 **13.93**	5.63 **13.46**
5	6.61 **16.26**	5.79 **13.27**	5.41 **12.06**	5.19 **11.39**	5.05 **10.97**	4.95 **10.67**	4.82 **10.27**	4.68 **9.89**	4.53 **9.47**	4.36 **9.02**
6	5.99 **13.74**	5.14 **10.92**	4.76 **9.78**	4.53 **9.15**	4.39 **8.75**	4.28 **8.47**	4.15 **8.10**	4.00 **7.72**	3.84 **7.31**	3.67 **6.88**
7	5.59 **12.25**	4.74 **9.55**	4.35 **8.45**	4.12 **7.85**	3.97 **7.46**	3.87 **7.19**	3.73 **6.84**	3.57 **6.47**	3.41 **6.07**	3.23 **5.65**
8	5.32 **11.26**	4.46 **8.65**	4.07 **7.59**	3.84 **7.01**	3.69 **6.63**	3.58 **6.37**	3.44 **6.03**	3.28 **5.67**	3.12 **5.28**	2.93 **4.86**
9	5.12 **10.56**	4.26 **8.02**	3.86 **6.99**	3.63 **6.42**	3.48 **6.06**	3.37 **5.80**	3.23 **5.47**	3.07 **5.11**	2.90 **4.73**	2.71 **4.31**
10	4.96 **10.04**	4.10 **7.56**	3.71 **6.55**	3.48 **5.99**	3.33 **5.64**	3.22 **5.39**	3.07 **5.06**	2.91 **4.71**	2.74 **4.33**	2.54 **3.91**
11	4.84 **9.65**	3.98 **7.20**	3.59 **6.22**	3.36 **5.67**	3.20 **5.32**	3.09 **5.07**	2.95 **4.74**	2.79 **4.40**	2.61 **4.02**	2.40 **3.60**

TABLE F—(Continued)

Degrees of freedom for greater mean square

	1	2	3	4	5	6	8	12	24	∞
12	4.75 9.33	3.88 6.93	3.49 5.95	3.26 5.41	3.11 5.06	3.00 4.82	2.85 4.50	2.69 4.16	2.50 3.78	2.30 3.36
13	4.67 9.07	3.80 6.70	3.41 5.74	3.18 5.20	3.02 4.86	2.92 4.62	2.77 4.30	2.60 3.96	2.42 3.59	2.21 3.16
14	4.60 8.86	3.74 6.51	3.34 5.56	3.11 5.03	2.96 4.69	2.85 4.46	2.70 4.14	2.53 3.80	2.35 3.43	2.13 3.00
15	4.54 8.68	3.68 6.36	3.29 5.42	3.06 4.89	2.90 4.56	2.79 4.32	2.64 4.00	2.48 3.67	2.29 3.29	2.07 2.87
16	4.49 8.53	3.63 6.23	3.24 5.29	3.01 4.77	2.85 4.44	2.74 4.20	2.59 3.89	2.42 3.55	2.24 3.18	2.01 2.75
17	4.45 8.40	3.59 6.11	3.20 5.18	2.96 4.67	2.81 4.34	2.70 4.10	2.55 3.79	2.38 3.45	2.19 3.08	1.96 2.65
18	4.41 8.28	3.55 6.01	3.16 5.09	2.93 4.58	2.77 4.25	2.66 4.01	2.51 3.71	2.34 3.37	2.15 3.01	1.92 2.57
19	4.38 8.18	3.52 5.93	3.13 5.01	2.90 4.50	2.74 4.17	2.63 3.94	2.48 3.63	2.31 3.30	2.11 2.92	1.88 2.49
20	4.35 8.10	3.49 5.85	3.10 4.94	2.87 4.43	2.71 4.10	2.60 3.87	2.45 3.56	2.28 3.23	2.08 2.86	1.84 2.42
21	4.32 8.02	3.47 5.78	3.07 4.87	2.84 4.37	2.68 4.04	2.57 3.81	2.42 3.51	2.25 3.17	2.05 2.80	1.81 2.36
22	4.30 7.94	3.44 5.72	3.05 4.82	2.82 4.31	2.66 3.99	2.55 3.75	2.40 3.45	2.23 3.12	2.03 2.75	1.78 2.30
23	4.28 7.88	3.42 5.66	3.03 4.76	2.80 4.26	2.64 3.94	2.53 3.71	2.38 3.41	2.20 3.07	2.00 2.70	1.76 2.26

Degrees of freedom for smaller mean square

APPENDIX OF TABLES • 431

n_1										
24	4.26 / 7.82	3.40 / 5.61	3.01 / 4.72	2.78 / 4.22	2.62 / 3.90	2.51 / 3.67	2.36 / 3.36	2.18 / 3.03	1.98 / 2.66	1.73 / 2.21
25	4.24 / 7.77	3.38 / 5.57	2.99 / 4.68	2.76 / 4.18	2.60 / 3.86	2.49 / 3.63	2.34 / 3.32	2.16 / 2.99	1.96 / 2.62	1.71 / 2.17
26	4.22 / 7.72	3.37 / 5.53	2.98 / 4.64	2.74 / 4.14	2.59 / 3.82	2.47 / 3.59	2.32 / 3.29	2.15 / 2.96	1.95 / 2.58	1.69 / 2.13
27	4.21 / 7.68	3.35 / 5.49	2.96 / 4.60	2.73 / 4.11	2.57 / 3.78	2.46 / 3.56	2.30 / 3.26	2.13 / 2.93	1.93 / 2.55	1.67 / 2.10
28	4.20 / 7.64	3.34 / 5.45	2.95 / 4.57	2.71 / 4.07	2.56 / 3.75	2.44 / 3.53	2.29 / 3.23	2.12 / 2.90	1.91 / 2.52	1.65 / 2.06
29	4.18 / 7.60	3.33 / 5.42	2.93 / 4.54	2.70 / 4.04	2.54 / 3.73	2.43 / 3.50	2.28 / 3.20	2.10 / 2.87	1.90 / 2.49	1.64 / 2.03
30	4.17 / 7.56	3.32 / 5.39	2.92 / 4.51	2.69 / 4.02	2.53 / 3.70	2.42 / 3.47	2.27 / 3.17	2.09 / 2.84	1.89 / 2.47	1.62 / 2.01
35	4.12 / 7.42	3.26 / 5.27	2.87 / 4.40	2.64 / 3.91	2.48 / 3.59	2.37 / 3.37	2.22 / 3.07	2.04 / 2.74	1.83 / 2.37	1.57 / 1.90
40	4.08 / 7.31	3.23 / 5.18	2.84 / 4.31	2.61 / 3.83	2.45 / 3.51	2.34 / 3.29	2.18 / 2.99	2.00 / 2.66	1.79 / 2.29	1.52 / 1.82
45	4.06 / 7.23	3.21 / 5.11	2.81 / 4.25	2.58 / 3.77	2.42 / 3.45	2.31 / 3.23	2.15 / 2.94	1.97 / 2.61	1.76 / 2.23	1.48 / 1.75
50	4.03 / 7.17	3.18 / 5.06	2.79 / 4.20	2.56 / 3.72	2.40 / 3.41	2.29 / 3.19	2.13 / 2.89	1.95 / 2.56	1.74 / 2.18	1.44 / 1.68
60	4.00 / 7.08	3.15 / 4.98	2.76 / 4.13	2.52 / 3.65	2.37 / 3.34	2.25 / 3.12	2.10 / 2.82	1.92 / 2.50	1.70 / 2.12	1.39 / 1.60
70	3.98 / 7.01	3.13 / 4.92	2.74 / 4.07	2.50 / 3.60	2.35 / 3.29	2.23 / 3.07	2.07 / 2.78	1.89 / 2.45	1.67 / 2.07	1.35 / 1.53

Degrees of freedom for smaller mean square

TABLE F—(Continued)

Degrees of freedom for smaller mean square	Degrees of freedom for greater mean square							
	1	2	3	4	5	6	8	12	24	∞
80	3.96 / 6.96	3.11 / 4.88	2.72 / 4.04	2.49 / 3.56	2.33 / 3.26	2.21 / 3.04	2.06 / 2.74	1.88 / 2.42	1.65 / 2.03	1.31 / 1.47
90	3.95 / 6.92	3.10 / 4.85	2.71 / 4.01	2.47 / 3.53	2.32 / 3.23	2.20 / 3.01	2.04 / 2.72	1.86 / 2.39	1.64 / 2.00	1.28 / 1.43
100	3.94 / 6.90	3.09 / 4.82	2.70 / 3.98	2.46 / 3.51	2.30 / 3.21	2.19 / 2.99	2.03 / 2.69	1.85 / 2.37	1.63 / 1.98	1.26 / 1.39
125	3.92 / 6.84	3.07 / 4.78	2.68 / 3.94	2.44 / 3.47	2.29 / 3.17	2.17 / 2.95	2.01 / 2.66	1.83 / 2.33	1.60 / 1.94	1.21 / 1.32
150	3.90 / 6.81	3.06 / 4.75	2.66 / 3.91	2.43 / 3.45	2.27 / 3.14	2.16 / 2.92	2.00 / 2.63	1.82 / 2.31	1.59 / 1.92	1.18 / 1.27
200	3.89 / 6.76	3.04 / 4.71	2.65 / 3.88	2.42 / 3.41	2.26 / 3.11	2.14 / 2.89	1.98 / 2.60	1.80 / 2.28	1.57 / 1.88	1.14 / 1.21
300	3.87 / 6.72	3.03 / 4.68	2.64 / 3.85	2.41 / 3.38	2.25 / 3.08	2.13 / 2.86	1.97 / 2.57	1.79 / 2.24	1.55 / 1.85	1.10 / 1.14
400	3.86 / 6.70	3.02 / 4.66	2.63 / 3.83	2.40 / 3.37	2.24 / 3.06	2.12 / 2.85	1.96 / 2.56	1.78 / 2.23	1.54 / 1.84	1.07 / 1.11
500	3.86 / 6.69	3.01 / 4.65	2.62 / 3.82	2.39 / 3.36	2.23 / 3.05	2.11 / 2.84	1.96 / 2.55	1.77 / 2.22	1.54 / 1.83	1.06 / 1.08
1000	3.85 / 6.66	3.00 / 4.63	2.61 / 3.80	2.38 / 3.34	2.22 / 3.04	2.10 / 2.82	1.95 / 2.53	1.76 / 2.20	1.53 / 1.81	1.03 / 1.04
∞	3.84 / 6.64	2.99 / 4.60	2.60 / 3.78	2.37 / 3.32	2.21 / 3.02	2.09 / 2.80	1.94 / 2.51	1.75 / 2.18	1.52 / 1.79		

TABLE G To facilitate the calculation of T-scores

The percents refer to the percentage of the total frequency below a given score $+ 1/2$ of the frequency on that score. T-scores are read directly from the given percentages.

Percent	T-score	Percent	T-score
.0032	10	53.98	51
.0048	11	57.93	52
.007	12	61.79	53
.011	13	65.54	54
.016	14	69.15	55
.023	15	72.57	56
.034	16	75.80	57
.048	17	78.81	58
.069	18	81.59	59
.097	19	84.13	60
.13	20	86.43	61
.19	21	88.49	62
.26	22	90.32	63
.35	23	91.92	64
.47	24	93.32	65
.62	25	94.52	66
.82	26	95.54	67
1.07	27	96.41	68
1.39	28	97.13	69
1.79	29	97.72	70
2.28	30	98.21	71
2.87	31	98.61	72
3.59	32	98.93	73
4.46	33	99.18	74
5.48	34	99.38	75
6.68	35	99.53	76
8.08	36	99.65	77
9.68	37	99.74	78
11.51	38	99.81	79
13.57	39	99.865	80
15.87	40	99.903	81
18.41	41	99.931	82
21.19	42	99.952	83
24.20	43	99.966	84
27.43	44	99.977	85
30.85	45	99.984	86
34.46	46	99.9890	87
38.21	47	99.9928	88
42.07	48	99.9952	89
46.02	49	99.9968	90
50.00	50		

	0	1	2	3	4	5	6	7	8	9	10	11	12	13	14	15	16	17	18	19	20	21	22	23
1	270	218	196	181	170	160	151	144	137	131	125	120	115	110	106	102	97	94	90	86	82	79	76	72
2	244	207	189	175	165	156	148	141	134	128	122	118	112	108	104	99	95	92	88	84	81	77	74	71
3	228	198	182	170	160	152	144	137	131	125	120	115	110	106	102	97	94	90	86	82	79	76	72	69
4	216	191	177	165	156	148	141	134	128	123	118	113	108	104	100	96	92	88	84	81	77	74	71	67
5	210	185	172	161	152	145	138	131	126	120	115	111	106	102	98	94	90	86	82	79	76	72	69	66
6	199	179	167	157	149	141	135	129	123	118	113	108	104	100	96	92	88	84	81	77	74	71	68	64
7	192	174	163	153	145	138	132	126	121	116	111	106	102	98	94	90	86	83	79	76	72	69	66	63
8	186	170	159	150	142	135	128	124	118	113	109	104	100	96	92	88	84	81	77	74	71	68	64	61
9	181	165	155	147	139	133	126	121	116	111	106	102	98	94	90	86	83	79	76	73	69	66	63	60
10	176	161	151	143	136	130	124	119	114	109	104	100	96	92	88	85	81	78	74	71	68	65	62	59
11	171	158	148	140	134	127	122	116	111	107	102	98	94	90	87	83	79	76	73	69	66	63	60	57
12	167	154	145	138	131	125	119	114	109	105	100	96	92	89	85	81	78	74	71	68	65	62	59	56
13	163	151	142	135	128	122	117	112	107	103	99	94	91	87	83	80	76	73	70	66	63	60	57	54
14	159	147	139	132	126	120	115	110	105	101	97	93	89	85	81	78	75	71	68	65	62	59	56	53
15	156	144	136	129	123	118	113	108	103	99	95	91	87	83	80	76	73	70	66	63	60	57	54	51
16	152	141	134	127	121	116	111	106	101	97	93	89	85	82	78	75	71	68	65	62	59	56	53	50
17	149	139	131	125	119	113	109	104	99	95	91	87	84	80	77	73	70	67	64	60	57	54	52	49
18	146	136	129	122	117	111	106	102	98	93	89	86	82	78	75	72	68	65	62	59	56	53	50	47
19	143	133	126	120	114	109	105	100	96	92	88	84	80	77	73	70	67	64	61	58	55	52	49	46
20	140	131	124	118	112	107	103	98	94	90	86	82	79	75	72	69	65	62	59	56	53	50	47	45
21	137	128	121	116	110	105	101	96	92	88	84	81	77	74	70	67	64	60	58	55	52	49	46	43
22	135	126	119	113	108	103	99	95	90	87	83	79	76	72	69	66	62	59	56	53	50	48	45	42
23	132	124	117	111	106	101	97	92	89	85	81	78	74	71	67	64	61	58	55	52	49	46	43	41
24	130	121	115	109	104	100	95	91	87	83	80	76	73	69	66	63	60	57	54	51	48	45	42	39
25	127	119	113	107	102	98	93	89	85	82	78	74	71	68	64	61	58	55	52	49	46	43	41	38
26	125	117	111	105	101	96	92	88	84	80	76	73	70	66	63	60	57	54	51	48	45	42	39	37
27	123	115	109	104	99	94	90	86	82	78	75	71	68	65	62	58	55	52	49	46	44	41	38	35
28	120	113	107	102	97	92	88	84	80	77	73	70	67	63	60	57	54	51	48	45	42	39	37	
29	118	111	105	100	95	91	87	83	79	75	72	68	65	62	59	56	53	50	47	44	41	38		
30	116	109	103	98	93	89	85	81	77	74	70	67	64	60	57	54	51	48	45	42	40			
31	114	107	101	96	92	87	83	79	76	72	69	65	62	59	56	53	50	47	44	41				
32	112	105	99	94	90	86	82	78	74	71	67	64	61	58	54	51	48	46	43					
33	110	103	98	93	88	84	80	76	73	69	66	63	59	56	53	50	47	44						
34	108	101	96	91	86	82	79	75	71	68	64	61	58	55	52	49	46							
35	106	99	94	89	85	81	77	73	70	66	63	60	56	53	50	47								
36	104	97	92	88	83	80	75	72	68	65	61	58	55	52	49									
37	102	96	91	86	82	78	74	70	67	63	60	57	54	51										
38	100	94	89	84	80	76	72	69	65	62	59	55	52											
39	98	92	87	83	79	75	71	67	64	61	57	54												
40	97	91	86	81	77	73	69	66	62	59	56													
41	95	89	84	80	75	72	68	64	61	58														
42	93	87	82	78	74	70	66	63	60															
43	91	85	81	76	72	69	65	62																
44	90	84	79	75	71	67	64																	
45	88	82	78	73	69	66																		
46	86	81	76	72	68																			
47	85	79	75	70																				
48	83	78	73																					
49	81	76																						
50	80																							

	24	25	26	27	28	29	30	31	32	33	34	35	36	37	38	39	40	41	42	43	44	45	46	47	48	49
1	69	66	63	60	57	54	51	48	45	43	40	37	35	32	29	27	24	21	19	16	14	11	09	06	04	01
2	67	64	61	58	55	52	50	47	44	41	39	36	33	31	28	25	23	20	18	15	13	10	08	05	03	
3	66	63	60	57	54	51	48	45	43	40	37	35	32	29	27	24	21	19	16	14	11	09	06	05		
4	64	61	58	55	52	50	47	44	41	39	36	33	31	28	25	23	20	18	15	13	10	08	05			
5	63	60	57	54	51	48	45	43	40	37	35	32	29	27	24	21	19	16	14	11	09	06				
6	61	58	55	53	50	47	44	41	39	36	33	31	28	25	23	20	18	15	13	10	08					
7	60	57	54	51	48	45	43	40	37	35	32	29	27	24	21	19	16	14	11	09						
8	58	55	52	50	47	44	41	39	36	33	31	28	25	23	20	18	15	13	10							
9	57	54	51	48	46	43	40	37	35	32	29	27	24	21	19	16	14	11								
10	56	53	50	47	44	41	39	36	33	31	28	25	23	20	18	15	13									
11	54	51	48	46	43	40	37	35	32	29	27	24	22	19	16	14										
12	53	50	47	44	41	39	36	33	31	28	25	23	20	18	15											
13	51	48	46	43	40	37	35	32	29	27	24	22	19	16												
14	50	47	44	42	39	36	33	31	28	25	23	20	18													
15	49	46	43	40	37	35	32	29	27	24	22	19														
16	47	44	42	39	36	33	31	28	26	23	20															
17	46	43	40	37	35	32	29	27	24	22																
18	44	42	39	36	33	31	28	26	23																	
19	43	40	38	35	32	30	27	24																		
20	42	39	36	34	31	28	26																			
21	40	38	35	32	30	27																				
22	39	36	34	31	28																					
23	38	35	32	30																						
24	36	34	31																							
25	35	32																								
26	34																									

TABLE H Mean σ-distances from the mean, of various percents of a normal distribution

Average distance from the mean, in terms of σ, of each single percentage of a normal distribution (decimals omitted). Figures along the top of the table represent percentages of area from either extreme. Figures down the side of the table represent percentages measured from given points in the distribution.

Examples: The average distance from the mean of the highest 10% of a normally distributed group is 1.76σ (entry opposite 10 in first column). The average distance from the mean of the *next* 20% is .86σ (entry opposite 20 in column headed 10). The average distance from the mean of the *next* 30% is

$$\frac{.26 \times .20 + (-.13 \times .10)}{.30}$$

or .13σ (20% lie to the right of mean and 10% to left, see page 320).

TABLE I A table to infer the value of $\sqrt{1-r^2}$ from a given value of r

r	$\sqrt{1-r^2}$	r	$\sqrt{1-r^2}$	r	$\sqrt{1-r^2}$
.0000	1.0000	.3400	.9404	.6800	.7332
.01	.9999	.35	.9367	.69	.7238
.02	.9998	.36	.9330	.70	.7141
.03	.9995	.37	.9290	.71	.7042
.04	.9992	.38	.9250	.72	.6940
.05	.9987	.39	.9208	.73	.6834
.06	.9982	.40	.9165	.74	.6726
.07	.9975	.41	.9121	.75	.6614
.08	.9968	.42	.9075	.76	.6499
.09	.9959	.43	.9028	.77	.6380
.10	.9950	.44	.8980	.78	.6258
.11	.9939	.45	.8930	.79	.6131
.12	.9928	.46	.8879	.80	.6000
.13	.9915	.47	.8827	.81	.5864
.14	.9902	.48	.8773	.82	.5724
.15	.9887	.49	.8717	.83	.5578
.16	.9871	.50	.8660	.84	.5426
.17	.9854	.51	.8617	.85	.5268
.18	.9837	.52	.8542	.86	.5103
.19	.9818	.53	.8480	.87	.4931
.20	.9798	.54	.8417	.88	.4750
.21	.9777	.55	.8352	.89	.4560
.22	.9755	.56	.8285	.90	.4359
.23	.9732	.57	.8216	.91	.4146
.24	.9708	.58	.8146	.92	.3919
.25	.9682	.59	.8074	.93	.3676
.26	.9656	.60	.8000	.94	.3412
.27	.9629	.61	.7924	.95	.3122
.28	.9600	.62	.7846	.96	.2800
.29	.9570	.63	.7766	.97	.2431
.30	.9539	.64	.7684	.98	.1990
.31	.9507	.65	.7599	.99	.1411
.32	.9474	.66	.7513	1.00	.0000
.33	.9440	.67	.7424		

TABLE J Coefficients of correlation significant at the 5% level and at the 1% level for varying degrees of freedom

Degrees of Freedom	Number of Variables						
	2	3	4	5	6	7	9
1	.997 **1.000**	.999 **1.000**	.999 **1.000**	.999 **1.000**	1.000 **1.000**	1.000 **1.000**	1.000 **1.000**
2	.950 **.990**	.975 **.995**	.983 **.997**	.987 **.998**	.990 **.998**	.992 **.998**	.994 **.999**
3	.878 **.959**	.930 **.976**	.950 **.983**	.961 **.987**	.968 **.990**	.973 **.991**	.979 **.993**
4	.811 **.917**	.881 **.949**	.912 **.962**	.930 **.970**	.942 **.975**	.950 **.979**	.961 **.984**
5	.754 **.874**	.836 **.917**	.874 **.937**	.898 **.949**	.914 **.957**	.925 **.963**	.941 **.971**
6	.707 **.834**	.795 **.886**	.839 **.911**	.867 **.927**	.886 **.938**	.900 **.946**	.920 **.957**
7	.666 **.798**	.758 **.855**	.807 **.885**	.838 **.904**	.860 **.918**	.876 **.928**	.900 **.942**
8	.632 **.765**	.726 **.827**	.777 **.860**	.811 **.882**	.835 **.898**	.854 **.909**	.880 **.926**
9	.602 **.735**	.697 **.800**	.750 **.836**	.786 **.861**	.812 **.878**	.832 **.891**	.861 **.911**

TABLE J—(Continued)

Degrees of Freedom	Number of Variables						
	2	3	4	5	6	7	9
10	.576 **.708**	.671 **.776**	.726 **.814**	.763 **.840**	.790 **.859**	.812 **.874**	.843 **.895**
11	.553 **.684**	.648 **.753**	.703 **.793**	.741 **.821**	.770 **.841**	.792 **.857**	.826 **.880**
12	.532 **.661**	.627 **.732**	.683 **.773**	.722 **.802**	.751 **.824**	.774 **.841**	.809 **.866**
13	.514 **.641**	.608 **.712**	.664 **.755**	.703 **.785**	.733 **.807**	.757 **.825**	.794 **.852**
14	.497 **.623**	.590 **.694**	.646 **.737**	.686 **.768**	.717 **.792**	.741 **.810**	.779 **.838**
15	.482 **.606**	.574 **.677**	.630 **.721**	.670 **.752**	.701 **.776**	.726 **.796**	.765 **.825**
16	.468 **.590**	.559 **.662**	.615 **.706**	.655 **.738**	.686 **.762**	.712 **.782**	.751 **.813**
17	.456 **.575**	.545 **.647**	.601 **.691**	.641 **.724**	.673 **.749**	.698 **.769**	.738 **.800**
18	.444 **.561**	.532 **.633**	.587 **.678**	.628 **.710**	.660 **.736**	.686 **.756**	.726 **.789**
19	.433 **.549**	.520 **.620**	.575 **.665**	.615 **.698**	.647 **.723**	.674 **.744**	.714 **.778**
20	.423 **.537**	.509 **.608**	.563 **.652**	.604 **.685**	.636 **.712**	.662 **.733**	.703 **.767**
21	.413 **.526**	.498 **.596**	.552 **.641**	.592 **.674**	.624 **.700**	.651 **.722**	.693 **.756**
22	.404 **.515**	.488 **.585**	.542 **.630**	.582 **.663**	.614 **.690**	.640 **.712**	.682 **.746**
23	.396 **.505**	.479 **.574**	.532 **.619**	.572 **.652**	.604 **.679**	.630 **.701**	.673 **.736**
24	.388 **.496**	.470 **.565**	.523 **.609**	.562 **.642**	.594 **.669**	.621 **.692**	.663 **.727**
25	.381 **.487**	.462 **.555**	.514 **.600**	.553 **.633**	.585 **.660**	.612 **.682**	.654 **.718**
26	.374 **.478**	.454 **.546**	.506 **.590**	.545 **.624**	.576 **.651**	.603 **.673**	.645 **.709**
27	.367 **.470**	.446 **.538**	.498 **.582**	.536 **.615**	.568 **.642**	.594 **.664**	.637 **.701**
28	.361 **.463**	.439 **.530**	.490 **.573**	.529 **.606**	.560 **.634**	.586 **.656**	.629 **.692**

TABLE J—(Continued)

Degrees of Freedom	Number of Variables						
	2	3	4	5	6	7	9
29	.355 .456	.432 .522	.482 .565	.521 .598	.552 .625	.579 .648	.621 .685
30	.349 .449	.426 .514	.476 .558	.514 .591	.545 .618	.571 .640	.614 .677
35	.325 .418	.397 .481	.445 .523	.482 .556	.512 .582	.538 .605	.580 .642
40	.304 .393	.373 .454	.419 .494	.455 .526	.484 .552	.509 .575	.551 .612
45	.288 .372	.353 .430	.397 .470	.432 .501	.460 .527	.485 .549	.526 .586
50	.273 .354	.336 .410	.379 .449	.412 479	.440 .504	.464 .526	.504 .562
60	.250 .325	.308 .377	.348 .414	.380 .442	.406 .466	.429 .488	.467 .523
70	.232 .302	.286 .351	.324 .386	.354 .413	.379 .436	.401 .456	.438 .491
80	.217 .283	.269 .330	.304 .362	.332 .389	.356 .411	.377 .431	.413 .464
90	.205 .267	.254 .312	.288 .343	.315 .368	.338 .390	.358 .409	.392 .441
100	.195 .254	.241 .297	.274 .327	.300 .351	.322 .372	.341 .390	.374 .421
125	.174 .228	.216 .266	.246 .294	.269 .316	.290 .335	.307 .352	.338 .381
150	.159 .208	.198 .244	.225 .270	.247 .290	.266 .308	.282 .324	.310 .351
200	.138 .181	.172 .212	.196 .234	.215 .253	.231 .269	.246 .283	.271 .307
300	.113 .148	.141 .174	.160 .192	.176 .208	.190 .221	.202 .233	.223 .253
400	.098 .128	.122 .151	.139 .167	.153 .180	.165 .192	.176 .202	.194 .220
500	.088 .115	.109 .135	.124 .150	.137 .162	.148 .172	.157 .182	.174 .198
1000	.062 .081	.077 .096	.088 .106	.097 .115	.105 .122	.112 .129	.124 .141

TABLE OF SQUARES AND SQUARE ROOTS
OF THE NUMBERS FROM 1 TO 1000

442 • STATISTICS IN PSYCHOLOGY AND EDUCATION

TABLE OF SQUARES AND SQUARE ROOTS OF THE NUMBERS FROM 1 TO 1000

Number	Square	Square Root	Number	Square	Square Root
1	1	1.000	51	26 01	7.141
2	4	1.414	52	27 04	7.211
3	9	1.732	53	28 09	7.280
4	16	2.000	54	29 16	7.348
5	25	2.236	55	30 25	7.416
6	36	2.449	56	31 36	7.483
7	49	2.646	57	32 49	7.550
8	64	2.828	58	33 64	7.616
9	81	3.000	59	34 81	7.681
10	1 00	3.162	60	36 00	7.746
11	1 21	3.317	61	37 21	7.810
12	1 44	3.464	62	38 44	7.874
13	1 69	3.606	63	39 69	7.937
14	1 96	3.742	64	40 96	8.000
15	2 25	3.873	65	42 25	8.062
16	2 56	4.000	66	43 56	8.124
17	2 89	4.123	67	44 89	8.185
18	3 24	4.243	68	46 24	8.246
19	3 61	4.359	69	47 61	8.307
20	4 00	4.472	70	49 00	8.367
21	4 41	4.583	71	50 41	8.426
22	4 84	4.690	72	51 84	8.485
23	5 29	4.796	73	53 29	8.544
24	5 76	4.899	74	54 76	8.602
25	6 25	5.000	75	56 25	8.660
26	6 76	5.099	76	57 76	8.718
27	7 29	5.196	77	59 29	8.775
28	7 84	5.292	78	60 84	8.832
29	8 41	5.385	79	62 41	8.888
30	9 00	5.477	80	64 00	8.944
31	9 61	5.568	81	65 61	9.000
32	10 24	5.657	82	67 24	9.055
33	10 89	5.745	83	68 89	9.110
34	11 56	5.831	84	70 56	9.165
35	12 25	5.916	85	72 25	9.220
36	12 96	6.000	86	73 96	9.274
37	13 69	6.083	87	75 69	9.327
38	14 44	6.164	88	77 44	9.381
39	15 21	6.245	89	79 21	9.434
40	16 00	6.325	90	81 00	9.487
41	16 81	6.403	91	82 81	9.539
42	17 64	6.481	92	84 64	9.592
43	18 49	6.557	93	86 49	9.644
44	19 36	6.633	94	88 36	9.695
45	20 25	6.708	95	90 25	9.747
46	21 16	6.782	96	92 16	9.798
47	22 09	6.856	97	94 09	9.849
48	23 04	6.928	98	96 04	9 899
49	24 01	7.000	99	98 01	9 950
50	25 00	7.071	100	1 00 00	10 000

TABLE OF SQUARES AND SQUARE ROOTS • 443

TABLE OF SQUARES AND SQUARE ROOTS—*Continued*

Number	Square	Square Root	Number	Square	Square Root
101	1 02 01	10.050	151	2 28 01	12.288
102	1 04 04	10.100	152	2 31 04	12.329
103	1 06 09	10.149	153	2 34 09	12.369
104	1 08 16	10.198	154	2 37 16	12.410
105	1 10 25	10.247	155	2 40 25	12.450
106	1 12 36	10.296	156	2 43 36	12.490
107	1 14 49	10.344	157	2 46 49	12.530
108	1 16 64	10.392	158	2 49 64	12.570
109	1 18 81	10.440	159	2 52 81	12.610
110	1 21 00	10.488	160	2 56 00	12.649
111	1 23 21	10.536	161	2 59 21	12.689
112	1 25 44	10.583	162	2 62 44	12.728
113	1 27 69	10.630	163	2 65 69	12.767
114	1 29 96	10.677	164	2 68 96	12.806
115	1 32 25	10.724	165	2 72 25	12.845
116	1 34 56	10.770	166	2 75 56	12.884
117	1 36 89	10.817	167	2 78 89	12.923
118	1 39 24	10.863	168	2 82 24	12.961
119	1 41 61	10.909	169	2 85 61	13.000
120	1 44 00	10.954	170	2 89 00	13.038
121	1 46 41	11.000	171	2 92 41	13.077
122	1 48 84	11.045	172	2 95 84	13.115
123	1 51 29	11.091	173	2 99 29	13.153
124	1 53 76	11.136	174	3 02 76	13.191
125	1 56 25	11.180	175	3 06 25	13.229
126	1 58 76	11.225	176	3 09 76	13.266
127	1 61 29	11.269	177	3 13 29	13.304
128	1 63 84	11.314	178	3 16 84	13.342
129	1 66 41	11.358	179	3 20 41	13.379
130	1 69 00	11.402	180	3 24 00	13.416
131	1 71 61	11.446	181	3 27 61	13.454
132	1 74 24	11.489	182	3 31 24	13.491
133	1 76 89	11.533	183	3 34 89	13.528
134	1 79 56	11.576	184	3 38 56	13.565
135	1 82 25	11.619	185	3 42 25	13.601
136	1 84 96	11.662	186	3 45 96	13.638
137	1 87 69	11.705	187	3 49 69	13.675
138	1 90 44	11.747	188	3 53 44	13.711
139	1 93 21	11.790	189	3 57 21	13.748
140	1 96 00	11.832	190	3 61 00	13.784
141	1 98 81	11.874	191	3 64 81	13.820
142	2 01 64	11.916	192	3 68 64	13.856
143	2 04 49	11.958	193	3 72 49	13.892
144	2 07 36	12.000	194	3 76 36	13.928
145	2 10 25	12.042	195	3 80 25	13.964
146	2 13 16	12.083	196	3 84 16	14.000
147	2 16 09	12.124	197	3 88 09	14.036
148	2 19 04	12.166	198	3 92 04	14.071
149	2 22 01	12.207	199	3 96 01	14.107
150	2 25 00	12.247	200	4 00 00	14.142

Table of Squares and Square Roots—Continued

Number	Square	Square Root	Number	Square	Square Root
201	4 04 01	14.177	251	6 30 01	15.843
202	4 08 04	14.213	252	6 35 04	15.875
203	4 12 09	14.248	253	6 40 09	15.906
204	4 16 16	14.283	254	6 45 16	15.937
205	4 20 25	14.318	255	6 50 25	15.969
206	4 24 36	14.353	256	6 55 36	16.000
207	4 28 49	14.387	257	6 60 49	16.031
208	4 32 64	14.422	258	6 65 64	16.062
209	4 36 81	14.457	259	6 70 81	16.093
210	4 41 00	14.491	260	6 76 00	16.125
211	4 45 21	14.526	261	6 81 21	16.155
212	4 49 44	14.560	262	6 86 44	16.186
213	4 53 69	14.595	263	6 91 69	16.217
214	4 57 96	14.629	264	6 96 96	16.248
215	4 62 25	14.663	265	7 02 25	16.279
216	4 66 56	14.697	266	7 07 56	16.310
217	4 70 89	14.731	267	7·12 89	16.340
218	4 75 24	14.765	268	7 18 24	16.371
219	4 79 61	14.799	269	7 23 61	16.401
220	4 84 00	14.832	270	7 29 00	16.432
221	4 88 41	14.866	271	7 34 41	16.462
222	4 92 84	14.900	272	7 39 84	16.492
223	4 97 29	14.933	273	7 45 29	16.523
224	5 01 76	14.967	274	7 50 76	16.553
225	5 06 25	15.000	275	7 56 25	16.583
226	5 10 76	15.033	276	7 61 76	16.613
227	5 15 29	15.067	277	7 67 29	16.643
228	5 19 84	15.100	278	7 72 84	16.673
229	5 24 41	15.133	279	7 78 41	16.703
230	5 29 00	15.166	280	7 84 00	16.733
231	5 33 61	15.199	281	7 89 61	16.763
232	5 38 24	15.232	282	7 95 24	16.793
233	5 42 89	15.264	283	8 00 89	16.823
234	5 47 56	15.297	284	8 06 56	16.852
235	5 52 25	15.330	285	8 12 25	16.882
236	5 56 96	15.362	286	8 17 96	16.912
237	5 61 69	15.395	287	8 23 69	16.941
238	5 66 44	15.427	288	8 29 44	16.971
239	5 71 21	15.460	289	8 35 21	17.000
240	5 76 00	15.492	290	8 41 00	17.029
241	5 80 81	15.524	291	8 46 81	17.059
242	5 85 64	15.556	292	8 52 64	17.088
243	5 90 49	15.588	293	8 58 49	17 117
244	5 95 36	15.620	294	8 64 36	17.146
245	6 00 25	15.652	295	8 70 25	17.176
246	6 05 16	15.684	296	8 76 16	17.205
247	6 10 09	15.716	297	8 82 09	17.234
248	6 15 04	15.748	298	8 88 04	17.263
249	6 20 01	15.780	299	8 94 01	17.292
250	6 25 00	15.811	300	9 00 00	17.321

TABLE OF SQUARES AND SQUARE ROOTS—Continued

Number	Square	Square Root	Number	Square	Square Root
301	9 06 01	17.349	351	12 32 01	18.735
302	9 12 04	17.378	352	12 39 04	18.762
303	9 18 09	17.407	353	12 46 09	18.788
304	9 24 16	17.436	354	12 53 16	18.815
305	9 30 25	17.464	355	12 60 25	18.841
306	9 36 36	17.493	356	12 67 36	18.868
307	9 42 49	17.521	357	12 74 49	18 894
308	9 48 64	17.550	358	12 81 64	18.921
309	9 54 81	17.578	359	12 88 81	18.947
310	9 61 00	17.607	360	12 96 00	18.974
311	9 67 21	17 635	361	13 03 21	19.000
312	9 73 44	17 664	362	13 10 44	19.026
313	9 79 69	17.692	363	13 17 69	19.053
314	9 85 96	17.720	364	13 24 96	19.079
315	9 92 25	17.748	365	13 32 25	19.105
316	9 98 56	17.776	366	13 39 56	19.131
317	10 04 89	17.804	367	13 46 89	19.157
318	10 11 24	17 833	368	13 54 24	19.183
319	10 17 61	17.861	369	13 61 61	19.209
320	10 24 00	17.889	370	13 69 00	19.235
321	10 30 41	17.916	371	13 76 41	19.261
322	10 36 84	17 944	372	13 83 84	19.287
323	10 43 29	17 972	373	13 91 29	19.313
324	10 49 76	18.000	374	13 98 76	19.339
325	10 56 25	18.028	375	14 06 25	19.363
326	10 62 76	18.055	376	14 13 76	19.391
327	10 69 29	18.083	377	14 21 29	19.416
328	10 75 84	18.111	378	14 28 84	19.442
329	10 82 41	18.138	379	14 36 41	19.468
330	10 89 00	18.166	380	14 44 00	19.494
331	10 95 61	18.193	381	14 51 61	19.519
332	11 02 24	18.221	382	14 59 24	19.545
333	11 08 89	18.248	383	14 66 89	19.570
334	11 15 56	18.276	384	14 74 56	19.596
335	11 22 25	18.303	385	14 82 25	19.621
336	11 28 96	18.330	386	14 89 96	19.647
337	11 35 69	18.358	387	14 97 69	19.672
338	11 42 44	18.385	388	15 05 44	19.698
339	11 49 21	18.412	389	15 13 21	19.723
340	11 56 00	18.439	390	15 21 00	19.748
341	11 62 81	18.466	391	15 28 81	19.774
342	11 69 64	18.493	392	15 36 64	19.799
343	11 76 49	18.520	393	15 44 49	19.824
344	11 83 36	18.547	394	15 52 36	19.849
345	11 90 25	18.574	395	15 60 25	19.875
346	11 97 16	18.601	396	15 68 16	19.900
347	12 04 09	18.628	397	15 76 09	19.925
348	12 11 04	18.655	398	15 84 04	19.950
349	12 18 01	18.682	399	15 92 01	19.975
350	12 25 00	18.708	400	16 00 00	20.000

TABLE OF SQUARES AND SQUARE ROOTS—*Continued*

Number	Square	Square Root	Number	Square	Square Root
401	16 08 01	20.025	451	20 34 01	21.237
402	16 16 04	20.050	452	20 43 04	21.260
403	16 24 09	20.075	453	20 52 09	21.284
404	16 32 16	20.100	454	20 61 16	21.307
405	16 40 25	20.125	455	20 70 25	21.331
406	16 48 36	20.149	456	20 79 36	21.354
407	16 56 49	20.174	457	20 88 49	21.378
408	16 64 64	20.199	458	20 97 64	21.401
409	16 72 81	20.224	459	21 06 81	21.424
410	16 81 00	20.248	460	21 16 00	21.448
411	16 89 21	20.273	461	21 25 21	21.471
412	16 97 44	20.298	462	21 34 44	21.494
413	17 05 69	20.322	463	21 43 69	21.517
414	17 13 96	20.347	464	21 52 96	21.541
415	17 22 25	20.372	465	21 62 25	21.564
416	17 30 56	20.396	466	21 71 56	21.587
417	17 38 89	20.421	467	21 80 89	21.610
418	17 47 24	20.445	468	21 90 24	21.633
419	17 55 61	20.469	469	21 99 61	21.656
420	17 64 00	20.494	470	22 09 00	21.679
421	17 72 41	20.518	471	22 18 41	21.703
422	17 80 84	20.543	472	22 27 84	21.726
423	17 89 29	20.567	473	22 37 29	21.749
424	17 97 76	20.591	474	22 46 76	21.772
425	18 06 25	20.616	475	22 56 25	21.794
426	18 14 76	20.640	476	22 65 76	21.817
427	18 23 29	20.664	477	22 75 29	21.840
428	18 31 84	20.688	478	22 84 84	21.863
429	18 40 41	20.712	479	22 94 41	21.886
430	18 49 00	20.736	480	23 04 00	21.909
431	18 57 61	20.761	481	23 13 61	21.932
432	18 66 24	20.785	482	23 23 24	21.954
433	18 74 89	20.809	483	23 32 89	21.977
434	18 83 56	20.833	484	23 42 56	22.000
435	18 92 25	20.857	485	23 52 25	22.023
436	19 00 96	20.881	486	23 61 96	22.045
437	19 09 69	20.905	487	23 71 69	22.068
438	19 18 44	20.928	488	23 81 44	22.091
439	19 27 21	20.952	489	23 91 21	22.113
440	19 36 00	20.976	490	24 01 00	22.136
441	19 44 81	21.000	491	24 10 81	22.159
442	19 53 64	21.024	492	24 20 64	22.181
443	19 62 49	21.048	493	24 30 49	22.204
444	19 71 36	21.071	494	24 40 36	22.226
445	19 80 25	21.095	495	24 50 25	22.249
446	19 89 16	21.119	496	24 60 16	22.271
447	19 98 09	21.142	497	24 70 09	22.293
448	20 07 04	21.166	498	24 80 04	22.316
449	20 16 01	21.190	499	24 90 01	22.338
450	20 25 00	21.213	500	25 00 00	22.361

Table of Squares and Square Roots—Continued

Number	Square	Square Root	Number	Square	Square Root
501	25 10 01	22.383	551	30 36 01	23.473
502	25 20 04	22.405	552	30 47 04	23.495
503	25 30 09	22.428	553	30 58 09	23.516
504	25 40 16	22.450	554	30 69 16	23.537
505	25 50 25	22.472	555	30 80 25	23.558
506	25 60 36	22.494	556	30 91 36	23.580
507	25 70 49	22.517	557	31 02 49	23.601
508	25 80 64	22.539	558	31 13 64	23.622
509	25 90 81	22.561	559	31 24 81	23.643
510	26 01 00	22.583	560	31 36 00	23.664
511	26 11 21	22.605	561	31 47 21	23.685
512	26 21 44	22.627	562	31 58 44	23.707
513	26 31 69	22.650	563	31 69 69	23.728
514	26 41 96	22.672	564	31 80 96	23.749
515	26 52 25	22.694	565	31 92 25	23.770
516	26 62 56	22.716	566	32 03 56	23.791
517	26 72 89	22.738	567	32 14 89	23.812
518	26 83 24	22.760	568	32 26 24	23.833
519	26 93 61	22.782	569	32 37 61	23.854
520	27 04 00	22.804	570	32 49 00	23.875
521	27 14 41	22.825	571	32 60 41	23.896
522	27 24 84	22.847	572	32 71 84	23.917
523	27 35 29	22.869	573	32 83 29	23.937
524	27 45 76	22.891	574	32 94 76	23.958
525	27 56 25	22.913	575	33 06 25	23.979
526	27 66 76	22.935	576	33 17 76	24.000
527	27 77 29	22.956	577	33 29 29	24.021
528	27 87 84	22.978	578	33 40 84	24.042
529	27 98 41	23.000	579	33 52 41	24.062
530	28 09 00	23.022	580	33 64 00	24.083
531	28 19 61	23.043	581	33 75 61	24.104
532	28 30 24	23.065	582	33 87 24	24.125
533	28 40 89	23.087	583	33 98 89	24.145
534	28 51 56	23.108	584	34 10 56	24.166
535	28 62 25	23.130	585	34 22 25	24.187
536	28 72 96	23.152	586	34 33 96	24.207
537	28 83 69	23.173	587	34 45 69	24.228
538	28 94 44	23.195	588	34 57 44	24.249
539	29 05 21	23.216	589	34 69 21	24.269
540	29 16 00	23.238	590	34 81 00	24.290
541	29 26 81	23.259	591	34 92 81	24.310
542	29 37 64	23.281	592	35 04 64	24.331
543	29 48 49	23.302	593	35 16 49	24.352
544	29 59 36	23.324	594	35 28 36	24.372
545	29 70 25	23.345	595	35 40 25	24.393
546	29 81 16	23.367	596	35 52 16	24.413
547	29 92 09	23.388	597	35 64 09	24.434
548	30 03 04	23.409	598	35 76 04	24.454
549	30 14 01	23.431	599	35 88 01	24.474
550	30 25 00	23.452	600	36 00 00	24.495

TABLE OF SQUARES AND SQUARE ROOTS—*Continued*

Number	Square	Square Root	Number	Square	Square Root
601	36 12 01	24.515	651	42 38 01	25.515
602	36 24 04	24.536	652	42 51 04	25.534
603	36 36 09	24.556	653	42 64 09	25.554
604	36 48 16	24.576	654	42 77 16	25.573
605	36 60 25	24.597	655	42 90 25	25.593
606	36 72 36	24.617	656	43 03 36	25.612
607	36 84 49	24.637	657	43 16 49	25.632
608	36 96 64	24.658	658	43 29 64	25.652
609	37 08 81	24.678	659	43 42 81	25.671
610	37 21 00	24.698	660	43 56 00	25.690
611	37 33 21	24.718	661	43 69 21	25.710
612	37 45 44	24.739	662	43 82 44	25.729
613	37 57 69	24.759	663	43 95 69	25.749
614	37 69 96	24.779	664	44 08 96	25.768
615	37 82 25	24.799	665	44 22 25	25.788
616	37 94 56	24.819	666	44 35 56	25.807
617	38 06 89	24.839	667	44 48 89	25.826
618	38 19 24	24.860	668	44 62 24	25.846
619	38 31 61	24.880	669	44 75 61	25.865
620	38 44 00	24.900	670	44 89 00	25.884
621	38 56 41	24.920	671	45 02 41	25.904
622	38 68 84	24.940	672	45 15 84	25.923
623	38 81 29	24.960	673	45 29 29	25.942
624	38 93 76	24.980	674	45 42 76	25.962
625	39 06 25	25.000	675	45 56 25	25.981
626	39 18 76	25.020	676	45 69 76	26.000
627	39 31 29	25.040	677	45 83 29	26.019
628	39 43 84	25.060	678	45 96 84	26.038
629	39 56 41	25.080	679	46 10 41	26.058
630	39 69 00	25.100	680	46 24 00	26.077
631	39 81 61	25.120	681	46 37 61	26.096
632	39 94 24	25.140	682	46 51 24	26.115
633	40 06 89	25.159	683	46 64 89	26.134
634	40 19 56	25.179	684	46 78 56	26.153
635	40 32 25	25.199	685	46 92 25	26.173
636	40 44 96	25.219	686	47 05 96	26.192
637	40 57 69	25.239	687	47 19 69	26.211
638	40 70 44	25.259	688	47 33 44	26.230
639	40 83 21	25.278	689	47 47 21	26.249
640	40 96 00	25.298	690	47 61 00	26.268
641	41 08 81	25.318	691	47 74 81	26.287
642	41 21 64	25.338	692	47 88 64	26.306
643	41 34 49	25.357	693	48 02 49	26.325
644	41 47 36	25.377	694	48 16 36	26.344
645	41 60 25	25.397	695	48 30 25	26.363
646	41 73 16	25.417	696	48 44 16	26.382
647	41 86 09	25.436	697	48 58 09	26.401
648	41 99 04	25.456	698	48 72 04	26.420
649	42 12 01	25.475	699	48 86 01	26.439
650	42 25 00	25.495	700	49 00 00	26.458

TABLE OF SQUARES AND SQUARE ROOTS—Continued

Number	Square	Square Root	Number	Square	Square Root
701	49 14 01	26.476	751	56 40 01	27.404
702	49 28 04	26.495	752	56 55 04	27.423
703	49 42 09	26.514	753	56 70 09	27.441
704	49 56 16	26.533	754	56 85 16	27.459
705	49 70 25	26.552	755	57 00 25	27.477
706	49 84 36	26.571	756	57 15 36	27.495
707	49 98 49	26.589	757	57 30 49	27.514
708	50 12 64	26.608	758	57 45 64	27.532
709	50 26 81	26.627	759	57 60 81	27.550
710	50 41 00	26.646	760	57 76 00	27.568
711	50 55 21	26.665	761	57 91 21	27.586
712	50 69 44	26.683	762	58 06 44	27.604
713	50 83 69	26.702	763	58 21 69	27.622
714	50 97 96	26.721	764	58 36 96	27.641
715	51 12 25	26.739	765	58 52 25	27.659
716	51 26 56	26.758	766	58 67 56	27.677
717	51 40 89	26.777	767	58 82 89	27.695
718	51 55 24	26.796	768	58 98 24	27.713
719	51 69 61	26.814	769	59 13 61	27.731
720	51 84 00	26.833	770	59 29 00	27.749
721	51 98 41	26.851	771	59 44 41	27.767
722	52 12 84	26.870	772	59 59 84	27.785
723	52 27 29	26.889	773	59 75 29	27.803
724	52 41 76	26.907	774	59 90 76	27.821
725	52 56 25	26.926	775	60 06 25	27.839
726	52 70 76	26.944	776	60 21 76	27.857
727	52 85 29	26.963	777	60 37 29	27.875
728	52 99 84	26.981	778	60 52 84	27.893
729	53 14 41	27.000	779	60 68 41	27.911
730	53 29 00	27.019	780	60 84 00	27.928
731	53 43 61	27.037	781	60 99 61	27.946
732	53 58 24	27.055	782	61 15 24	27.964
733	53 72 89	27.074	783	61 30 89	27.982
734	53 87 56	27.092	784	61 46 56	28.000
735	54 02 25	27.111	785	61 62 25	28.018
736	54 16 96	27.129	786	61 77 96	28.036
737	54 31 69	27.148	787	61 93 69	28.054
738	54 46 44	27.166	788	62 09 44	28.071
739	54 61 21	27.185	789	62 25 21	28.089
740	54 76 00	27.203	790	62 41 00	28.107
741	54 90 81	27.221	791	62 56 81	28.125
742	55 05 64	27.240	792	62 72 64	28.142
743	55 20 49	27.258	793	62 88 49	28.160
744	55 35 36	27.276	794	63 04 36	28.178
745	55 50 25	27.295	795	63 20 25	28.196
746	55 65 16	27.313	796	63 36 16	28.213
747	55 80 09	27.331	797	63 52 09	28.231
748	55 95 04	27.350	798	63 68 04	28.249
749	56 10 01	27.368	799	63 84 01	28.267
750	56 25 00	27.386	800	64 00 00	28.284

TABLE OF SQUARES AND SQUARE ROOTS—*Continued*

Number	Square	Square Root	Number	Square	Square Root
801	64 16 01	28.302	851	72 42 01	29.172
802	64 32 04	28.320	852	72 59 04	29.189
803	64 48 09	28.337	853	72 76 09	29.206
804	64 64 16	28.355	854	72 93 16	29.223
805	64 80 25	28.373	855	73 10 25	29.240
806	64 96 36	28.390	856	73 27 36	29.257
807	65 12 49	28.408	857	73 44 49	29.275
808	65 28 64	28.425	858	73 61 64	29.292
809	65 44 81	28.443	859	73 78 81	29.309
810	65 61 00	28.460	860	73 96 00	29.326
811	65 77 21	28.478	861	74 13 21	29.343
812	65 93 44	28.496	862	74 30 44	29.360
813	66 09 69	28.513	863	74 47 69	29.377
814	66 25 96	28.531	864	74 64 96	29.394
815	66 42 25	28.548	865	74 82 25	29.411
816	66 58 56	28.566	866	74 99 56	29.428
817	66 74 89	28.583	867	75 16 89	29.445
818	66 91 24	28.601	868	75 34 24	29.462
819	67 07 61	28.618	869	75 51 61	29.479
820	67 24 00	28.636	870	75 69 00	29.496
821	67 40 41	28.653	871	75 86 41	29.513
822	67 56 84	28.671	872	76 03 84	29.530
823	67 73 29	28.688	873	76 21 29	29.547
824	67 89 76	28.705	874	76 38 76	29.563
825	68 06 25	28.723	875	76 56 25	29.580
826	68 22 76	28.740	876	76 73 76	29.597
827	68 39 29	28.758	877	76 91 29	29.614
828	68 55 84	28.775	878	77 08 84	29.631
829	68 72 41	28.792	879	77 26 41	29.648
830	68 89 00	28.810	880	77 44 00	29.665
831	69 05 61	28.827	881	77 61 61	29.682
832	69 22 24	28.844	882	77 79 24	29.698
833	69 38 89	28.862	883	77 96 89	29.715
834	69 55 56	28.879	884	78 14 56	29.732
835	69 72 25	28.896	885	78 32 25	29.749
836	69 88 96	28.914	886	78 49 96	29.766
837	70 05 69	28.931	887	78 67 69	29.783
838	70 22 44	28.948	888	78 85 44	29.799
839	70 39 21	28.965	889	79 03 21	29.816
840	70 56 00	28.983	890	79 21 00	29.833
841	70 72 81	29.000	891	79 38 81	29.850
842	70 89 64	29.017	892	79 56 64	29.866
843	71 06 49	29.034	893	79 74 49	29.883
844	71 23 36	29.052	894	79 92 36	29.900
845	71 40 25	29.069	895	80 10 25	29.916
846	71 57 16	29.086	896	80 28 16	29.933
847	71 74 09	29.103	897	80 46 09	29.950
848	71 91 04	29.120	898	80 64 04	29.967
849	72 08 01	29.138	899	80 82 01	29.983
850	72 25 00	29.155	900	81 00 00	30.000

TABLE OF SQUARES AND SQUARE ROOTS · 451

TABLE OF SQUARES AND SQUARE ROOTS—*Continued*

Number	Square	Square Root	Number	Square	Square Root
901	81 18 01	30.017	951	90 44 01	30.838
902	81 36 04	30.033	952	90 63 04	30.854
903	81 54 09	30.050	953	90 82 09	30.871
904	81 72 16	30.067	954	91 01 16	30.887
905	81 90 25	30.083	955	91 20 25	30.903
906	82 08 36	30.100	956	91 39 36	30.919
907	82 26 49	30.116	957	91 58 49	30.935
908	82 44 64	30.133	958	91 77 64	30.952
909	82 62 81	30.150	959	91 96 81	30.968
910	82 81 00	30.166	960	92 16 00	30.984
911	82 99 21	30.183	961	92 35 21	31.000
912	83 17 44	30.199	962	92 54 44	31.016
913	83 35 69	30.216	963	92 73 69	31.032
914	83 53 96	30.232	964	92 92 96	31.048
915	83 72 25	30.249	965	93 12 25	31.064
916	83 90 56	30.265	966	93 31 56	31.081
917	84 08 89	30.282	967	93 50 89	31.097
918	84 27 24	30.299	968	93 70 24	31.113
919	84 45 61	30.315	969	93 89 61	31.129
920	84 64 00	30.332	970	94 09 00	31.145
921	84 82 41	30.348	971	94 28 41	31.161
922	85 00 84	30.364	972	94 47 84	31.177
923	85 19 29	30.381	973	94 67 29	31.193
924	85 37 76	30.397	974	94 86 76	31.209
925	85 56 25	30.414	975	95 06 25	31.225
926	85 74 76	30.430	976	95 25 76	31.241
927	85 93 29	30.447	977	95 45 29	31.257
928	86 11 84	30.463	978	95 64 84	31.273
929	86 30 41	30.480	979	95 84 41	31.289
930	86 49 00	30.496	980	96 04 00	31.305
931	86 67 61	30.512	981	96 23 61	31.321
932	86 86 24	30.529	982	96 43 24	31.337
933	87 04 89	30.545	983	96 62 89	31.353
934	87 23 56	30.561	984	96 82 56	31.369
935	87 42 25	30.578	985	97 02 25	31.385
936	87 60 96	30.594	986	97 21 96	31.401
937	87 79 69	30.610	987	97 41 69	31.417
938	87 98 44	30.627	988	97 61 44	31.432
939	88 17 21	30.643	989	97 81 21	31.448
940	88 36 00	30.659	990	98 01 00	31.464
941	88 54 81	30.676	991	98 20 81	31.480
942	88 73 64	30.692	992	98 40 64	31.496
943	88 92 49	30.708	993	98 60 49	31.512
944	89 11 36	30.725	994	98 80 36	31.528
945	89 30 25	30.741	995	99 00 25	31.544
946	89 49 16	30.757	996	99 20 16	31.559
947	89 68 09	30.773	997	99 40 09	31.575
948	89 87 04	30.790	998	99 60 04	31.591
949	90 06 01	30.806	999	99 80 01	31.607
950	90 25 00	30.822	1000	100 00 00	31.623

REFERENCES

The following books will be found useful by students in psychology and in education.

EDWARDS, A. L. *Statistical Analysis.* New York: Rinehart and Co., Inc., 1946.
GUILFORD, J. P. *Fundamental Statistics in Psychology and Education.* 2nd ed.; New York: McGraw-Hill Book Co., Inc., 1950.
LINDQUIST, E. F. *A First Course in Statistics.* Rev. ed.; Boston: Houghton-Mifflin Co., 1942.
McNEMAR, QUINN. *Psychological Statistics.* New York: John Wiley and Sons, 1949.
MODE, E. B. *The Elements of Statistics.* New York: Prentice Hall, Inc., 1946.
WALKER, HELEN M. *Elementary Statistical Methods.* New York: Henry Holt and Co., 1943.

More advanced books are:

EDWARDS, A. L. *Experimental Design in Psychological Research.* New York: Rinehart and Co., 1950.
FISHER, R. A. *The Design of Experiments.* London: Oliver and Boyd, 1935.
FISHER, R. A. *Statistical Methods for Research Workers.* New York: Hafner Publishing Co., 1950.
JOHNSON, P. O. *Statistical Methods in Research.* New York: Prentice Hall, Inc., 1949.
LINDQUIST, E. F. *Statistical Analysis in Educational Research.* Boston: Houghton-Mifflin Co., 1940.
RIDER, P. R. *An Introduction to Modern Statistical Methods.* New York: John Wiley and Sons, 1939.
SNEDECOR, G. W. *Statistical Methods.* Ames, Iowa: The Collegiate Press, Inc., 1946.
TRELOAR, A. E. *Elements of Statistical Reasoning.* New York: John Wiley and Sons, 1939.

Computation aids

ARKIN, H., AND COLTON, R. *Tables for Statisticians.* New York: Barnes and Noble, Inc., 1950.

BARLOW'S TABLES OF SQUARES, etc. London: E. and F. N. Spon, Ltd., 1935.

FISHER, R. A., AND YATES, F. *Statistical Tables.* New York: Hafner Publishing Co., Inc., 1948.

INDEX

Accuracy, standards of, in computation, 20–24
Ackerson, L., 340
Actuarial prediction, through correlation, 164
Adkins, D. C., 303, 351
Analysis of variance: principles of, 268–273; how variances are analyzed, 269–273; in determining significance of difference between independent means, 273–284; between correlated means, 285–296
Anastasi, A., 346, 400
Anderson, J. E., 350
Arkin, H., 454
Array, in a correlation table, 130
Attenuation: correction of correlation coefficient for, 346–347; assumptions underlying, 347
Average: definition of, 28; of correlation coefficients, 146–147. See also Mean, Median, and Mode.

Bar diagram, 80–82
Barlow's Tables, 454
Beta coefficients: in partial and multiple correlation, 393–394, 396–397; as "weights," 393; calculation of, in Wherry-Doolittle method, 415–417
Bias in sampling. See Sampling
Binomial expansion: use in probability, 87–92; graphic representation of, 91
Bi-serial correlation, 356–362; calculation of r_{bis}, 357–359; SE of r_{bis}, 359; alternate formula for, 360–361; point bi-serial coefficient, 361–362
Brigham, C. C., 214
Burks, B. S., 420

Central tendency, measures of, 28. See also Mean, Median, and Mode
Chesire, L., 365
Chi-square test, 254; as a measure of divergence from the null hypothesis, 255–257, and from the normal distribution, 257–258; when table entries are small, 258–261; when table entries are in percentages, 261–262; in contingency tables, 262–265; additive property of, 265
Classification of measures into a frequency distribution, 4–9
Class-interval: definition of, 6–8; methods of expressing, 7–8; midpoint of, 7–8; limits of, 7–8
Clayton, B., 340
Coefficient: of variation, or V, 57–60; of alienation, 174–176; of determination, in the interpretation of r, 176–178
Coefficient of correlation: meaning of, 126–134; as a ratio, 126–128; represented graphically, 131; computation of, deviations from assumed means, 134–139; computation of, deviations from means, 139–142; computation of, deviations from zero, 142–145; averaging of, 146–147; effect of variability upon, 166–167; interpretations of, 172–178; reliability of, 197–201
Colton, R., 454
Column diagram. See Histogram
Comparison: of obtained distribution with normal probability curve, 101–103; of groups in terms of overlapping, 107–108. See also Chi-square, Skewness, and Kurtosis
Computation, rules for, 20–24
Confidence-intervals for the true mean, meaning of, 187–189
Conrad, H. S., 176
Contingency, coefficient of (C), 368–371; relation of C to chi-square, 368; methods of computing C, 369–370; comparison of C with r, 371
Continuous series: definition of, 2–3;

455

scores in, 3–4; tabulation of measures in, 4–9
Correlation, linear, 122, 131–134; positive, negative, and zero, 122–124; expressed as a ratio, 126–127; construction of table, 128–130; graphic representation of, 131–134; product-moment method in, 134–139; from ungrouped data, 139–146; difference formula in, 145–146; effect of errors of observation upon, 346–347; rank difference method of computing, 353–356; spurious, 399–401. See also Partial correlation and Multiple correlation
Correlation-ratio (eta), in non-linear relationship, 372
Covariance, analysis of, 289–295
Criterion: value of, in determining the validity of tests, 345–346; prediction of by multiple regression equation, 391–394
Critical ratio, definition of, 215. See also t-test
Cumulative frequencies, method of computing, 63–64
Cumulative frequency graph: construction of, 63–65; smoothing of, 76–77
Cureton, E. E., 389
Curvilinear relationship, 371–373

Data, continuous and discrete, 2–4
Davis, F. B., 351
Deciles. See Percentiles
Degrees of freedom: meaning of, 193–194; in analysis of variance, 278, 283, 287
Deviation. See Quartile deviation, Mean deviation, and Standard deviation
Differences, significance of: between means, 213–232; between medians, 232; between standard deviations, 232–236; between percentages, 236–239; between r's, 239–240. See also Standard error and Probable error
Discrete series, 2
Distribution, frequency. See Frequency distribution
Dunlap, J. W., 196, 389

Edgerton, H. A., 161
Edwards, A. L., 268, 299, 453

Elliott, R. M., 405
Equivalent groups, method of, 228–230
Error, curve of, 85–87. See also Normal curve
Errors: of sampling, 201–208; constant, 209. See also Probable and Standard errors
Experimental hypotheses: testing of, 247–254; null hypothesis, 247–248
Ezekiel, M., 389, 418

Ferguson, G. A., 350
Fertig, J. W., 298
Fiducial limits (Fisher), 189; probability, 189
Fisher, R. A., 189, 198, 203, 249, 270, 428, 453, 454
Flanagan, J. C., 351
Franzen, R., 59
Frequency distribution: construction of, 4–8; graphical representation of, 9–20; normalizing a, 307–311; rectangular and normal, 313–315
Frequency polygon: construction of, 11–12; smoothing of, 14–16; comparison with histogram, 18, 20; comparison of two, on same axes, 18, 19
Froelich, G. J., 336
F-test: in comparing two σ's, 233–234; in analysis of variance, 280–281

Garrett, H. E., 186, 280, 400
Goulden, C. H., 270
Graphic representation: principles of, 9–10; of correlation coefficient, 131. See also Frequency polygon, Histogram, Cumulative frequency graph, Percentile curve or Ogive, Line graph, Bar diagram
Grouping: in tabulating a frequency distribution, 4–9; assumptions in, 8–9
Guilford, J. P., 351, 368, 453
Gulliksen, H., 348, 351

Hartshorne, H., 236
Hawkes, Lindquist, and Mann, 115, 351
Heterogeneity, effect of: upon correlation, 166–167; upon the reliability coefficient, 344–345

Hillegas, M. B., 317
Histogram: definition of, 16–17; comparison of, with frequency polygon, 18, 20
Holtzman, W. H., 189, 224
Holtzinger, K. J., 340
Homogeneity, 43; effect of, upon correlation, 166–167
Hull, C. L., 117, 324

Inferences, errors in, 219–222
Interaction, in analysis of variance, 287
Interval. *See* Class-interval
Item analysis: problem of, 349; and selection, 349; and difficulty of, 350; and validity, 350–351

Jackson, J. D., 340
Johnson, P. O., 241, 453
Jones, D. C., 94
Jones, H. E., 173
Jones, L. V., 217

Kelley, T. L., 99, 342, 368
Kelly, E. L., 340
Kendall, M. G., 371, 395
Kuder, G. F., 335
Kurtosis: calculation of, 100–101; standard error of, 242–243
Kurtz, A. K., 196

Levels of confidence, 186–187
Lewis, D., 190, 254
Likert, R., 319
Lindquist, E. F., 270, 453
Line graphs, 78–80
Long, J. A., 351, 361

Martin, G. B., 176
Matched groups, method of, 230–233
May, M. A., 236, 380
McCall, W. A., 308
McNemar, Q., 85, 94, 219, 238, 268, 294, 343, 453
Mean, arithmetic: calculation of, from ungrouped scores, 28, from frequency distribution, 29–31, by "assumed mean" method, 36–39; when to use, 39; reliability of, 182–185; limits of accuracy for, 186–187
Mean deviation, or MD: calculation of, from ungrouped data, 48–49; from grouped data, 49–50; when to use, 61
Median: calculation of, from ungrouped scores, 31–32; from frequency distribution, 32–34; in special cases, 34–35; when to use, 39; reliability of, 194
Merrill, M. A., 170, 343
Method: single group, 225–228; equivalent groups, 228–230; matched groups, 230–232
Midpoint of interval, as representative of all of the scores on the interval, 7–8
Mode: calculation of, 35–36; when to use, 40
Mode, E. B., 453
Moore, T. V., 420
Morgan, J. J. B., 248
Moving average, use of in smoothing a curve, 14–16
Multiple coefficient of correlation, R, 380; computation of, in a three-variable problem, 387; formulas for, 395–397; beta coefficients in, 396–397; significance of, 397; "shrinkage" in, 407; limitations to use of, 419–420
Multiple regression equations: for n variables, 391; for three variables (special form), 391–393; partial regression coefficients (b), 392–393; beta coefficients, 393–394

Non-linear relationship, measurement of, 371–373
Normal probability curve, 85–87; illustrations of, 85–86; deduction from binomial expansion, 90–92; in psychological measurement, 92–94; equation of, 94; properties of, 94–96; constants of, 94, 97; comparison of obtained distribution with, 101–103; use in solution of a variety of problems, 103–113; in scaling test scores, 323–326; in scaling judgments, 326–327
Normality: divergence of frequency distribution from, 113–118; normalizing a frequency distribution, 307–311; T-scores, 307–313
Null hypothesis: in determining significance of coefficient of correlation, 199–201; in testing reliability of dif-

ferences, 213; advantages of, 246–247; testing of, against direct determination of probable outcomes, 248–251; testing of, against normal curve frequencies, 251–253
Numbers: rounded, 20–21; exact and approximate, 22

Ogburn, W. F., 420
Ogive: construction of, 69–71; percentiles and percentile ranks from, 70–75; uses of, 73–75; smoothing of, 76–77
Order of merit, ranks, 323–327; changing into numerical scores, table for, 324
Otis, A. S., 334
Overlapping, in the measurement of groups, 107–108

Parallel forms method, in reliability of test scores, 333–334
Parameter, definition of, 181
Partial correlation: value of, in analysis, 378–379; illustrations of, in a three-variable problem, 380–387; notation in, 387–388; formulas for partial r's, 387–389; significance of, 389; limitations to the use of, 419–420
Paterson, D. G., 315, 405
Pearson, K., 128
Percentages: standard error of, 196; standard error of the difference between two, 237–238
Percentile, ranks (PR): computation of, 68–69; construction of curve of, 69–73; graphic method of finding ranks, 71–73; uses of curve of, 73–75; norms, 75–77; scale, use of, in combining test scores, 313–315; scale, disadvantages of, 315
Percentiles: calculation of, 66–69; graphic method of finding, 70–74
Perry, N. C., 368
Peters, C. C., 168, 365, 371
Phi-coefficient, calculation of, 367–368; relation to χ^2, 368
Pintner, R., 315, 400
Predictions: accuracy of, from regression equations, 161–163; accuracy of group, 163–166; "regression effect" in, 171–172; from multiple regression equations, 386–387, 394–395

Probability, elementary principles of, 87–92
Probable error: relation to Q, 47; relation to σ, 97
Product-moment method of finding r, 134–139

Quartile deviation (Q): calculation of, 44–48; when to use, 61; reliability of, 195
Quartiles, Q_1 and Q_3, computation of, 44–48

Range, as a measure of variability, 44; when to use, 60–61; influence upon the coefficient of correlation, 166–167
Rank-difference method of computing correlations, 354–356; when to use, 356
Ranks, transmutation of, into units of amount, 323–327
Rational equivalence, method of, in test reliability, 335–337
Rectangular distribution, and normal, 313–315
Regression coefficient, 154–156; in partial and multiple correlation, 392–394
Regression effect, reasons for, 171–172
Regression equations, 151–154; in deviation form, 154–157; in correlation table, 157–158; in score form, 159–160; value of, in prediction and control, 160–161; limitations to use of, 162–166; formulas for, in partial and multiple correlation, 391–394
Relative variability, coefficient of, 57–60. See also Coefficient of variation
Reliability: meaning of, 180–183; of the mean, 182–185; in small samples, 189–193; of the median, 194; of Q, 195; of σ, 195; of a percentage, 196–197; sampling and reliability, 201–209; of differences, independent means, 213–216, 222–225; of differences, correlated means, 225–232; of test scores, 332–344; index of, 341–342; dependence of coefficient of, upon the size and variability of the group, 344
Remmers, H. H., 340

Rhine, J. B., 248
Richardson, M. W., 335, 351, 361
Rider, P. R., 453
Ruch, G. M., 340
Russell, J. T., 165

Saffir, M., 365
Sampling: random, 202–205; stratified, 205–206; incidental, 206; purposive, 207; size of, 207–208; and errors of measurement, 208; bias and constant errors in, 209
Sandiford, P., 351, 361
Scale, definition of, 1
Scaling: of test items (σ-scaling), 301–305; of total scores, 305–307; of judgments, 316–318; of answers to a questionnaire, 319–322; of ratings, 322–323. See also Percentile scale, T-scale
Scatter diagram, 128–129
Scores: definition of, 1; in continuous and in discrete series, 2–3
Selection of tests in a battery, factors in, 397–399
Semi-interquartile range, 44–48. See also Quartile deviation
Shartle, C. L., 161, 174, 345, 404
Shock, N. W., 340
Sigma scores, and standard scores, 305–307
Significance: meaning of, 212; levels of, 216–217; two- and one-tailed tests of, 217–219; table for determining, 427; .05 and .01 tables of, for r, 437–439
Significant figures, 21
Skewness: measurement of, 97–99; causes of, 114–118; standard error of measure of, 241–242
Snedecor, G. W., 193, 270, 453
Spearman-Brown prophecy formula in test reliability, 339–341
Split-half method, in reliability of test scores, 334–335
Spurious correlation, 399; arising from heterogeneity, 399–400; of indices, 400–401; of averages, 401
Stalnaker, J. L., 361
Standard deviation or σ, 50; calculation of, 51–52; calculation of, by Short Method, 52–54; calculation of, from raw scores, 54–56; in special cases, 56–57; when to use, 61; reliability of, 194–195; estimation of true value of, 347–348; formulas for, in partial correlation, 389–391
Standard error, of a mean, in large samples, 182; in small samples, 190; of a median, 194; of σ, 195; of Q, 195; of a percentage, 196; of r, 197; of the difference between means, 213–232; of the difference between medians, 232; of the difference between r's, 239
Standard error of an obtained score, 342–343
Standard error, of estimate, 161–163; in the interpretation of r, 174–175; in partial and multiple correlation, 394–395
Standard scores, 305–307; compared with T-scores, 312–313
Statistic, definition of, 181
Stead, W. H., 161, 174, 345, 404
Student's distribution, table of, 427
Symonds, P. M., 145

Tabulation: of measures in a frequency distribution, 4–9; in a correlation table, 128–130
Taylor, H. C., 165
Terman, L. M., 170, 343
Test items: relative difficulty of, 302–305; analysis of, 349–350
Test-retest method, in reliability of test scores, 333
Test scores, factors affecting reliability of, 337–341
Tetrachoric correlations, 362; calculation of, 362–365; diagrams in, 365; SE of, 365–366; use of, in test evaluation, 366–367
Thomson, G. H., 400
Thorndike, E. L., 86, 115
Thorndike, R. L., 171, 387, 398
Thurstone, L. L., 59, 316, 365
Transmutation of measures, 316–327; of judgments, 316–323; of orders of merit, 323–327
Treloar, A. E., 219, 453
T-scale, 307–312; comparison with standard scores, 312–313; advantages of, 313
t-test, meaning of, 190–192; comparison with CR, 223; in analysis of variance, 275, 283–284, 285; table of t (Table D), 427

Validity: relation of, to reliability, 344; measurement of, in a test, 344–349; in terms of criteria, 345–346; indirect measures of, 345–346; of test battery, 348–349
Van Voorhis, W. R., 168, 365, 371
Variability: meaning of, 42; measures of, 43; coefficient of relative variability, 57–60; reliability of measures of, 194–195. *See also* Mean deviation, Quartile deviation, Range, Standard deviation
Variance (σ^2): analysis of, 268–273; components of, 274–281

Walker, H. M., 128, 154, 191, 453
Wherry, R. J., 407
Wherry-Doolittle Test Selection Method, 404; illustration of, 405–418; shrinkage formula for R in, 407; regression equations in, 416–417; beta weights and multiple R, 417–418
Wilks, S. S., 230
Woo, T. L., 263
Woodworth, R. S., 317

Yates, F., 203, 454
Yule, G. U., 86, 90, 197, 371, 395, 400

z-function (Fisher), use in determining reliability of r, 198–199; significance of difference between two r's, 239–240
Zubin, J., 280